Perspectives In Exercise Science and Sports Medicine
Volume 2: Youth, Exercise, and Sport

Edited by

Carl V. Gisolfi, Ph.D.
University of Iowa

David R. Lamb, Ph.D.
Ohio State University

Benchmark Press, Inc.
Indianapolis, Indiana

Library of Congress Cataloging in Publication Data:
LAMB, DAVID R., 1939-
GISOLFI, CARL V., 1942-
PERSPECTIVES IN EXERCISE SCIENCE AND SPORTS MEDICINE
VOLUME 2: YOUTH EXERCISE AND SPORT

Cover Design: Gary Schmitt
Copy Editor: Becky Claxton

Manufactured By: Edwards Brothers
                Ann Arbor, Michigan

Library of Congress Catalog Card number: 88-70343

ISBN: 0-936157-32-1

Printed in the United States of America
10 9 8 7 6 5 4 3 2 1

The Publisher and Author disclaim responsibility for any adverse effects or consequences from the misapplication or injudicious use of the information contained within this text.

Contributors

Ken Baldwin, Ph.D.
Department of Physiology
   and Biophysics
University of California-Irvine
Irvine, CA

Oded Bar-Or, M.D.
Department of Pediatrics
McMaster University
Chedoke-McMaster Hospitals
Hamilton, Ontario, Canada

Steven Blair, P.E.D.
Institute for Aerobics Research
Dallas, TX

Cameron Blimkie, Ph.D.
School of Physical Education
McMaster University
Hamilton, Ontario, Canada

Claude Bouchard, Ph.D.
University of Laval
Ste-Foy, Canada

David S. Braden, M.D.
Department of Pediatrics
Pediatric Physical Performance
   Laboratory
Medical College of Georgia
Augusta, GA

George Brooks, Ph.D.
Department of Physical Education
University of California-Berkeley
Berkeley, CA

Debra Clark
Institute for Aerobics Research
Dallas, TX

Priscilla Clarkson, Ph.D.
Department of Exercise Science
University of Massachusetts
Amherst, MA

Edward Coyle, Ph.D.
Department of Physical Education
University of Texas
Austin, TX

Kirk Cureton, Ph.D.
Department of Physical Education
University of Georgia
Athens, GA

J. Mark Davis, Ph.D.
Department of Physical Education
University of South Carolina
Columbia, SC

Jerome Dempsey, Ph.D.
Department of Preventive Medicine
University of Wisconsin Health Science
   Center
Madison, WI

Rod Dishman, Ph.D.
Department of Physical Education
University of Georgia
Athens, GA

Barbara Drinkwater, Ph.D.
Department of Medicine
Pacific Medical Center
Seattle, WA

Patty Freedson, Ph.D.
Department of Exercise Science
University of Massachusetts
Amherst, MA

Carl Gisolfi, Ph.D.
Department of Exercise Science
   and Physical Education
University of Iowa
Iowa City, IA

William Gonyea, Ph.D.
Department of Cell Biology
University of Texas
Austin, TX

iii

George Halaby, Ph.D.
The Quaker Oats Company
Barrington, IL

Kathe Henke, Ph.D.
Pulmonary Fellow-University
  of Wisconsin
University of Sydney
Sydney, Australia

John Holloszy, M.D.
Department of Medicine
Washington University School
  of Medicine
St. Louis, MO

Edward Horton, M.D.
College of Medicine
University of Vermont
Burlington, VT

Frederick James, M.D.
Division of Cardiology
Children's Hospital
Cincinnati, OH

David Lamb, Ph.D.
School of Health, Physical Education,
  and Recreation
The Ohio State University
Columbus, OH

Ronald Lauer, M.D.
Division of Pediatric Cardiology
University Hospital
University of Iowa
Iowa City, IA

Robert Lemanske, M.D.
Clinical Science Center
University of Wisconsin
Madison, WI

Peter Lemon, Ph.D.
Applied Physiology Research
  Laboratory
Kent State University
Kent, OH

Timothy Lohman, Ph.D.
Department of Exercise Science
University of Arizona
Tucson, AZ

Ann Loucks, Ph.D.
College of Osteopathic Medicine
Ohio University
Athens, OH

Robert Malina, Ph.D.
Department of Anthropology
University of Texas
Austin, TX

Jerry Maynard, Ph.D.
Department of Exercise Science
  and Physical Education
University of Iowa
Iowa City, IA

Janet McArthur, Ph.D.
Boston, MA

Lyle Micheli, M.D.
Children's Hospital Medical Center
Boston, MA

Jere Mitchell, M.D.
Southwestern Medical School
University of Texas
Austin, TX

William Morgan, Ed.D.
Sport Psychology Laboratory
University of Wisconsin
Madison, WI

Ethan Nadel, Ph.D.
John B. Pierce Foundation Laboratory
New Haven, CT

David Orenstein, Ph.D.
Cystic Fibrosis Center
Children's Hospital of Pittsburgh
Pittsburgh, PA

Lawrence Oscai, Ph.D.
Exercise Research Division
Department of Physical Education
University of Illinois-Chicago
Chicago, IL

Russell Pate, Ph.D.
Department of Physical Education
University of South Carolina
Columbia, SC

Kenneth Powell, M.D.
Division of Health Education
Centers for Disease Control
Atlanta, GA

Alan Rogol, M.D., Ph.D.
Department of Pediatrics
University of Virginia
Charlottesville, VA

Digby Sale, Ph.D.
Department of Physical Education
McMaster University
Hamilton, Ontario, Canada

Tara Scanlon, Ph.D.
Department of Kinesiology
University of California-
  Los Angeles
Los Angeles, CA

Vern Seefeldt, Ph.D.
Michigan State University
East Lansing, MI

Roy Shephard, M.D., Ph.D.
School of Health and Physical
  Education
University of Toronto
Toronto, Ontario, Canada

William Strong, M.D.
Pediatric Physical Performance
  Laboratory
Department of Pediatrics
Medical College of Georgia
Augusta, GA

John Sutton, M.D.
McMaster University Medical
  Center
Hamilton, Ontario, Canada

Charles Tipton, Ph.D.
Department of Exercise
  and Sport Science
University of Arizona
Tucson, AZ

Art Vailas, Ph.D.
Biodynamics Laboratory
University of Wisconsin
Madison, WI

Acknowledgement

The Quaker Oats Company and The Gatorade Sports Science Institute are proud to have facilitated the publication of this second volume in the series *"Perspectives in Exercise Science and Sports Medicine."* The symposium on "Youth, Exercise, and Sport" and this publication represent the collective deliberations and contributions of many eminent scientists.

We at The Quaker Oats Company and the Gatorade Sports Science Institute will continue our support of research and education in exercise science and sports medicine. By working with the scientific community, we hope to make a significant contribution to the science and medicine of exercise and sports.

Philip A. Marineau
Executive Vice President
The Quaker Oats Company

George A. Halaby
Vice President
Research and Development

Foreword

The Quaker series of sports medicine and exercise science conferences offer a unique opportunity for experts within a well-defined area of interest to join together in a comprehensive review of the research on that topic. In 1988 the theme of the conference was "Youth, Sport, and Exercise," and this volume represents the results of those deliberations. Hopefully, it will provide a stimulus for further research on the many important issues relating to youth fitness.

This is an area of particular concern to the American College of Sports Medicine. The college recently issued an Opinion Statement, "Physical Fitness in Children and Youth," which encourages a greater emphasis on health-related fitness programs for children but also points out the need for more definitive data in this area. If this book is successful in stimulating greater interest in how exercise and sport affect the child, it will have made a great contribution.

The Quaker Oats Company has graciously donated the proceeds from this series, *Perspectives in Exercise Science and Sports Medicine,* to the American College of Sports Medicine Foundation. We appreciate Quaker's continuing interest in the sports sciences and support of the ACSM Foundation and look forward to the results of the next conference in this series.

Barbara L. Drinkwater, Ph.D.
President
American College of Sports Medicine

Preface

This is the second volume of the series *Perspectives in Exercise Science and Sports Medicine*. We believe that this book contains the most current and comprehensive reviews available of critical topics in the field of youth, exercise, and sport. Realizing the dearth of information available on most of these topics for very young persons, we asked the authors to concentrate on children but to include literature where apppropriate on youths up to the age of 18 years. We hope this volume will stimulate others to help fill in the gaps in our knowledge of how young people respond and adapt to physical exercise.

The contributors to this volume, all internationally known authorities, participated in a conference in Bermuda in June of 1988 to help produce the best possible manuscripts for the book. Each of the chapter authors had provided drafts of their manuscripts to each of two expert reactors in advance of the conference. The reactors responded with suggestions for revisions, most of which were made in advance of the conference. At the conference, each author presented the highlights of the revised chapter, the reactors responded briefly, and all conference participants then jumped into the fray with vigorous criticism, praise, and suggestions for further revisions. This discussion is included following each chapter. The beauty of this format is that expert review is provided by the two reactors and a broader perspective is then given by the remaining conference participants who are eager to find connections among their own disciplines and those of each author. All contributors to both volumes of this series have found this conference format to be very exciting and informative.

The conduct of a scientific conference and the production of a book such as this is a prodigious undertaking and would be impossible without a great deal of personal commitment by all involved and without some mechanism of financial support. We are grateful that sponsorship of this series on *Perspectives in Exercise Science and Sports Medicine* is one of many ways that The Quaker Oats Company and Gatorade Thirst Quencher have shown their support for exercise science and sports medicine. There are many thoughtful individuals at The Quaker Oats Company who have helped bring this series to fruition, and we are grateful to each of them; we especially wish to acknowledge the steadfast encouragement and support of George A. Halaby, Ph.D., and Robert Murray, Ph.D., without whom this series would not be possible.

We also acknowledge the contributions of a world-class meeting organizer, Leslie Walczak, and her colleagues at McCord Travel. Leslie has the remarkable ability to manage 47 tasks at once and to give the appearance of never being frustrated, frazzled, flustered, or fatigued, no matter what crises develop and no matter how impossible our demands.

Finally, we appreciate the efficient, enthusiastic, and courteous efforts of Butch Cooper and Becky Claxton at Benchmark Press. It always amazes us how they can produce such a high-quality finished product from the reams of smudges, arrows, and hieroglyphics that we mail to them.

C. V. Gisolfi
D. R. Lamb

Contents

1

Characteristics of Physical Fitness in Youth

RUSSELL R. PATE, PH.D.

ROY J. SHEPHARD, M.D., PH.D.

INTRODUCTION

There seems to be wide agreement that maintenance of adequate physical fitness levels in children is important. The scientific community, professional groups, and the public all appear to believe that children should be physically fit, that physical fitness carries important short- and long-term benefits for youngsters, and that society should take action to ensure participation by youngsters in enough physical activity to maintain adequate fitness.

However, one need delve only slightly below the surface of the youth fitness issue to encounter substantial controversy and discord. While there is general agreement that "physical fitness" is important, there is no clear consensus as to how this term should be defined or operationalized. Although most interested groups agree that physical fitness should be systematically measured in children, the various professional groups have recommended approaches to fitness measurement that differ markedly in underlying philosophy and in methodology. Despite the fact that most interested parties contend that there is a "youth fitness problem," there is no unanimity as to the magnitude of the problem or how it can best be attacked. In the United States over the past decade, youth fitness has become a "political football" as various government agencies, professional organizations, and private groups have struggled with each other and with society's changing view of physical fitness.

Clearly, the field of youth fitness is not without controversy. Nonetheless, this chapter is based on two rather optimistic assumptions. The first is that, despite the existence of different philosophies and traditions, the various interest groups are motivated by a common concern for the well-being of children. Second, it is assumed that scientific inquiry can and will contribute to the development of consensus and to the ultimate resolution of the various contentious issues. It seems that a place to begin the development of consensus is with a careful analysis of the scientifically documentable physical fitness characteristics of children. Hence, this chapter is intended to provide a concise summary and analysis of selected physical fitness characteristics of youngsters in the age range of 6–18 years. Because youth fitness is an expansive issue and because it has been fraught with controversy, it is necessary to delimit the topic and to define terminology. Accordingly, this chapter begins with preliminary discussions of the concept of physical fitness and methods of fitness measurement as applied to children.

I. PHYSICAL FITNESS: CONCEPTS AND METHODS OF MEASUREMENT

This section is intended to set the stage for development of a characterization of physical fitness in children by answering several basic questions. Among these are: How is physical fitness to be defined? How is the adopted definition to be operationalized? And, how can physical fitness (as operationalized) be measured in the laboratory and in the field?

A. A Definition of Physical Fitness

Many formal definitions of physical fitness have been proposed over the years. These have varied in scope, concept, specificity, and language. Typically, physical fitness has been defined in rather broad terms and, as will be discussed below, has been viewed as including a rather varied array of components. This chapter focuses on an aspect of physical fitness that has frequently been labelled "health-related" physical fitness. This term has come into common use in recent years as some scientists and practitioners have felt the need to differentiate their view of fitness from the more traditional and broader concept of "motor fitness." As will be discussed below, motor fitness generally has been seen as including some physical abilities that relate primarily to athletic performance, whereas health-related physical fitness has been viewed as a narrower concept focusing on the aspects of fitness that are related to day-to-day function and health maintenance (Blair et al., 1982; Corbin & Fox, 1985; Falls, 1980; Pate, 1983).

A suitable definition of health-related physical fitness should meet the following criteria.

- It should convey a concept of physical fitness that is applicable and relevant to the vast majority of people.
- It should convey a concept that is consistent with the current body of knowledge in the exercise sciences.
- It should convey a concept that is based on the scientifically established relationships among physical activity, functional capacities, and health.

- It should employ language that is clear and specific enough to facilitate operationalization of the definition.

For the purpose of this chapter, health-related physical fitness is defined as a state characterized by:

(1) an ability to perform daily activities with vigor, and (2) traits and capacities that are associated with low risk of premature development of the hypokinetic diseases (i.e., those associated with physical inactivity).

The rationale for this definition has been presented in detail elsewhere (Pate, 1983). Briefly, this definition conveys a concept of fitness that is broad enough to apply to essentially everyone and that is consistent with our current knowledge of the health benefits of regular exercise and lends itself to operationalization by practitioners and scientists.

The definition cited, by including the word "state," implies that health-related physical fitness is a dichotomous variable (i.e., you either have it or you do not). Such an approach is consistent with the trend toward establishment of criterion-referenced standards for physical fitness tests (see chapter by Blair et al. in this volume). However, it is acknowledged that health-related physical fitness and each of its components vary along a continuum and that the current knowledge base does not allow us to draw a clear line between "too low" and "acceptable" fitness levels. Nonetheless, we would argue that the proposed definition describes a condition that is desirable, even though it cannot now be described in precise biological terms.

B. Operationalizing The Definition of Physical Fitness

In order to measure physical fitness or to design programs for its improvement, a definition of physical fitness must be operationalized. Fitness authorities have been essentially unanimous in viewing physical fitness, regardless of how it is defined, as a multidimensional trait. Consequently, "physical fitness" typically has been operationalized by identifying the "dimensions" or "components" of fitness that fall within the concept defined.

A component of fitness might be defined as a unique physical characteristic or ability that is related in a significant way to the capacity for movement. To qualify as a component, a charactertistic or ability should not share a large fraction of variance with (i.e., it should not be highly correlated with) another component. Fleishman (1964), in his landmark factor analytic studies, identified 11 fitness components. Fleishman's factor labels and some of the test items used in his studies are listed in Table 1-1. An examination of this table leads to the conclusion that Fleishman took a very broad view

TABLE 1-1. *Fitness components as identified in the factor analytic studies of Fleishman (1964) and selected test items employed in those studies.*

Component	Sample Test Items
Explosive strength	Shuttle run 50 yard dash Standing broad jump Softball throw
Static strength	Hand grip Medicine ball put Trunk pull-dynamometer
Dynamic strength	Pull-up Bent arm hang Rope climb Push-ups
Trunk strength	Leg lifts Sit-ups
Extent flexibility	Toe touching Twist and touch
Dynamic flexibility	Lateral bend Squat, twist, and touch
Gross body equilibrium	Two-foot cross balance-eyes closed Rail walking
Balance—visual cues	One foot cross balance-eyes open
Speed of limb movement	Plate tapping Rotary aiming
Gross body coordination	Cable jump Soccer dribble
Cardiovascular endurance	600 yard run-walk Step test

of the concept of physical fitness. Indeed, he defined physical fitness as ". . . functional capacity of individuals to perform certain kinds of tasks requiring muscular activity" (Fleishman, 1964).

Broad definitions of fitness such as that of Fleishman encompass an awkwardly large number of diverse fitness components. As a result, efforts have been made to describe different types of fitness and to operationalize these with sub-groups of the fitness components. For example, Clarke has employed the terms "general motor ability," "motor fitness," and "physical fitness" and has operationalized these as shown in Table 1-2 (Clarke, 1967). Definitions of the fitness components included in Clarke's concept of motor fitness are provided in Table 1-3. Within the realm of youth fitness testing and programming, the motor fitness concept as described by Clarke has been dominant through most of the 20th century (Clarke, 1975; Van Dalen et al., 1953). The relevance of motor fitness and each of its components to athletic populations is obvious, but its importance

TABLE 1-2. *Components of general motor ability, motor fitness and physical fitness as proposed by Clarke (1967).*

Component	Motor Ability	Motor Fitness	Physical Fitness
Arm-eye Coordination	X		
Muscular Power	X	X	
Agility	X	X	
Muscular Strength	X	X	X
Muscular Endurance	X	X	X
Cardiorespiratory Endurance	X	X	X
Flexibility	X	X	
Speed	X	X	
Foot-eye Coordination	X		

to nonathletic groups has been questioned (Blair et al., 1983; Blair et al., 1982; Corbin & Fox, 1985; Pate, 1983; Plowman & Falls, 1978; Pate, Corbin, et al., 1987).

Over the past decade the concept of health-related physical fitness, as defined above and as distinct from motor fitness, has gained broad acceptance. In operationalizing the definition of health-related physical fitness, two major criteria have been applied in selecting relevant components. First, a component of health-related physical fitness should be related to day-to-day functional capacity, health promotion, and/or disease prevention. Furthermore, these relationships should be documented by convincing scientific evidence. Second, the component should be related to physical activity habits. That is, epidemiological and/or experimental studies should demonstrate that status on the component is better in more phys-

TABLE 1-3. *Definitions of motor and physical fitness components (Clarke, 1967).*

AGILITY —	Speed in changing direction or in changing body position; speed and coordination.
ANAEROBIC POWER —	Maximum rate of force generation and work performance.
BALANCE —	Maintenance of a stable body position.
BODY COMPOSITION —	Fatness; ratio of fat weight to total body weight
CARDIORESPIRATORY ENDURANCE —	Ability to sustain moderate intensity, whole body activity for extended time periods.
FLEXIBILITY —	Range of motion in a joint or series of joints.
MUSCULAR ENDURANCE —	Ability to perform repeated, high resistance muscle contractions.
MUSCULAR STRENGTH —	Maximum force applied with a single muscle contraction.
SPEED —	Maximum rate of movement.

ically active people or that exercise training improves status on the component.

Application of these criteria to the components of physical fitness identified by Fleishman and Clarke has led most authorities to select three of them for inclusion in the health-related physical fitness concept. These are cardiorespiratory endurance, muscular strength/endurance (abdominal and upper body) and flexibility (low back/hamstring). In addition, body composition has become recognized in recent years as a physical fitness component. Because it meets the two aforementioned criteria of a health-related fitness component, body composition is now typically included with other such components. Table 1-4 provides a summary of the rationale for selection of each of the four health-related components. Also provided is a small number of key supporting references. More expansive discussions of the scientific rationale for selection of health-related physical fitness components have been published previously (AAHPERD, 1985; Pate, 1983; Simons-Morton et al., 1987).

The principal focus of this chapter is on health-related physical fitness. Therefore, the following sections of the chapter will deal primarily with the four fitness components listed in Table 1-4.

TABLE 1-4. *Health-related physical fitness components and the rationale for designation of each as health-related. Rationales are stated as benefits associated with maintenance of each component at an acceptable level.*

Component	Rationale	Selected References
Cardiorespiratory Endurance	Enhanced physical working capacity Reduced fatigue Reduced risk of coronary heart disease	(Blair et al., 1982; Haskell et al., 1985; Shephard, 1984) (Cooper et al., 1976; Gibbons et al., 1983; Paffenbarger et al., 1986; Powell et al., 1987)
Body Composition	Reduced risk of hypertension, coronary heart disease, and diabetes	(Bjorntorp, 1987; Lohman et al., 1984)
Muscular Strength	Enhanced functional capacity (lifting, carrying) Reduced risk of low back pain	(Haskell et al., 1985; Kein & Kirkaldy—Willis, 1980; Melleby, 1982)
Flexibility	Enhanced functional capacity (bending, twisting) Reduced risk of low back pain	(Haskell et al., 1985; Kein & Kirkaldy—Willis, 1980; Melleby, 1982)

C. Measurement of Physical Fitness in Children

Since physical fitness is multidimensional, its measurement requires administration of multiple tests. A thorough discussion of measurement of physical fitness is beyond the scope of this chapter. However, some treatment of this topic is necessary because physical fitness is ordinarily characterized in terms of performance or status on tests that are taken as valid measures of the selected components.

Table 1-5 provides a summary of the methods for measurement of the four health-related fitness components. The tests listed are those that have been most commonly applied with children. Both laboratory and field tests are listed. Included are references in which each test (or type of test) is described. Following are brief discussions of some of the methods listed in Table 1-5. In these discussions, emphasis is given to examining the validity and limitations of those tests that are used later in this chapter as the basis for characterizing the fitness of children.

1. Cardiorespiratory Endurance. As has been true for adults, in children the most widely used criterion measure of cardiorespiratory endurance has been directly measured maximal aerobic power ($\dot{V}O_2$max). Techniques for measurement of $\dot{V}O_2$max in children have been reviewed elsewhere (Bar-Or, 1983), and the best method for expressing data ($L \cdot min^{-1}$, $mL \cdot kg^{-1} \cdot min^{-1}$ or $mL \cdot cm^2 \cdot min^{-1}$) is discussed by Shephard (1982). Since $\dot{V}O_2$max provides a clear indication of the subject's oxygen transport/utilization capacity, this test is attractive from a physiological perspective. However, it should be noted that $\dot{V}O_2$max testing in younger children is subject to some methodological limitations and that results of the $\dot{V}O_2$max test must be interpreted with particular caution in children. As has been noted by Bar-Or (1987) and as will be discussed later in this chapter, $\dot{V}O_2$max is not always an accurate indicator of physical working capacity in children.

In the field setting, distance runs of various structures and lengths have been used extensively to measure cardiorespiratory endurance. Validation studies in children generally have reported correlations between weight-relative $\dot{V}O_2$max and distance run performance in the range of 0.40–0.80 (AAHPERD, 1985; Jackson & Coleman, 1976). Distance runs have advantages in terms of ease of administration with groups of children. However, they usually have been structured so as to require a maximal effort, and eliciting such an effort is often difficult in children. Furthermore, knowledge of proper pacing technique is also needed with these tests.

Recently, modified approaches to distance run tests have been

TABLE 1-5. *Methods for measurement of health-related physical fitness components in children. Detailed descriptions of methods provided in the references listed.*

Cardiorespiratory Endurance—Laboratory

Maximal aerobic power, $\dot{V}O_2$ max (treadmill)	(Astrand, 1952; Bar-Or, 1983; Cureton et al., 1977)
Maximal aerobic power, $\dot{V}O_2$ max (leg cycle)	(Astrand, 1952; Bar-Or, 1983)
PWC_{170}	(Bar-Or, 1983)

Field

9 min or 12 min run for distance	(AAHPERD, 1976, 1980)
20 m shuttle run	(Leger & Lambert, 1982)
Mile (1.6 km), 1.5 mile (2.4 km) or 0.5 mile (0.8 km) run/walk for time	(AAHPERD, 1988; Ross & Gilbert, 1985; Ross & Pate, 1987)
600 yd walk/run	(AAHPERD, 1976)
Canadian Home Fitness Test	(Shephard, 1982)

Body Composition—Laboratory

Hydrostatic weight	(Lohman, 1982; Slaughter, Lohman &
Deuterium oxide dilution	Boileau, 1978; Boileau et al., 1984)
Potassium counting	

Field

Skinfold thickness	(Lohman, 1982; Slaughter et al., 1988)
Body mass indices	
Girth measures	

Muscular Strength—Laboratory

Isometric dynamometer	(Berger & Medlin, 1969; Clarke, 1967;
Isokinetic dynamometer	Molnar & Alexander, 1977)
Isotonic one-repetition maximum	
Cable tensiometer	

Field

Pull-ups	(AAHPERD, 1988)
Modified pull-ups	(Pate et al., 1987)
Push-ups	(Bos & Mechling, 1985)
Flexed arm hang	(Reiff et al., 1985)
Sit-ups	(AAHPERD, 1988)

Flexibility—Laboratory

Leighton flexometer	(Leighton, 1942)
Goniometer	

Field

Sit-and-reach	(AAHPERD, 1980; Wells & Dillon, 1952)
Stand-and-reach	(Kraus & Hirshland, 1954)

developed. The Fit Youth Today program (American Health and Fitness Foundation, 1986) includes a submaximal, 20 min run with which the child is evaluated, in part, on his or her ability to run/jog continuously for 20 min, regardless of pace. Another modification is the 20-m shuttle run test, in which running pace is increased incrementally each minute and the child continues until unable to maintain the designated pace (Leger & Lambert, 1982).

   2. **Muscular strength.** In the laboratory setting, muscular strength is typically measured with isometric dynamometers, isokinetic dynamometers or isotonic one-repetition maximum tests. Each of these approaches has been used with children (see references in Table 1-5). In the field, muscular strength is commonly measured with calisthenic exercises that involve repetitive movement of the body or a body part (e.g., sit-ups, pull-ups). These tests are usually structured in one of two ways. Either the subject performs as many repetitions as possible in a specified time, or the subject performs as many repetitions as possible before encountering fatigue. Consequently, for subjects who are able to perform multiple repetitions, these tests have an endurance component. As a result, field tests such as sit-ups and pull-ups usually have been labelled as tests of "muscular strength/endurance." Relatively little is known about the concurrent validity of field tests such as sit-ups and pull-ups (i.e., correlations with absolute measures of strength). However, it is clear that body weight is a confounding factor in performance of such tests (Berger & Medlin, 1969). It seems likely that these common field tests of muscular strength/endurance function best as measures of weight-relative muscular strength and that they are less useful as indicators of absolute strength. This view is corroborated by the results of a recent study in which pull-up test performance was found to correlate significantly with weight-relative muscular strength ($r = 0.51$) but to associate much less strongly with absolute strength ($r = 0.10$) (Pate & Lonnett, unpublished manuscript).

   In recent years, several efforts have been made to enhance the validity of field tests of muscular strength/endurance through modification of traditional test protocols. Bent-knee curl-ups have been recommended over sit-ups as a means of maximizing involvement of the abdominal musculature while minimizing the involvement of the hip flexors (Flint & Gudgell, 1965; Robertson & Magnusdottir, 1987; Walters & Partridge, 1975). Several modified pull-up tests have been developed (Baumgartner, 1978; Pate & Lonnett, unpublished manuscript; Pate et al., 1987). In general, these tests involve moving less than the full body mass and thereby tend to yield fewer zero scores than the traditional pull-up test. The flexed arm hang test, which in the past has often been used with girls only, has recently been used with both boys and girls (Reiff et al., 1985).

3. **Flexibility.** Perhaps the most commonly applied criterion measure of flexibility is joint range of motion as measured with the Leighton flexometer or goniometer (Leighton, 1942). Among the more common field tests of flexibility are the sit-and-reach, stand-and-reach and trunk extension tests. Of these, the sit-and-reach test has been the most widely applied with children. At present, all of the national physical fitness test batteries in the United States of America include a sit-and-reach test. The validity of field tests of flexibility, such as the sit-and-reach test, has not been studied extensively. However, a recent study found performance on the sit-and-reach test to be reasonably well-correlated with hamstring flexibility (r = 0.60 − 0.73) but not highly correlated with low back flexibility (r = 0.27 − 0.30) (Jackson & Baker, 1986). Inter-individual variability in anthropometric characteristics such as height and leg length are associated with sit-and-reach test performance, but only outlying values seem to affect performance to a significant extent (Broer & Galles, 1958).

4. **Body composition.** Measurement of body composition in children has been particularly difficult because of the lack of a suitable criterion measure. Body density can be effectively measured in children using the same techniques as are commonly applied with adults (e.g., hydrostatic weight). Other laboratory methods include whole-body radioactive counting of potassium and dilution techniques with deuterium oxide to estimate total body water (Lohman, 1982, 1986).

Unfortunately, transformation of measured body density to estimated percentage of body fat (% fat) has involved incorrect assumptions and calculations (Lohman, 1986). Application of body density-to-% fat transformation equations developed for adults (Siri, 1961) to children has been considered inappropriate because bone content of the fat-free body is known to be lower and water content higher in children than adults. Recently, Lohman and colleagues have reported technical advances in this area, and acceptable estimates of % fat can now be made in children (Lohman, 1986; Slaughter et al., 1988).

In recent years, as body composition has become accepted as a component of health-related physical fitness, field-based measurement of body composition in children has become common. Most frequently, field testing of body composition has been approached by measuring skinfold thicknesses at one or more anatomical sites (AAHPERD, 1980, 1988; Johnston et al., 1972, 1974; Lohman, 1986; Slaughter et al., 1988). Because of the previously mentioned concerns about the validity of transforming body density to % fat in children, most investigators have reported raw skinfold thickness data without transformation to estimated % fat (AAHPERD, 1980, 1985, 1988; Johnston et al., 1972, 1974). However, with the recent advances cited above, it seems likely that transformation of skinfold thickness measurements to % fat in children will be more common in the future, and standards have been proposed based on these advances (Lohman, 1986).

5. **Physical Fitness Test Batteries.** In the United States, most physical fittness testing of youngsters occurs in school physical education programs. Accordingly, most of the current physical fitness test batteries were developed for administration in the school setting. Over the past 15 y profound changes have occurred in the makeup of the physical fitness tests that have been developed and promoted by various national organizations in the United States. The reasons for the changes in testing methods have been discussed in previous publications (Blair et al., 1983; Pate, Corbin, et al., 1987; Plowman & Falls, 1978). Briefly, it appears that the changes have resulted from the expansion of two bodies of knowledge. First and most importantly, our greater knowledge of the relationships among physical activity, physical fitness and health factors has tended to highlight the importance of the health-related fitness components. Second, specific testing methods have been modified as our knowledge of test item validity, reliability, and practicality has grown.

Table 1-6 is presented to demonstrate the evolution in the makeup of physical fitness test batteries over recent decades. This table lists the physical fitness components and specific test items included in the test batteries promoted by the American Alliance for Health, Physical Education, Recreation and Dance across the 30 y period from 1958 to 1988. An examination of the information in Table 1-6 leads to several conclusions about recent trends in physical fitness testing in children in the United States. These include:

- There has been a gradual de-emphasis of measurement of motor skill and of components of fitness that fall primarily in the motor fitness domain (i.e., speed, agility, leg power).
- A greater focus on the components of health-related physical fitness, including body composition, has become evident.
- Methods for measurement of certain fitness components have been modified as new knowledge concerning validity of test items has become available.

As indicated by the information in Table 1-6, youth fitness testing practices have changed dramatically over the past 30 y. However, it would be incorrect to conclude that we currently have unanimity among professional groups as to the appropriate methods for fitness testing in children. Table 1-7 (adapted from Safrit, unpublished manuscript) provides a summary of the composition of several physical fitness test batteries that are currently being promoted nationally in the United States. Also included are the batteries that were administered in the two National Children and Youth Fitness Studies (NCYFS) (Ross & Gilbert, 1985; Ross & Pate, 1987) and a test battery developed by the International Council of Sport Science and Physical Education (Bos & Mechling, 1985). A review of the tests described in Table 1-7 indicates that most of the emphasis is being placed on health-related fitness components but that some of the batteries are continuing to include motor fitness test items.

6. **Purposes and Applications of Physical Fitness Testing.** In the protracted debate over appropriate fitness testing methods, there has been a tendency to overlook the broad purposes and long-term effects of physical fitness testing in children. The purposes of physical fitness testing have been discussed elsewhere (Pate, 1978) and will not be discussed in detail here. Briefly, fitness test batteries should be viewed primarily as educational tools that, if properly administered, can promote acquisition of important knowledges and skills. Also, fitness tests that are used in a sensitive and educationally sound fashion can contribute to the development of positive attitudes toward fitness. Such attitudes, it is assumed, should promote development of physically active lifestyles that carry into adulthood. This should be the major goal of our physical activity programs for youngsters. This philosophic position has been endorsed recently by the American College of Sports Medicine (1988) and the American Academy of Pediatrics (1987). We recommend that future research be directed toward describing the effects of participating in a physical fitness test and toward optimizing the techniques for administering such tests.

7. **Interpretation of Physical Fitness Test Performances.** In concluding this section, it seems important to comment on several issues related to interpretation of fitness test performances in children. Fitness test data are often evaluated by comparison of individual scores or group means with normative data or with previously collected data on the same individual or group. However, as noted above, there is currently a strong trend toward application of criterion-referenced fitness standards that are based on the established fitness-health relationship. Whether fitness scores are compared with norms, standards, or previously determined scores in the same individual or group, the following issues should be considered:

TABLE 1-6. *Fitness components and test items included in the physical fitness test batteries promoted by the American Alliance for Health, Physical Education, Recreation and Dance (AAHPERD), 1958 to 1988*

Fitness Component	AAHPER Youth Fitness Test (1958)	AAHPER Youth Fitness Test (1965)	AAHPER Youth Fitness Test (1975)	AAHPERD Health-Related Physical Fitness Test (1980)	AAHPERD Physical Best (1988)
Cardiorespiratory endurance	600 yd (550 m) walk/run	600 yd (550 m) walk/run	600 yd (550 m) walk/run Options: 1 mi (1.6 km) or 9 min run (ages 10–12); 1.5 mi (2.4 km) or 12 min run (ages ≥ 13)	1 mi (1.6 km) or 9 min run Option: 1.5 mi (2.4 km) or 12 min run	1 mi (1.6 km) run/walk
Body composition	—	—	—	Sum of skinfolds (triceps & subscapular)	Sum of skinfolds (triceps & calf) Options: —sum of triceps & subscapular —triceps only —body mass index

TABLE 1-6. (continued)

Flexibility	—	—	—	Sit-and-reach	Sit-and-reach
Muscular strength & endurance —Abdominal	Sit-ups: (straight leg, hands behind head; elbow touches opposite knee; maximal number)	Sit-ups: (same as 1958)	Sit-ups: (bent knee; arms across chest; number in 1 min)	Sit-ups: (arms across chest; curl up to sitting position; elbows touch thighs; number in 1 min)	Sit-ups: (same as 1980)
—Upper body	Pull-ups	Pull-ups (boys) Flexed arm hang (girls)	Pull-ups (boys) Flexed arm hang (girls)	—	Pull-ups
Anaerobic Power	Standing Long Jump	Standing Long Jump	Standing Long Jump	—	—
Speed	50 yd (45.9 m) Dash	50 yd (45.9 m) Dash	50 yd (45.9 m) Dash	—	—
Agility	Shuttle Run	Shuttle Run	Shuttle Run	—	—
Motor Skill	Softball Throw for Distance	Softball Throw for Distance	—	—	—

TABLE 1-7. *Fitness components and test items included in selected current physical fitness test batteries (1988)*

Fitness Component	AAHPERD Physical Best	Fitness-Gram	President's Challenge	Fit Youth Today
Cardiorespiratory	1 mi (1.6 km) walk/run for time Options: 1/2 mi walk/run (younger) 1 1/2 mi walk/run (older)	1 mi (1.6 km) walk/run for time	1 mi (1.6 km) walk/run for time	20 min steady state jog
Body composition	Sum of skinfolds (triceps & calf) Options: —Sum of triceps & subscapular, —triceps only, —body mass index	Sum of skinfolds (triceps & calf) Option: —body mass index	—	Sum of skinfolds (triceps & calf)
Flexibility	Sit-and-reach	Sit-and-reach	V-sit and reach Option: sit-reach	Sit-and-reach
Muscular strength and endurance —Abdominal	Sit-ups: (bent knees; arms across chest; elbows touch thighs; number in 1 min)	Sit-ups: (bent knees; arms across chest; number in 1 min)	Sit-ups: (bent knees; arms across chest; number in 1 min)	Sit-ups: (bent knees; arms across chest; number in 2 min)
—Upper body	Pull-ups	Pull-ups Option: Fl. arm hang	Pull ups	—
Agility/speed/anaerobic power	—	Shuttle run (optional)	Shuttle run	—

TABLE 1-7. *(continued)*

Fitness Component	NCYFS I	NCYFS II	Int'l Physical Performance Test Profile
Cardiorespiratory	1 mi (1.6 km) walk/run for time	1/2 mi (0.8 km) run/walk (ages 6 & 7) 1 mi (1.6 km) run/walk (ages 8 & 9)	6 min run
Body Composition	Sum of skinfolds (triceps & subscapular)	Sum of skinfolds (triceps, subscapular, calf)	—
Flexibility	Sit-and-reach	Sit-and-reach	—
Muscular Strength and endurance			
—Abdominal	Sit-ups: (bent knees; arms across chest; number in 1 min)	Sit-ups: (bent knees; arms across chest; number in 1 min)	Sit-ups: (bent knees; holding ball behind head; number in 30 sec)
—Upper body	Chin-ups	Modified pull-ups (pull up apparatus used)	Push-ups (30 sec) and medicine ball throw
Agility/speed/anaerobic power	—	—	20 m dash and standing long jump

Genetic endowment. The determinants of physical fitness in children are not well understood. However, it seems likely that a child's fitness is a function of his genetic endowment as well as his habitual physical activity characteristics (Bouchard, 1978). Therefore, those who interpret fitness test scores should consider that a child performs within the limits established by his genome. Because genetic profiles vary considerably across individuals, not all children can be expected to attain high levels of fitness.

Developmental status. Children of the same age can vary markedly in body size and in maturity level. Since both growth and development affect fitness test performances, the child's developmental status should be considered when his fitness test scores are evaluated. Children who are particularly "early" or "late" maturers should be expected to manifest physical fitness profiles that are typical of children of greater or lesser chronological age, respectively.

Standardization of test protocols. If fitness test scores are compared with previously established scores or standards, it is important that the testing methods be appropriately standardized. The concern for standardization operates at two levels. First, it is, of course, important that the same test items be employed. As was discussed in a previous section of this chapter, not all of the widely promoted test batteries use the same test items. At a second level, it is critical that field tests be administered in a consistent and standardized manner. Children should be carefully prepared for execution of tests, and examiners must follow prescribed guidelines with rigor.

II. PHYSICAL FITNESS CHARACTERISTICS OF CHILDREN AND YOUTH

In considering the physical fitness characteristics of youngsters, several pertinent questions come to mind. How does physical fitness change with aging? How do the sexes differ at the various stages of growth and development? Has the physical fitness of children changed over recent decades? How do measures of physical fitness associate with one another in children? These questions will be addressed in the following sections of this chapter. However, because each of these issues could be the basis for a very expansive discussion, some limitations must be imposed. First, major attention will be given only to the four health-related physical fitness components. Second, whenever possible, discussions will be based on data recently collected from nationally representative samples of children in the United States. Results of three large-scale surveys published since 1985 will be used (Reiff et al., 1985; Ross & Gilbert, 1985; Ross & Pate, 1987). In interpreting the results of these field-based surveys, pertinent laboratory-based studies will be referenced.

A. Physical Fitness In Children With Regard To Age and Sex

It is, of course, well-established that many physical performance characteristics are related to body size (Malina, 1975; Shephard, 1982). Accordingly, it seems appropriate to begin an examination of fitness characteristics of children with a brief review of the changes in body size that occur across the age-span of interest, in this case 6–18 years. Figures 1-1 and 1-2 demonstrate the age trends in mean height and weight for children included in the two National Children and Youth Fitness Studies. Across the 6–13 year age range, mean height and weight increase linearly with age in both boys and girls. However, above age 13 in girls, both height and weight gradually reach a plateau, whereas boys continue to increase steadily in mean height through age 15 and in mean weight through age 17.

Since body size increases dramatically during childhood, interpretation of the physical fitness characteristics of children of different ages must consider body size as a potential confounding factor. Thus, various conventions have been adopted to control for body size differences across age groups of children. The most common technique involves expression of a variable relative to body mass, and it is this procedure that will be employed in this chapter. However, it should be noted that fitness traits are sometimes expressed relative to body surface area and to various functions of height. More

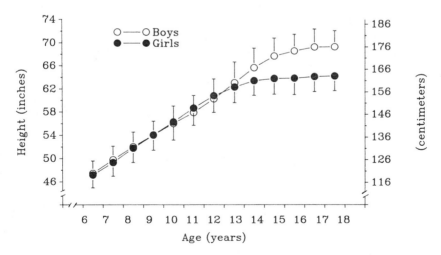

FIGURE 1-1. *Mean height (± SD) of U.S. boys and girls ages 6–18 years as determined in the National Children and Youth Fitness Studies (Ross and Gilbert, 1985; Ross and Pate, 1987).*

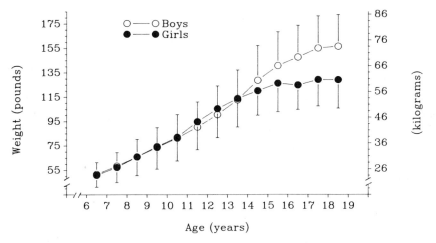

FIGURE 1-2. *Mean weight (± SD) of U.S. boys and girls ages 6–18 years as determined in the National Children and Youth Fitness Studies (Ross and Gilbert, 1985; Ross and Pate, 1987).*

detailed discussions of techniques for dimensional analysis of physical fitness data in children are available in other references (Astrand & Rodahl, 1986; Shephard, 1982).

In the following sections, developmental trends in physical fitness variables will be examined by reviewing cross-sectional studies in which subjects were grouped by sex and chronological age. However, it should be noted that cross-sectional data tend to obscure the effects of developmental phenomena such as the adolescent growth spurt, which occurs at different ages in different children. The effects of the growth spurt are better represented via longitudinal tracking of fitness variables with age expressed relative to the age at "peak height velocity" (Beuner & Malina, 1988; Mirwald & Bailey, 1986). To date, developmental trends for fitness variables have not been recorded longitudinally in large, nationally representative samples of children.

1. Body Composition. Skinfold thickness data from the two National Children and Youth Fitness Studies (NCYFS) are presented in Figure 1-3. This figure shows that mean skinfold fat increases steadily in girls up to the age of 15. In boys skinfold thicknesses increase up to the age of 10, then remain approximately constant through age 18. Thicker skinfolds are found in girls than boys across the entire age range, although the difference is not great up through age 11. After that age, the mean sex difference increases substantially for about three years and ultimately levels at age 15, with a

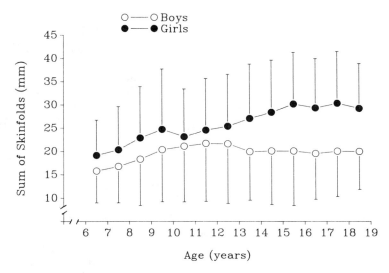

FIGURE 1-3. *Mean sum of triceps and subscapular skinfold thickness (± SD) in U.S. boys and girls as determined in the National Children and Youth Fitness Studies (Ross and Gilbert, 1985; Ross and Pate, 1987).*

difference of about 18 mm for the sum of triceps and subscapular skinfolds.

The age-related increases in skinfold fat observed in children almost certainly reflect increases in overall body fatness. For example, Lohman (1986) has estimated % body fat from the skinfold data collected by the National Center for Health Statistics (Johnston et al., 1972, 1974) and has determined that in boys, body fat increases from a mean of 11% to 16% from the ages of 6 to 11 y. In girls, body fat increases progressively from 14% at 6 y to 27% at 17 y.

2. Cardiorespiratory Endurance. In general, the capacity of children to perform sustained exercise that relies primarily on aerobic metabolism improves with age. However, the manifestation of this improvement varies with method of measurement. As shown by the data in Figure 1-4, mean 1.6 km (one mile) run/walk performance improves gradually in both boys and girls across the 8–14 y age range. Beyond that age, boys continue to improve, but mean performance in girls plateaus at about 12 min. In an adult, this would correspond to a maximum oxygen uptake of only 28 $mL \cdot kg^{-1} \cdot min^{-1}$. Mean performance in boys improves through age 16 before leveling at performances of about 8 min. Boys perform better than girls across the entire age range, and the sex difference increases steadily through age 15.

The 1.6 km run/walk is, of course, a performance test that involves weight-bearing exercise. The data in Figure 1-4 show clearly the capacity of children to perform such exercise improves with aging up to about age 14 for girls and age 16 for boys and that, on average, boys perform better than girls at all ages. As discussed in a previous section, endurance runs have been validated against directly measured $\dot{V}O_2$max and, therefore, it is true that children with higher weight-relative $\dot{V}O_2$max values tend to perform better on tests such as the mile run. However, this interpretation is correct only when applied to children within a narrow age range. It would be *incorrect* to conclude from the trends observed in the data in Figure 1-4 that weight-relative $\dot{V}O_2$max increases with aging in children. Indeed, available evidence suggests that mean $\dot{V}O_2$max ($mL \cdot kg^{-1} \cdot min^{-1}$) is roughly equal across age groups of children (Bar-Or, 1983; Pate & Blair, 1978; Shephard, 1984). It seems likely that the observed age-wise improvement in 1.6 km run performance is explained primarily by the decrease in the weight-relative oxygen cost of running that occurs with increasing leg length and perhaps other developmental changes and improved choice of pace (Bar-Or, 1983; Daniels & Oldridge, 1971; Krahenbuhl et al., 1985).

Because body weight increases with age while mean weight-relative $\dot{V}O_2$max remains approximately constant, it is clear that

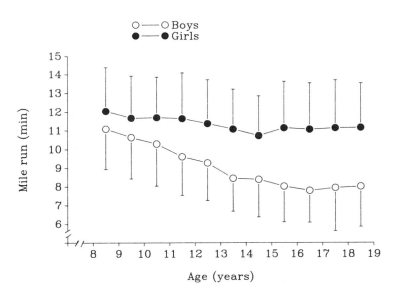

FIGURE 1-4. *Mean mile run/walk time (± SD) in U.S. boys and girls as determined in the National Children and Youth Fitness Studies (Ross and Gilbert, 1985; Ross and Pate, 1987).*

$\dot{V}O_2$max expressed in absolute terms ($L \cdot min^{-1}$) increases with age. Such an increase is well-documented and explains the age-wise improvements in performance on endurance tests that involve work against external resistances that are not scaled to body weight. An example is the PWC_{170} test, which has been used extensively with children.

The data presented in Figure 1-4 demonstrate a rather marked sex difference in performance on the 1.6 km run/walk test. Because the oxygen cost of running does not differ greatly between boys and girls (Astrand, 1952), the sex difference in 1.6 km run performance probably does reflect a sex difference in weight-relative $\dot{V}O_2$max. The existence of such a difference is corroborated by the results of laboratory studies indicating a small sex difference in $\dot{V}O_2$max in younger children, but larger differences in older youth (Bar-Or, 1983; Pate & Blair, 1978; Shephard, 1982). The observed sex differences in $\dot{V}O_2$max and related performance tests are probably explained in part by gender-related differences in body composition (see previous section) and hemoglobin concentration (Astrand, 1952; Bar-Or, 1983). Also, it seems likely that the observed performance differences may be partly accounted for by differences in habitual activity levels (Rode & Shephard, 1971; Shephard, 1982).

3. Muscular Strength. Muscular strength, measured in absolute terms via dynamometry, increases with aging in children. The observed increases in strength mirror rather closely the muscle mass that develops during childhood (Malina, 1975). Shephard (1982) has reported that, before puberty, isometric muscle strength tends to increase progressively in both boys and girls and that the boys manifest values about 10% greater than the girls. However, beyond the age of 12, boys show a continued increase in strength (about 50% from ages 12 to 14), whereas strength scores in girls tend to reach a plateau.

As was discussed above, field measures of muscular strength usually involve resisting or moving part or all of the body mass. A typical example is the flexed arm hang test, in which subjects move their chins up to a high bar, which is grasped with an over-hand grip. Figure 1-5 presents flexed arm hang test data for a representative sample of U.S. children. The data in Figure 1-5 indicate that mean upper body muscular strength (relative to body weight) remains fairly constant from the ages of 6 to 12 years but increases markedly in boys during puberty (ages 13–15 years). In girls, mean flexed arm hang performance changes little across the 6–17 y age range.

A rather different developmental pattern is observed for sit-up test scores. Performance on the timed sit-up test presumably reflects

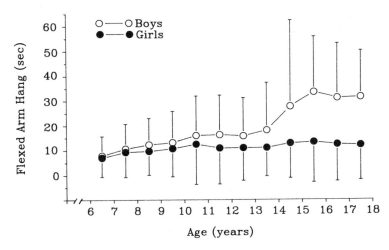

FIGURE 1-5. *Mean flexed arm hang time (± SD) in U.S. boys and girls as determined in the National School Population Fitness Survey (Reiff, et al., 1985).*

the ratio between abdominal muscular strength and the mass of the upper body (i.e., torso, head, arms). As shown in Figure 1-6, the number of sit-ups performed in one minute increases steadily in both boys and girls from ages 6 to 12. After age 12, mean test per-

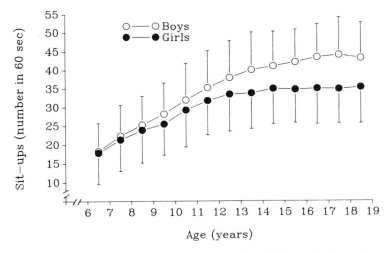

FIGURE 1-6. *Mean sit-up test performance (± SD) in U.S. boys and girls as determined in the National Children and Youth Fitness Studies (Ross and Gilbert, 1985; Ross and Pate, 1987).*

24 *PERSPECTIVES IN EXERCISE*

formance plateaus in girls but continues to increase in boys, albeit at a rate that is slower than that observed before puberty. The different developmental trends for flexed arm hang and sit-up test performances may be associated with age-related changes in the distribution of the body mass. During childhood, body proportions change so the mass of the upper body relative to total body mass declines (Spurgeon et al., 1959). Therefore, it appears likely that the strength of the abdominal muscles increases more rapidly than the mass of the upper body. In contrast, tests such as the flexed arm hang require resisting the entire body weight, which increases at roughly the same rate as muscle mass and strength.

    4. Flexibility. As indicated by the data in Figure 1-7, performance on the sit-and-reach test remains fairly constant in boys and girls across the 6–10 y age range. After age 10, girls manifest a gradual improvement in performance that continues through age 16. In boys, an improvement in performance is noted, but it begins at age 14 and continues through age 17. A sex difference in performance is observed across the entire age range. However, in contrast to observations with the other fitness components, greater flexibility is found in girls than boys. The magnitude of the mean differences in sit-and-reach test performance is only about 2.5 cm (1 in) at the younger ages, but the difference increases markedly during puberty to about 7.6 cm (3 in).

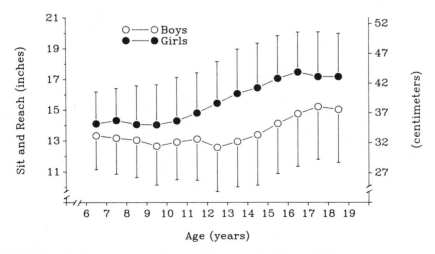

FIGURE 1-7. *Mean sit-and-reach test performance (± SD) in U.S. boys and girls as determined in the National Children and Youth Fitness Studies (Ross and Gilbert, 1985; Ross and Pate, 1987).*

B. Secular Trends In Physical Fitness Of Children

One of the most common public perceptions in the youth fitness domain is that contemporary children are less physically fit than their counterparts of previous decades. This perception has been created by regular reports from respected fitness authorities that today's children are "unfit" or "fail to meet acceptable fitness standards." Such reports are apparently readily accepted by parents and others who are concerned about societal trends such as increased television watching by children and reduced dependence on "human energy" for transportation (e.g., walking or bicycling to school). However, common perceptions are not always consistent with pertinent scientific evidence.

Regrettably, a comprehensive analysis of secular trends in health-related fitness of children cannot now be performed because health-related fitness surveys of representative samples of children have only recently been conducted. In the United States, three national surveys of fitness in 10- to 17-year-old youths were conducted in 1958, 1965, 1975, and 1985 by the President's Council on Physical Fitness and Sports (Reiff et al., 1985). However, these surveys have focused primarily on motor fitness components (e.g., 45.7 m (50 yd) dash, standing long jump, shuttle run). All four of the surveys included the pull-up test for boys, and the first three surveys included the flexed-arm hang test for girls. Examination of the age-group means for these strength tests reveals no clear performance trends across the four surveys. Some improvements were noted between 1958 and 1965, but this could reflect in part greater familiarity of children with the test battery.

The best method now available for assessing secular trends in fitness is evaluation of skinfold thickness data collected on children in the United States since the early 1960s. Gortmaker and colleagues (1987) recently studied the prevalence of obesity in 6- to 17-year-old children by comparing triceps skinfold thickness data collected in cycles 2 and 3 of the National Health Examination Survey (NHES) (1963–1970) and the first and second National Health and Nutrition Examination Survey (1971–74 and 1976–80, respectively). Defining obesity as being at or above the 85th percentile for triceps skinfold thickness determined in the earlier survey, Gortmaker et al. found 54% and 39% increases in the prevalence of this condition in 6–11 and 12–17 year old groups, respectively. In a somewhat similar unpublished study comparing NHES skinfold data from the 1960s and NCYFS skinfold data from the 1980s, Lohman, Going, Houtkooper, Pate, and Ross reported that average estimated % body fat was approximately 2% greater in the latter survey.

The results of these longitudinal studies of skinfold thickness certainly suggest that children have become fatter. Because physical activity is a determinant of body composition, it may well be that today's children are fatter because they are less active. Indeed, both Dietz and Gortmaker (1985) and Pate and Ross (1987) have reported significant associations between measures of physical activity and skinfold thickness in children. A particularly important culprit may be time spent viewing television, which, in both of the aforementioned studies, was found to be positively correlated with skinfold thickness.

If reduced physical activity is an underlying cause of the reported increased fatness in children, it is possible that today's children rank lower than their predecessors in other aspects of physical fitness. However, as mentioned previously, data that would allow a direct examination of this possibility are not currently available.

C. Associations Among Measures Of Physical Fitness In Children

In a previous section of this chapter it was noted that youth fitness testing practices have evolved toward greater emphasis on health-related physical fitness and away from a focus on motor fitness. Also, it was noted that health-related physical fitness has been operationalized in multidimensional terms and measured with test batteries that include four or five test items. These recent trends in fitness testing practices have been driven by several beliefs about the relationships between the two types of fitness. Among these are:

- Health-related physical fitness and motor fitness are overlapping yet distinct concepts.
- Motor fitness components such as anaerobic power, speed, and agility have a common biological basis that is related to the contractile properties and amount of skeletal muscle.
- The components of health-related physical fitness are essentially independent of each other and therefore warrant measurement via separate test items.

The validity of these three beliefs can be tested, to a limited extent, by examining the associations among performances on the common fitness test items in children.

1. Associations Between Health-related Fitness And Motor Fitness Tests. After considering the recent trends mentioned above, the skeptic might wonder whether the distinction between health-related fitness and motor fitness goes beyond the philosophical. Are the two concepts different at the practical level? Or, put another way, do not the same children perform well on fitness tests regardless of the nature of the test?

The data presented in Table 1-8 indicate that, from a measurement perspective, health-related fitness and motor fitness are largely independent. The correlation coefficients between common health-related fitness and motor fitness test items are generally in the low to moderate range (<0.35). Only four of the 36 correlation coefficients reported in Table 1-8 were greater than 0.35, and all of these were for associations among running tests. These tests, regardless of duration, presumably have some underlying basis related to skill in running. Such a presumption is consistent with the finding of Cureton et al. (1977) that 50 yd dash performance is an apparent determinant of distance running performance in children.

2. Associations Among Motor Fitness Test Items. The data presented in Table 1-9 indicate that performances on the common

TABLE 1-8.   *Zero-order correlations* between selected motor fitness and health-related physical fitness test items (Reiff et al., 1985)*

| | BOYS | | |
	Age	50 yd (45.9 m) dash	Shuttle run
Flexed Arm Hang	7	0.35	0.20
	11	0.39	0.34
	16	0.28	0.29
Sit-and-Reach	7	0.16	0.04
	11	0.02	0.06
	16	0.09	0.16
Mile Run	7	0.31	0.11
	11	0.51	0.40
	16	0.45	0.25
	GIRLS		
	Age	50 yd (45.9 m) dash	Shuttle run
Flexed Arm Hang	7	0.27	0.14
	11	0.20	0.01
	16	0.28	0.32
Sit-and-Reach	7	0.22	0.24
	11	0.33	0.14
	16	0.17	0.20
Mile Run	7	0.36	0.26
	11	0.38	0.34
	16	0.26	0.54

*Signs of correlation coefficients were not reported. It is assumed that a positive correlation indicates that "Better Performance" on one test was positively associated with "Better Performance" on the other.

TABLE 1-9. *Zero-order correlations* among selected motor fitness test items (Reiff et al., 1985).*

| | BOYS | | |
	Age	50 yd (45.9 m) Dash	Shuttle Run
Standing Long Jump	7	0.55	0.36
	11	0.58	0.59
	16	0.43	0.36
50 yd Dash	7		0.45
	11	—	0.47
	16		0.31
	GIRLS		
	Age	50 yd (45.9 m) Dash	Shuttle Run
Standing Long Jump	7	0.48	0.29
	11	0.51	0.48
	16	0.50	0.54
50 yd Dash	7		0.51
	11	—	0.43
	16		0.55

*Signs of correlation coefficients were not reported. It is assumed that a positive correlation indicates that "Better Performance" on one test was positively associated with "Better Performance" on the other.

motor performance test items tend to be at least moderately correlated with each other. Of the 18 zero-order correlation coefficients presented in Table 1-9, 14 are greater than 0.40. Clearly these items tend to associate more strongly with each other than with the health-related fitness test items. This finding is consistent with the nature of the test items and with the relevant information from the field of muscle biochemistry. Each of the test items included in Table 1-9 (standing long jump, 50 yd dash, shuttle run) requires high rates of power output by the leg musculature. Ability to perform such activity is dependent, to a considerable extent, on fiber type distribution in skeletal muscle (Costill et al., 1976). Since test items such as the 45.7 m (50 yd) dash and standing long jump have a common biological basis and tend to be highly correlated, there appears to be no compelling reason to include both items in a test battery.

3. **Associations Among Health-Related Fitness Test Items.** In contrast to the data for motor fitness items, performances on health-related fitness test items are not correlated highly with each other. Of the 60 correlation coefficients presented in Table 1-10, only six are greater than 0.35. This suggests that these test items are essentially independent of each other and that inclusion of each in test

batteries is warranted. However, it is also noted that the low correlations may reflect in part the limited reliability of the measurements.

It may be noteworthy that the sit-and-reach test is apparently the most independent test of those included in Table 1-10. Also, it should be noted that sum of skinfolds does not associate more strongly with performance on the other items than those items do with each other. While body composition may be an underlying determinant of performance on tests such as the distance run, the data in Table 1-10 indicate that performance on a distance run test is not highly correlated with sum of skinfold thickness in children.

TABLE 1-10. *Zero-order correlations* among health-related physical fitness test items as observed in NCYFS I and II (Ross & Gilbert, 1985; Ross & Pate, 1987).*

| | | BOYS Sum of | | | |
Variable	Age	Skinfolds	Sit-reach	Sit-ups	Pull-ups
Distance Run	6–7	0.34	−0.01	−0.27	−0.30
	10–11	0.41	−0.14	−0.24	−0.29
	15–16	0.32	−0.09	−0.31	−0.24
Sum of Skinfolds	6–7		−0.02	−0.23	−0.26
	10–11	—	−0.12	−0.25	−0.42
	15–16		−0.03	−0.16	−0.42
Sit-reach	6–7			−0.11	0.15
	10–11	—	—	−0.17	0.19
	15–16			−0.19	0.18
Sit-ups	6–7				0.48
	10–11	—	—	—	0.32
	15–16				0.29

| | | GIRLS Sum of | | | |
Variable	Age	Skinfolds	Sit-reach	Sit-ups	Pull-ups
Distance Run	6–7	0.31	−0.03	−0.34	−0.34
	10–11	0.33	−0.16	−0.35	−0.23
	15–16	0.26	−0.12	−0.42	−0.19
Sum of Skinfolds	6–7		−0.02	−0.20	−0.30
	10–11	—	−0.07	−0.24	−0.29
	15–16		−0.06	−0.17	−0.18
Sit-reach	6–7			0.16	0.17
	10–11	—	—	0.23	0.05
	15–16			0.19	0.06
Sit-up	6–7				0.46
	10–11	—	—	—	0.26
	15–16				0.25

*Correlation coefficients greater than 0.15 are statistically significant at the 0.001 probability level.

D. Cross-Cultural Comparisons

The information presented to this point is drawn mainly from children in the United States. However, it may be useful to attempt some comparisons with available information from other parts of the world.

1. Limitations To Comparisons. Any comparisons must be made with considerable caution. Most large-scale surveys have used simple field tests, and small differences in test design, motivation, environmental conditions, and recent practice of the required skills all have a major impact upon test results. Thus, the performance test battery of the California Association for Health, Physical Education and Recreation (CAHPER), superficially similar to that devised by AAHPERD, has many differences of detail; for example, the CAHPER shuttle run is begun from a lying rather than a standing position (Shephard, 1982). In many countries, the concept of competition is less developed than in the United States, and there is corresponding difficulty in motivation for speed-based tests. Likewise, the running speed possible in an air-conditioned gymnasium differs markedly from that observed on rough ground in tropical heat. Finally, children in the United States have out-performed their European counterparts on a soft-ball throw, probably not because of superior explosive strength in their arms, but because the game of softball is almost unknown in Europe.

If laboratory tests are used, systematic errors may again arise from differences in measuring equipment and technique. However, several international organizations, including the World Health Organization, the International Biological Program, and the International Committee for Physical Fitness Research have proposed standardized procedures to minimize this source of difficulty (Andersen et al., 1971; Larson, 1974; Weiner & Lourie, 1981).

Finally, many comparisons are complicated by differences among samples in body size, secular trends, nutritional status, maturity, and general health. The scores on most field tests of performance are heavily influenced by both height and body mass (Shephard, 1982). In most countries, children increase in height by about 1 cm per decade, so account must be taken of the age at which observations were made. When laboratory measurements such as maximum oxygen uptake are expressed per kg of body mass or per cm^2 of height, they are adversely influenced by over-nutrition, but severe protein malnutrition or anemia due to parasitic infection may also limit maximum oxygen transport. Maturation occurs earlier in countries such as the United States, where favorable average socioeconomic conditions lead to earlier increases of muscle strength in boys and of body fat in girls.

2.   **Height.** The overall stature of children seems influenced much more by socioeconomic factors than by ethnic groupings (Shephard, 1978); thus, growth patterns are widely accepted as one important measure of the adequacy of community nutrition.

The heights of Canadian children were comparable to those of children from Hungary and the United Kingdom in 1966, are much greater than those of children in Bahrain, but are less than those of children in Belgium and the United States (Table 1-11). One reason for the shorter average stature of the Canadian group relative to the sample from the United States is that there are large regional differences. The lowest figures are seen for the Inuit and some of the Indian populations; Francophone children have also traditionally been smaller than the Anglophones, although with the improved socioeconomic status of Quebec, there is now a strong secular trend to obliterate this difference (Shephard, 1986).

3.   **Body Mass.** Because body mass necessarily varies with stature, cross-cultural comparisons are conveniently made in terms of various mass/height ratios; we will here use units of g/cm (Table 1-12). Before considering the data, two points of interpretation must be stressed. First, illness and selective sampling tend to exclude the extremes of heavy and light individuals, and the extent of exclusion of the heaviest children depends on the extent of disapproval of obesity in any given culture. Secondly, in some societies, such as the Inuit of the Canadian Arctic, a high body mass reflects well-developed muscles rather than an accumulation of adipose tissue.

TABLE 1-11.   *Height (cm) of prepubescent children—some international comparisons (for sources of data, see Shephard, 1986). U.S. data from NCYFS I and II.*

Age (years *)	U.S.A. 1985–87	Canada 1981	BOYS U.K. 1966	Belgium 1969	Hungary 1979	Bahrain 1983
7	126.5	123.5	123.5	126.3	124.8	—
8	132.2	129.3	128.0	131.2	129.9	—
9	137.3	134.8	134.2	136.1	135.3	128.7
10	142.4	140.2	139.4	141.2	140.4	130.9
11	147.1	145.0	144.9	146.0	145.6	135.6
Age (years *)	U.S.A. 1985–87	Canada 1981	GIRLS U.K. 1966	Belgium 1969	Hungary 1979	Bahrain 1983
7	125.3	124.2	122.4	124.7	124.4	—
8	131.6	129.2	127.9	129.9	129.9	—
9	137.3	134.8	133.5	135.0	135.7	—
10	143.0	141.2	139.7	141.4	141.4	131.8
11	149.1	145.9	146.2	148.3	146.9	135.5

*Age at last birthday (that is, 7 equals 7.00–7.99 years); other values interpolated where necessary.

TABLE 1-12. *Weight for height ratios (g/cm) in selected populations; for details of sources see Shephard (1986). U.S. data from NCYFS I and II.*

BOYS

Age (years *)	U.S.A.	Canada	Belgium	Czechoslovakia	France	Hungary	U.K.
	1985–87	1981	1969	1970	1964	1979	1966
7–9	0.224	0.214	0.194	0.186	0.196	0.207	0.198
10–12	0.277	0.264	0.232	0.261	0.234	0.254	0.239
13–14	0.330	0.318				0.265	0.304
15–19	0.384	0.386		0.335	0.287	0.358	0.346

GIRLS

Age (years *)	U.S.A.	Canada	Belgium	Czechoslovakia	France	Hungary	U.K.
	1985–87	1981	1969	1970	1964	1979	1966
7–9	0.225	0.214	0.200	0.188	0.193	0.204	0.201
10–12	0.285	0.267	0.242	0.264	0.238	0.256	0.250
13–14	0.329	0.328			0.300	0.314	0.320
15–19	0.351	0.351		0.333		0.341	0.344

* Age at last birthday (that is, 7 equals 7.00 to 7.99 years)

CHARACTERISTICS OF PHYSICAL FITNESS **33**

The current body mass to height ratios for children from the United States and Canada are higher than for most other national samples. It could be argued that in some populations the group tested was less representative, with a selective sampling of more active children; also, the sports popular among Canadian adolescent boys (ice hockey and Canadian football) favor heavier players. At least a part of the additional mass seems to be muscle, but skinfold readings are also greater for North American youths than for some European samples (Table 1-13).

   4.   Body Composition. Most of the large-scale population data on body composition are based upon the measurement of skinfold thicknesses (Table 1-13). The percentage of body fat, and thus the mass of lean tissue per cm of stature, has been estimated by the application of standard prediction formulae (Table 1-14).

   The North American children seem to have somewhat more subcutaneous fat than some of their European counterparts, including those from Belgium, West Germany, and the United Kingdom. However, interpopulation differences are much greater between more and less developed societies. In Canadian Inuit boys, for example, the average skinfold thickness is only 4.6 mm at 13–14 y, and 5.5 mm at 15–19 y; moreover, the lesser thickness of subcutaneous fat seems compatible with normal health.

   Unfortunately, much of the world data on lean body mass is derived from small and unrepresentative samples. Moreover, the [40]potassium method (used in the study of West German children) yields systematically different answers from those obtained by either skinfold measurements or hydrostatic weighing. The skinfold estimates from North America nevertheless seem lower than the figures obtained in Czechoslovakia and the United Kingdom, the latter being based upon hydrostatic weighing.

   5.   Maximum Oxygen Uptake. While there have now been a substantial number of international studies that used direct measurements of maximum oxygen uptake, only small samples of subjects have been so tested. Subjects are commonly of above-average fitness. One survey of the world literature (Shephard, 1966) tabulated data for 6,633 nonathletic males and 653 nonathletic females, mostly fitness test volunteers (Table 1-15). Other large samples have been tested in Czechoslovakia and West Germany, whereas in Canada, representative population samples have performed the Canadian Home Fitness Test and the PWC_{170} test.

   In the youngest age category, scores for the world population are biased upward by a Swedish sample that was probably above the average fitness for that country. The U.S. population data fall well below the world averages, although smaller U.S. samples have

Table 1-13. Skinfold readings for selected populations (in some cases, values have been interpolated). Average of 2-4 skinfolds, mm. For sources of data see Shephard (1986). U.S. data from NCYFS I and II.

BOYS

Age (years *)	U.S.A. 1985–87	Canada 1981	Belgium 1969	Czechoslovakia 1970	W. Germany 1972	Holland 1979	U.K. 1962
7–9	9.3	6.8	—	4.8	6.4	10.0	6.4
10–12	10.8	8.3	7.2	6.2	7.2	9.7	7.0
13–14	10.0	7.9	7.4	8.2	7.8	9.0	7.5
15–19	9.9	8.5	7.4	8.5	—	—	7.5

GIRLS

Age (years *)	U.S.A. 1985–87	Canada 1981	Belgium 1969	Czechoslovakia 1970	W. Germany 1972	Holland 1979	U.K. 1962
7–9	11.3	8.3	—	6.3	7.8	11.3	7.7
10–12	12.2	9.6	—	8.5	9.1	11.3	9.0
13–14	13.9	11.1	—	12.0	10.5	11.2	10.5
15–19	14.9	12.5	—	13.5	—	—	12.1

* Age at last birthday (that is 7 equals 7.00–7.99 years)

TABLE 1-14. *Lean mass (g/cm) in selected population. In some cases, values have been interpolated. For sources of data, see Shephard (1986). U.S. data from NCYFS I and II.*

			BOYS		
Age	U.S.A.	Canada	Czechoslovakia	W. Germany	U.K.
(years *)	1985–87	1981	1970	1967	1977
7–9	185	182	—	121	—
10–12	223	219	226	145	—
13–14	273	265	283	177	—
15–19	322	311	327	227	350

			GIRLS		
Age	U.S.A.	Canada	Czechoslovakia	W. Germany	U.K.
(years *)	1985–87	1981	1970	1967	1977
7–9	174	169	—	—	—
10–12	219	207	—	—	—
13–14	250	244	—	—	—
15–19	264	256	—	—	270

*Age at last birthday (that is, 7 equals 7.00 to 7.99 years)

sometimes matched these figures. The Home Fitness Test data from Canada conform fairly closely to the world averages in the older age categories, although lower figures were predicted from the PWC_{170} results.

In many under-developed societies, probably because of malnutrition and disease, the maximum oxygen uptake is no higher than the world average for industrialized countries (Shephard, 1978).

TABLE 1-15. *Maximum oxygen uptake data ($mL \cdot kg \cdot min^{-1}$) for selected populations (data interpolated where necessary); Canadian data based on results of Canadian Home Fitness Test (CHFT) or Physical Working Capacity at a heart rate of 170 (PWC_{170}). See Shephard (1986) for sources of data.*

			BOYS		
Age	Canada		World	Czechoslovakia	W. Germany
(years *)	1981		1966	1970	1961
	CHFT	PWC_{170}			
7–9	49.9	41.3	54.3	—	—
10–12	50.4	41.8	50.0	45.0	45.0
13–14	50.7	43.3	49.8	—	48.0
15–19	49.3	43.7	46.4	45.4	45.0

			GIRLS		
Age	Canada		World	Czechoslovakia	W. Germany
(years *)	1981		1966	1970	1961
	CHFT	PWC_{170}			
7–9	42.7	36.8	49.8	—	38.0
10–12	42.8	37.5	46.5	37.5	39.0
13–14	42.5	35.9	42.1	—	38.0
15–19	40.9	36.8	43.3	35.4	38.0

*Age in completed year (that is, 7 equals 7.00 to 7.99 years)

However, high figures have been reported for some arctic communities, particularly the Canadian Inuit, where prolonged physical labor in hunting has been the norm; the advantage of these groups has been steadily lost as they have become acculturated to a "western" lifestyle (Rode & Shephard, 1984).

      6. **Handgrip Force.** Readings for handgrip force are somewhat vulnerable to the type of measuring instrument that is used. Recent North American data have been obtained mainly with the accepted Stoelting handgrip dynamometer (Table 1-16). Figures using this instrument seem generally a little higher than those reported from Europe, and the Stoelting data greatly exceed the figures for Bahrain. Other values from less urbanized societies (including the Inuit) show lower grip strengths than those observed in urban North America; this may reflect in part a lesser willingness to undertake a maximal effort rather than a true difference of muscular strength.

      7. **Speed Sit-ups.** Current figures for one min, speed sit-ups are fairly comparable in the United States and Canada, and appear to exceed figures for some other countries (Table 1-17). Again, it is unclear the extent to which this reflects a true difference of muscular strength and endurance, and the extent to which it reflects motivation and recent practice of the required skills.

      8. **Flexibility.** While there is much published data on the sit-and-reach test, comparisons have all too often been vitiated by a failure to indicate the zero position of the measuring scale. Canadian students seem marginally inferior to U.S. and Dutch students on this test, but Canadians out-perform Scottish students (Table 1-18).

TABLE 1-16. *Handgrip force (N) for selected populations; data interpolated where necessary. See Shephard (1986) for sources of data.*

			BOYS			
Age	Canada	Belgium	Czechoslovakia	Bahrain	Holland	Scotland
(years *)	1981	1969	1970	1983	1979	1980–83
7–9	147	132	—	108	122	—
10–12	218	201	—	147	141	—
13–14	326	—	—	201	183	204
15–19	469	—	489	336	—	364
			GIRLS			
Age	Canada	Belgium	Czechoslovakia	Bahrain	Holland	Scotland
(years *)	1981	1969	1970	1983	1979	1980–83
7–9	132	—	—	—	104	—
10–12	192	—	—	131	122	—
13–14	268	—	—	191	150	224
15–19	294	—	306	221	—	289

*Age in completed years (that is, 7 equals 7.00–7.99 years).

TABLE 1-17. *Speed sit-ups in one minute—some international comparisons. For sources of data see Shephard (1986). U.S. data from NCYFS I and II.*

Age	U.S.A.	Canada	BOYS W. Germany	Israel	Scotland
(years *)	1985–87	1981	1978	1978	1983
7–9	25.3	28.0	13	14	—
10–12	35.4	34.9	18	21	—
13–14	40.5	38.5	20	24	—
15–19	43.2	38.2	—	—	—

Age	U.S.A.	Canada	GIRLS W. Germany	Israel	Scotland
(years *)	1985–87	1981	1978	1978	1983
7–9	23.6	26.1	13	13	—
10–12	31.7	32.6	18	18	—
13–14	34.4	33.7	18	18	25
15–19	34.9	31.6	—	—	25

*Age in completed years (that is, 7 equals 7.00–7.99 years).

9. Conclusions. There remain many problems in comparing youth fitness data from one laboratory to another because of differences in equipment, technique, and sociocultural factors. However, the general impression that emerges from such comparisons is that the urban North American child is fatter, somewhat stronger, and has a poorer maximum oxygen uptake than those from other societies; these differences are particularly marked in communities where a high level of physical activity is important to normal daily living. Given that children from countries having poorer economies can develop a higher level of health-related fitness, it appears that

TABLE 1-18. *Flexibility (sit-and-reach test, 25.0 cm equals ability to touch toes). For sources of data, see Shephard (1986). U.S. data from NCYFS I and II.*

Age	U.S.	BOYS Canada	Holland	Scotland
(years *)	1985–87	1981	1982	1980–83
7–9	27.3	27.9	—	—
10–12	27.3	26.5	27.0	—
13–14	28.0	26.2	29.0	25.7
15–19	32.1	29.8	32.0	28.8

Age	U.S.	GIRLS Canada	Holland	Scotland
(years *)	1985–87	1981	1982	1980–83
7–9	30.3	31.8	—	—
10–12	32.4	30.9	31.0	—
13–14	35.9	32.8	34.0	28.7
15–19	38.2	34.1	37.0	32.8

the average child in North America participates in an insufficient amount of daily physical activity to realize his or her physiological potential.

III. SUMMARY AND CONCLUSIONS

Physical fitness in children has been a concern of physical educators, exercise scientists, physicians, and the public for many years. Over the past three decades profound changes have developed in the operational definition of "physical fitness" as it is applied with children. The major trend has been toward greater and more exclusive emphasis on the components of physical fitness that are known to be health-related. This trend has been manifested in the implementation of physical fitness test batteries for children that focus on the health-related fitness components, i.e., cardiorespiratory endurance, body composition, muscular strength/endurance and flexibility.

Examination of age trends in health-related physical fitness test performances in nationally representative samples of children in the United States yield the following observations:

1. Skinfold thicknesses increase with aging in both boys and girls from the ages of 6 to 12. After age 12, girls show a continued increase in skinfold fat, whereas a plateau is reached for boys.
2. Distance running performance improves with aging in both boys and girls, though to a greater extent in boys. Performance essentially reaches a plateau in both sexes after age 15.
3. Upper body muscular strength, relative to body weight, is slightly greater in boys than in girls through age 12. At puberty, weight-relative upper body strength increases markedly in boys but stays constant in girls. Abdominal muscle strength, as manifested in a timed sit-up test, increases in both boys and girls up to age 14, then reaches a plateau.
4. Across the 6–18 y age range, girls perform better than boys in a sit-and-reach test of low back/hamstring flexibility. Both sexes show steady performance improvements from the ages of 12 to 16 y.

Some evidence suggests that in the United States, today's children are less physically fit than those of previous decades, although in countries such as Canada there has been improvement of physical working capacity, particularly among teenage girls. However, a conclusion of diminished fitness is supported only by studies in which skinfold thickness data collected in the 1960s and 1970s have been compared with similar data collected in the 1980s. Nationally representative data on most other health-related fitness components were not available before the 1980s.

Finally, associations among common field tests of physical fitness in children indicate that traditional motor fitness test items, such as the 50 yd dash and standing long jump, tend to be more highly intercorrelated than do the tests of health-related fitness (e.g., skinfolds, distance run, etc.). Also, the motor fitness and health-related test items tend not to be highly correlated with each other, supporting the concept that the two types of fitness are largely independent.

BIBLIOGRAPHY

1. AAHPER (1976). *Youth Fitness Test manual*. Washington, D.C.: American Alliance for Health, Physical Education, Recreation and Dance.
2. AAHPERD (1980). *Health Related Physical Fitness Test manual*. Reston, VA: American Alliance for Health, Physical Education, Recreation and Dance.
3. AAHPERD (1985). *Technical manual*. Reston, VA: American Alliance for Health, Physical Education, Recreation and Dance.
4. AAHPERD (1988). *The AAHPERD Physical Best Program*. Reston, VA: American Alliance for Health, Physical Education, Recreation and Dance.
5. American Academy of Pediatrics. Physical fitness and the schools. *Pediatrics 80:* 449–450, 1987.
6. American College of Sports Medicine (1988). Opinion Statement on Physical Fitness in Children and Youth. *Medicine and Science in Sports and Exercise 20:* 422–423.
7. American Health and Fitness Foundation (1986). *Fit Youth Today*. Austin, TX: American Health and Fitness Foundations.
8. Anderson, K.L., Shephard, R.J., Denolin, J., Varnauskas, E., & Massironi, R. (1971). *Fundamentals of exercise testing*. Geneva:World Health Organization.
9. Astrand, P.-O. (1952). *Experimental studies of physical working capacity in relation to sex and age*. Copenhagen:Ejnar Munkgaard.
10. Astrand, P.-O. & Rodahl, K. (1986). *Textbook of Work Physiology*, 3rd ed. New York:McGraw-Hill Book Co.
11. Bar-Or, O. (1983). *Pediatric Sports Medicine for the Practitioner*. New York:Springer-Verlag.
12. Bar-Or, O. (1987). A commentary to children and fitness: A public health perspective. *Research Quarterly for Exercise and Sport 58:*304–307.
13. Baumgartner, T.A. (1978). Modified pull-up test. *Research Quarterly 49:*80–84.
14. Berger, R.A., & Medlin, R.L. (1969). Evaluation of Berger's 1-RM chin test for junior high males. *Research Quarterly 40:*460–463.
15. Beuner, G. & Malina, R.M. (1988). Growth and physical performance relative to the timing of the adolescent spurt. In: K.B. Pandolf, ed. *Exercise and Sport Sciences Reviews 16:*503–540.
16. Blair, S.E., Falls, H.B., Pate, R.R. (1983). A new physical fitness test. *The Physician and Sportsmedicine 11:*87–95.
17. Blair, S.N., Pate, R.R., & McClenaghan, B. (1982). Current approaches to physical fitness education. In: T. Kratchowill (ed.), *Annual Reviews of School Psychology*, (Vol.2. 315–361). Hillsdale, NJ:Erlbaum.
18. Bjorntorp, P. (1987). Classification of obese patients and complications related to the distribution of surplus fat. *The American Journal of Clinical Nutrition 45:*1120–1125.
19. Boileau, R.A., Lohman, T.G., Slaughter, M.H., Ball, T.E., Going, S.B. & Hendrix, M.K. (1984). Hydration of the fat-free body in children during maturation. *Human Biology 56:*651–666.
20. Bos, K. & Mechling, H. (1985). *Technical Studies: International Physical Performance Test Profile*. Cologne, West Germany: International Council of Sport Science and Physical Education.
21. Bouchard, C. (1978). Genetics, growth and physical activity. In: F. Landry, and W.R. Orban, eds. *Physical activity and Human Well-being*. Miami, FL:Symposia Specialists.
22. Broer, M. & Galles, N. (1958). Importance of relationship between various body measure-

ments and performance of the toe-touch test. *Research Quarterly for Exercise and Sport 29:*253–263.

23. Clarke, H.H. (1967). *Application of measurement to health and physical education,* 4th ed. Englewood Cliffs, NJ:Prentice-Hall, Inc.
24. Clarke, H.H., ed. (1975). Physical fitness testing in schools. *Physical Fitness Research Digest 5:*1–23.
25. Chrysler Fund-Amateur Athletic Union (1987). *Physical fitness program.* Bloomington, IN: The Chrysler Fund-Amateur Athletic Union.
26. Cooper, K.H., Pollock, M.L., Martin, R.P., White, S.R., Linnerrud, A.C., & Jackson, A. (1976). Physical fitness levels vs. selected coronary risk factors: a cross-sectional study. *Journal of the American Medical Association 236:*166–169.
27. Corbin, C.B. & Fox, K.R. (1985). Fitness for a lifetime. *British Journal of Physical Education 16:*44–46.
28. Costill, D.C., Daniels, J., & Evans, W. (1976). Skeletal muscle enzymes and fiber composition in male and female track athletes. *Journal of Applied Physiology 40:*149–154.
29. Cureton, K.J., Boileau, R.A., Lohman, T.G., & Misner, J.E. (1977). Determinants of distance running performance in children: Analysis of a path model. *Research Quarterly 48:*270–279.
30. Daniels, J., & Oldridge, N. (1971). Changes in oxygen consumption of young boys during growth and running training. *Medicine and Science in Sports 3:*161–165.
31. Dietz, W.H. & Gortmaker, S.L. (1985). Do we fatten our children at the television set? Obesity and television viewing in children and adolescents. *Pediatrics 75:*807–812.
32. Falls, H.B. (1980). Modern concept of physical fitness. *Journal of Physical Education and Recreation 41:*25–27.
33. *Fitnessgram User's Manual.* (1987). Dallas, TX:Institute for Aerobics Research.
34. Fleishman, E.A. (1964). *The structure and measurement of physical fitness.* Englewood Cliffs, NJ:Prentice-Hall, Inc.
35. Flint, M.M., & Gudgell, J. (1965). Electromyographic study of abdominal muscular activity during exercise. *Research Quarterly 36:*29–37.
36. Gibbons, L.W., Blair, S.N., Cooper, K.H., & Smith, M. (1983). Association between coronary heart disease risk factors and physical fitness in healthy adult women. *Circulation 67:*977–983.
37. Gortmaker, S.L., Dietz, W.H., Sobol, A.M., & Weber, C.A. (1987). Increasing pediatric obesity in the U.S. *American Journal of Diseases in Children 14:*535–540.
38. Haskell, W.L., Montoye, H.J., & Orenstein, D. (1985). Physical activity and exercise to achieve health-related physical fitness components. *Public Health Reports 100:*202–212.
39. Jackson, A.S., & Coleman, A.E. (1976). Validation of distance run tests for elementary school children. *Research Quarterly 47:*86–94.
40. Jackson, A.W., & Baker, A.A. (1986). The relationship of the sit-and-reach test to criterion measures of hamstring and back flexibility in young females. *Research Quarterly for Exercise and Sport 3:*183–186.
41. Johnston, F.E., Hamill, P.V.V., & Lemeshow, S. (1972). *Skinfold thickness of children 6–11 years.* (Series 11, No.120). Washington, DC:U.S. Center for Health Statistics.
42. Johnston, F.E., Hamill, P.V.V., & Lemeshow, J. (1974). *Skinfold Thickness of Youth 12–17 Years.* (National Health Survey, Series 11, No. 132, U.S. Department of Health, Education, and Welfare) Washington, D.C.:U.S. Government Printing Office.
43. Kein, H.A. and Kirkaldy-Willis, W.H. (1980). *Clinical Symposia: Low Back Pain* 1(6). Summit, New Jersey: CIBA Pharmaceutical.
44. Krahenbuhl, G.S., Skinner, J.S., & Kohrt, W.M. (1985). Developmental aspects of maximal aerobic power in children. In: R.L. Terjung (ed.), *Exercise and Sport Sciences Reviews. Vol. 13.* New York:Macmillan. 503-538.
45. Kraus, H., & Hirshland, R.P. (1954). Minimum muscular fitness tests in school children. *Research Quarterly 25:*178–187.
46. Larson, L.A. (1974). *Fitness, health and work capacity.* New York:MacMillan.
47. Leger, L.A., & Lambert, J. (1982). A maximal multistage 20-metre shuttle run test to predict VO_2 max. *European Journal of Applied Physiology 49:*1–12.
48. Leighton, J.R. (1942). A simple objective and reliable measure of flexibility. *Research Quarterly 13:*205.
49. Lohman, T.G. (1982). Measurement of body composition in children. *Journal of Physical Education, Recreation, and Dance 53:*67–70.
50. Lohman, T.G. (1986). Applicability of body composition techniques and constants for children and youth. K.B. Pandolf (ed.), *Exercise and Sport Sciences Reviews 14:*325–357. New York:Macmillan Publishing Company.
51. Lohman, T.G., Boileau, R.A. & Slaughter, M.H. (1984). Body composition in children and youth. In: *Advances in Pediatric Sport Sciences, Vol. 1* Champaign, IL:Human Kinetics.

CHARACTERISTICS OF PHYSICAL FITNESS **41**

52. Malina, R.M. (1975). Anthropometric correlates of strength and motor performance. In: J.H. Wilmore, & J.F. Keogh, (eds.) *Exercise and Sport Sciences Reviews. Vol. 3,* New York:Academic Press. 249–274.
53. Melleby, A. (1982). *The Y's Way to a Healthy Back,* Piscataway New Jersey:New Century Publishers.
54. Mirwald, R.L., & Bailey, D.A. (1986). *Maximal Aerobic Power, A longitudial analysis.* London, Ontario:Sports Dynamics.
55. Molnar, G.E., & Alexander, J. (1977). Objective, quantitative muscle testing in children: a pilot study. *Archives of Physical Medicine and Rehabilitation* 58:254–257.
56. Paffenbarger, R.S., Jr., Hyde, R.T., Wing, A.L., & Hsieh, C. (1986). Physical activity, all-cause mortality, and longevity of college alumni. *New England Journal of Medicine* 314:605–613.
57. Pate, R.R. (1978). Fitness testing with a realistic purpose. *Journal of Physical Education and Recreation* 49:47–48.
58. Pate, R.R. (1983). A new definition of youth fitness. *The Physician and Sportsmedicine* 11:77–83.
59. Pate, R.R., & Blair, S.N. (1978). Exercise and the prevention of atherosclerosis: Pediatric implications. In W. Strong (ed.), *Pediatric aspects of atherosclerosis.* (251–286). New York:Grune & Stratton.
60. Pate, R.R., Corbin, C.B., Simons-Morton, B.G., & Ross, J.G. (1987). Physical education and its role in school health promotion. *Journal of School Health* 57:445–450.
61. Pate, R.R., & Lonnett, M. (1988). Validity of field test of upper body muscular strength and endurance. Unpublished manuscript.
62. Pate, R.R., & Ross, J.G. (1987). Factors associated with health-related fitness. *Journal of Physical Education, Recreation and Dance* 58:93–95.
63. Pate, R.R., Ross, J.G., Baumgartner, T.A., & Sparks, R.E. (1987). The modified pull-up. *Journal of Physical Education, Recreation and Dance* 58:71–73.
64. Plowman, S.A., & Falls, H.B. (1978). AAHPERD Youth Fitness Test revision: How fit? and for what? *Journal of Physical Education and Recreation* 49:22–24.
65. Powell, K.E., Thompson, P.D., Caspersen, C.J., & Kendrick, J.S. (1987). Physical activity and the incidence of coronary heart disease. *Annual Review of Public Health* 8:281–287.
66. Reiff, G.G., Dixon, W.R., Jacoby, D., Ye, G.X., Spain, C.G., & Hunsicker, P.A. (1985). *National School Population Fitness Survey. The President's Council on Physical Fitness and Sports 1985.* Research Project 282-84-0086, Ann Arbor:University of Michigan.
67. Robertson, L.D., & Magnusdottir, H. (1987). Evaluation of criteria associated with abdominal fitness testing. *Research Quarterly for Exercise and Sport* 58:355–359.
68. Rode, A., & Shephard, R.J. (1971). The cardiorespiratory fitness of an arctic community. *Journal of Applied Physiology* 31:519–526.
69. Rode, A., & Shephard, R.J. (1984). Ten years of "civilization." Fitness of the Canadian Inuit. *Journal of Applied Physiology,* 56:1472–1477.
69. Ross, J.G., & Gilbert, G.G. (1985). The national children and youth fitness study: A summary of findings. *Journal of Physical Education, Recreation and Dance* 56:45–50.
70. Ross, J.G., & Pate, R.R. (1987). The national children and youth fitness study II: A summary of findings. *Journal of Physical Education, Recreation and Dance* 58:51–56.
71. Shephard, R.J. (1978). *Human physiological work capacity.* London:Cambridge University Press.
72. Shephard, R.J. (1982). *Physical Activity and Growth,* Chicago:Year Book Medical Publishers.
73. Shephard, R.J. (1984). Physical activity and "wellness" of the child. In: R.A. Boileau, (ed.). *Advances in Pediatric Sport Sciences, Vol. 1.* Champaign, IL:Human Kinetics.
74. Shephard, R.J. (1986). *Fitness of a nation. Lessons from the Canada Fitness Survey.* Basel:Karger.
75. Simons-Morton, B.G., O'Hara, N.M., Simons-Morton, D.G., & Parcel, G.S. (1987). Children and fitness: A public health perspective. *Research Quarterly for Exercise and Sport* 58:295–302.
76. Simons-Morton, B.G., Parcel, G.S., O'Hara, N.M., Blair, S.N., & Pate, R.R. (1988). Health-related physical fitness in childhood: status and recommendations. *Annual Reviews of Public Health* 9:403–425.
77. Siri, W.E. (1961). Body composition from fluid spaces and density. In J. Brozek and H. Hanschel. (eds.). *Techniques for Measuring Body Composition.* Washington:National Academy of Science.
78. Slaughter, M.H., Lohman, T.G., Boileau, R.A., Horswill, C.A., Stillman, R.J., Van Loan, M.D., & Bemben, D.A. (1988). Skinfold equations for estimation of body fatness in children and youth. *Human Biology* 60: 709–723.
79. Slaughter, M.H., Lohman, T.G., & Boileau, R.A. (1978). Relationship of anthropometric dimensions to lean body mass in children. *Annals of Human Biology* 5:469–482.
80. Spurgeon, J.H., Young, N.D. & Meredith, H.V. (1959). Body size and form of American-born boys of Dutch ancestry in Michigan. *Growth* 23:55–71.

81. Tucker, L.A. (1986). The relationship of television viewing to physical fitness and obesity. *Adolescence, 21:*797–806.
82. Van Dalen, D.B., Mitchell, E.D., & Bennett, B.C. (1953). *A World History of Physical Education.* Englewood Cliffs, NJ:Prentice-Hall.
83. Walters, C.E., & Partridge, M.J. (1975). Electromyographic study of the differential action of the abdominal muscles during exercise. *American Journal of Physical Medicine 36:*259–268.
84. Weiner, J.S., & Lourie, J.A. (1981). *Practical human biology.* New York:Academic Press.
85. Wells, K., & Dillon, E. (1952). The sit and reach—a test of back and leg flexibility. *Research Quarterly 23:*115–118.

DISCUSSION

BAR-OR: We often use chronological age as an independent variable when we talk about the changes in fitness, but I think an attempt should be made to find some other items on the abscissa that can help us understand what really goes on during the developmental years. Probably height would be available in most surveys, and I imagine some effort could be made to express data relative to height.

To demonstrate the problem of cultural/cross-cultural issues, we were involved in a study of children in Burma some years ago. Two items for the girls were sit-ups and flexed arm-hang. Some girls in the rural areas could not do a single sit-up. But when we put them on the bar, they could hang for a long time. I think this distinct specificity of "strength" tests to different muscle groups is of concern and is something that we should be addressing for the future. Finally, perhaps some attempt should be made to discuss racial differences in fitness.

PATE: I agree that it would be interesting to express the data relative to height. Roy Shephard suggested height squared, and I think that would be appropriate. Also, I certainly agree that more attention should be given to cross-cultural and interracial issues.

SUTTON: From an epidemiological perspective, one always wonders about problems with sampling. Are you confident that the studies you cited have taken into account various other factors, such as social-economic status within communities and groups as well as racial differences? Also, it seems to me that the simple assessment of pubertal status may well be one of the critical issues for future studies in this field. My final point is that we're throwing around the term "hypokinetic disease" as if it's something we all understand. I'm not sure I do. Before we use this as just another catch phrase, I would be much happier if we all knew what we were talking about.

PATE: Unfortunately, in NCYFS 1 and 2 there are no pure maturity measures available against which to plot the data. Regarding racial differences in fitness, to be honest with you, I cannot remember with certainty whether race is in the NCYFS data set or not. I agree that it has rarely been addressed in studies of this sort, and probably should be.

GONYEA: Are you saying that the phrase "with vigor" implies a level of fitness? I think activity and fitness are two different issues. I think you address activity in the paper, but I'm not left with any sense that I know what a fit youth is. I know what the norms are, but are you implying that the norms we see are actually measuring fitness or measuring activity levels?

PATE: I think the data measure fitness and not activity. I think one of the most important needs that we have in this field is to settle on manageable, useful, criterion-referenced standards for these fitness tests, so that we can answer that question, "What is a physically fit youth?"

GONYEA: How a child improves in body composition should certainly be a concern of all of us. One way is to increase the activity level; the other is to restrict caloric intake. Hopefully, you are not recommending a dramatic restriction in caloric intake; we have enough trouble with anorexia and bulimia as it is, especially with some of the teenagers.

PATE: I certainly agree that we would not want to be interpreted as making that sort of statement. My belief is that we can administer skinfold tests to kids and provide feedback to them and their parents in a cautious and sensitive way.

MALINA: I think we are overlooking the fact that by 6 years of age not all children are physically skilled within the normal range of variation of motor skills. I'm just wondering if we're not pushing fitness testing at too early an age. Secondly, I'm puzzled about why we call it "health-related" fitness. I'm still not convinced that there is a relationship between strength and health, and between flexibility and health, especially in children. Many of these items you mentioned, e.g., cardiorespiratory endurance, strength, and fatness, don't track very well through childhood, except perhaps for some of the extremes of the population. So why do you call it "health-related" fitness?

PATE: It's clear that the documentation for a link between fitness and health is tenuous at best for muscular strength and flexibility, and we know far less about those relationships than we need to or than we do for aerobic power or body composition.

MALINA: How about the testing of children as young as 6 years of age, many of whom simply don't have the running skills to run a mile?

PATE: This is clearly a problem. On the other hand, when NCYFS 1 was conducted, it started at age 10, but as soon as the data were published, there was a hue and cry about the need for data on younger kids. In response to that, the government funded the follow-up—NCYFS 2.

MALINA: Perhaps we should measure other things at the younger ages. I think other factors might be developmentally much more important.

PATE: There have been occasional responses to that concern, for example, the half-mile run instead of the mile run in the younger children.

MALINA: How about simple things such as how motorically skilled the kids are? That would tell us a lot more. I would suspect that skilled children would be able to do the fitness test, but those who are delayed in motor development, and there are some 8 and 9 year olds who are delayed, should probably be tested on motor skill development before going on to their level of fitness.

PATE: I think you have raised a good question. I'm not sure that the data that can answer the question are available at the present time. If they are, it would be interesting to know just how strong that association is.

BROOKS: I would like to see an organization such as the American College of Sports Medicine thoughtfully and carefully develop and implement one set of fitness standards for youth.

FREEDSON: I am concerned about the validity of flexed arm hang pull-up as a measure of strength in children. It seems to me that the criterion measure should be quite specific to the pull-up movement or to an isometric flexed arm hang.

2

Exercise and Sport Psychology in Youth 6 to 18 Years of Age

Rod K. Dishman, Ph.D.

INTRODUCTION
I. COMPETITIVE SPORT
Theory and Research
A. Outcomes
    1. Attitudes and Values
    2. Moral Development, Cooperation, Aggression, Delinquency
    3. Emotional Stress
B. Determinants
II. PHYSICAL ACTIVITY
Theory and Research
A. Outcomes
    1. Mental Health
    2. Body Image
    3. Self-Esteem
B. Determinants
    1. Schools and the Doctor's Office
    2. Behavioral Interventions
    3. Population-Based Retrospective Surveys in Adults
    4. Psychological Theories of Behavior as Models for Youth
    5. Age or Developmental Stages
SUMMARY
ACKNOWLEDGEMENTS
FOOTNOTES
BIBLIOGRAPHY
DISCUSSION

INTRODUCTION

Recent policy and position statements issued by the U.S. Centers for Disease Control (CDC) (U.S. Department of Health and Human Services, 1986) and the Canadian Association of Sports Sciences (CASS) (Hughson, 1986) have addressed psychological aspects of participation in physical activity and competitive sport that apply to youths 6–18 years of age. These statements are important because they reflect the social significance that North America places on youthful participation in sport and exercise and because they imply critical research agendas for pediatric sports medicine and science.

My purpose in this chapter is to examine theory and research from the field of sport psychology that bear on the recommendations by CDC and CASS. Methodological limitations, research directions, and practical implications are included. My review will reveal that, in most instances, the recommendations by CDC and CASS stem from general theory or professional consensus rather than from a consensus of scientific evidence on children in sport and exercise settings.

First, psychological outcomes and determinants associated with competitive sport are considered. Outcomes and determinants of physical activity follow. I chose this organization for the convenience of the reader, and because it characterizes the topical literature in sport psychology. My approach will be to provide a broad overview in order to introduce the area to sports medicine readers who are not familiar with sport psychology. This approach necessitates a broad and superficial coverage. More detail can be found in the references provided. Because the strength of scientific inference varies widely among the studies reviewed, I have provided summaries of the current knowledge and research dilemmas for each topical area rather than critical evaluations of individual studies. When too little research is available to permit conclusions about an important question, I have discussed what I perceive to be representative studies that illustrate the type of research taking place in that area or the type of research needed to advance our knowledge.

COMPETITIVE SPORT

The Canadian Association of Sport Sciences has recommended the following . . . "be applied to all sport situations, from local recreational leagues to elite championship performances" (Hughson, 1986, p. 163).

- The psychological well-being of children in sport programs can best be achieved by providing an environment which allows children to achieve a sense of competence, to feel that they have some control over their actions, and to develop a sense of reward from within the activity itself.
- Adults involved with competitive sport programs for children must ensure that these programs teach children to react to

adverse situations by constructive problem-solving rather than by means of aggressive behavior.

- Effort must be made to permit and to encourage sport participation by all people, regardless of gender, race, age, or economic status.

Theory and Research

Most of the literature from sport psychology relevant for the CASS Position Statement comes from theory and research on attitudes and values, moral development, cooperation, aggression, delinquency, emotional stress, and motivation for participation.

The consensus by social anthropologists holds that sport and playful activity is crucial to a child's cognitive and social development. Piaget (1965) concluded, for example, that the practice of rules and the consciousness of rules associated with play leads to the development of moral values. Mead (1934) hypothesized that the roles children assume while playing teach them to perceive what others are doing in relation to themselves and that this perception is a necessary function for participation. Also, Bruner et al. (1976) stated that the random play of childhood is an important precursor to adult competence.

On the basis of these theoretical views and popular attitudes toward physical activity and sports, it is generally believed that involvement in sport and physical activity contributes to the development of positive psychological and social attributes. Whether this is actually true is not yet scientifically verified, however. As the discussion that follows will reveal, there is little well-controlled, experimental, and/or longitudinal research to document most claims about the benefits or risks associated with sport for youth under the age of 18 y.

Outcomes

Attitudes and Values. One of the most widely cited studies on attitudes and values related to sport was conducted by Webb (1969), who examined value orientations toward competition. As young boys and girls studied by Webb advanced in age, attitudes toward play changed. Specifically, "skill" became more important than "fairness." Winning became increasingly important. Subsequent studies based on Webb's research have generally found that participants in sports are more likely to value "winning," whereas non-participants are more likely to value "fair play" (Kidd and Woodman, 1975; Mantel & Vander Velden, 1974; Maloney & Petrie, 1972). Differences between males and females have been noted in the general population but not among high caliber athletes. In the general population, males are more likely to value "winning" than are females, while among high level athletes, males and females value "winning" equally (Kane, 1982). These studies seem to indicate that in those involved in sport, the value of fair play decreases relative to an increased value of winning. This has not, however, been experimentally determined. Until experimental and longitudinal studies are conducted, it is not possible to conclude that participation in sport is responsible for this change in attitude, nor is it now possible to conclude that "fair play" is socially more desirable than is winning. Results on these questions that are generalizable to the youth population are not available.

The balance of fair play, winning, and losing is, however, essential to the attitude of sportsmanship. Generally it has been found that people with more experience in organized sports display poorer sportsmanship attitudes than nonparticipants (Allison, 1982; Bovyer, 1963; Kroll & Peterson, 1965; Lakie, 1964). As in the studies on attitude toward winning and fair play, however, these cross-sectional results have not been determined by experimental or prospective studies. Thus, the differences reported could be the result of subject selection effects, whereby children who do not value winning drop out of sport. The causality underlying the descriptive cross-sectional studies done remains unknown. Also, the various self-report assessments employed have uncertain construct validity.

Moral Development, Cooperation, Aggression, Delinquency. Sportsmanship is often equated with morality. However, sportsmanship is typically defined as social conventional behavior. This is behavior that "conforms to prescribed social norms and is intended to maintain social organization" (Weiss & Bredemeier, 1986, p. 3), such as shaking hands before or after a contest. Social conventional behaviors are distinguished from moral behaviors, which are defined as "those which are concerned with the physical or psychological welfare of others and the protection of rights and responsibilities" (Weiss & Bredemeir, 1986, p. 4), such as lying about a game score when there are no referees present.

It is difficult to distinguish moral behavior from social convention based on observation, and this has impeded scientific studies in this area. In addition, moral development has also been researched under a variety of theoretical models, and this diversity has led to conflicting results. Two prominent theories that have been used are Bandura's (1977b) social learning theory and a structural developmental approach such as Kohlberg's (1981) Stage Theory of moral development. In the former theory, moral development is evaluated in terms of behaviors as they conform to social norms, whereas theories such as Kohlberg's evaluate moral development in terms of the cognition or reasoning behind the behavior. It is evident that a distinction between social conventional behavior and moral behavior is not clear on the basis of theory. This lack of clarity becomes increasingly evident when theory is translated into measurable variables. In other words, while studies of moral development seem to have validity by appearance, it is questionable whether they have demonstrated construct validity. For this reason, although it has been reported that physical education activities can promote moral development (Breswsan & Woolacott, 1983), it is not possible to conclude that this, in fact, has been the case. This is perplexing because theories about the impact of physical activity and physical education on character development were published as early as 1930 (McCloy, 1930).

It is disappointing that more convincing empirical evidence is unavailable. Bredemeier (1988) has discussed the cross-sectional and correlational evidence linking contact sport participation with less mature moral reasoning and aggressive dispositions, but selection bias has not been discounted in these studies. Nonaggressive, morally mature children may not choose or may not be successful in

TABLE 2-1. *Social learning and structural developmental approaches to moral development. From Weiss & Bredemeier (1986). Moral development. In V. Seefeldt (ed.),* Physical Activity and Well-Being. *Reston, VA: American Alliance for Health, Physical Education, and Recreation.*

TWO APPROACHES to MORAL DEVELOPMENT

	Basis for Ethical Practices	Source of Moral Growth	Definition of Morality
I. Social Learning Approach	socialization & internalization of conventional social mandates	clear, consistent, & reinforcing feedback from significant others	action in accordance with social definitions of prosocial behavior
II. Structural Developmental Approach			
A. Cognitivist Model	role taking & the application of abstract moral principles	cognitive disequilibrium resulting when moral reasoning at current stage does not resolve moral conflicts	making individual judgments about the intrinsic merits and consequences of behaviors
B. Interactionist Model	interpersonal exchanges and the development of consensual agreements	social disequilibrium leading to dialogue & negotiation to achieve moral balance in relationships & groups	using interpersonal skills to optimize everyone's mutual interest in a particular setting

TABLE 2-2. *Proposed intervention strategies for moral development in sport and physical activity settings. Adapted from Weiss & Bredemeier (1986). Moral development. In V. Seefeldt (ed.), Physical Activity and Well-Being. Reston, VA: American Alliance for Health, Physical Education, and Recreation.*

STRATEGIES FOR MORAL GROWTH

1. Allow disorganizing experiences to occur
2. Allow student/athletes to design group experiences
3. Link moral issues in sport to general life situations
4. Use inductive discipline (why rules must be followed) in place of "time-out" penalties

contact sports. Thus, the causal influence of sport remains unknown. Despite this absence of causal data, Weiss and Bredemeier (1986) have proposed interventions for enhancing moral development in sport and physical education settings (Table 2-2). However, convincing experimental data to support these hypotheses and recommendations are not yet available (Bredemeier et al., 1986).

Recent extension of Haan's (1978) Structural-Interactionist model to children's sport and physical education shows theoretical promise, but a recent field study at a youth sport camp (Bredemeier & Shields, 1986) showed that instruction based on social learning theory or on structural developmental theory both increased moral intentions compared with a control group. On the other hand, neither instructional approach affected moral maturity for distributing justice. The construct validity of the dependent measures used in this study is unclear, however, and a measurement technology must be validated in order to test moral development hypotheses in sport and physical activity settings.

Moral behavior can be said to be also constituted from a variety of behaviors such as cooperativeness and altruism. Studies on the development of these behaviors as a function of physical fitness and sport have provided evidence for two opposing points of view. One point of view holds that cooperative behaviors are undermined by sports activities. The other states that cooperative behaviors can be developed as a result of participation in sports. Kleiber and Roberts (1981), for example, found that sports experience can inhibit cooperative behaviors. However, it is difficult to separate these effects from the larger social context. According to Kagen and Madsen (1972), with advancing age competitiveness and winning become increasingly valued over cooperation. Moreover these are behaviors emphasized by the larger culture as well as the sport subculture. Thus, sport or physical activity per se may not be the determining factors for the adoption of competitiveness or prosocial behaviors such as cooperation; rather, the process by which values and behaviors are transmitted and learned in sport and society are likely the keys. Orlick (1981) has conducted research, for example, in which games and play were structured in a way designed to produce positive cooperative behavior among children.

Similar issues hold for the study of aggressive behavior. While some scholars hypothesize that frustration associated with competition promotes aggressive behavior, others believe that sport is a way to channel aggressive behavior in a socially acceptable manner. Again, it is probably not the activity that is responsible for learning aggressive behavior or learning self-control, but the fact that the behavior is sanctioned and reinforced by a variety of socializing agents.

The many theories proposed to explain sport aggression must also stand against common experience. Penetrating observations such as that by Paul Dyment, chairman of the Sports Medicine Committee of the American Academy of Pediatrics (Strauss, 1988), deserve the attention of sport psychologists who rely on general theories of morality and aggression to explain sport behavior in the absence of empirical support from actual competitive sport settings. While the generalizability of Dr. Dyment's comments is unknown, their apparent internal validity warrants study:

> Hockey is probably the most violent sport we tolerate in public schools, but in my ten years as a team physician for a high school hockey team, I've seen only one fight. These boys see their role models—the pros—fighting all the time, yet they themselves don't fight. The moment a boy takes a glove off, he's out of the game for unsportmanlike conduct. If he throws a punch, he's out for two games. The penalty is immediate and automatic; there's no appeal. So even though high school boys get just as angry as the pros, they stop themselves. They're learning to control themselves—just one more positive result of participation in sports. (p. 3).

Whether indicative of moral self-control or incentive-motivated behavior to avoid an undesired outcome–expulsion, Dr. Dyment's anecdotal view somehow rings as more true in its simplicity than good portions of prevailing social theories of sport aggression; it deserves testing.

Another notion akin to prosocial behavior is the idea that "sound programs of health, physical education, and recreation can help lessen delinquency" (p. 3) (American Association for Health, Physical Education, and Recreation, 1954). Research of the last 20 years has been recently reviewed by Segrave (1983), who concluded that there is evidence that delinquency among athletic groups is significantly lower than among nonathletic groups. However, it cannot be concluded that involvement in athletics actually deters delinquent behavior. The research in this area is primarily descriptive and correlational. Therefore, it is possible that the inverse relationship between athletics and delinquency is the result of a self-selection process rather than participation in sport.

The completed research on social dynamics in sport reveals a need to better understand the social learning process as it occurs through physical activity and sport. Future studies need to examine the manner in which sports are taught and played, the relationships between social behaviors in sport and moral reasoning, the generalizability of social behaviors and moral reasoning from sport settings to other social settings, and the extent to which sport and activity contexts contribute to, or are coincidental with, the natural development of social values and behaviors associated with increasing age in a competitive culture.

Emotional Stress. A great deal of controversy has been generated among coaches, parents, physicians, and physical educators concerning the implications of athletic competition for children. On one side, proponents advocate athletic competition for its psychosocial benefits (e.g., cooperation, leadership). Opponents claim that participation creates excessive emotional stress. The research generated in response to this controversy indicates that positive and negative outcomes both occur. A survey of Norwegian children conducted by Railo (1982) concluded, "that 20–30% (of children skilled in sports) are subject to many negative psychosocial pressures in their sports environment while the remaining 70–80% appear to have predominantly positive incentives" (p. 139).

Comparable population surveys of children in the United States and other countries are not available, but the available small sample research on U.S. youth suggests the incidence of emotional stress is typically less than the estimated exposure rate. Studies with athletes 9 to 16 years old show that both physiological and subjective measures of anxiety states are increased above resting levels in anticipation of competitive sport events and critical situations during actual competition (Skubic & Hilgendorf, 1964; Skubic, 1955; Hanson, 1967; Scanlan, 1984; Lowe & McGrath, 1971). However, psychophysiologic studies collectively suggest that the stress attributed to emotion during competitive sport in children is no greater, and usually less, than the accompanying metabolically induced stress of exertion and recreational sport. For example, epinephrine excretion is typically viewed as an indicator of emotional stress, yet in young ice hockey players the epinephrine response following competition

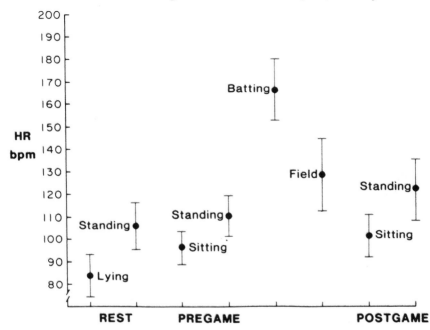

FIGURE 2-1. *Heart rate responses in Little League baseball competition compared with resting responses in boys 9–10 years old. Adapted from Hanson, D.L. (1967). Cardiac response to participation in Little League baseball competition as determined by telemetry.* Research Quarterly for Exercise and Sport *38:381–388. Resting values are taken from known normative values.*

has been found to be no different than that seen during recreational play or bicycle ergometry (Cunningham et al., 1973) (Fig. 2-4). A study of high-level youth wrestlers showed that less than half reported subjective stress associated with competition (Gould et al., 1983), and although young athletes report anxiety after losing, the degree of increases in both precompetitive and postcompetitive anxiety have consistently been seen to remain well within a clinically normal range (i.e., within one standard deviation) (Scanlan & Passer, 1978; Scanlan & Passer, 1979). Also, changes are typically temporary.

Subjective self-evaluations and adult observations of anxiety (Seymour, 1956) have not been linked with physiological signs of stress that might signal clinical significance for the health of youth. Some children can have psychological problems associated with sport that are of clinical magnitude (Pillemer & Micheli, 1988; Smith, 1984), but the population incidence and prevalence of emotional or be-

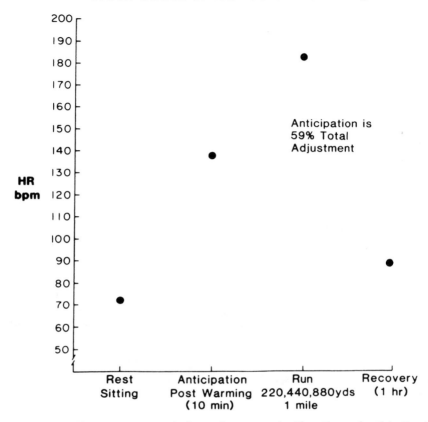

FIGURE 2-2. *Heart rate responses in foot racing compared with resting and anticipation in girls 14–17 years old. Adapted from Scubic & Hilgendorf (1964). Anticipatory, exercise, and recovery rates of girls affected by four running events.* Journal of Applied Physiology 19:853–856.

havioral disorders among child athletes has not been determined by epidemiologic methods nor compared with expected rates in non-athletes.

Although the potential negative effects of sports do not seem to occur in most participating children, it is important to understand the characteristics of those who experience negative effects and why those effects occur. Scanlan and colleagues have found that children who demonstrate high trait and state anxiety and low self-esteem, who have low personal and team expectations, and who have low sport enjoyment exhibit more stress than children who feel capable (Scanlan, 1984; Scanlan & Lewthwait, 1984; 1988). Furthermore, be-

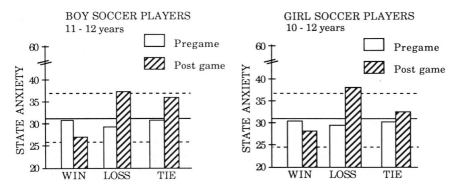

FIGURE 2-3. *Subjective state anxiety responses to soccer competition in boys and girls 10–12 years old. Adapted from Scanlan & Passer (1978). Factors related to competitive stress among male youth sport participants.* Medicine and Science in Sports 10:103–108. *Scanlan & Passer (1979). Sources of competitive stress in young female athletes.* Journal of Sport Psychology 1:151–159. *The solid line represents the population mean under non-stressful conditions, and the broken lines indicate one standard deviation above and below the norm. Sport competition does not influence subjective anxiety to a clinically significant level in most children aged 10–12.*

cause sport occurs in a context that involves extensive social evaluation, stress can be exacerbated by peers, coaches, and parents. Railo (1982) reported that 30–35% of Norwegian children felt they received too little encouragement from parents and trainers. Furthermore, it was found that perceived overexpectation from peers was substantially less than from parents. Similarly, Scanlan & Lewthwaite (1984) have reported that worries over meeting per-

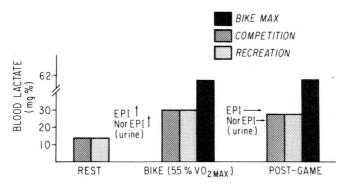

FIGURE 2-4. *Metabolic and catecholamine responses to the stress of exertion and recreational and competitive ice hockey in boys 10 years old. Adapted from Cunningham et al., (1973). Catecholamine excretion in young hockey players. In* Abstracts of the First Canadian Congress for the Multidiciplinary Study of Sport and Physical Activity.

ceived expectations of parents and the coach are related to precompetition stress. A study by Smith and Smoll (1982) showed that when youth coaches increase positive reinforcement of play and reduce criticism, athletes' attitudes toward the coaches becomes more favorable, but the performance or health impact of this attitude change was not demonstrated.

These correlational studies do not, however, establish that such "worries" cause stress or directly influence performance or health in children. It may be argued, for example, that overexpectation of parents is no greater for sport than for other psychosocial contexts. Indeed, it has been found that twice as many fathers have excessive expectations for academic performance as for sport performance (Raillo, 1982). Also, competitive athletics have been found to produce no more transient anxiety than do academic tests, and significantly less anxiety than a band solo (Simon & Martens, 1979)!

On the basis of this evidence it would seem that concerns about excessive stress associated with competitive sport are largely unfounded. Most studies that have suggested that sport increases emotional stress have relied exclusively on subjective reports by athletes or behavioral ratings by parents or coaches. These estimates have not been corroborated by neurologic or neuroendocrine measures of stress, and the validity of most of the subjective assessments used is uncertain when gauged by standard psychometric criteria.

Moreover, it remains unclear if youth sport contributes to stress in children in ways or degrees different from other socially evaluated settings where ability is encouraged, evaluated, and rewarded by others. However, coaches, parents, physical educators, and physicians need to be able to develop methods for identifying children who are particularly prone to stressful situations and to develop performance goals, standards, and interventions that are based on appropriate criteria for the skill level and psychological maturity of the child. In this regard it is perplexing that current guidelines for youth sport competition endorsed by the American Academy of Pediatrics (1988a) do not include provisions for the psychological well-being of youth participants. Preparation of such guidelines should be considered by groups such as the American College of Sports Medicine.

Determinants

Bodies of literature in sport psychology have developed that focus on the motivation for participation in youth sport and on factors leading to youth dropping out of sport. Representative findings from this literature are illustrated in Table 2-3 and have been thoroughly

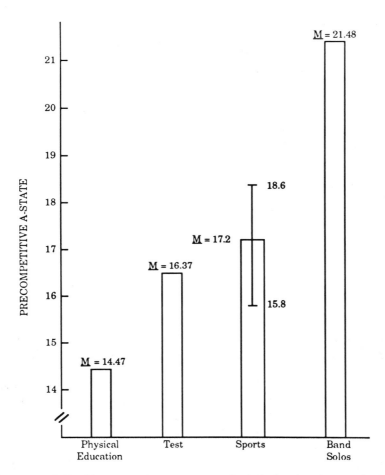

FIGURE 2-5. *Subjective state anxiety responses to physical education class, academic testing, sport competition, and a solo band performance in high school boys. The mean for sports comes from seven sports and is depicted by a 99% confidence band indicating no difference from the anxiety of academic testing. Adapted from Simon & Martens (1979). Children's anxiety in sport and non-sport evaluative activities.* Journal of Sport Psychology 1:160–169.

discussed elsewhere (Feltz & Ewing, 1987; Gould & Horn, 1984; Roberts, 1982; Vallerard et al., 1987). Concern has been expressed that dropping out of youth sport is often caused by excessive stress or feelings of low personal competence, yet studies show that children are more likely to withdraw because of interpersonal problems with a coach or because they prefer another leisure activity. Often the other activity is simply another sport or team (Gould & Horn, 1984).

TABLE 2-3. *Representative results from studies of self-reported reasons for dropping out from a sport in athletes 10 to 18 years of age. From Pooley (1981).*

YOUTH SPORT DROPOUTS

SOCCER (POOLEY, 1981)
(N=50, 10-15 YRS)

Too Much Competition	33%
Other Things To Do	54%
Young More Likely	

SWIMMING (GOULD, 1982)
(N=50, 10-18 YRS)

Other Things To Do	84%
Other Sports	80%
Not Fun	
Not Reaching Own Standards	
Too Hard	40%
Didn't Like Coach	
Boring	

The information reported about determinants of sport participation is virtually impossible to evaluate, however. Studies have typically involved cross-sectional and correlational comparisons of static groups or surveillance studies of single teams, and the validity of the self-reports used to assess the determinants of dropout (Gould et al., 1983) and sport participation (Gill et al., 1983; Gould et al., 1985) has not been confirmed by conventional psychometric standards for construct validity and reliability (Nunnally, 1978). Because the available data are descriptive rather than predictive or experimental, guidelines for interventions to increase youth sport participation are not available. Finally, the public health impact of understanding the determinants of youth sport participation and dropout cannot now be determined because the incidence and prevalence rates of youth sport participation and dropout have not been established by epidemiologic methods. This area will be an important one for future investigations, but measurement technologies must first be refined to enhance both internal and external validity (Wankel & Kreisel, 1985a; 1985b).

Studies must also adopt biometric approaches rather than rely exclusively on social psychological models as done in the past. Many children may simply leave a sport or sports altogether in favor of other pursuits where their ability or potential for success is greater. Thus, studies of participation motivation and dropout must adjust the behavioral measures used according to objective measures of sport ability rather than continuing to rely on subjective measures alone.

PHYSICAL ACTIVITY

In the midcourse review of the 1990 Objectives for Physical Fitness and Exercise (U.S. Department of Health and Human Services, 1986), the U.S. Centers for Disease Control (CDC) recommend that by the year 2000: ". . . (a) 80 percent or more of persons 10 years of age and older will know that regular physical activity reduces . . . the symptoms of depression and anxiety (p. 44), (b) . . . 50 percent or more of children and adolescents 6 to 17 years of age will participate in daily school physical education programs, (c) . . . 90 percent or more of high schools will have physical education classes devoting at least 50 percent of class time to activities that are commonly done by adults (p. 18), and (d) . . . the relationship between participation in various types of physical activities during childhood and adolescence and the physical activity practices of adults will be known (p. 71)."

These recommendations assume a public health consensus that mental health benefits are associated with habitual physical activity and that there is a basis for understanding the determinants of physical activity participation which can serve as targets for interventions and promotions designed to increase youthful and adult participation in physical activity.

Theory and Research

Most of the research from sport psychology relevant to the CDC recommendations (U.S. Department of Health and Human Services, 1986) comes from studies of the psychological effects of physical activity and the determinants of participation in supervised exercise programs and physical activity in the population by youth 6 to 18 years of age. As was the case for sport, however, the scientific evidence available to support the professional consensus is outstripped by the public importance of understanding and promoting the outcomes and determinants of physical activity for youth.

Outcomes

Mental Health. Thirty to 40% of American adults will have an episode of psychiatric significance during their lifetimes (Robins et al., 1984), but just 20% of those who suffer will seek professional care (Shapiro, Skinner, & Kessler, 1984). This suggests that the mental health of the population might benefit if personal coping skills for mental disorders and stress could be developed. Because many mental health problems have a childhood onset or origin, establishing the developmental role of physical activity and exercise as mental health-related behaviors for youth 18 y and younger should be a national priority (Taylor, Sallis, & Needle, 1985).

The psychiatric epidemiology of childhood exercise and fitness is an undeveloped field of study, but the current opinion among allied health professionals holds that exercise has beneficial emotional effects across all ages and in both sexes (Morgan & Goldston, 1987). The mechanisms through which mental health outcomes occur with exercise are not well-defined, but the association between physical activity and mental well-being does not appear to result solely from the fact that mentally healthy people choose to be active and the unhealthy choose to be sedentary (Ross & Hayes, 1988). According to the National Institute of Mental Health workshop on exercise (Morgan & Goldston, 1987), available scientific evidence indicates that physical fitness is positively associated with mental health and well-being, and acute exercise is associated with the reduction of signs and symptoms of stress emotions such as state anxiety, neuromuscular tension, and mild to moderate depression. Studies also suggest that for some individuals, medically supervised exercise can serve as a successful adjunct to treatment for disorders of sleep, eating behavior, and alcohol abuse, and for psychotic episodes of depression and schizophrenia (Dishman, 1986).

Studies of children are fewer in number and less well controlled than those with adults. For example, in one of the few clinical studies available (Jankowski et al., 1976[1]), Polish inpatient and outpatient adolescent boys who had problems with learning, family, and substance abuse were treated with either thioridazine, psychotherapy or fitness training, and sport activity. This paper has been interpreted in the literature as indicating that psychiatric outcomes were equivalent for all conditions (e.g., Greist et al., 1978, p. 263). However, several methodological problems cloud the interpretation of the paper by Jankowski et al. (1976)[1]: (a) patients were not randomly assigned to treatments, (b) raters were not blinded to the patients' treatments, (c) there were no statistical analyses, (d) some of the rating scales were not validated, and (e) measures of physical fitness were not defined. Moreover, the results reported were mixed: (a) kinetic therapy did not improve fitness in the *inpatients*, (b) kinetic therapy *and* psychotherapy influenced fitness in the *outpatients*, (c) psychotherapy was more effective than kinetic therapy in reducing depression and anti-social behavior in the *outpatients*, and (d) the kinetic therapy subjects and waiting-list controls became *more neurotic* during the intervention period.

Thus, results of the research by Jankowski et al. (1976) do not clearly support the view that fitness or sport activity (i.e., kinetic therapy) is equivalent to psychotherapy or drug therapy. There was evidence that kinetic therapy was actually *inferior* to psychotherapy in the outpatient cohort. The apparent positive effect in the case of kinetic therapy with inpatients may reflect the influence of "any treatment versus no treatment" (i.e., placebo effect) because fitness was unchanged. This study is, however, instructive because it illustrates many of the methodological and interpretive pitfalls characteristic of the sparse research literature on the psychological effects of physical activity on youth (Brown, 1982; Pillemer & Micheli, 1988).

Carefully designed and controlled prospective studies with various age and developmental groups of children are needed, and future studies of physical activity must consider the epidemiology of mental health. For example, boys are much more likely than girls to show disorders of attention deficits, anxiety and sleep, but 95% of anorexia nervosa and most cases of bulimia are restricted to girls (Oakes, 1984). Clinical estimates indicate that girls are three times as likely as boys to attempt suicide at ages 14 to 15 y, and more than 60% of adolescent suicide attempts are superimposed on a current psychiatric diagnosis and previous contact with psychosocial services (Garfinkel et al., 1982). For these reasons, sport and exercise research in these areas would be particularly informative.

Because one sign of anorexia is compulsive physical activity, concern has been expressed that sport involvement might predispose one to affliction with eating disorders, specifically in sports where a low fat body composition is rewarded (McSherry, 1984). Although early cross-sectional studies of female gymnasts and ballerinas showed higher than expected rates of anorexia and bulimia, it appears that most sport-related eating problems are the results of premorbid personality problems or temporary goal-appropriate diet restrictions and not the effects of sport-induced pathology (Dishman, 1985).

A provocative article by Yates et al. (1983) implied that adult anorectics present profiles that are similar to adults who are excessive exercisers, particularly obligatory runners. However, this article was apparently based on unverified case illustrations. Controlled research (Blumenthal et al., 1985) has shown that for the most part, exercise commitment and anorexia nervosa are separate entities. In fact, psychotherapy combined with running has been found to be an effective treatment for anorexia in some case studies (Kostrubala, 1976). Anorectic patients and committed exercisers differ widely on cardiopulmonary fitness, resting hormone profiles, and scores on standard tests of psychopathology. Comparison favors the exerciser

TABLE 2-4. *Clinical features of anorectic and athletic girls. From McSherry (1984). The diagnostic challenge of anorexia nervosa.* American Family Physician 29(4):144.

Shared features

Dietary faddism
Controlled calorie consumption
Specific carbohydrate avoidance
Low body weight
Resting bradycardia and low blood pressure
Increased physical activity
Amenorrhea or oligomenorrhea
Anemia (may or may not be present)

Distinguishing features

Athlete

Purposeful training
Increased exercise tolerance
Good muscular development
Accurate body image
Body fat level within defined normal range

Anorexic

Aimless physical activity
Poor or decreasing exercise performance
Poor muscular development
Flawed body image (patient believes herself to be overweight)
Body fat level below normal range
Biochemical abnormalities if abusing laxatives and/or diuretics

(Blumenthal et al., 1985; McSherry, 1984). Because, however, high achieving adolescent girls are at high risk for eating disorders, it is important that controlled prospective exercise and sport studies with this group be conducted.

Concerns have also been expressed about exercise dependence and addiction, whereby social and vocational development or medical health can suffer from obsessive or compulsive goal striving through exercise (Morgan, 1979). Although the population prevalence of abusive exercise behaviors is unknown, clinical estimates suggest a much lower rate than that for sedentary living (Dishman et al. 1985). Nevertheless, abusive exercise is a serious clinical concern for some adults and possibly for some children. The impact of childhood exercise experience on dependence or abuse in both early years and later in adulthood warrants examination. A recent study suggests, however, that participation motivation among young runners is psychologically healthy and differs little from that seen in participants in other youth sports (Feltz & Albrecht, 1987).

Body Image. The image of self is believed to be fundamentally based on one's body image (Freud, 1958). Experiences in the process of development, particularly comparisons with personal and social standards, also teach children the value of the self, or self-esteem. Some traits, such as temperament, appear to be largely heritable and relatively resistant to change due to age or environment. Others change predictably according to age or maturity, while still others, such as self-perceptions like body image, are more sensitive to life events. Physical activity experiences should be expected to most readily affect the latter.

Body image can be defined as the cognitive and affective representations that a person has about his or her body (Secord & Jourard, 1953). Correlational studies and clinical observations of children and adolescents have generally shown a positive relationship between physical fitness, body image, and self-image (Vander Velde, 1985). Self-image is the expression of qualities, attitudes, and values that a person consciously experiences as his or hers (Eide, 1982).

Because studies have often not specified the type of activity that is most associated with body image, whereas subjective measures of fitness or ability often yield the highest relationships with self-image, it is important to determine the effects of physical training on body image and self-image. This permits a true measure of physical activity impact upon which to base perceptions of the change. Other methodological concerns in the exercise literature on body image stem from the populations studied and the law of initial values. For example, experimental studies have demonstrated that those people who are least physically fit achieve greater gains than those who are initially more physically fit (Sonstroem, 1984). An analogous process may be operating in relation to psychological fitness. A ceiling effect can reduce the potential for improvement if a child's self-image is already relatively positive. Likewise, if subjective changes in fitness are directly linked with objective fitness or performance gains, a diminishing psychological benefit will parallel the diminishing rate of biological change at the upper range of the fitness spectrum.

This line of reasoning is supported by the data of Koocher (1971). Sixty-five boys from the ages of 7 to 15 y were examined on pre- and posttest discrepancies between their ideal image and self-image. Results showed a significant improvement in self-image in those who learned to swim but not in those who did not learn or who were able to swim before the camp. Effects such as these, however may be transitory and largely specific to the setting studied. That is, the duration and generalizability of increases in self-image from sport settings to other contexts is not established (Sonstroem, 1984).

In summary, there are circumstances where physical fitness and physical activity seem to contribute to body-image and self-image.

However, this relationship may be moderated by several factors: (1) the initial levels of body image or self-image and physical fitness; (2) the probability of eventual success in performance, and (3) the duration and intensity of the training. Further inquiry should take these variables into account to more clearly define their interactions and how they affect specific children.

Self-Esteem. Self-esteem is the evaluative component of self-image. It is the value that individuals learn to place on themselves. Its source is the interaction between the person and environmental/social experiences. Because studies examining the relationship between physical fitness and self-esteem belong to the same domain as studies examining the effect on self-image, similar results would be expected. Indeed, this is the case (Sonstroem, 1984), thus strengthening the idea that physical fitness activities can lead to improved self-esteem.

A meta-analysis by Gruber (1986) of 84 correlational, case, and experimental studies involving mostly preadolescent children concluded that physical fitness activity contributes to the development

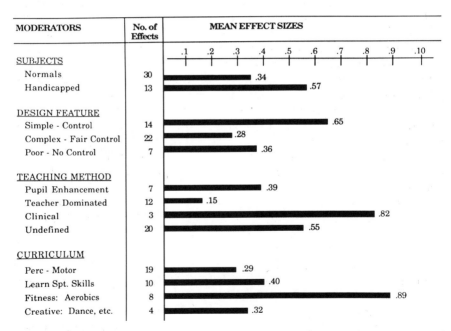

FIGURE 2-6. *The effects of physical education and physical activity on the self-esteem of children. Adapted from Gruber (1986). Physical activity and self-esteem development in children: a meta-analysis. In G.A. Stull & H.M. Eckert (eds.). Effects of Physical Activity on Children. The Academy Papers 19:30–48. Champaign, IL: Human Kinetics.*

of self-esteem. Over all the experimental studies, it was found that the average self-esteem of children who participated in directed play and physical education programs was two-thirds of one standard deviation higher than children who were in a control group. But, several variables were found to moderate this effect.

One important moderator was the subjects studied. There was a large difference in effect size between normal children and children who were classified as handicapped; i.e., 0.34 and 0.57, respectively. Handicapped children in this case included children who were emotionally disturbed, trainable mentally retarded, economically disadvantaged, educable mentally retarded, and perceptually handicapped. This evidence supports an earlier point that those who are in the most need will demonstrate the greatest gains.

A second moderator of the relationship between self-esteem and physical activity in Gruber's study was the teaching method used. In school settings, allowing children to interact with teachers and share in the decision making showed a somewhat greater effect than the traditional teacher-dominated style. The most marked effects, however, were observed in clinical settings or with clinical groups.

The type of curriculum also influenced effect size. Physical fitness and aerobic activities had a greater effect than perceptual-motor or motor development programs, programs designed to teach sport skills, and programs of creative dance, mime, or creative movement. Physical fitness and aerobic activities were found to have a mean effect size of 0.89 compared with 0.41 for the three other types of activities listed.

Another important moderator in the Gruber analysis was the experimental design used. Simple designs consisting of one experimental and one control group were found to have nearly twice the effect size as more complex factorial designs. This finding is important for future studies examining the relationship between self-esteem and physical activity, because it suggests that the results of the meta-analysis were not dependent on the quality of research designs. Future studies must include, however, a control group that receives an equal amount of attention or social reinforcement compared with the physical activity group. In order to be more conclusive about the effects of exercise on self-esteem, it is important to rule out the possibility of placebo or Hawthorne effects (i.e., any treatment is better than none) and subjects' expectancies of benefits.

In addition to understanding the practical significance of effect size and the variables that can influence this relationship, it is also important to understand the mechanisms responsible for the improvement in self-esteem (Sonstroem, 1984). Because a greater effect size has been found for aerobic activity over four other types of activity, biologically based explanations are appealing. However, they are untested in children and youth.

The impact of physical fitness training on self-esteem may also have roots in social learning. Changes in body image or in self-perceptions of physical ability are most reliable when actual increases in fitness or ability occur. These relationships can be expected to contribute to overall self-esteem and perceived competence when physical attributes are highly valued relative to other dimensions of self-concept, such as social status and academic success. Among children, physical competence appears central to overall self-esteem, but its relative importance tends to diminish with age as more varied experiences provide other areas where comparisons with personal goals and other people can occur.

In summary, exercise and sport can be as effective as other social or achievement settings that influence feelings of competence. This effectiveness depends principally on fostering self-perceptions of personally valued attributes, either by direct means of increasing fitness and skill or indirectly by social reinforcement. In these ways, children's values and the evaluations about their sport and exercise performance imparted by parents, teachers, coaches, peers, and physicians can have an impact as great as the activities and their actual outcomes.

Carefully designed and controlled prospective studies with various age groups and developmental groups of children are needed, but available evidence consistently indicates that mental health gains accompany fitness activities with little apparent mental health risk. This reinforces the importance to mental well-being of fitness and

TABLE 2-5. *Possible explanations for the association between increased self-esteem and physical activity. From Sonstroem (1984).* **Exercise and Sport Sciences Reviews 12**:*139.*

Program Agents

Increase in physical fitness
Goal achievement
Feelings of somatic well-being
Sense of competence, mastery, or control
Adoption of associated health behaviors
Social experiences
Experimental attention
Reinforcement of significant others

Score Agents

Self-presentation strategies
Defensiveness
Social desirability
Perceived task demands
Expectancy, suggestion
Perceived leader or group pressures

exercise habits previously linked with physical health. Unfortunately, the effectiveness of exercise prescription for reducing symptoms of stress disorders among children remains largely uninvestigated. Present research has focused primarily on assessing the reliability and validity of instruments for diagnosing stress-related factors such as Type A Behavior Pattern and anger (Matthews & Angulo, 1980; Matthews & Siegel, 1985; Murray & Bruhn, 1983; Wolf et al., 1982). Once these instruments are validated, the use of exercise as a viable treatment modality can then be evaluated.

Determinants

Much remains to be learned about health-related outcomes associated with childhood exercise and fitness. A principal contribution by sport psychology to preventive sport medicine will come from research on determinants of physical activity patterns during early years and how these patterns and determinants might have an impact later on exercise, fitness, health behaviors, and health outcomes in adult years.

Little is known about the determinants and health outcomes of physical activity patterns among youth under the age of 18 (Dishman et al., 1985). This is disturbing, because the consensus of public health officials is that the likelihood of reaching the 1990 exercise and fitness objectives for children is poor (Centers for Disease Control, 1985) and that behavioral interventions will be required if participation rates are to be increased. Though physical activity profiles are beginning to be known, their trends and reliable determinants for children and youth are empirically unknown (Dishman et al., 1985; Stephens et al., 1985). As a result, the information needed to guide effective interventions to increase physical activity and exercise in these age groups is not available.

Also, it is commonly assumed that patterns of exercise and health habits for adulthood are established during early years. However, the influence of childhood fitness or physical activity history on adult fitness or physical activity patterns remains unstudied.

The level of physical activity necessary for fitness and health in children is not well-known (LaPorte et al., 1982). But, based on adult requirements, available studies converge in showing that few children spontaneously participate in activity with enough intensity (e.g., to elevate heart rate to 160/min), duration (20–60 min), or frequency (3–5 d/wk) to maintain cardio-respiratory fitness (Gilliam et al., 1981). Moreover, it remains unclear what portion of daily caloric expenditure among children is due to activity from vigorous or fitness-producing play (Waxman & Stunkard, 1980) or daily routines (Epstein et al., 1984). This lack of quantification of physical activity has

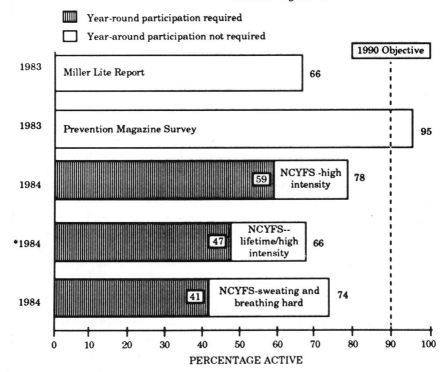

**Principal National Surveys
of Physical Activity, 1983-1984
Children -- Ages 10-17**

▦ Year-round participation required

☐ Year-around participation not required

| | | 1990 Objective |

1983 Miller Lite Report — 66

1983 Prevention Magazine Survey — 95

1984 NCYFS -high intensity — 59 — 78

*1984 NCYFS-- lifetime/high intensity — 47 — 66

1984 NCYFS-sweating and breathing hard — 41 — 74

PERCENTAGE ACTIVE

*Best estimate of status of the objective.

FIGURE 2-7. *Physical activity rates in the U.S. population for ages 10–17 years. Adapted from U.S. Department of Health and Human Services (1986). Midcourse Review of 1990 Objectives for Physical Fitness and Exercise. U.S. Government Printing Office: Washington, DC., and Caspersen, Christenson, & Pollard (1986). Status of the 1990 physical fitness and exercise objectives—evidence from NHIS. Public Health Reports 101:587–592.*

been a major problem in studies investigating the relationship between exercise and cardiovascular disease risk in youth under 18 years of age (Linder & Durant, 1982; Saris, 1986).

In addition to determining effective physical activity levels, studies need to take into account medical, social, environmental, and psychological determinants of physical activity. For example, children classified as sedentary may have health problems associated with chronic disease or health risk factors or may have other problems that predispose them to both inactivity and disease. Cross-sectional and longitudinal studies with children and restrospective studies with adults can clarify these questions.

Schools and the Doctor's Office. In their recent review of physical activity promotion programs in the United States, Iverson et al. (1985) discussed evidence on the effectiveness of schools and the physician's office in promoting physical activity. They concluded:

> It appears that a major opportunity to influence favorable physical activity in the United States is being missed in schools. A large majority of students are enrolled in physical education classes, but the classes appear to have little effect on the current physical fitness levels of children and, furthermore, have little impact on developing lifelong physical activity skills. (p. 212)

> Physicians do not regularly ask about the physical activity patterns of their patients. Although most physicians believe that being physically active is important, most do not counsel their patients about physical activity. . . . It appears that physicians can be effective in altering patient behavior. (p. 214)

Although direct experimental tests of these views have not been published, results from several controlled small-sample studies, cross-sectional population surveys of children, and a retrospective survey of adults are consistent with the conclusions of Iverson et al. (1985).

Studies suggest that exercise program interventions in the school can be effective in increasing fitness and leisure activity. Gilliam and co-workers (Gilliam et al., 1981; MacConnie et al., 1982) describe an eight month program for 6-and 7-year-old boys and girls that consisted of aerobic dances, running, rhythmic activity, and rope jumping 4 d/wk, 25 min/d, at heart rates greater than 150 beats/min. This activity reinforced a once-per-week, 20 min, classroom session on the relationships between exercise, nutrition, and coronary artery disease. Compared with controls who maintained normal weekly activities, including a single 40 min physical education class, experimental children spent more time in high level activity (heart rate > 160/min) and less time in low level activity (heart rate < 110/min). Notably, this increase appeared to include more high intensity exercise during leisure time as well. The maintenance of this increased activity after the study period was not examined.

Although a few small-sample reports indicate that controlled behavioral interventions in school settings can be associated with increased frequency, intensity, and duration of physical activity, and in some cases desirable health outcomes (Brownell & Kaye, 1982), they do not specify the determinants of the increases observed. Thus, their effectiveness in other settings cannot be predicted; the critical components of the interventions or their target behavioral variables have not been identified and assessed, and this prevents a standardized evaluation or application of the results. The studies also fail to address the impact of the interventions, i.e., the increased activity, on activity at later time periods. Further, because subjects are sampled for convenience and not representativeness, the generalizability of results across school settings, gender, grade level, race, and socioeconomic status is unknown. A recent educational trial with 37 schools in New York showed changes in dietary intake and health knowledge, and modest reductions in total plasma cholesterol (1 to 1.7 mg/dL), but physical activity was unchanged (Walter et al. 1988).

Community-based and school-based (Dwyer et al., 1983) exercise and education programs (Kuntzleman, 1985) suggest that school interventions have efficacy for increasing fitness and reducing known cardiovascular risk factors among many child population segments. However, it is unclear to what degree typical school systems are doing so. Thus, the effectiveness of such programs remains undemonstrated in the population. Moreover, the available research in this area reveals little about determinants of existing school-age activity patterns or how early habits relate to activity in later years.

The National Children and Youth Fitness Study (NCYFS) conducted by the School Health Initiative of the Public Health Service (U.S. Department of Health and Human Services, 1985) showed that of the national random sample of 8,800 boys and girls from grades 5 through 12, 80% were enrolled in physical education, with a weekly average of 3.6 class meetings of 46.7 min duration each. Yet, only 36.3% of students took physical education daily, and of the average 11.8 different activities engaged in during a year, less than one-half of the curriculum was based on lifetime activities believed to have health significance. The more recent NCYFS II study of 2,435 representative U.S. children from grades 1–4 shows similar results. Although 96% are enrolled in physical education, only 36% participate daily (U.S. Department of Health and Human Services, 1987). The 1990 Public Health Service goal calls for 60% daily participation in health-related physical education activity in the school (U.S. Department of Health and Human Services, 1980).

The typical adolescent student reports that over 80% of total physical activity comes from leisure or sport activities outside the physical education class. The average girl devotes 70.7% of nonschool activity to what can be regarded as lifetime physical activities, compared with 55.7% for the typical boy.

The degree to which this activity involvement reflects sufficient intensity and regularity for cardiorespiratory fitness and health is not encouraging. If activity appropriate for health and fitness is de-

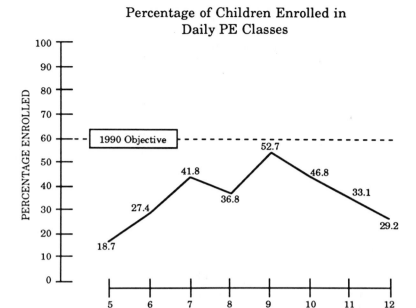

FIGURE 2-8. *Percentage of U.S. children enrolled in daily physical education classes in grades 5–12. From U.S. Department of Health and Human Services (1986). Midcourse Review of 1990 Objectives for Physical Fitness and Exercise. U.S. Government Printing Office: Washington, DC.*

fined by minimum standards of large muscle, dynamic movements for 20 min duration, three or more times weekly at an intensity of 60% of cardiorespiratory capacity, about one-half of boys and girls appear active enough to benefit. According to self-report, 58.9% are appropriately active year-round; 46.9% use a lifetime activity to achieve this level, but only 41.0% state that they regularly exert themselves during exercise so that they breathe hard and sweat. Based on teacher and parent ratings, only about 35–40% of children in grades 1–4 have activity levels above average for their age and sex. Just 13–17% are rated as a lot more active than their peers (U.S. Department of Health and Human Services, 1987).

The 1990 Public Health Service goals call for more than a 90% rate of regular participation among 10 to 17 year olds. Much of the physical activity involvement of children and youth appears to be in team sports or recreational pursuits, where fitness gains are negligible and health benefits are unknown.

Greater health-related fitness in the NCYFS sample was associated with (1) greater participation in high intensity physical activ-

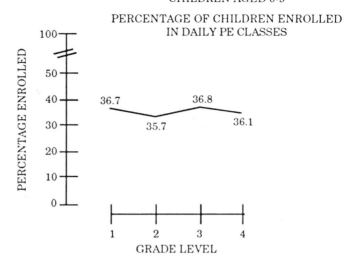

FIGURE 2-9. *Percentage of U.S. children enrolled in daily physical education classes in grades 1–4. Adapted from U.S. Department of Health and Human Services (1987). National Children and Youth Fitness Study II.* Journal of Physical Education and Recreation 58(9):49–96.

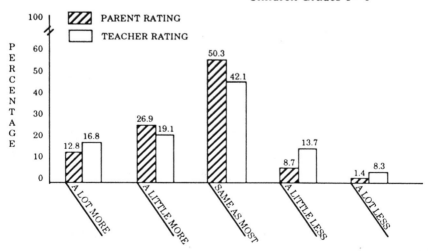

FIGURE 2-10. *Parent and teacher ratings of physical activity levels for U.S. children in grades 1–4. Adapted from U.S. Department of Health and Human Services (1987). National Children and Youth Fitness Study II.* Journal of Physical Education and Recreation 58(9):49–96.

ity during nonsummer months, (2) enrollment in physical education classes with frequent weekly meetings and a variety of activities, and (3) greater number and variety of nonschool activities during the past year. In the NCYFS II sample, mile walk/run performance and skinfold sum was associated with (a) participation in community-based physical activities, (b) parent and teacher activity ratings, (c) mother's activity habits, and (d) daily hours of television watching. The cross-sectional designs of these surveys cannot, however, address the degree to which these factors lead to greater fitness or, conversely, the degree to which higher initial fitness level (and other behavioral or environmental factors) selectively dispose children to more and varied activity. Also, the year-round behavioral differences noted for the NCYFS sample appeared only when extreme fitness groups were contrasted (i.e., students at or above the 75th percentile vs. students below the 40th percentile), and even then the behavior-fitness association was modest. This further obscures the origins and meaning of the fitness and activity relationship.

These results hint at other activity trends that are also disturbing for public health. First, the portion of the adolescent student population that is active drops substantially during fall and winter months, then rises in spring and summer. The authors of the NCYFS report surmise that this may set an unhealthy precedent for adult activity patterns, where consistent participation is desirable. Second, while enrollment in physical education is at a rate of 96–97% at grades 1 through 6, only 50% of 11th and 12th grade students are enrolled. This corresponds with the rapid decrease in exercise patterns later seen as children leave school and enter the work force (Stephens et al., 1985). Finally, when contrasted with a comparable sample of American children from the 1960s, the subjects in the NCYFS sample appeared significantly fatter (2–3 mm) as indicated by triceps brachii skinfold assessment. This finding suggests that current activity levels in school-age children and youth do not adequately offset dietary habits. A recent study (Dietz & Gortmaker, 1985) attributes much of this gain in body fat to excessive television watching and inadequate exercise habits. It is not clear, however, from the NCYFS study if the apparent increase in childhood fatness is significant from a practical or epidemiologic standpoint.

The American Academy of Pediatrics (1986) Committee on Nutrition recommendations for a Prudent Life-style for Children state that "counseling on the maintenance of ideal body weight and a regular exercise program . . . should be a routine part of all health supervision visits (p. 523)." However, it was estimated in 1984 that less than 50% of physicians actually counseled patients about exercise (U.S. Department of Health and Human Services, 1986). The physician readership of *The Physician and Sportsmedicine* reported that 85%, 60%, and 43%, respectively, recommended exercise for depression, anxiety, and substance dependence, yet this likely represented a biased sample and did not address childhood counseling. A recent and more representative random sample of 2,000 pediatrician members of the 22,000 member American Academy of Pediatricians indicated that more than 70% of primary care pediatricians encouraged exercise for well children 6 y or older, even if they were not at high risk for illness. This rate exceeds U.S. Department of Health and Human Services (1986) recommendations for the year 2000. Among primary care physicians, 50–65% believed that exercise was very important for these ages—more important than diet but less important than cigarette smoking (Nader et al., 1987), but only 25% believed they could be effective in changing patient behavior.

There is little evidence, however, that physician counseling will increase children's physical activity, even though great potential exists for this to occur (Iverson et al., 1985). Research has suggested that less than 10% of physicians believe they are successful in helping patients change behavior (Weschsler et al., 1983), and this belief might hinder their attempts or their effectiveness. Recent study is more encouraging in suggesting that physicians can increase physical activity (Iverson et al., 1985; Wells, Lewis, & Leake, 1986). In the future, physicians should be exposed to exercise promotion and behavior change principles (Dishman, 1988a) as they apply to exercise adherence in youth under the age of 18 y and to adults.

Behavioral Interventions. Behavioristic and educational techniques have been used to increase physical activity in mentally retarded children (Allen & Iwata, 1980) and boys and girls with obesity (Epstein et al., 1984a,b) and insulin-dependent diabetes (Marrero, Fremion, & Golden, 1988). However, few controlled studies of self-selected leisure activity in youth 6 to 18 years of age have been reported, and these have involved descriptions of small samples. This makes it difficult to establish a population baseline against which to compare the effectiveness of interventions designed to increase physical activity.

Observation, questionnaires, diaries kept by parents, heart rate monitors, estimates of energy expenditure or caloric balance, and changes in fitness (Baranowski et al., 1984; Bradfield et al., 1971; Campaigne et al., 1984; Epstein et al., 1984b; Gilliam et al., 1981; Ilmarinen & Rutenfranz, 1980; Lussier & Buskirk, 1977; Spady, 1980; Waxman & Stunkard, 1980) have been used to estimate activity during the school year, during recess periods, and during summer months when school is not in session (Gilliam et al., 1981; Howell et al., 1978; LaPorte et al., 1982; Saris et al., 1980; Wallace et al., 1985). Daily exercise diaries, weight loss, and fitness changes have also been contrasted as estimates of exercise compliance among children outpatients undergoing supervised treatment for obesity (Epstein et al., 1984a,b). Although exercise and physical activity are effective adjuncts to weight loss therapy, both fitness changes and weight loss are poor estimates of activity patterns in obese children. Advances in understanding the determinants of free-living physical activity in children and youth cannot occur until the concurrent validity of activity estimates is established for ages 6 to 18 y.

Population-Based Retrospective Surveys in Adults. Available evidence on the relationship between childhood and adulthood exercise patterns is not compelling; it comes exclusively from cross-sectional and retrospective surveys with adults and is limited to sport and physical education experiences.

A 1972 National Adult Physical Fitness Survey (Clarke, 1973) estimated that just 36% of Americans had taken physical education or gym classes in elementary school, whereas 42% and 57% had such classes in junior and senior high school, respectively. Nearly all of the 76 million Americans who had school physical education felt their experience was good for them, but 1.1 million felt it was a bad experience, and 9.8 million were neutral in their opinion. However, the impact of physical education or school sports on adult activity patterns was unclear in this survey. Although 90 to 91% of the total public felt children should have physical education at all education levels from elementary school through college, 45% of those surveyed were themselves completely sedentary. In addition, although former participants in more than one school sport reported they were twice as likely to be active than inactive in adulthood, former participants in just one sport, or adults with no school sport background, were each equally likely to be inactive or to be active.

The influence of school sport participation on adult physical activity patterns is an important area of study for exercise epidemiology. Not only should early activity history be expected to be a strong influence on contemporary activity during adulthood, but were participation in school sports to be causally linked to adult activity, it could be modified by public policy. Morbidity and mortality studies of former athletes must also consider physical activity patterns during the adult years to control for the confounding effect of interactions between activity history and subject self-selection. The association between school sport and adult activity is a phenomenon that has received little research attention. In their recent review, Powell and Dysinger (1987) located only six empirical articles on childhood participation in sport and physical education as antecedents to adult activity patterns. They concluded that the existing evidence is equivocal.

The results of past studies have collectively been difficult to interpret because of a number of design and measurement limitations. Cross-sectional and retrospective studies have yielded associations that may merely be coincidental; other unmeasured variables may account for causal predictions. In particular, a number of subject-selection biases may confound the associations of principal interest. For example, any comparison of contemporary activity between former athletes and non-athletes should first adjust for differences in age, physical fitness, and health status that might exist between the two groups. Each factor has been related to adult physical activity (Dishman et al., 1985) and could confound an observed association with sport history. Both the internal and external validity of results have also been limited. Population-based studies with potential for high generalizability across different types of subjects and activities have relied on activity recall without objective fitness measures to verify the self-report. Conversely, studies of small groups in supervised settings have permitted objective measurements of activity, but they apply to only a narrow range of population segments and have not assessed free-living activity outside the supervised setting.

Studies reporting greater adult activity among former athletes have employed cross-sectional or retrospective designs and relied solely on self-report measures of sport involvement and adult activity history. Studies that have used objective definitions of sport history or of adult activity (e.g., program attendance or physical fit-

TABLE 2-6. *Recommendations for Retrospective Study of Youth Sport and Adult Activity*

1. Define physical activity, exercise, fitness, sport, and setting (e.g. supervised vs. free-living)

2. Limit, stratify or adjust for age, gender, education, health

3. Use objective measures of sport participation

4. Consider skill development: interest, opportunities, diversity of sport experience

5. Conduct prospective studies to confirm retrospective associations

ness) consistently show no differences among former athletes and non-athletes in both cross-sectional and prospective designs. Our recent findings (Dishman, 1988b) indicate that contemporary physical activity in adult Caucasian males is not different between former school athletes and non-athletes. This was observed for both a cross-section of free-living activity and a propsective supervised setting in which the potential confounding influences of age, fitness, and health status were statistically controlled. Moreover, the recall estimate of free-living activity was verified by its patterning with other subjective and objective concurrent estimates of physical activity, including exercise tolerance and body mass index. Based on our results and those from other reports methodologically similar to ours, school sport participation does not appear promising as a target for promotions designed to increase physical activity in adult Caucasian males. Future studies should examine, however, the quality of the school sport experience, employ objective measures of sport history, and study females and other races or ethnic groups. Moreover, the influences of participation motivation or dropping out of youth sport upon adult physical activity should be studied prospectively and retrospectively.

Personality, Heredity, and Behavior[2]. The social-psychological approach that has exclusively characterized the literature on youth sport participation cannot account for biological predispositions to activity. The potential impact on physical activity of learning-based interventions cannot be accurately evaluated without an understanding of innate personality influences on activity patterns.

It is widely agreed that personality structure is governed in large measure by heredity, and both the pervasiveness and stability of extraversion-introversion and neuroticism-stability is well-documented (Holden, 1987). Also, the influence of extraversion and emotional stability on sport performance is also well documented (Morgan, 1986b). There are several theoretical reasons why extroverts should be more successful in sport than introverts. First, extroverts have a higher level of sensory input than introverts for a given subjective intensity (Eysenck, 1967), and this explains, in part, why extroverts have a higher pain tolerance than introverts. This difference in pain tolerance has been found to exist from as early as 5 years of age (Elliott, 1972). The work of Kagan, Reznick, and Snidman (1988) has led to the conclusion that differences in "inherited variation in the threshold of arousal in selected limbic sites may contribute to shyness in childhood and even extreme degrees of social avoidance in adults." (p. 167) The work by Kagan et al. (1988) has relied on the use of longitudinal research designs in which children were first tested at 2 years of age and again at 7 years. In this work, it has been found that "inhibited" versus "uninhibited" behavioral responses are governed largely by biological factors.

In addition, it has been reported that neuroticism is influenced by heredity as well, and this trait is correlated 0.85 in identical twins as compared with 0.22 in fraternal twins (Eysenck, 1947, 1967). Since personality structure is influenced so dramatically by the genotype (Holden, 1987; Kagan et al., 1988), it is unlikely that any personality differences observed between athletes and non-athletes in cross-sectional comparisons are caused by involvement in sport. Therefore, it is imperative that longitudinal designs be employed in the study of this question. The limited longitudinal research suggests that psychological differences observed between athletes and non-athletes exist from the very outset (Morgan, 1976; Morgan, 1986a). This preliminary research suggests that gravitation toward sport, or self-selection, is responsible for the unique psychological profile observed in the athlete.

It has also been demonstrated that not only are maximal aerobic power, endurance performance, and anaerobic performance influenced by the genotype (Bouchard, 1988; Klissouras, 1970), but trainability is influenced by heredity as well (Bouchard, 1988). Success for certain athletes is also governed in part by somatotype (e.g., diver, gymnast, football lineman, basketball player, cox, heavyweight wrestler, lightweight wrestler, etc.). It is therefore perplexing why social psychologists have failed to acknowledge the influence of biological factors in their efforts to understand phenomena such as "dropout" in sport settings. There has been an effort to describe the social and/or psycho-social factors responsible for "dropout" with a general failure to entertain the possibility that young children drop out of sport programs because they lack ability. Social psychologists have looked for the answers to problems such as dropout with the tools and research methodologies they have been trained to employ. In this sense, they are method-bound, and while the environment (e.g., coaching style, parental role, peer and sibling influences, etc.) may certainly influence adherence versus dropout from a sport, it is quite likely that individuals who are "outgoing, stable, strong, tall, and possess high pain tolerance in concert with good muscular endurance, aerobic power, and anaerobic power" may tend to enjoy involvement in sport to a greater degree than does the individual who is "shy, neurotic, weak, short, etc." In other words, it is possible that success and enjoyment in sport is governed by personality structure and physiological capacity to an extent greater than that offered by the environment.

Social psychologists have not only failed to realize that outcomes and/or products are governed largely by psychobiological traits, but there has also been a complete failure to recognize that millions of young children are "cut" from sport teams each year; that is, they do not *drop out*, they are *thrown out* (i.e., discarded). What is the psychological impact of being rejected? Is rejection any better or worse than a stressful environment that provokes volitional recidivism? Put another way, possibly the stress in sport should be preserved, and our efforts should be directed toward developing strategies that will optimize involvement in, exposure to, and successful adaptation to exercise-sport stressors.

It has also been reported by Johnson and Morgan (1981) that athletes (n = 865) and non-athletes (n = 500) differ psychologically at 18 years of age. While this cross-sectional study cannot rule out the possibility that sport may have caused the observed differences, related research suggests that such differences usually exist from the outset. In other words, it appears that a selection factor accounts for most of the differences reported in cross-sectional comparisons of athletes and non-athletes (Morgan, 1976; Morgan, 1986a). In the study by Johnson and Morgan (1981) the personality profiles of athletes and non-athletes not only differed significantly at 18 years of age, but those athletes who went on to enjoy success in their various sports possessed significantly less psychopathology from the outset than did the unsuccessful.

The work by Johnson and Morgan (1981) was extended to include a 20-y follow-up of athletes and non-athletes who were tested at 18 years of age and 20 years later at 38 years of age (Morgan, 1986a). The mood state, quality of life, and exercise patterns at 38 years of age were predicted with 76%, 73%, and 78% accuracy using personality data collected at 18 years of age. In other words, it is possible to predict who will be active versus sedentary in the middle years on the basis of psychological status in the early years. Of equal importance in this study was the finding that athleticism in the early years was unrelated to exercise patterns in the middle years. Furthermore, health status (physical and mental), quality of life, and socioeconomic status (Duncan index) at 38 years of age, were not related to athleticism in the early years (i.e., 18–22 years of age). These findings serve to support an extensive literature that suggests personality structure and mood state in the middle and later years is governed largely by heredity and early developmental factors.

Psychological Theories of Behavior as Models for Determinants of Physical Activity and Exercise for Youth 6 to 18 Years Old. It is important to determine the degree to which fitness, physical activity, and exercise are similar or different in origins or patterns when compared with other health behaviors and risk factors. Exercise or fitness might augment or diminish the impact of other health risk factors, and exercise might reinforce or create barriers for other health behaviors. If models unique to exercise and physical activity are required to account for habitual participation, successful interventions will need to focus on determinants that are different from, or may complement, those encompassed by existing health education and promotion principles and techniques. However, research in this area on children is essentially nonexistent (Dishman et al., 1985). Although nearly all exercise studies have exclusively examined adults, there are implications from the theoretical models for physical activity relationships and behavioral impact from childhood to adulthood. These health behavior models and related studies are summarized in Table 2-7.

The models summarized are limited to accounting for the variability in health behaviors due to attitudes, values, beliefs, self-perceptions, and affect. These factors are important for public health interventions because they provide targets for mass information or persuasion campaigns and education. But, it is clear that additional forces influence some health actions.

Existing models of health behavior do not place an emphasis on biological aspects that may distinguish physical activity and exercise from other health behaviors. Yet it is commonly recognized that other health behaviors are not homogenous in origin. Differences in determinants and health outcomes make it useful to regard most health behaviors as either illness-reducing or health-promoting. Janz and Becker (1984) recently distinguished between preventive health behavior, sick role behavior, and clinic utilization. Also, a distinction between health-related and health-directed behavior is an illustrative contrast. It is recognized that actions may be initiated purposely for health or that health outcomes may result from behaviors motivated by nonhealth reasons. Also, many health behaviors may occur due to predisposition or environmental bias that is independent of conscious decisions. This is evidenced by the prevailing main effects that age, sex, and socioeconomic status exert on many health behaviors and their associated morbidity and mortality rates.

Age or Developmental Stages. The role of age or developmental stage is another important component that needs to be taken into account to guide research/interventions with health beliefs, attitudes and behaviors. As Roberts, Maddux, and Wright (1984) point out, children are different from adults in their ability to understand health issues and to assume personal responsibility for their health. What's more, the rapid changes that occur in childhood may call for different strategies with regard to questions of determinants and effective interventions.

A few studies have tried to assess differences by age among the

Table 2-7. *General Behavior Models for Exercise in Youth*

Behavior Model and Summary	Conclusions
1. **Health Belief Model** (Rosenstock, 1974). Compliance with any health behavior depends on perceived vulnerability to a disorder, belief that health risk is increased by noncompliance, and belief that health effectiveness of the behavior outweighs barriers.	It is not known how health beliefs about exercise are formed in children or if they predict exercise patterns. How health beliefs from childhood affect later adult beliefs and habits is also not known (Dielman et al., 1982; Green et al., 1980; Holcomb et al., 1984). A valid technology for assessing exercise and health beliefs for children is not available.
2. **Theory of Reasoned Action** (Ajzen & Fishbein, 1977). Attitudes about a specific exercise prescription (i.e., time, place, and type of exercise) can predict behavior through its interaction with social norms. Both influence exercise intention.	The extent to which physical activity patterns in children stem from reasoned action and how exercise intentions interact with other activity influences is not known. The model has predicted less than half of exercise intentions in children (Godin & Shephard, 1986). Contrasts between general and specific exercise attitudes as predictors across time, settings, activities, and age groups are needed.
3. **Self-Efficacy** (Bandura, 1977a). To attempt and persist at a behavior change, one must perceive a personal ability to carry out the behavior when the outcome is known. Self-efficacy develops by (a) actual mastery, (b) modeling, (c) verbal persuasion, and (d) emotional signs of coping ability.	It is important to understand the incentives to engage in health-related exercise during childhood and how they change and/or remain in adulthood. Beliefs about general physical ability vs. self-efficacy in specific exercise settings needs to be studied with children across activities, time, and settings. Based on exercise results with adult patient groups, self-efficacy may best predict exercise patterns among youth with disabling conditions that have restricted past activity.
	Feelings of self-efficacy most accurately predict when they are specific to a narrow range of behavior and time. However, general feelings of physical ability might be a better predictor of overall exercise patterns across time, settings, and activities than specific self-efficacy beliefs, but this has not been tested. Self-efficacy is influenced by actual experience and subjective signs of inability. Therefore, there is a need to take into account past activity history and perceived exertional strain. Self-efficacy does not predict persistence of behavior change when incentives are not present.

TABLE 2-7. (*Continued*)

Behavior Model and Summary	Conclusions
4. **Physical Activity Model** (Sonstroem, 1978). Attraction to physical activity is reinforced by increased self-esteem; mediated by perceived increases in physical ability and fitness due to increased activity.	Although its predictions are not as precisely stated as the preceding models, the Physical Activity Model is attractive because it provides a link between past activity history, fitness, self-perceptions of ability, and attitude. It permits an empirical contrast with other models of attitude (e.g., Ajzen & Fishbein, 1977) and perceived ability (e.g., Bandura, 1977a). The model has not been experimentally tested, but cross-sectional evidence supports its validity for spontaneous exercise in children. This is the only available model designed specifically for youth physical activity patterns.
5. **Health Locus of Control** (Wallston et al., 1978). This model is also concerned with perceived competence but extends the concept to beliefs about the source of control over health and behavior reinforcements.	No studies on children's exercise have employed locus of control models, and exercise-specific measures and reinforcement value have received little attention. Studies of adult exercise have yielded mixed results and have not been uniform in method. Because this model and the ones that follow (perceived competence, personal investment, and outcome expectancy value) encompass a developmental or social learning perspective and offer targets for social psychology interventions with exercise, they should be contrasted among children and youth.
6. **Theory of Planned Behavior** (Ajzen, 1985). Expands the theory of reasoned action by including perceived and actual control over behavior. It acknowledges that intentions are often not implemented because of inability, situational barriers, or transcience of intentions.	No physical activity studies reported, but the model may help explain why the theory of reasoned action has provided incomplete explanations in exercise settings. The inclusion of internal control and self-efficacy variables with attitudes, norms, intentions, and activity history within the planned behavior model should be tested in children, but it is likely to be more appropriate for ages 10–17 than for younger ages.

TABLE 2-7. (Continued)

Behavior Model and Summary	Conclusions
7. **Expectancy-Value Decision Theories.** Behavior is a function of self-expectations of the outcomes from a behavior and the evaluation of these outcomes in contrast to outcomes of alternative actions.	May predict intention or interest in adopting free-living physical activity but has not predicted participation in either free-living or supervised activity. Useful global framework for understanding the unique aspects of the preceding six models; each has emanated from the broader decision-theory base. Integration of self-efficacy and planned behavior within an expectancy value umbrella may offer a parsimonious model for explaining adoption of physical activity.
8. **Self-Regulatory Theory.** Behavior is controlled much like a servomechanism in which goal setting, self-monitoring of behavior, and self-reinforcement are necessary skills to implement behavioral intentions and overcome personal and situational barriers to motivation.	Some evidence supports the effectiveness of interventions which include goal setting, self-monitoring, and self-reinforcement. Cross-sectional study suggests these skills combine with self-motivation to explain variance in free-living activity. Most effective in multiple component packages, particularly using principles of relapse prevention. Appears particularly important for explaining maintenance and periodicity of physical activity in free-living physical activity. Can be an important adjunct to prevent or reduce the incidence of dropout in supervised settings.
9. **Opponent-Process Theory.** A two-phase process underlies motivated behavior. The primary phase to a stimulus is excitatory and it initiates a secondary, inhibitory or opponent phase which returns arousal to a hedonic neutrality acceptable to the individual. The opponent process grows faster and stronger with stimulus exposure while the initial phase grows weaker and decays more rapidly. Thus, an initially pleasurable or aversive response requires increasing stimulus exposure, while its absence produces a growing opponent response.	No physical activity studies reported. May help explain maintenance or adherence to habitual physical activity. The theory's biobehavioral nature can account for tangible sensations that may reinforce continued participation. The exclusive reliance of the previous models on cognition has been inadequate for conceptualizing tangible or concrete reinforcing mechanisms for participation among the active.
10. **Perceived Competence** (Harter, 1982). The focus of this model is on goal directed behavior and self-perceptions in social, academic, and physical activity settings. It is similar to Sonstroem's (1978) Physical Activity Model.	No studies related to exercise behavior in children although the model has been tested in youth sport settings (Feltz & Petlichkoff, 1983).
11. **Personal Investment** (Maehr, 1984). Based on congruence between beliefs, attitudes, values, intentions, perceived competence, and behavior. Emphasis on goal setting.	No studies related to exercise behavior in children.

seven health and risk behaviors studied by Breslow and associates in the Human Population Laboratory (Belloc & Breslow, 1972). For example, Glynn (1983) studied health and illness behaviors in second to 10th graders in the Milwaukee, Wisconsin school system. It was found that there was a gradual and consistent decline in health behaviors from second to 10th grade, with the decline being somewhat greater for females than for males. The majority of the decline was due to changes in regular sleeping and eating patterns. Other factors that contributed to this decline were cigarette smoking, consumption of alcoholic beverages, and a decline in physical activity.

Studies that examine cross-sectional relationships between exercise or physical activity and other health behaviors among adults show little overlap. Exercise-related variables tend to group alone, although dietary behavior is frequently correlated with activity patterns. Research with high school students shows a similar pattern (Hays et al., 1984). Exercise habits were not linked to meal regularity; drug, alcohol, or cigarette use; and hours of sleep.

A cross-sectional random survey of 3,106 Finnish school children 11 to 19 years of age (Telama & Silvennoinen, 1979) illustrates methodologic and conceptual concerns for socially based interventions and research. Across age, near-linear shifts in self-perceived motivation for exercise occurred. Performance-oriented competitive motivation and a normative emphasis on health (e.g., fitness exercise is everybody's duty; exercise is one of the healthy habits of life; physical activity is useful at a later age) decreased with age, whereas recreation for relaxation increased. Most importantly, the motives most strongly linked to frequency and intensity of volitional physical activity were perceived fitness and physical competence, recreation for relaxation, and functional health (e.g., maintaining one's health; improving endurance). There were also noteworthy gender differences in activity motivation. Boys, particularly at the younger ages, tended to endorse competition and fitness motivation, whereas girls, particularly at older ages, endorsed recreation.

Other research in the United States is consistent with the Finnish observations in suggesting that health and exercise beliefs differ in stability across age. When more than 300 young adults from Madison, Wisconsin, who had been tested as children in 1961 were followed up 16 y later in 1977, Mechanic (1979) observed a limited degree of stability in perceived health and illness over time. Factors related to health-care utilization appeared very pliable across age. Communication of illness feelings to others and feeling at ease with seeing a doctor were unrelated from childhood to adulthood. However, factors related to self-monitoring and self-regulating health showed moderate stability. Denial of pain, risk taking, and perceived illness susceptibility were the most predictable from childhood to adulthood. Young children who did not pay attention to pain seemed more likely to become adults who deny pain, maintain normal activities when ill, do not discuss illness symptoms, and take health risks.

Among the Wisconsin adults, the reporting of exercise was related to enjoyment of exercise and to feelings of physical health and personal control over health, but not to illness symptoms or health care utilization. These data may have relevance for defining the part of exercise and health behaviors that remains stable or self-regulated across age. Because Mechanic (1979) observed factors relating to self-regulation that showed moderate stability over time, these may have important implications for maintenance of exercise behavior. For example, interventions are best targeted at determinants sensitive to change agents, whereas more resistant determinants should be accommodated.

Harter (1982) has proposed a framework for understanding how self-regulatory health behaviors develop in youth. The framework hypothesizes that the order of self-regulatory component processes in children occurs in the reverse order of how self-regulation is thought to operate in adulthood. In other words, self-regulation in adulthood is thought to operate sequentially through the processes of: (1) self-monitoring; (2) self-evaluation; and (3) self-reinforcement. However, children first learn to imitate verbal approval. This is applied before they learn the processes of self-evaluation. In turn, self-evaluation must be learned before they can apply it to situations where it is necessary to self-monitor. There have been no studies conducted to test this developmental model for exercise. However, other researchers (Magrab, 1978; Matthews & Angulo, 1980; Melamed & Siegel, 1980) have advocated the use of interventions designed to enhance self-regulatory skills, particularly for children who have difficulty complying with a health regimen.

In summary, the lack of information concerning (1) what constitutes "healthful" physical activity from childhood to adulthood; (2) how social, psychological, and biological mechanisms interact to promote self-regulatory behaviors across life span; (3) which self-regulatory skills most facilitate exercise adherence in children and adults; and (4) how self-regulatory behaviors are acquired in the developmental process, indicate that there is a need for a conceptual framework to guide future research and interventions. In addition, it will be important to determine the influences of concrete or intrinsically reinforcing aspects of youthful participation in physical activity. Constructs such as enjoyment and preferred exertion have not yet been studied in youths 6 to 18 years of age. Of the behavior models outlined in Table 2-7, outcome-expectancy value theories and opponent-process theory appear particularly well-suited for describing the development of intrinsic incentives and rewards for physical activity participation in youth, but they have not been tested in youths 6 to 18 y.

SUMMARY

The available literature in sport psychology reveals the following for youth aged 6 to 18 y:

1. The effectiveness of competitive sport participation for promoting psychological and social benefits has not yet been verified by scientific methods. The same can be said for psychological and social risks often attributed to sport. Social psychology and social anthropology theories demonstrate how sport *can* be a positive or negative experience, but most of the empirical evidence from actual sport settings indicates that sport has little psychological impact on most children. When parents and coaches promote a sport environment that permits a balance between cooperation and competition and offers opportunity for learning skills and mastering challenging goals without exaggerated threat of injury or social criticism, most children seem to enjoy sports. Perceived competence is a worthwhile goal for sport, but its role for motivating sport behavior is not yet empirically clear. The social roles and rules inherent in the structure of sport make it a potential vehicle for instructing moral development, but the extent to which moral development and prosocial behaviors are being influenced by sport is not yet known. Thus, while competitive sport has potential efficacy for aiding the psychological and social development of children, its effectiveness for doing so has not been convincingly demonstrated.

2. Knowledge about the population benefits, risks, and rates of sport participation among children and youth cannot advance unless epidemiologic methods are employed. Currently, the sport psychology findings in these areas are of unknown generalizability. Likewise, the internal validity of the small-sample studies that have been conducted is unclear because there has been nearly exclusive reliance on a self-report methodology without concern for conventional psychometric theory or concurrent measures of behavior, physiology, or pathology.

3. Similar conclusions can be drawn for the psychological outcomes associated with physical activity. Although physical activity increases self-esteem for most children, this effect is most likely when physical successes occur and when they are rewarded socially. The effects of physical activity on anxiety and depression are unknown for youth 6 to 18 years of age, but the consensus by mental health professionals holds that the mental health efficacy of activity seen in adults should also be seen in children.

4. The determinants of physical activity in children 6 to 18 years of age are unknown, and a measurement technology for assessing population activity is currently being developed. The best available estimates indicate that national goals for leisure activity rates and daily physical education will not be reached. Parents, schools, and physicians can have efficacy in increasing physical activity and its determinants, but their effectiveness in doing so is not now known (e.g., Nader et al., 1987).

5. At present, sport psychology lacks the measurement, technology and applied theory to predictably meet the important North American policy and position goals. The means to develop this technology and theory are available in the traditions of epidemiology, psychiatry, psychometry, psychophysiology, psychopharmacology, and exercise science. However, these traditions are not employed by the vast majority of child sport psychologists, who rely on social psychology or social anthropology theory and techniques. These are important and effective traditions, but used exclusively they cannot continue to advance our understanding in the areas of participation rates, determinants, and outcomes in sport and physical activity. Because less than 1% of the members of the American College of Sports Medicine are sport psychologists, psychiatrists, or sociologists, it is unlikely these views will be diffused to most sport psychologists.

A recent review by Malina (1988) of a new child sport psychology volume is representative of the current state of affairs in pediatric sport psychology and offers a solution:

> The focus of the volume is, with few exceptions, exclusively behavioral to the neglect of biology. This is puzzling for sport and is unique in that the biological organism must physically perform the neuromuscular skills demanded of a sport in the context of situations which

are socially or culturally determined. To exclude the biological is myopic. Sport, like many other aspects of culture, should be treated in a biocultural or biosocial manner.

BIBLIOGRAPHY

1. Ajzen, I. and M. Fishbein. Attitude-behavior relations: A theoretical analysis and review of empirical research. *Psychological Bulletin* 84:888–918, 1977.
2. Allen, C.D. and B.A. Iwata. Reinforcing exercise maintenance: using existing high rate activities. *Behavior Modification* 4:337–354, 1980.
3. Allison, M.T. Sportsmanship: Variations based on sex and degree of competitive experience. In A.O. Dunleavy, A.W. Miracle, and C.R. Rees, (eds.) *Studies in the sociology of sport.* Fort Worth, TX: Texas Christian University Press, 153–165, 1982.
4. American Academy of Pediatrics. Committee on Nutrition. Prudent Life-style for Children: Dietary Fat and Cholesterol. *Pediatrics* 78:521–523, 1986.
5. American Academy of Pediatrics. Recommendations for participation in competitive sports. *Pediatrics* 81:737–739, 1988.
6. American Association for Health, Physical Education, and Recreation. Resolutions, 58th National Convention. Washington, D.C.: AAHPERD Publications, 1954.
7. Bandura, A. Self-efficacy: Toward a unifying theory of behavioral change. *Psychological Review* 84(2):191–215, 1977a.
8. Bandura, A. *Social learning theory.* Englewood Cliffs, NJ: Prentice-Hall, 1977b.
9. Belloc, N.B. and L. Breslow. Relationship of physical health status and family practices. *Preventive Medicine* 1:409–421, 1972.
10. Binkhorst, R.A., H.C.G. Kemper, and W.H.M. Saris, (eds.) *Children and Exercise XI,* Champaign, IL: Human Kinetics, 1985.
11. Blumenthal, J.A., S. Rose, and J.L. Chang. Anorexia nervosa and exercise. *Sports Medicine* 2:247–247, 1985.
12. Bouchard, C. Gene-environment interaction in human adaptability. In R.M. Malina and H.M. Eckert (eds). *Physical Activity in Early and Modern Populations.* Champaign, IL: Human Kinetics, 56–66, 1988.
13. Bovyer, G. Children's concepts of sportsmanship in the 4th, 5th, and 6th grade. *Research Quarterly* 34:282–287, 1963.
14. Bradfield, R.B., H. Chan, N.E. Bradfield, and P.R. Payne. Energy expenditures and heart rates of Cambridge boys at school. *American Journal of Clinical Nutrition* 24:1461–1466, 1971.
15. Bredemeier, B. The moral of the youth sport story. In E.W. Brown and C.F. Branta (eds.) *Competitive Sports for Children and Youth* (pp. 285–296). Champaign, IL: Human Kinetics, 1988.
16. Bredemeier, B. and D. Shields. Moral growth among athletes and non-athletes. A comparative analysis of females and males. *Journal of Genetic Psychology* 147:7–18, 1986.
17. Bredemeier, B., M. Weiss, D. Shields, and R. Shewchuk. Promoting moral growth in a summer sport camp: The implementation of theoretically grounded instructional strategies. *Journal of Moral Education* 15:212–220, 1986.
18. Breswsan, E.S. and M.H. Woolacott. A prescriptive paradigm for sequencing instruction in physical education. *Human Movement Science* 1:155–175, 1983.
19. Brown, R.S. Exercise and mental health in the pediatric population. *Clinics in Sports Medicine* 1(3):515–527, 1982.
20. Brownell, K.D. and F.S. Kaye. A school-based behavior modification, nutrition education, and physical activity program for obese children. *The American Journal of Clinical Nutrition* 35:277–283, 1982.
21. Bruner, J., A. Jolly, and K. Sylva. (eds.) *Play: Its role in evolution and development.* New York: Penguin, 1976.
22. Campaigne, B.N., T.B. Gilliam, M.L. Spencer, and E.R. Gold. Heart rate holter monitoring of 6- and 7-year-old children with insulin dependent diabetes mellitus, cardiovascular and short term metabolic response to exercise: a pilot study. *Research Quarterly for Exercise and Sport* 55:69–73, 1984.
23. Centers for Disease Control. Status of the 1990 physical fitness and exercise objectives. *Morbidity and Mortality Weekly Report.* U.S. Department of Health and Human Services, 34(34), 521–524; 529–531, 1985.
24. Clarke, H.H. (Ed.). National adult physical fitness survey. *President's Council on Physical Fitness and Sports Newsletter* (Special Edition). Washington, D.C., May, 1973.
25. Cunningham, D.A., R. Dorner, J.B. Critz, J. Griffiths, and M. Lefcoe. Catecholamine ex-

cretion in young hockey players. In *Abstract of the First Canadian Congress for the Multidisciplinary Study of Sport and Physical Activity*, 1973.

26. Dielman, T.E., S. Leech, M.H. Becker, I.M. Rosenstock, W.J. Horvath, and S.M. Radius. Parental and child health beliefs and behavior. *Health Education Quarterly* 9(2 and 3):60–77, 1982.
27. Dietz, W.H. and S.L. Gortmaker. Do we fatten our children at the television set? Obesity and television viewing in children and adolescents. *Pediatrics* 75(5):807–812, 1985.
28. Dishman, R.K. Medical psychology in exercise and sport. *Medical Clinics of North America* 69:123–143, 1985.
29. Dishman, R.K. Mental health. In Seefeldt, V. (ed.) *Physical Activity and Well-being* (pp. 304–341). Reston, VA: American Alliance for Health, Physical Education, Recreation and Dance, 1986.
30. Dishman, R.K. (ed.). *Exercise adherence: Its impact on public health.* Champaign, IL: Human Kinetics, 1988a.
31. Dishman, R.K. Supervised and free-living physical activity: No differences in former athletes and non-athletes. *American Journal of Preventive Medicine, 4,* 153–160, 1988b.
32. Dishman, R.K. and A.L. Dunn. Exercise adherence in children and youth: implications for adulthood. In R.K. Dishman (ed.) *Exercise adherence: Its impact on public health.* Champaign, IL: Human Kinetics, 1988a.
33. Dishman, R.K. and A.L. Dunn. Pediatric sport psychology. In *Pediatric Sports Medicine.* New York: Sport Medical Spectrum Publications, 1988b.
34. Dishman, R.K., J.F. Sallis, and D. Orenstein. The determinants of physical activity and exercise. *Public Health Reports* 100:158–171, 1985.
35. Dwyer, T., W.E. Coonan, D.R. Leitch, B.S. Hetzel, and R.A. Baghurst. An investigation of the effects of daily physical activity on the health of primary school students in South Australia. *International Journal of Epidemiology* 12:308–313, 1983.
36. Eide, R.The relationship between body image and physical activity. *Scandinavian Journal of Social Medicine, Supplement* 29:109–112, 1982.
37. Elliott, C.D. Extroverts and introverts. *Science News* 18:282, 1972.
38. Epstein, L.H., R. Koeske, and R. Wing. Adherence to exercise in obese children. *Journal of Cardiac Rehabilitation* 4:185–195, 1984.
39. Eysenck, H.J. *Dimensions of Personality.* London: Kegan Paul, 1947.
40. Eysenck, H.J. *Biological Basis of Personality.* Springfield: Charles C. Thomas Co, 1967.
41. Feltz, D.L. and L. Petlichkoff. Perceived competence among interscholastic sport participants and dropouts. *Canadian Journal of Applied Sport Sciences* 8:231–235, 1983.
42. Feltz, D.L. and R.R. Albrecht. Psychological implications of competitive running. In M.R. Weiss and D. Gould (eds.) *Sport for Children and Youth: 1984 Olympic Scientific Congress Proceedings.* Champaign, IL: Human Kinetics, 1987.
43. Feltz, D.L. and M.E. Ewying. Psychological characteristics of elite young athletes. *Medicine and Science in Sports and Exercise 19* (Supplement):S98–S105, 1987.
44. Freud, S. On narcissism. In *Complete standard edition of the psychological works of Sigmund Freud.* London: Hagarth, 69–102, 1958.
45. Garfinkel, B.D., A. Froese, and J. Hood. Suicide attempts in children and adolescents. *American Journal of Psychiatry* 139:1257–1261, 1982.
46. Gill, D.L., J.B. Gross, and S. Huddleston. Participation motivation in youth sport. *International Journal of Sport Psychology* 14:1–14, 1983.
47. Gilliam, T.B., P.S. Freedson, D.L. Geener, and B. Shabraray. Physical activity patterns determined by heart rate monitoring in 6- to 7-year-old children. *Medicine and Science in Sports and Exercise* 13(1):65–67, 1981.
48. Glynn, W. Juvenile illness behavior: Effect of age, sex, personality, and distress. Unpublished doctoral dissertation, University of Wisconsin, Madison, 1983.
49. Godin, G. and R.J. Shephard. Psychosocial factors influencing intentions to exercise of young students from grades 7 to 9. *Research Quarterly for Exercise and Sport* 57:41–52, 1986.
50. Gould, D., D. Feltz, T. Horn, and M. Weiss. Reasons for attrition in competitive swimming. *Journal of Sport Behavior* 5:155–165, 1983.
51. Gould, D., D.L. Feltz, and M.R. Weiss. Motives for participating in competitive youth swimming. *International Journal of Sport Psychology* 16:126–140, 1985.
52. Gould, D. and T. Horn. Participation motivation in young athletes. In J. Silva and R. Weinberg, (eds.) *Psychological Foundations of Sport* Human Kinetics, Champaign, IL: pp. 359–370, 1984.
53. Gould, D., R. Horn, and J. Spreeman. Sources of stress in junior elite wrestlers. *Journal of Sport Psychology* 5:159–171, 1983.
54. Green, L.W., P. Heit, D.C. Iverson, L.J. Kolbe, and M. Kreuter. The school health curriculum project: its theory, practice, and measurement experience. *Health Education Quarterly* 7(1):14–34, 1980.

55. Greist, J.H., M.H. Klein, R.R. Eischens, J. Faris, A.S. Gurman, and Morgan, W.P. Running through your mind. *Journal of Psychosomatic Research* 22:259–294, 1978.
56. Gruber, J.J. Physical activity and self-esteem development in children: A meta-analysis. In G.A. Stull and H.M. Eckert, (eds.). *Effects of Physical Activity on Children,* American Academy of Physical Education Papers, 19:30–48. Human Kinetics, Champaign, IL, 1988.
57. Haan, N. Two moralities in action contexts: relationship to thought, ego regulation and development. *Journal of Personality and Social Psychology* 36:286–305, 1978.
58. Hanson, D.L. Cardiac response to participation in Little League baseball competition as determined by telemetry. *Research Quarterly* 38:381–388, 1967.
59. Harter, S. A developmental perspective on some parameters of self-regulation in children. In P. Karoly and F.H. Kanfer (eds.) *Self-management and behavior change: From theory to practice.* New York: Pergamon Press, 1982.
60. Hays, R., A.W. Stacy, and M.R. DiMatteo. Covariation among health related behaviors. *Addictive Behaviors* 9:315–318, 1984.
61. Holcomb, J.D., J.P. Carbonari, R.V. Ingersoll, W.M. Luce, and J. Nelson. The long term impact of a cardiovascular school health curriculum. *Health Education* October/November:19–23, 1984.
62. Holden, C. The genetics of personality. *Science* 237:598–601, 1987.
63. Hovell, M.F., J.H. Bursick, B. Sharkey, and J. McClure. An evaluation of elementary students' voluntary physical activity during recess. *Research Quarterly for Exercise and Sport* 49(4):460–474, 1978.
64. Hughson, R. Children in competitive sports—a multi-disciplinary approach. *Canadian Journal of Applied Sport Sciences* 11:162–172, 1986.
65. Ilmarinen, J. and Rutenfranz. Longitudinal studies of the changes in habitual physical activity of school children and working adolescents. In K. Berg and B.O. Eriksson, (eds). *Children and Exercise IX.* University Park Press, Baltimore, pp. 149–159, 1980.
66. Iverson, D.C., J.E. Fielding, R.S. Crow, and G.M. Christenson. The promotion of physical activity in the United States population: The status of programs in medical, worksite, community, and school settings. *Public Health Reports* 100(2):212–224, 1985.
67. Jankowski, K., E. Andrzejewska, J. Endicott, A. Fraczek, K. Jankowska, S. Kozlowski, L. Markiewicz, and J. Reykowski. Psychotherapie, pharmokotherapie and sporttherapie bei emotional gestorten Jugendlichen: Eine vergleichende Analyse von stationarer und ambulanter Therapie mit Hilfe physiologischer und psychologisher Methoden. *Zeitschrift fur Klinische Psychologie und Psychotherapie* 24:251–255, 1976.
68. Janz, N.K. and M.H. Becker. The health belief model: a decade later. *Health Education Quarterly* 11(1):1–47, 1984.
69. Johnson, R.W. and W.P. Morgan. Personality characteristics of college athletes in different sports. *Scandinavian Journal of Sports Science* 3:41–49, 1981.
70. Kagan, J., J.S. Reznick, and N. Snidman. Biological bases of childhood shyness. *Science* 240:167–171, 1988.
71. Kagen, S. and M.C. Madsen. Experimental analyses of cooperation and competition in Anglo-American and Mexican-American children. *Developmental Psychology* 6:49–59, 1972.
72. Kane, M.J. The influence of level of sport participation and sex-role orientation on female professionalization of attitudes toward play. *Journal of Sport Psychology* 4:290–294, 1982.
73. Kidd, T.R. and W.F. Woodman. Sex orientations toward winning in sport. *Research Quarterly* 46:476–483, 1975.
74. Kleiber, D.A. and G.C. Roberts. The effects of sport experience in the development of social character: An exploratory investigation. *Journal of Sport Psychology* 3:114, 122, 1981.
75. Klissouras, V. Heritability of adaptive variation. *Journal of Applied Physiology* 29:358–367, 1970.
76. Kohlberg, L. *The philosophy of moral development: Moral stages and the idea of justice.* San Francisco: Harper and Row, 1981.
77. Koocher, G.P. Swimming, competence, and personality change. *Journal of Personal and Social Psychology* 18:275–278, 1971.
78. Kostrubala, T. *The joy of running.* New York: J.B. Lippincott, 1976.
79. Kroll, W. and K.H. Peterson. Study of values test and collegiate football teams. *Research Quarterly* 36:441–447, 1965.
80. Kuntzleman, C.T. W.K. Kellogg Feeling Good Project. Technical Report. Fitness Finders, Spring Arbor, Michigan, 1985.
81. Lakie, W.L. Expressed attitudes of various groups of athletes toward athletic competition. *Research Quarterly* 35:497–501, 1964.
82. LaPorte, R.E., J.A. Cauley, C.M. Kinsey, W. Corbett, R. Robertson, R. Black-Sandler, C.H. Kuller, and J. Falkel. The epidemiology of physical activity in children, college students, middle-aged men, menopausal females, and monkeys. *Journal of Chronic Diseases* 35:787–795, 1982.

83. Linder, C.W. and R.H. DuRant. Exercise, serum lipids, and cardiovascular disease—risk factors in children. *Pediatric Clinics of North America* 29(6):1341–1354, 1982.
84. Lowe, R. and J.E. McGrath. Stress, arousal, and performance: Some findings calling for a new theory. Project Report AF 1161–1167, Air Force Office of Scientific Research, 1971.
85. Lussier, L. and E.R. Buskirk. Effects of an endurance training regimen on assessment of work capacity in prepubertal children. *Annals New York Academy of Sciences* 301:734–747, 1977.
86. MacConnie, S.E., T.B. Gilliam, D.L. Geenen, and A.E. Pels. Daily physical activity patterns of prepubertal children involved in a vigorous exercise program. *International Journal of Sports Medicine* 3:202–207, 1982.
87. Maehr, M. Meaning and motivation: toward a theory of personal investment. *Research on Motivation in Education: Student Motivation* 1:115–144, 1984.
88. Magrab, P.R. (Ed.). *Psychological management of pediatric problems*, Vol. 1. Baltimore: University Park Press, 1978.
89. Malina, R.M. Review of *Advances in Pediatric Sport Sciences, Volume 2: Behavioral Issues. Sports Medicine Bulletin* 23:19, 1988.
90. Maloney, T. and B. Petrie. Professionalization of attitudes toward play among Canadian school pupils as a function of sex, grade, and athletic participation. *Journal of Leisure Research* 4:184–195, 1972.
91. Mantel, R. and L. Vander Velden. The relationship between the professionalization for attitudes toward play of preadolescent boys and participation in organized sports. In G.H. Sage, (ed.) (pp. 172–178) *Sport in American Society*, 2nd ed. Reading, MA: Addison-Wesley, 1974.
92. Marrero, D.G., A.S. Fremion, and M.P. Golden. Improving compliance with exercise in adolescents with insulin dependent diabetes mellitus: Results of a self-motivated home exercise program. *Pediatrics* 81:519–525, 1988.
93. Matthews, K.A. and J. Angulo. Measurement of Type A behavior pattern in children: Assessment of children's competitiveness, impatience-anger, and aggression. *Child Development* 51:466–475, 1980.
94. Matthews, K.A. and J.M. Siegel. The Type A behavior pattern in children and adolescents: Assessment, development, and associated coronary risk. In A.R. Baum and J.E. Singer, (eds.). *Handbook of Health and Medical Psychology* Vol. 2, Hillsdale, N.J.: Lawrence Erlbaum Associates, 1985.
95. McCloy, C. Character building through physical education. *Research Quarterly* 1:41–61, 1930.
96. McSherry, J.A. The diagnostic challenge of anorexia nervosa. *American Family Physician* 29:141–45, 1984.
97. Mead, G. *Mind, Self, and Society*. Chicago: University of Chicago Press, 1934.
98. Mechanic, D. The stability of health and illness behavior: Results from a 16-year follow-up. *American Journal of Public Health* 69:1142–1145, 1979.
99. Melamed, B.G. and L.J. Seigel. *Behavioral Medicine: Practical Applications in health care*. New York: Springer, 1980.
100. Morgan, W.P. Psychological consequences of vigorous physical activity and sport. In *The Academy Papers*, M.G. Scott (ed.), Iowa City: American Academy of Physical Education, pp. 15–30, 1976.
101. Morgan, W.P. Negative addiction in runners. *The Physician and Sportsmedicine* 7:57–70, 1979.
102. Morgan, W.P. Athletes and nonathletes in the middle years of life. In B.D. McPherson, (ed.) *Sport and Aging*, pp. 167–186, Champaign, IL: Human Kinetics, 1986a.
103. Morgan, W.P. Selected psychological factors limiting performance: A mental health model. In *Limits of Human Performance*, D.N. Clarke and E.H. Eckert (eds.). Champaign, IL: Human Kinetics. 70–80, 1986b.
104. Morgan, W.P. and S.N. Goldston (eds.). *Exercise and Mental Health*. Washington, D.C.: Hemisphere Publishing Corporation, 1986.
105. Murray, J.L. and J.G. Bruhn. Reliability of the MYTH scale in assessing Type A behavior in preschool children. *Journal of Human Stress* 9(4):23–28, 1983.
106. Nader, P.R., H.L. Taras, J.F. Sallis, and T.L. Patterson. Adult heart disease prevention in childhood: A national survey of pediatricians' practices and attitudes. *Pediatrics* 79:843–850, 1987.
107. Nunnally, J.C. *Psychometric Theory*. New York: McGraw-Hill, 1978.
108. Oakes, R. Sex patterns in DSM-III: Bias or basis for theory development. *American Psychology* 39, 1320–1322, 1984.
109. Orlick, T.D. Positive socialization via cooperative games. *Developmental Psychology* 17:426–429, 1981.
110. Piaget, J. *The moral judgment of the child*. New York: Norton, 1965.
111. Pillemer, F.G. and L.J. Micheli. Psychological considerations in youth sports. *Clinics in Sports Medicine* 7(3):679–689, 1988.

112. Powell, K.E. and W. Dysinger. Childhood sports and physical education as precursors of adult physical activity. *American Journal of Preventive Medicine* 3:276–281, 1987.
113. Railo, W.S. The relationship of sport in childhood and adolescence to mental and social health. *Scandinavian Journal of Social Medicine Supplement* 29:135–145, 1982.
114. Roberts, C.C., J.E. Maddux, and Wright. Developmental perspectives on behavioral health. In J.D. Matarazzo, S.M. Weiss, J.A. Herd, N.E. Miller and S.M. Weiss (eds.) *Behavioral Health* pp. 56–68. New York: Wiley Interscience, 1984.
115. Roberts, G.C. Achievement motivation in sport. *Exercise and Sport Sciences Reviews* 10:236–269, 1982.
116. Robins, L.N., J.E. Helzer, and M.M. Weissman. Lifetime prevalence of specific psychiatric disorders in three sites. *Archives of General Psychiatry* 41:949–958, 1984.
117. Rosenstock, I.M. Historical origins of the health belief model. *Health Education Monographs* 2(4):1–9, 1974.
118. Ross, C.E. and D. Hayes. Exercise and psychologic well-being in the community. *American Journal of Epidemiology* 127:762–771, 1988.
119. Saris, W.H.M. Habitual physical activity in children: Methodology and findings in health and disease. *Medicine and Science in Sports and Exercise* 18:253–263, 1986.
120. Saris, W.H.M., R.A. Binkhorst, A.B. Cramwinckel, F. van Waesberghe, and A.M. van der Veen-Hezemans. The relationship between working performance, daily physical activity, fatness, blood lipids and nutrition in school children. In K. Berg and B.O. Eriksson, (eds.). *Children and Exercise IX* pp. 166–174. Baltimore: University Park Press, 1980.
121. Scanlan, T.K. Competitive stress and the child athlete. In J.M. Silva, III and R.S. Weinberg (pp. 118–129). *Psychological foundations of sport*. Champaign, IL: Human Kinetics, 1984.
122. Scanlan, T.K. and R. Lewthwaite. Social psychological aspects of competition for male youth sport participants: Predictors of competitive stress. *Journal of Sport Psychology* 6:208–226, 1984.
123. Scanlan, T.K. and R. Lewthwaite. From stress to enjoyment: parental and coach influences on young participants. In E.W. Brown and C.F. Branta (eds.) *Competitive Sports for Children and Youth* (pp. 41–48). Champaign, IL: Human Kinetics, 1988.
124. Scanlan, T.K. and M.W. Passer. Factors related to competitive stress among male youth sport participants. *Medicine and Science in Sports* 10:103–108, 1978.
125. Scanlan, T.K. and M.W. Passer. Sources of competitive stress in young female athletes. *Journal of Sport Psychology* 139:1257–1261, 1979.
126. Secord, P.F. and S.M. Jourard. The appraisal of body-cathexis. Body-cathexis and the self. *Journal of Consulting Psychology* 17:343–347, 1953.
127. Segrave, J.O. Sport and juvenile delinquency. In R.E. Terjung, (ed.). *Exercise and Sport Sciences Reviews*, Vol. 2 (pp. 181–209). Philadelphia: Franklin Institute 1983.
128. Seymour, E.W. Comparative study of certain behavioral characteristics of participant and non-participant boys in Little League baseball. *Research Quarterly* 27:338–346, 1956.
129. Shapiro, S., E.A. Skinner and L.G. Kessler. Utilization of health and mental health services. *Archives of General Psychiatry* 41:971–978, 1984.
130. Simon, J.A. and R. Martens. Children's anxiety in sport and nonsport evaluative activities. *Journal of Sport Psychology* 1:151–159, 1979.
131. Skubic, E. Emotional responses of boys to Little League and Middle League competitive baseball. *Research Quarterly* 26:342–352, 1955.
132. Skubic, E. and J. Hilgendort. Anticipatory, exercise, and recovery heart rates of girls was affected by four running events. *Journal of Applied Physiology* 19:853–856, 1964.
133. Smith, R.E. and F.L. Smoll. Psychological stress: A conceptual model and some intervention strategies in youth sports. In R.A. Magill, M.J. Ash and F.L. Smoll, (eds.) *Children in sport: A contemporary anthology*, 2nd ed. Champaign, IL: Human Kinetics, 1982.
134. Smith, R.E. The dynamics and prevention of stress-induced burnout in athletics. *Primary Care* 11:115–127, 1984.
135. Sonstroem, R.J. Exercise and self-esteem. In R.L. Terjung, (ed.). *Exercise and Sport Sciences Reviews*, Vol. 12, 123–155. Lexington, MA: Collamore Press, 1984.
136. Spady, D.W. Total daily energy expenditure of healthy, free-ranging school children. *The American Journal of Clinical Nutrition* 33:766–775, 1980.
137. Stephens, T., D.R. Jacobs, and C.C. White. A descriptive epidemiology of leisure-time physical activity. *Public Health Reports* 100(2):147–158, 1985.
138. Strauss, R.H. Theoretical sports medicine. *The Physician and Sportsmedicine* 16(5):3, 1988.
139. Taylor, C.B., J.F. Sallis, and R. Needle. The relation of physical activity and exercise to mental health. *Public Health Reports* 100(2):195–202, 1985.
140. Telama, R. and M. Silvennoinen. Structure and development of 11- to 19-year-olds' motivation for physical activity. *Scandinavian Journal of Sports Science* 1:23–31, 1979.
141. U.S. Department of Health and Human Services. National Children and Youth Fitness Study. *Journal of Physical Education, Recreation and Dance.* 56(1):44–90, 1985.

142. U.S. Department of Health and Human Services. Midcourse review 1990 objectives for physical fitness and exercise. U.S. Government Printing Office, Washington, DC, 1986.
143. U.S. Department of Health and Human Services. National children and youth fitness study II. *Journal of Physical Education and Recreation* 58(9):49–96, 1987.
144. Vallerand, R.J., E.L. Deci, and R.M. Ryan. Intrinsic motivation in sport. *Exercise and Sport Sciences Reviews* 15:389–425, 1987.
145. Vander Velde, C. Body images of one's self and others: Developmental and clinical significance. *American Journal of Psychiatry* 142:527–537, 1985.
146. Wallace, J.P., T.L. McKenzie, and P.R. Nader. Observed vs. recalled exercise behavior: a validation of a seven-day exercise recall for boys 11 to 13 years old. *Research Quarterly for Exercise and Sport* 56:161–165, 1985.
147. Wallston, K.A., B.S. Wallston, and M.R. DeVellis. Development of a multi-dimensional health locus of control (MHLC) scale. *Health Education Monographs* 6:160–170, 1978.
148. Walter, H.J., A. Hofman, R.D. Vaughan, and E.L. Wynder. Modification of risk factors for coronary heart disease. *New England Journal of Medicine* 318:1093–1100, 1988.
149. Wankel, L.M. and P.S.L. Kreisel. Factors underlying enjoyment of youth sports: sport and age group comparisons. *Journal of Sport Psychology* 7:51–64, 1985a.
150. Wankel, L.M. and P.S.J. Kreisel. Methodological considerations in youth sport motivation research: A comparison of open-ended and paired comparison approaches. *Journal of Sport Psychology* 7:65–74, 1985b.
151. Waxman, M. and A.J. Stunkard. Caloric intake and expenditure of obese boys. *The Journal of Pediatrics* 96(2):187–193, 1980.
152. Webb, H. Professionalism of attitudes toward playing among adolescents. In G. Kenyon, (ed.) *Aspects of contemporary sport sociology*. p. 161. Chicago: Athletic Institute, 1969.
153. Weiss, M.R. and B.J. Bredemeier. Moral development. In V. Seefeldt, (ed.). *Physical activity and human well-being*. Reston, VA: AAHPERD, 1986.
154. Weschler, H., S. Levine, R.K. Idelson, M. Rohman, and J.O. Taylor. The physician's role in health promotion—a survey of primary care practitioners. *New England Journal of Medicine* 308:97–100, 1983.
155. Wolf, T.M., M.C. Sklov, P.A. Wenzl, S.M. Hunter, and G.S. Berenson. Validation of a measure of Type A behavior pattern in children: Bogalusa Heart Study. *Child Development* 53:126–135, 1982.
156. Yates, A., K. Leehey, and C.M. Shisslak. Running—An analogue of anorexia? *New England Journal of Medicine* 308:251–255, 1983.

ACKNOWLEDGMENTS

Thanks go to Andrea Dunn for her help in writing two review articles from which portions of this paper were drawn (Dishman & Dunn, 1988a; Dishman & Dunn, 1988b) and to Donna Smith for preparing the manuscript and Marlee Stewart for preparing the figures and tables. Thanks are also extended to Drs. William P. Morgan and Tara Scanlan for providing their unique perspectives in formal reactions to the paper and to Drs. Priscilla Clarkson, Lyle Micheli, Alan Rogol, and Art Vaillas for helpful suggestions.

FOOTNOTES

[1]My appreciation is extended to William P. Morgan, Gernot Presting, and Patrick O'Connor of the University of Wisconsin for bringing their translation and critical review of the Jankowski et al. (1976) paper to my attention.
[2]Special thanks go to Dr. Morgan for his specific insights and for providing the section on personality, heredity, and behavior.

DISCUSSION

SHEPHARD: In thinking about psychological responses to physical activity we need to consider the situation in which the activity occurs and not merely think of the activity as a clearly defined independent variable. For example, Finnish research has shown that gymnastics presented to teenagers in an indoor setting produces quite negative attitudes toward the activity, whereas a positive attitude was associated with the activity when presented in an outdoor setting. Also, Outward Bound types of experiences, in which the emphasis is placed on helping members of the group achieve goals, have had very positive effects on attitudes toward physical activity. I think such situational effects on attitudes toward activity need to be addressed.

DISHMAN: That question bears attention. I attempted to mention it in the paper but perhaps not as emphatically as I should have.

SUTTON: Has there been any attempt by psychologists to delineate stress that has positive outcomes from stress that has negative outcomes, especially in youth?

DISHMAN: I am not comfortable with generalizing from the rather weak available evidence on the activity participation rates, the incidence of "stress", or any of the psychological effects associated with participation by youth either in sport or physical activity, especially because these phenomena have mostly been studied with nonuniform methods in very small samples with unknown generalizability. I don't believe we have any solid idea of what the true population prevalence or incidence rates of stress are in the area of youth sport.

Stress is not a psychological response, it's not a systemic physiological response, but it is an organismic response to real or imagined events. If you looked at the few physiological studies that use neuroendocrine or heart rate responses, for example, as measures of psychological stress, you will find that the psychological stress response is not remarkable. Such stress occurs, but it is lower than or equal to physical exertion stress, and it is soon over. Moreover, studies of "stress" in youth sport have not examined health or social outcomes linked with the acute stress responses to sport. This is necessary to distinguish clearly positive outcomes from negative outcomes, and it will require accelerated research using clinical and epidemiological methods.

DRINKWATER: I was intrigued when I read recently that self-esteem is associated more with aerobic and fitness types of activity than it is with skilled and creative activities. I wondered how strong this relationship is and how it can be explained.

DISHMAN: The relationship you describe is probably not terribly strong. Nevertheless, assuming it has some validity, it may be that if someone is active, they improve a skill or they at least perceive they've improved a skill; such improvements may be more readily seen in fitness types of activities than in creative or in sports skill activities.

DRINKWATER: Do you know of any relationship between the increased self-esteem seen with fitness activities and the readiness to continue that type of activity in the future?

DISHMAN: Bob Sonstroem's work early on with this topic suggested that there indeed was a relationship between measurable fitness, the perception that children had of that fitness, and their attitude or orientation toward being active. That orientation then apparently stimulated more physical activity. In cross-sectional studies, there are data that support such a notion in children. But to carry that over into adult years, I think, is not very well established.

SHEPHARD: It may well be that the greater self-esteem seen with fitness activities can be accounted for by the fact that a very small gain in aerobic power, for example, with cycling training, allows one to pedal an additional 60 or 70 miles in relative comfort. Thus, a large increase in exercise duration results from a relatively modest training effort, and this may lead to greater feelings of accomplishment and an improved self-esteem.

3

Age- and Sex-Associated Variation in Strength During Childhood: Anthropometric, Morphologic, Neurologic, Biomechanical, Endocrinologic, Genetic, and Physical Activity Correlates.

CAMERON J. R. BLIMKIE, PH.D.

INTRODUCTION

I. SCOPE

Muscular strength has long been considered an important and separate component of physical fitness. Strength is required for movement, and one's level of strength determines, in part, the ease and effectiveness of performance in many day-to-day, occupational, recreational, and sports activities. Strength testing of children is performed routinely by rehabilitation therapists to assess degree of muscle disability and to diagnose rate of recovery from injury, by physical educators to grade student performance, and by coaches to select athletes for sports teams. Although beyond the scope of this chapter, strength testing is also commonly used in the adult population for selection into certain occupations and for determination of competency in various work-related tasks.

Given the diversity of application and the significance of strength testing and measurement, it is important that administrators of such tests be familiar with the normal age- and sex-associated variations in strength performance and with the various factors that can both influence performance scores and confound interpretation of the results of investigations of strength. These issues are discussed in detail in this chapter.

The purpose of this chapter is to describe age- and sex-associated changes in skeletal muscle strength during childhood and to discuss these changes in terms of selected biologic, anthropometric, morphologic, neurologic, biomechanical, endocrinologic, genetic, and physical activity influences. The reader is directed to earlier excellent reviews on the topic of strength development during childhood by Malina (1975, 1978, 1986) and to a recent review by Beunen and Malina (1988).

For the purposes of this chapter, childhood will encompass the age range from birth to late adolescence (18 y) and may sometimes be used interchangeably with youth. For ease of discussion, this age range may be subdivided into the various categories outlined in Table 3-1, namely: early childhood; mid-childhood; early adolescence, which includes puberty; and late adolescence.

This chapter will deal solely with the topic of muscle strength and will not address the equally important issues of either skeletal muscle power or endurance. Strength is discussed in terms of the peak force or torque development during a) maximal voluntary isometric contractions, b) electrically evoked single twitch isometric muscle contractions, c) electrically evoked tetanic isometric muscle contractions, and d) maximal voluntary isokinetic muscle contrac-

TABLE 3-1. *Age Categories During Childhood.*

Category	Age Range
Early Childhood	0–6 y, Females
	0–6 y, Males
Mid-Childhood	7–10 y, Females
	7–12 y, Males
Early Adolescence	11–13 y, Females
(includes puberty)	13–15 y, Males
Late Adolescence	14–18 y, Females
	16–18 y, Males

TABLE 3-2. *Characteristics Of Different Types Of Muscle Contractions.*

Variable	Description
Force	Peak tension (measured externally by a strain gauge or dynamometer) developed during voluntary or involuntary (electrically evoked) activation of muscle. Because of the mechanical disadvantage of the musculotendonous-skeletal system, the measured external tension is less than that developed within the muscle tendon.
Torque	Peak force (tension) developed about a joint. Torque is the product of force applied at the point of contact with the dynamometer and the moment arm or distance from the point of application of force to the center of the joint axis.
Maximal Isometric Contraction	Voluntary and electrically evoked activation of muscle against an immovable resistance, resulting in maximal tension development with no change in muscle length.
Maximal Isokinetic Contraction	Voluntary activation of muscle against a movable and varying resistance, resulting in maximal tension development throughout the joint's full range of motion, with a constant or fixed movement speed.
Evoked Twitch Contraction	Activation of muscle by a single percutaneous supramaximal electrical stimulation that results in a single isometric contraction lasting a few hundred msec.
Evoked Tetanic Contraction	Activation of muscle by repetitive percutaneous electrical stimulation that results in a fused isometric contraction usually lasting a few sec.
Maximal Voluntary Contraction	Activation of muscle achieved during an all-out voluntary isometric or isokinetic muscle contraction. Maximal voluntary isometric contractions usually last a few sec, whereas the duration of isokinetic contractions will vary from less than a sec to a few sec, depending on the speed of movement.

tions. A brief description of the key characteristics of these contraction types is presented in Table 3-2. A more detailed explanation of the physiologic and mechanical characteristics of the various types of muscle contractions and of terminologic considerations relevant to human muscle strength can be found in papers by Knuttgen and Kraemer (1987), Komi (1984), Kulig et al. (1984), Osternig (1986), Sale and Norman (1982), and Winter (1978).

Strength and strength measurement have received considerable attention over the years. The literature on adults is replete with descriptions of strength characteristics of virtually all human muscle groups under various physiologic conditions and includes subjects of all ages and states of health. The scope of this chapter will mainly include age- and sex-associated changes in strength for only selected measures of strength, namely: handgrip strength, elbow flexion and extension strength, knee extension and flexion strength, and plantar flexion strength. Strength changes for these measures will also be compared with changes in whole body strength as represented by composite strength scores (totaled scores from several individual strength measures).

The selection of muscle groups to be tested for strength was based primarily on the availability of comprehensive published strength data sets covering the age range of interest for this chapter. While there are numerous papers dealing with the topic of strength in children, there are considerably fewer studies with commonality in age ranges studied, muscle groups tested, strength testing methodology used, type of muscle contraction studied, and physiologic conditions under which muscles were tested.

Lastly, this review is primarily restricted to normal, healthy, nonathletic children. In some cases however, data were derived from control subjects in clinical studies or studies of young athletic populations.

II. ISOMETRIC STRENGTH

A. Grip Strength

By far the most abundant strength literature in children exists in the form of grip strength data. It is important to remember that absolute strength scores will vary depending upon the type of dynamometer utilized in testing and upon the nuances of the testing procedures, e.g., hand-arm position, degree of practice, level of motivation, hand dominance, and level of understanding about the purpose and nature of the test. Because data in this review were obtained under varying conditions, the reader is cautioned against making direct comparisons of strength scores across different studies. The more important emphasis is the pattern of variation in strength performance across ages and between sexes.

Numerous investigators have reported grip strength performance for various age groups within childhood. With a few noted exceptions, the summary of results in this section is restricted to studies that span at least the period from mid-childhood to adolescence and that use 18 years of age as the upper point of comparison. This period encompasses prepubertal, pubertal, and postpubertal developmental stages.

The age-related variation in absolute grip strength is shown for boys and girls in Figure 3-1. For boys, there appears to be a fairly linear increase in grip strength with advancing age from early childhood until the onset of puberty. Strength increases rapidly during the pubertal period and continues to increase considerably, albeit at a slower rate, during adolescence. The pattern is similar for girls until the onset of puberty. In contrast to boys, strength continues to increase in girls during puberty at a rate that does not appear substantially different from that seen during the prepubertal period. Additionally, there appears to be very little increase in strength among girls during adolescence. The pattern of strength development appears similar whether measures are made with one hand or both hands. The magnitude of the pubertal spurt in single hand grip strength for males appears dampened compared with the double

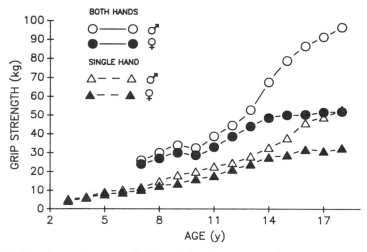

FIGURE 3-1. *Age- and sex-associated variation in grip strength performance. Points represent mean values for single and double hand performance scores. Drawn from data reported for females by: Canada Fitness Survey, 1985; Shephard, 1982; Smedley, 1900; Metheny, 1941; Montoye & Lamphier, 1977; and for males by: Canada Fitness Survey, 1985; Bookwalter et al., 1950; Clarke, 1971; Montoye & Lamphier, 1977; Shephard, 1982.*

hand performance; however, this is due primarily to the constriction of the ordinate for the single hand performance scores.

Sex-related differences in strength are evident as early as 3 years of age. Boys have consistently higher average single and double hand grip strength scores than girls from 3 to 18 years of age. Gender differences in grip strength are small, however, before the male adolescent growth spurt, at which time the difference becomes progressively larger with increasing age. There is considerable overlap of male and female strength scores before the male growth spurt. With increasing age during adolescence, however, the percentage of boys who outscore girls on various strength measures increases considerably (Faust, 1977; Jones, 1949; Malina, 1986a).

Using the strength score attained at 18 y (peak final strength) as a reference, it is apparent from Figure 3-2 that girls realize a higher proportion of their peak strength than boys at all chronological ages below 18. Girls and boys achieve 50% of their peak final strength performances by 10 and 12.5 y, respectively. Peak final strength at 18 y is, however, a rather arbitrary point of reference because grip strength in particular is known to increase at least into the early or mid-20s (Fisher & Birren, 1947; Montoye & Lamphear, 1977; Sale & Norman, 1982).

When grip strength performance is compared between genders, it is evident from Figure 3-3 that there is a progressive decrease in the female-male strength ratio with advancing age, whether ex-

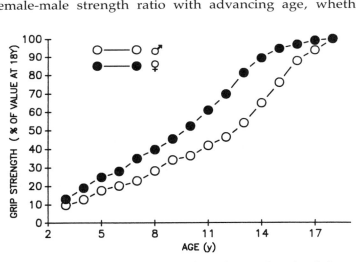

FIGURE 3-2. *Percent of peak final grip strength at 18 years of age in relation to age and sex. Drawn from data reported for females by: Canada Fitness Survey, 1985; Shephard, 1982; Smedley, 1900; Metheny, 1941; Montoye & Lamphier, 1977; and for males by: Canada Fitness Survey, 1985; Bookwalter et al., 1950; Clarke, 1971; Montoye & Lamphier, 1977; Shephard, 1982.*

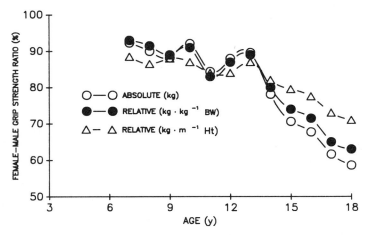

FIGURE 3-3. *Ratio of female-to-male hand grip strength in relation to age. Values are derived from the Canada Fitness Survey, 1985. Points are based on age- and sex-specific 50th percentile scores for total of two hand grip strength, weight, and height.*

pressed in absolute force or normalized for either body weight or height. Regrettably, there are no comparable data for grip strength normalized for lean body mass. Girls have about 92% of the absolute strength of boys at age 7, compared with less than 60% at 18 y. A similar age-related decline is evident for strength ratios normalized for height and weight, although the magnitude of the reduction is not as great. It is important to realize that these gender-based ratios are specific to hand grip strength and may not be generalizable to other muscle groups or to other types of muscle contractions.

Age-related differences in absolute strength between sexes are associated to some degree with differences in body size. As shown in Figure 3-4, boys are consistently stronger than girls for double hand grip strength normalized for body weight. Strength increases at about the same rate in both sexes from 7 to 13 y, but in contrast with girls, continues to increase with age for males during adolescence. Carron and Bailey (1974) demonstrated a similar increase in upper body, lower body and composite strength per kg body weight in males from 10 to 16 years of age.

The sex difference in relative strength (per kg mass) before puberty is at least in part due to the higher proportion of body fatness and lower proportion of lean tissue in females from mid-childhood onward (Faust, 1977; Kemper, 1986; Malina, 1986a; Saris et al., 1986). The divergence in strength between sexes during puberty and adolescence may be attributed in part to a continued increase in sub-

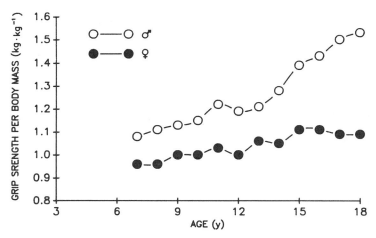

FIGURE 3-4. *Grip strength normalized for body weight in relation to age and sex. Values are derived from the Canada Fitness Survey, 1985. Data points are based on age-specific 50th percentile scores for two hand grip strength and weight.*

cutaneous fat in females (Canada Fitness Survey, 1985; Faust, 1977; Kemper, 1986) and to a proportionately greater increase in muscle size and mass in males (Malina, 1986a, in press; Malina & Johnston, 1967; Cheek, 1975).

While it is tempting to attribute sex differences in relative strength solely to the quantitative influence of body composition, other possible factors, e.g., neuromuscular, biochemical, and biomechanical differences between the sexes, cannot be discounted yet. Additionally, results from the Canada Fitness Survey (1983) indicated a substantial and progressive reduction in reported levels of physical activity for females beginning around puberty. The significance of age- and sex-associated differences in level and nature of physical activity on strength development will be addressed in greater detail later in this chapter.

A similar developmental pattern is evident for strength normalized for height (Figure 3-5). Boys have consistently higher scores than girls at all chronological ages, demonstrate a similar rate of strength increase to girls until 13 y, then show a progressive and substantial increase in strength from 13 to 18 y, during which time females exhibit a plateau in strength performance. Carron and Bailey (1974) reported a similar pattern of development for upper body, lower body, and composite strength normalized for height in boys from 10 to 16 y. This pattern is also similar to that for strength normalized for height reported in the classic studies of Asmussen (1973) and Asmussen and Heeboll-Nielsen (1955 and 1956).

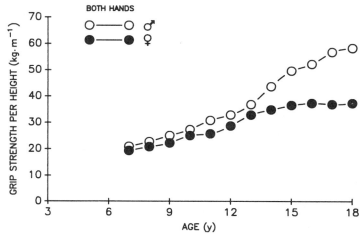

FIGURE 3-5. *Grip strength normalized for height in relation to age and sex. Values are derived from the Canada Fitness Survey, 1985. Data points are based on age-specific 50th percentile scores for two hand grip strength and height.*

These results indicate that strength increases at a faster rate than height for both sexes before puberty. The sex difference in strength and the relative acceleration in strength for males during puberty and adolescence may at least partially be attributed to the fairly well-defined and previously noted quantitative differences (anthropometric and morphologic) and as yet undefined qualitative differences (i.e., neuromuscular, biochemical, and biomechanical) between sexes. The importance of these quantitative and qualitative influences on strength performance will be discussed in greater detail later in this chapter.

B. Composite Strength

To this point the discussion has focused solely on isometric grip strength, largely because it represents strength of a fairly isolated muscle group performing a very specific function and because grip strength has been widely studied and reported for both genders throughout childhood and adolescence. The classic series of studies by Jones (1947; 1949) and later by Asmussen and Heeboll-Nielsen (1955; 1956) and Asmussen (1973) demonstrated that the developmental curves for strength will vary with the nature of the strength measures (grip vs. thrust strength) and that differences between sexes will vary with muscle group and muscle function tested. Given this variability, how representative are age-based grip strength performance curves of overall or general strength development?

Measures of composite strength (total of strength scores from several different muscle groups) provide an assessment of overall or general strength. The age and developmentally based performance curves for composite strength derived from the studies by Stolz and Stolz (1951) and Faust (1977) are presented in Figures 3-6a, b, and c. The pattern for absolute composite strength performance in both sexes is very similar to that previously described for grip strength. Females demonstrate consistently lower absolute composite strength scores than males, but a fairly similar rate of increase in strength during the prepubertal years. There is an acceleration in the rate of strength gain for males during the pubertal period, with a continued but abated increase during the postpubertal years. For females, there is only a slight increase in the rate of strength gain during the pubertal period, and this is followed by a plateau in strength performance during the postpubertal years. This pattern of composite strength performance is similar to that described by Carron and Bailey (1974) and Clarke (1971) for males, and by Carron et al. (1977) for females at comparable ages and stages of development. Based on these studies, the age-associated performance curves for absolute grip strength seem to accurately reflect composite or overall isometric strength development for both sexes during childhood. The reader is cautioned, however, that the degree of resemblance between grip and composite strength performances may vary as a function of both the number and nature of muscle groups comprising the composite strength performance, e.g., two of the four measures included in the composite strength scores shown in Figure 3-6 were grip strength scores.

To the author's knowledge, there are only three studies for males (Carron & Bailey, 1974; Clarke, 1971; Stolz & Stolz, 1951) and one for females (Faust, 1977) that permit the assessment of composite strength development with age, normalized for either weight or height during childhood. Based on these studies, it appears that composite strength increases only slightly faster than weight during the prepubertal years for both sexes (Figure 3-6b). Although not as conspicuous as for grip strength, there appears to be an acceleration in strength gain during the pubertal period for males, with a continued and similar rate of increase into adolescence. As for grip strength, there was little change in weight-normalized, composite strength for females between the onset of puberty and adolescence.

The pattern of composite strength performance normalized for height (Figure 3-6c) is similar to that previously described for grip strength for both sexes. Based on these few studies, it appears that normalized grip strength curves accurately reflect composite strength performances for both sexes throughout childhood when those performances are normalized for body weight and height.

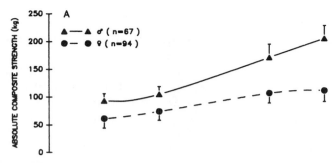

FIGURE 3-6a. *Composite isometric strength in relation to age, sex, and developmental status.*

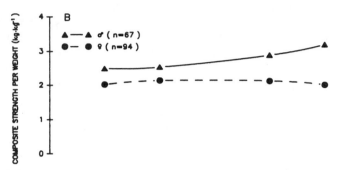

FIGURE 3-6b. *Composite isometric strength normalized for body weight, in relation to age, sex, and developmental status.*

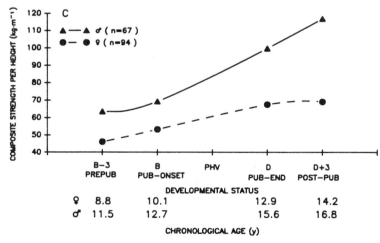

FIGURE 3-6c. *Composite isometric strength normalized for height, in relation to age, sex, and developmental status.*

Values are derived from Stolz and Stolz (1951), and Faust (1977) and are based on the total of four strength measures; right-hand grip, left-hand grip, shoulder pull, and shoulder thrust.

C. Elbow Flexion and Extension Strength

Compared with studies of grip strength, there are few studies of isometric strength performance of other isolated muscle groups covering the age range of interest in this review. Fowler & Gardner (1967) studied isometric elbow flexion and extension strength in boys during childhood and adolescence. The strength curves (Figure 3-7a) are similar to those previously described for grip and composite strength. Elbow flexor strength is greater than elbow extensor strength at each age, and the difference widens with advancing age. The elbow extensor-flexor strength ratio declines progressively with age from a peak of about 76% at 7.5 y to 57% during late adolescence (Figure 3-7b). These relationships must be interpreted with caution, however, because the absolute strength for these particular muscle groups (and therefore the strength ratio) is highly dependent upon the joint angle at which measurements are made. Elbow flexor and extensor strength measurements were made, however, at their respective optimal joint angles for peak force generation in the Fowler and Gardner study.

The development of isometric elbow flexion strength was also studied by Anderson et al. (personal communication) in a small group ($n = 5$) of untrained schoolboys from 10 to 16 y. Strength increased only moderately (approximately 27%) during the 2.5 y leading to the growth spurt in height (age at peak height velocity), but strength increased dramatically (approximately 93%) during the 3.5 y following the growth spurt. Lastly, Vos et al. (1986) reported that isometric arm flexion strength normalized for body weight was fairly

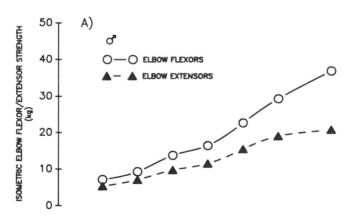

FIGURE 3-7a. *Isometric elbow flexor and elbow extensor strength for males in relation to age. Data are derived from Fowler and Gardner (1967) at joint angles of 115 degrees and 140 degrees, respectively, for flexion and extension (180 degrees is full extension).*

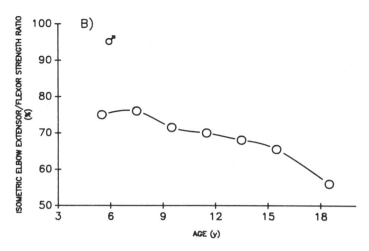

FIGURE 3-7b. *Isometric elbow extensor-to-flexor strength ratio for males in relation to age. Data are derived from Fowler and Gardner (1967) at joint angles of 115 degrees and 140 degrees respectively, for flexion and extension (180 degrees is full extension).*

constant from 13 to 18 years of age in two groups of girls followed longitudinally for 5 y. Regrettably, there are no published data for the elbow extensors or data that span both sides of puberty for these particular muscle groups for young females.

D. Knee Flexion and Extension Strength

As with elbow flexion and extension strength, there are likewise few studies of isometric leg strength performance for healthy, non-athletic children spanning the ages of interest for this review. The results from the most extensive of these studies of upper leg strength of Japanese children (Nemoto et al., 1988) are summarized in Figure 3-8a. Knee extensor strength increases in a linear fashion with age for both sexes in the prepubertal years. Boys demonstrate a substantial acceleration in knee extensor strength during puberty, with a somewhat attenuated, yet substantial rate of strength gain during adolescence. Based on extremely limited data, there appears to be little difference in knee extensor strength between boys and girls of the same age before puberty, and girls show the same rate of increase in strength as boys, at least until the onset of male puberty. Although girls demonstrate an accelerated rate of increase in knee extensor strength from 12 to 15 y, the rate is less than that of boys, and there is a progressive widening of the difference in strength between the sexes during adolescence due to an apparent plateau in knee extensor strength for females. This pattern of isokinetic knee extensor strength for males is similar to that reported by Fowler and

Gardner (1967) for North American boys of comparable ages. Additionally, Vos et al. (1986) recently reported a plateau in double leg extension strength normalized for body weight in females from 13 to 17 y. Regrettably, neither absolute strength nor body weight data were reported in this study.

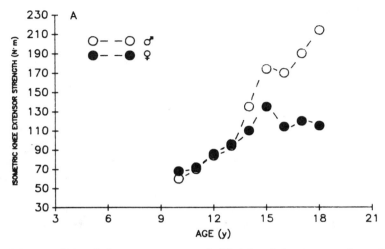

FIGURE 3-8a. *Isometric knee extensor strength (Nm) in relation to age and sex. Values are based on data from Nemoto et al. (1988) at a joint angle of 110 degrees (180 degrees is full extension).*

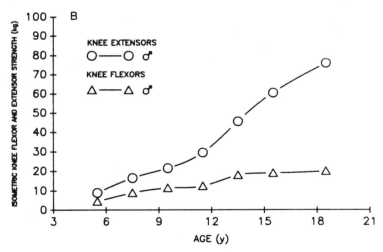

FIGURE 3-8b. *Isometric knee extensor and knee flexor strength (k/g) in relation to age. Values are based on data from Fowler and Gardner (1967) at joint angles of 115 degrees and 165 degrees (180 degrees is full extension), for knee extension and flexion, respectively.*

There are only limited data (Fowler & Gardner, 1967) on age-associated variability of knee flexor strength for boys and none for girls. As shown in Figure 3-8b, knee flexor strength increases progressively with age for boys before puberty, but at a slower rate than knee extension strength. There is a modest increase in knee flexor strength from 11.5 to 13.5 y; however, the rate of increase is less than that for knee extensor strength. In contrast to knee extensor strength, there appears to be very little further gain in knee flexor strength in boys during adolescence. Based on this single study (Fowler & Gardner, 1967), the knee flexor-extensor strength ratio decreases progressively with age from a peak value of 50% at age 5.5 years to 33% during late adolescence. As was the case for elbow strength, this ratio is specific to these particular muscle groups, and the magnitude of the ratio probably varies not only with age, but also with joint angle of the knee during testing. The degree to which these data accurately represent age-associated changes in isometric strength performance for these particular muscle groups in males remains to be verified. The age-associated variability for isometric knee extensor and flexor strength remains to be adequately described for females.

III. ISOKINETIC STRENGTH

Prior to the development of isokinetic dynamometry in the late 1960s, skeletal muscle function was characterized primarily by static or isometric strength measurements. The latter provided little information about the dynamic characteristics of muscle during contraction. An excellent review of the concept and application of isokinetic dynamometry has been provided by Osternig (1986).

While there are several descriptive studies of isokinetic strength characteristics of select pediatric groups (Brodie et al., 1986; Burnie & Brodie, 1986; Gilliam et al., 1979a, 1979b; Holmes & Alderink, 1984; Housh et al., 1984; Parker et al., 1982; Schlimkman, 1984; Tabin et al., 1985; Grace et al., 1984; Thorland et al., 1987), there are few extensive studies of isokinetic strength spanning childhood and adolescence (Alexander & Molnar, 1973; Miyashita & Kanehisa, 1979; Molnar & Alexander, 1973; Nemoto et al., 1988). These latter studies, although permitting assessment of age-associated variability in isokinetic strength performance, are limited in terms of their generalizability, first because of the small size of their samples (especially the studies by Alexander and Molnar [1973] and Molnar and Alexander [1973]) and secondly, by their population specificity (e.g., different nationalities).

A. Elbow Flexion and Extension Strength

There are no published studies of isokinetic elbow flexion and extension strength that span the entire age range of interest in this review. However, the rather limited data from the early studies by Alexander and Molnar (1973) and Molnar and Alexander (1973) provide a glimpse (Figure 3-9) of the functional changes in isokinetic strength of these muscle groups from prepuberty to adolescence. Elbow flexion strength (Figure 3-9a) appears to increase linearly with

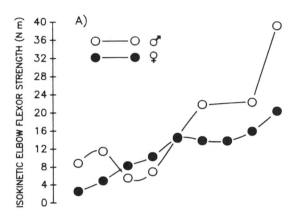

FIGURE 3-9a. *Isokinetic elbow flexor strength in relation to age and sex.*

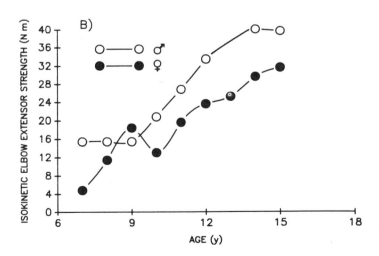

FIGURE 3-9b. *Isokinetic elbow extensor strength in relation to age and sex.*

Data for females and males are derived from Alexander and Molnar (1973) and Molnar and Alexander (1973), respectively, at an angular velocity of 30 deg/s.

advancing age for girls from 7 to 11 y. There is considerable variability in elbow flexion strength for boys from 7 to 10 y, but this is followed by a substantial linear increase from 9 to 12 y. There appears to be little further increase in elbow flexor strength for females from 11 to 14 y, and then a fairly sharp increase from 14 to 15 y. With the exception of a plateau from 12 to 14 y, there appears to be a substantial (more than twofold) and continued increase in elbow flexor strength for boys from 11 to 15 y. There are few consistent sex differences in isokinetic elbow flexor strength until age 11, when boys surpass girls and maintain this strength differential throughout adolescence.

Elbow extensor strength (Figure 3-9b) increases progressively with age (except from 9 to 10 y) from mid-childhood into adolescence for girls. There is no apparent change in elbow extensor strength for boys from 7 to 9 y and a substantial linear increase in strength from 9 to 14 y. There is no consistent sex difference for elbow extension strength before 10 y. Thereafter, boys have consistently greater elbow extensor strength than girls, and this difference seems to widen with advancing age.

It is evident from Figures 3-9a and b that elbow extensor strength exceeded elbow flexor strength for both sexes at most ages. The elbow flexor-extensor strength ratio (at a velocity of 30 deg/s) varied considerably with age, however, ranging from 41% to 79% for girls, and 32% to 100% for boys. There is obviously considerable variability in the data from these two studies, largely due to the restricted sample sizes. These summaries have been provided for comparative purposes, and the reader is cautioned that the age- and sex-associated variability in isokinetic strength performance for elbow flexors and extensors remains largely undefined for the pediatric population.

B. Knee Flexion and Extension Strength

There is also a dearth of performance studies of isokinetic knee flexion and extension strength in youth. Results from the studies by Alexander and Molnar (1973) and Molnar and Alexander (1973) for knee flexion strength are summarized in Figure 3-10a. Knee flexion strength increases slowly and fairly linearly from 7 to 11 y for girls, with little substantial increase from 11 to 15 y. For boys, there is a linear increase in strength from 7 to 11 y, a period (11 to 14 y) of only modest gain, and a sharp increase in strength from 14 to 15 y. The data point at age 15, however, represents the strength measurement for only one boy. There appears to be no consistent sex difference in isokinetic knee flexor strength until 11 y. At this point, boys surpass girls and achieve consistently higher strength values than girls throughout early adolescence. The sex difference widens only slightly from 11 to 14 y but appears to increase dramatically at 15 y.

Figure 3-10b summarizes the results from the studies of knee extensor strength by Alexander and Molnar (1973) and Molnar and Alexander (1973). Knee extensor strength increases linearly for girls

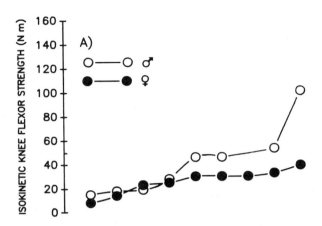

FIGURE 3-10a. *Isokinetic knee flexor strength in relation to age and sex. Data for females and males are derived from Alexander and Molnar (1973) and Molnar and Alexander (1973), respectively, at an angular velocity of 30 deg/s.*

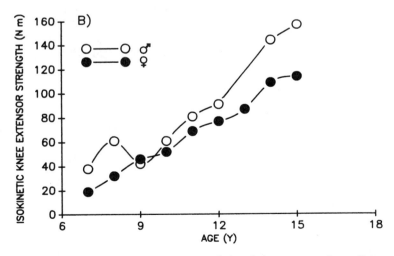

FIGURE 3-10b. *Isokinetic knee extensor strength in relation to age and sex. Data are derived from Alexander and Molnar (1973) and Molnar and Alexander (1973) at an angular velocity of 30 deg/s.*

from 7 to 15 y. There is no evident pubertal spurt in strength gain for girls, and strength appears not to increase beyond 15 y. For boys, there appears to be variable growth in knee extensor strength until about 10 y, followed by a nearly linear increase until about 12 or 13 y. Strength then continues to increase, but at an accelerated rate in boys from 12 to 15 y; strength gain slows slightly, but continues to increase throughout adolescence. Males have consistently greater strength than girls from about 10 onward, and the difference between the sexes widens with advancing age.

Based on the studies by Alexander and Molnar (1973), and Molnar and Alexander (1973) it appears that isokinetic knee extensor strength exceeds knee flexor strength for both sexes at all ages. The knee flexor-extensor isokinetic strength ratio (at a velocity of 30 deg/s) varied considerably with age, ranging from 30% to 51% for girls and 28% to 65% for boys. In the author's opinion, the age- and sex-associated variation in isokinetic knee flexion and extension strength, and the flexor-extensor strength ratio have not been adequately described for the pediatric population.

IV. SUMMARY—STRENGTH PERFORMANCE

There are considerably more studies of isometric hand grip strength among children and adolescents than there are for any other functional muscle groups or strength measures. The age- and sex-associated variation in grip strength performance is fairly well-defined for the pediatric age range. Characteristically, boys have slightly higher strength scores than girls, even during early and mid-childhood, and the difference widens with increasing age from puberty throughout adolescence and early adulthood.

There are fewer pediatric studies of isometric strength of the elbow flexors and extensors and of the knee flexors and extensors. For boys, the age-associated pattern of variation in elbow flexion strength is similar to that for hand-grip strength. Elbow extensor strength varies with age in a manner similar to elbow flexion strength until adolescence; thereafter, the rate of increase is substantially less for extensors than flexors. Additionally, the difference between flexor and extensor strength appears to widen with increasing age, beginning in mid-childhood. Regrettably, there are insufficient data for elbow flexors and extensors to define with confidence the age-associated variation in isometric strength for these muscle groups in females.

Isometric knee extensor strength varies with age in a pattern similar to grip strength for both sexes. However, unlike the results for grip strength, knee extensors in girls appear slightly stronger than in boys during the mid-childhood years. For boys, knee extension strength is consistently greater than knee flexion strength, and this difference widens with increasing age. There are insufficient data to describe the age-associated variation in knee flexor strength for females.

The influence of age and sex on isokinetic strength for the elbow flexors and extensors remains largely undefined, due to the highly restrictive nature of the existing studies in this area. Both elbow flexor and extensor strength appear to increase, albeit in a highly variable fashion, during the mid-childhood years, and there appears to be no consistent sex difference for either muscle group before puberty. Thereafter, strength of both muscle groups seems to increase throughout the circumpubertal period at least until early adolescence.

Isokinetic knee flexor strength increases fairly linearly with increasing age in both sexes during mid-childhood with no consistent sex difference. Boys show a substantial increase in isokinetic knee flexion strength during the circumpubertal years, whereas females show only a slight increase during puberty and early adolescence. Isokinetic knee extensor strength increases in a fairly linear manner for both sexes with increasing age during the mid-childhood years, with little consistent or substantial sex difference until the onset of male puberty. Thereafter, the difference between the sexes widens with age; females show little increase in isokinetic knee extensor strength during adolescence, whereas males demonstrate a dramatic increase with advancing age.

Other than for grip strength, the data presented in this review are based on only a few highly selected studies that vary considerably in terms of population characteristics, sample size, and strength testing procedures. Based on these studies, however, it appears that the pattern of strength performance varies with age between sexes for certain strength functions and sometimes varies within gender across different strength modes and functional muscle groups. Further research is needed to provide a clearer description of strength development during childhood and adolescence, particularly for females and for isometric and isokinetic strength modes for the major functional muscle groups.

V. CORRELATES AND DETERMINANTS OF STRENGTH

Regardless of the strength mode, it is apparent that strength increases dramatically from childhood to adolescence and that males are consistently stronger than females after having undergone puberty. This section discusses the following factors that are thought to influence and differentiate strength performance across ages and between sexes during childhood: a) age, b) body size, c) muscle size, d) muscle fiber type and size, e) muscle contractile characteristics, f) psycho-neurogenic influences, g) biomechanical influences, h) endocrinological influences, i) genetic influences, and j) physical activity influences.

Throughout this section, correlational analysis (Pearson product-moment correlation coefficients) is used to infer the degree of association between some independent factor and strength performance. The following arbitrary ranges, adopted from Malina (1975), have been used to indicate the relative strength of these correlational relationships: $r < 0.45$, low or poor; $0.45 < r < 0.80$, moderate; $r > 0.80$, strong or close relationship. The reader is directed to the review by Malina (1975) for a more detailed discussion of the statistical considerations inherent in the accurate interpretation of correlational data. Furthermore, although each of the factors listed above is thought to exert important independent influences on strength performance, many of these factors are interrelated and may influence strength through common or shared variance. The relative importance of each of these factors in the differentiation of strength performance can be determined using complicated analytical techniques (e.g., multiple regression analysis). While this approach has been applied on a limited basis with a few of these factors and within narrow age ranges, it has not been applied on a broader basis (including all of the factors identified in this paper and across the entire pediatric age range) to explain age- and sex-related variation in strength performance. Consequently, each of these factors is presented and discussed independently in this section. The reader is advised, however, that this is a rather simplistic approach to this topic and that the relative importance of each of these factors in differentiating strength performance probably varies at different ages and stages of development during childhood.

A. Age

The increase in maximal voluntary isometric strength for the elbow flexors and knee extensors is highly correlated (Figure 3-11a, b) with chronological age during childhood and adolescence, at least for males. Although to a lesser degree, a similar high positive correlation has also been found between evoked twitch torque (intrinsic strength of muscle) and chronological age for both elbow flexors and knee extensors (Figure 3-12a, b). Although no correlations were given, Davies (1985) has reported increases with age in twitch torque of the triceps surae muscle group for both males and females from 9 to 22 y. It is likely that a large proportion of this association between

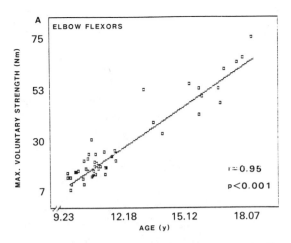

FIGURE 3-11a. *Relationship between maximal voluntary isometric elbow flexion strength and chronological age (n=46) in males. Strength was measured as torque (Nm) on a custom-made dynomometer at an elbow joint angle of 80 degrees (180 degrees is full extension). Previously unpublished data are from Blimkie et al.*

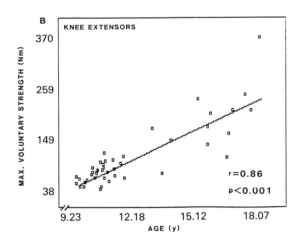

FIGURE 3-11b. *Relationship between maximal voluntary isometric knee extension strength and chronological age (n=46) in males. Strength was measured as torque (Nm) on a custom-made dynomometer at a knee joint angle of 120 degrees (180 degrees is full extension). Previously unpublished data are from Blimkie et al.*

strength and age is due to the shared variation of age with other biologic and morphologic factors (Table 3-3) that may influence strength performance. However, as reported by both Clarke & Degutis (1962) and Asmussen (1973), age per se might exert an independent influence, at least on maximal voluntary strength, possibly

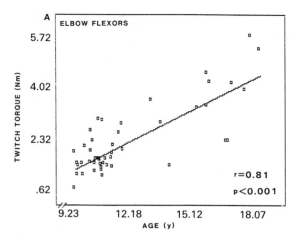

FIGURE 3-12a. *Relationship between elbow flexor evoked twitch torque and chronological age (n=46) in males. Torque was measured on a custom-made dynomometer at an elbow joint angle of 80 degrees (180 degrees is full extension), using percutaneous electrical stimulation. Previously unpublished data are from Blimkie et al.*

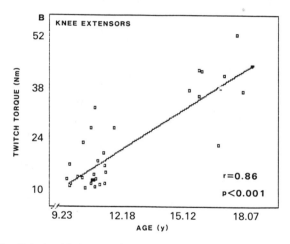

FIGURE 3-12b. *Relationship between knee extensor evoked twitch torque and chronological age (n=35) in males. Torque was measured on a custom-made dynomometer at a knee joint angle of 90 degrees (180 degrees is full extension), using percutaneouos electrical stimulation. Previously unpublished data are from Blimkie et al.*

through the mechanism of enhanced neurological maturation and control.

Given the apparent plateau in many strength functions in females during adolescence, it is likely that correlations between strength and age would be considerably less than those for males if determined across the entire pediatric age range. There should be few gender differences, however, in the magnitude of the correlations between age and strength throughout the early and mid-childhood years, since there is little gender difference for most strength performance measures during this period. In support of these generalizations, Carron and Bailey (1974) reported highly significant positive correlations between chronological age and strength in males from 10 to 16 y, whereas Faust (1977) reported moderate positive correlations between strength and age in females during prepuberty and onset of puberty, but low negative correlations at the end of puberty and during adolescence.

B. Body Size

The influence of body size, e.g., weight and height, on strength has been thoroughly reviewed by Malina (1975). As shown in Table 3-3, body weight is highly correlated with maximal voluntary isometric strength of both elbow flexors and knee extensors in males 9 to 18 y. Body weight is also moderately correlated with both elbow flexor and knee extensor evoked twitch torque (Table 3-3), at least for males. To the author's knowledge, there are no comparable pediatric data on these relationships for females.

Based on the relationship between age and grip strength nor-

TABLE 3-3. *Inter-relationship Between Selected Anthropometric, Morphologic and Isometric Strength Characteristics For Males 9 - 18 Years of Age*

Variable	+ Elbow Flexors					++ Knee Extensors				
	2	3	4	5	6	2	3	4	5	6
1) Age (y)	.924	.855	.865	.809	.950	.931	.854	.846	.861	.845
2) Height (cm)		.901	.837	.777	.930		.890	.887	.880	.846
3) Weight (kg)			.872	.769	.902			.866	.827	.905
4) EF⁺ and KE⁺⁺ CSA (cm²)				.708	.864				.867	.855
5) EF⁺ and KE⁺⁺ Evoked Twitch Torque (Nm)					.863					.849
6) EF⁺ and KE⁺⁺ Max. Voluntary Torque (Nm)					-					-

Cross-sectional area (CSA) of muscle was determined by computerized axial tomography at the mid-upper arm and mid-thigh, respectively, for the elbow flexors and knee extensors. Elbow flexor area is comprised of the biceps brachii and biceps brachialis muscles. Knee extensor area is comprised of the quadriceps muscle group. Evoked twitch torque was determined by percutaneous electrical stimulation (single supramaximal pulse, 50 ms) at 80 degrees of elbow flexion and 90 degrees of knee extension -180 degrees is full extension. Maximal voluntary torque was measured at the same joint angles as for evoked twitch torque. N = 46 for elbow flexors; N = 35 for knee extensors.

malized for body weight between mid-childhood and adolescence (Figure 3-4), one would expect a significant positive correlation between strength and weight for males, but a substantially lower association for females. Age-specific correlations between strength and weight for males are generally low to moderate during the mid-childhood years (Clarke, 1971; Carron & Bailey, 1974), tend to increase then peak during puberty, and abate during adolescence (Carron & Bailey, 1974; Clarke, 1971; Jones, 1947). Age-associated relationships between weight and strength are somewhat limited for females; however, Faust (1977) reported moderate positive correlations between strength and weight for females during the prepubertal years and at the onset of puberty and only low correlations at the end of puberty and during adolescence. Like the males, the magnitude of the correlation increased from prepuberty to onset of puberty then abated progressively from the end of puberty to adolescence. Similarily, Maglischo (1968) reported a progressive reduction in the strength of the correlation between weight and strength with increasing age (not specified) for females from the upper elementary, to junior high, to senior high school level.

Based on the relationship between age and grip strength normalized for height (Figure 3-5), one would predict fairly high positive correlations between strength and height for both sexes, with values for males being somewhat higher than for females. Table 3-3 indicates a high positive correlation between height and measures of maximal voluntary and evoked strength for elbow flexors and knee extensors in males. There are no comparable published data on these relationships for females.

Correlations between height and strength appear to vary with age for both females and males during childhood and adolescence. Correlations are generally significant but low during mid-childhood, increase to a peak of only a moderate level during puberty, and regress during adolescence for males (Carron and Bailey, 1974; Clarke, 1971). For females, the correlation between strength and height is significant and moderate during mid-childhood, increases somewhat but still within a moderate level by the onset of puberty, then decreases to a low and insignificant level during adolescence (Maglischo, 1968; Faust, 1977).

The relationship between strength development and body size can also be assessed using theoretical dimensional analysis (Asmussen & Heeboll-Nielsen, 1955; Asmussen, 1973). This theorem is based on geometric similarity between small and large children and constancy of tissue composition. Assuming that these relationships are invariable across ages and between sexes (Asmussen, 1973), then all areas of the body, including muscle cross-sectional area, will vary as height squared (h^2), during childhood and adolescence. Furthermore, assuming that strength varies in proportion to muscle cross-sectional area (Close, 1972; Ikai & Fukunaga, 1968), and that this relationship is constant across ages, then force or strength is also predicted to increase in proportion to the change in height squared during growth.

There have been limited applications of this dimensional analysis to strength development during growth. Asmussen (1973) demonstrated that strength in pulling for females developed fairly proportionally to height squared (exponent of 2.18) from 6 to 16 y. There was, however, considerable variability in this relationship among various muscle groups for females. Strength for most of the muscle groups investigated increased considerably more than had been predicted on the basis of changes in height squared. For males from 7 to 16 years old, leg extensor, finger flexor, and elbow flexor strength each increased substantially more than was expected based on changes in height squared (Asmussen & Heeboll-Nielsen, 1955). As with the females, there was considerable variability in the derived geometrical exponent among various muscle groups for males. Using a similar approach, Carron and Bailey (1974) found an approximate twofold greater average yearly percentage increase (22.7%) in composite strength in boys from 10 to 16 y than was predicted from the changes in height squared (12.1%) during this period.

There was a fairly linear relationship between strength and height when data for females in Asmussen's study (1973) were expressed as a logarithmic function. A parallel, but upward shifted relationship was found for boys up to the onset of puberty. At puberty there was a substantial break point in this linear relationship, with a disproportionate increase in strength for males that was most evident for upper extremity and trunk strength measures. These data indicated that boys tended to be stronger than girls of the same height throughout childhood, and that some factor or factors other than growth in stature take on a significant role in differentiating strength performance in males prior to puberty and especially during puberty and adolescence.

The discrepancy between actual strength performance and that predicted on the basis of height has been attributed both to quantitative differences (greater relative increase in muscle mass and cross-sectional area of muscle compared to height) and qualitative differences (neural or biochemical changes within motor units) between sexes and changes across ages, within the neuromuscular system (Asmussen & Heeboll-Nielsen, 1955; Asmussen, 1973; Carron & Bailey, 1974). Because strength increases faster than height in males before puberty (Carron & Bailey, 1974), i.e., at a time when muscle growth lags behind the increase in height, it seems likely that influences other than purely dimensional or quantitative factors contribute to the observed deviation from expected strength gains prior to puberty. On the other hand, Ball et al. (1987) reported disproportionate increases in muscle cross-sectional area relative to height squared during puberty and adolescence in males, thereby lending support to the quantitative argument in explaining at least part of the variance between expected and actual strength gains in relation to changes in height during these later periods of growth.

While dimensional analysis theory provides a useful quantitative model for the developmental assessment of various physiological functions, it is clear that there are difficulties with the application of this theorem to the study of age- and sex-associated variability in strength performance during growth. Despite Asmussen and Heeboll-Nielsen's (1955) assertion that the principle of geometric similarity applies to children, this issue has not been clearly established within the pediatric age range. Furthermore, the principle of constancy of tissue composition is questionable, given the recently identified variability in lean tissue densities during childhood (Lohman et al., 1984).

C. Muscle Size

Muscle strength under normal conditions will be highly dependent upon gross muscle size. Based on creatinine excretion rates, muscle mass increases approximately fivefold from 7.5 kg to 37 kg and from 42% to 53.6% of body weight in males from 5 to 17.5 y (Malina, 1969). Comparative values for females range from 6.9 kg to 24 kg (three-and-a-half-fold) and 40.2% to 42.5% of body weight in the same age range (Malina, 1969). At all ages beyond 7 y, males have a larger absolute and relative (kg muscle per kg body weight) amount of muscle compared to females. These patterns of muscle mass development probably account for a large proportion of the age-associated changes and gender differences observed in strength during childhood and adolescence. However, it must be noted that the actual increase in muscle mass and the percentage change during the course of growth will vary from muscle to muscle. The effect of this differential muscle growth on development of strength for specific muscle groups has not been adequately studied.

In addition to estimating muscle mass from creatinine excretion, muscle size has also been assessed by radiographic measurements of muscle width. The age-associated composite growth curve for forearm, thigh, and calf widths is virtually identical to the age-associated curve for height from birth to adulthood (Malina, 1969). There is little difference in muscle widths between the sexes before puberty. As shown in Figure 3-13a, b, there is a slight increase in the rate of gain in upper arm and calf muscle widths for females during puberty, resulting in slightly wider calf muscles, when compared to males, from 11 to 13 y (Maresh, 1970; Malina, 1978). This weak pubertal spurt in females is followed by a plateau during adolescence. For males, the spurt in muscle width lags behind that for females by about 2 y; however, the magnitude of the spurt during

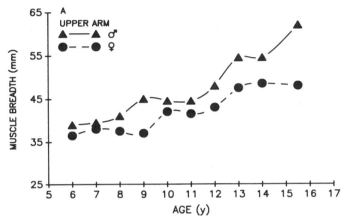

FIGURE 3-13a. *Relationship between age and muscle breadth for the upper left arm in females and males. Muscle breadth was measured from latero-medial radiographs. Data from Malina and Johnston (1966).*

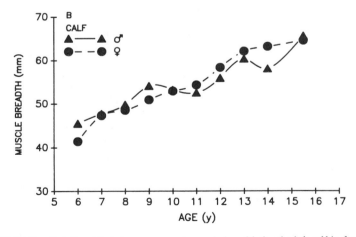

FIGURE 3-13b. *Relationship between age and muscle breadth for the left calf in females and males. Muscle breadth was measured from antero-posterior radiographs. Data from Malina and Johnston (1967).*

puberty is substantially greater in males, and muscle width contin-ues to increase throughout adolescence. Additionally, the shapes of the growth curves for these two muscle groups appear similar for males, but more variable for females. If strength performance is in-fluenced by muscle size, then these results suggest 1) that the shape of the strength curve may vary for different muscle groups within an individual and 2) that for certain muscle groups, girls may at times be stronger than boys, especially during their pubertal growth spurt.

It is likely that quantitative differences in muscle width account for a large proportion of the observed age and gender differences in strength development during childhood and adolescence. How-ever, as shown in Figure 3-14a, the peak gain in muscle strength occurs more typically after the peak gain in height and muscle cross-sectional area in boys (Carron & Bailey, 1974; Faust, 1977; Stolz & Stolz, 1951). This is not an invariable sequence, however, since, as shown in Figure 3-14b, a sizable proportion (23%) of boys may ex-perience peak strength gain before or coincident with the peak height velocity (Faust, 1977; Stolz & Stolz, 1951). For girls, peak strength gain occurs most often following peak gain in height; however, the timing is more variable than for boys, with a large proportion (51% of girls experiencing peak strength gain either before or coincident with peak height velocity (Faust, 1977). These observations suggest that in addition to the quantitative changes that occur in muscle size during puberty, other as yet unspecified factors may also be im-portant in the differentiation of muscle strength during puberty, es-pecially for the males.

The relationship between muscle width and strength has been thoroughly reviewed by Malina (1975). Correlations between strength and either areas or breadths of muscles in upper arm and calf are moderate ($r = 0.40$ and $r = 0.65$ for elbow flexors and ankle exten-sors, respectively) for boys during mid-childhood (Dempsey, 1955; Rarick & Thompson, 1956). Upper arm muscle breadth was mod-erately ($r = 0.60$) and positively correlated with elbow flexor strength in girls (Dempsey, 1955), but somewhat lower correlations ($r = 0.22$ to $r = 0.52$) were reported between ankle extensor strength and calf area and breadth during mid-childhood (Rarick & Thompson, 1956). Considering the slight gender difference in muscle sizes (approxi-mately 5% larger in boys), boys were disproportionately stronger than girls (11% to 13%) in these studies. This suggests that factors other than muscle size may also be important in the sexual differ-entiation of strength performance as early as the mid-childhood pe-riod.

While there are ample data describing age-associated changes

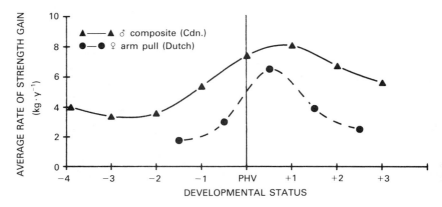

FIGURE 3-14a. *Relationship between yearly rate of strength gain and developmental status for females and males during the circumpubertal years (10–17 y). Values for males represent composite strength from seven muscle groups and are taken from Carron and Bailey (1974). Values for females are from Beunen and Malina (1988) and Kemper (1986), and represent the single measure of arm pull strength. Values are means an are aligned by age at peak height velocity (PHV).*

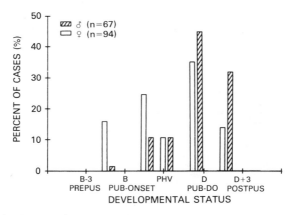

FIGURE 3-14b. *Percent of cases attaining composite strength velocity apex (peak velocity of strength gain) in relation to developmental status for females and males from 7 to 15, and 10 to 17, respectively. Data are taken from Stolz and Stolz (1951) and Faust (1977). See appendix A in Faust (1977) for a detailed description of the procedures used to determine developmental status. Composite strength is comprised of scores from right- and left- hand grip and from thrust and pull strength measurements.*

in muscle mass and proportions, there are surprisingly few studies of concomitant changes in muscle size and strength during growth. Lean body mass is comprised primarily of muscle and, therefore, serves as an indirect indicator of skeletal muscle mass. Not surprisingly, Forbes (1965) demonstrated a highly significant positive correlation ($r = 0.908$) between grip strength and lean body mass estimated by the potassium[40] technique for boys from 12 to 18 y. There are no comparable data describing this relationship in young females.

The relationship between muscle cross-sectional area and force production has been described for isolated animal muscle (Close, 1972) and for various human skeletal muscles under both maximal voluntary contractions (Chapman et al., 1984; Davies, 1985; De-Koning et al., 1986; Ikai & Fukunaga, 1968; Maughan, 1984; Maughan et al., 1983; Morris, 1948; Sale et al., 1987; Tsunoda et al., 1985) and electrically evoked contractions (Davies et al., 1983; Davies, 1985). A summary of these relationships for children is presented in Table 3-4.

Ikai and Fukunaga (1968) studied the relationship between voluntary isometric upper arm flexion strength and ultrasonically determined cross-sectional area of the upper arm flexors in a large number of subjects, including males and females from 12 to 18 y. Although correlation coefficients were not given, the published graph of this relationship indicated a fairly strong positive correlation between muscle cross-sectional area and strength for the boys. The data were more scattered and the relationship appeared weaker for girls than for boys. When normalized for muscle cross-sectional area,

TABLE 3-4. *Correlational Relationships Between Isometric Evoked and Voluntary Muscle Strength and Muscle Area*

Author	Age (y)	Sex	N	Area Measurement Technique	Muscle Group and Function	Regression Equation	Zero-Order Correlation
Blinkie et al, unpublished results	9-18	M	46	Computerized Axial Tomography, mid-upper arm -Cross-Sect. Area	Elbow Flexors Max. Vol. Force Twitch Force (1 Hz)	$y = 3.83 x -9.95$ $y = 0.20 x +.21$	$r = 0.86$ $r = 0.71$
	9-18	M	35		Quadriceps Max. Vol. Force Twitch Force (1 Hz)	$y = 3.64 x -52.54$ $y = 0.67 x - 9.57$	$r = 0.86$ $r = 0.87$
Chapman et al, 1984	10-35	M+F	22	Computerized Axial Tomography, mid-femur -Cross-Sect. Area	Quadriceps Max. Vol. Force	$y = 5.8 x +120$ $y = 6.9 x + 0.8$ $y = 7.6 x -23$	$r = 0.69$ (M) $r = 0.66$ (F) $r = 0.87$ (M+F)
Davies, 1985	19-21	M+F	91	Anthropometric Estimate -Cross-Sect. Area	Triceps Surae Max. Vol. Force	$y = 20.9 x -181.4$	$r = 0.92$
	11-21	M+F	42		Tetanic Force (50 Hz)	$y = 16.8 x -111.2$	$r = 0.86$
De Koning et al, 1986	15-36	M+F	281	Anthropometric Estimate -Cross-Sect. Area	Elbow Flexors Max. Vol. Force		$r = 0.83 - 0.90$
Dempsey, 1955	7	M+F		Anterio-posterior and Lateral x-ray -Muscle Depth and Breadth	Elbow Flexors Max. Vol. Force		$r = 0.41$ (M) $r = 0.60$ (F)
Funato et al, 1987	6-11	M+F M F	47 24 23	Ultrasound -Cross-Sect. Area	Elbow Flexors Max. Vol. Force Elbow Extensors Max. Vol. Force		$r = 0.62$ (M) $r = 0.79$ (F) $r = 0.58$ (M) $r = 0.72$ (F)
Ikai and Fukunaga, 1968	12-17 12-18	M F	101 93	Ultrasound -Cross-Sect. Area	Elbow Flexors Max. Vol. Force		not given not given
Rarick and Thompson, 1956	7	M F	32 19	Anterio-posterior and Lateral x-ray -Muscle Depth and Breadth	Ankle Extensors Max. Vol. Force		$r = 0.58-0.63$ (M) $r = 0.22-0.52$ (F)
Royce, 1958	18-20	M	100	Anthropometric Estimate -Muscle and Bone Radii	Elbow Flexors /Extensors Knee Flexors/Extensors		$r = 0.36-0.61$
Tsunoda et al, 1985	17-25	M	123	Ultrasound -Cross-Sect. Area	Quadriceps Max. Vol. Force		$r = 0.61$

Regression equations are in the form of $y = bx + a$, where $y =$ muscle force, $x =$ muscle cross-sectional area, and $b =$ constant.

there were no strength differences between sexes at given ages, and the ratio of strength to cross-sectional area was fairly constant from 12 to 18 y.

Davies et al. (1983) and Davies (1985) related both maximal voluntary and evoked strength of the triceps surae muscle to muscle cross-sectional area determined anthropometrically in males and females ranging from 9 to 21 y. Absolute maximal voluntary strength and evoked strength (at a stimulation frequency of 20 Hz) increased approximately twofold for females and 2.5-fold for males. Maximal voluntary strength was highly correlated ($r = 0.91$) with cross-sectional area for males and females combined. A strong positive correlation ($r = 0.86$) was also reported between muscle cross-sectional area and 50 Hz evoked strength for the triceps muscle group for males and females combined, from 11 to 21 y. When normalized for muscle cross-sectional area, the evoked strength to muscle area ratio (specific tension) was calculated at 33 N.cm^2 and was independent of age and sex (Davies, 1985).

Based on the mean values reported by Davies (1985), the calculated ratio of twitch strength (peak tension of maximal twitch) to maximal voluntary strength decreased from 11 to 21 y in males, but showed no consistent change with age in females. Given that twitch force represents the intrinsic strength of the muscle and that an increased ratio implies an improved ability to more fully tap this intrinsic strength capacity during voluntary effort, it appears from these data that the age-associated increase in voluntary strength in males may also be due in part to changes in the degree of voluntary activation of muscle that occur between childhood and adulthood. Whether this apparent increase in degree of muscle activation is caused by adaptations at the level of the central nervous system, segmental spinal level, or the level of the muscle itself remains undetermined.

Chapman et al. (1984) studied the relationship between cross-sectional area of the quadriceps muscle (determined by computerized axial tomography) and isometric knee extensor strength in two boys, 10 and 12 y, and in 20 adults from 22 to 35 y. A strong positive correlation ($r = 0.87$) was reported between muscle size and force for the combined results, which included data for the two boys.

Estimating muscle cross-sectional area by anthropometric means, DeKoning et al. (1986) studied the specific tension of the elbow flexor muscle group in untrained males and females (15 to 36 y) and in male athletes. There was no separate analysis of the relationship between strength and muscle area for adolescents. Untrained females had somewhat lower calculated specific tension values than the untrained males and male athletes.

Using ultrasound to measure muscle cross-sectional area, Funato et al. (1987) reported correlation coefficients of +0.624 and +0.792 between elbow flexor area and maximal voluntary elbow flexion strength, and +0.579 and +0.720 between elbow extensor area and elbow extension strength in Japanese boys and girls, respectively, from 6 to 11 y.

Lastly, Royce (1958) reported correlations ranging from +0.24 to +0.65 between calculated muscle cross-sectional areas and maximum limb strength in males 18 to 20 y.

The relationships between muscle cross-sectional area determined by computerized axial tomography and maximal voluntary isometric strength of the elbow flexor and knee extensor muscle groups are presented in Figure 3-15a,b for males from 9 to 18 y. The correlation coefficient for strength vs. area (0.86) for both muscle groups is moderately high. As shown in Figure 3-16a,b, the relationship between intrinsic muscle strength (twitch torque) and muscle cross-sectional area is also moderately strong for elbow flexors ($r = 0.71$) and knee extensors ($r = 0.87$) for males within this age range.

Generally, it appears from these studies that both maximal voluntary and evoked strength are moderately and positively correlated with muscle size within the age range of interest to this review. This association appears constant across several muscle groups and seems independent of the technique used to measure muscle cross-sectional area. The correlations are generally lower for narrower age ranges and appear to peak when spanning the period from mid-childhood to late adolescence. However, despite the strength of these relationships, it is also evident that muscle size alone does not account for all of the age-associated variation in strength from childhood to adulthood. Additionally, based on a limited number of studies and only a few muscle groups, there appears to be little if any age- or sex-associated variation in either voluntary or evoked specific tension within the pediatric age range. The relative importance of gross muscle size in differentiating strength among children of the same age, across ages, and between sexes remains to be determined, however.

D. Muscle Fiber Type and Size

Besides the influence of gross muscle size, muscle fiber composition and size might also affect skeletal muscle strength. It is now generally accepted that human skeletal muscle is comprised primarily of two muscle fiber types, slow-twitch, type I and fast-twitch, type II fibers and that the distribution of fiber types varies across different muscle groups. Additionally, type II fibers have been fur-

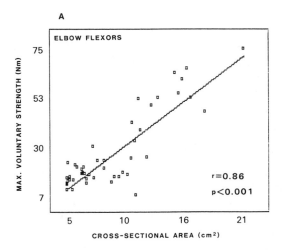

FIGURE 3-15a. *Relationship between muscle cross-sectional area and maximal voluntary isometric strength of the elbow flexors (n=46) in males from 9 to 18 y. Strength was measured as torque on a custom-made dynomometer at an elbow joint angle of 80 degrees (180 degrees is full extension). Muscle cross-sectional area of the elbow flexors (biceps brachii and brachialis muscles) was determined by computerized axial tomography taken at the mid-upper arm (right side), with the arm fully extended and relaxed. Previously unpublished data are from Blimkie et al.*

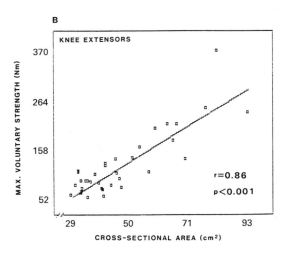

FIGURE 3-15b. *Relationship between muscle cross-sectional area and maximal voluntary isometric strength of the knee extensors (n=35) in males from 9 to 18 y. Strength was measured as torque on a custom-made dynomometer at a knee joint angle of 90 degrees (180 degrees is full extension). Muscle cross-sectional area of the knee extensors (quadriceps muscle) was determined by computerized axial tomography taken at the mid-thigh (right side), with the leg fully extended and relaxed. Previously unpublished data are from Blimkie et al.*

132 *PERSPECTIVES IN EXERCISE*

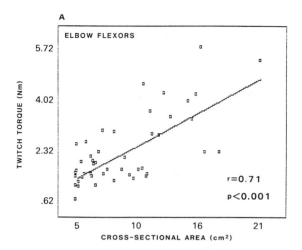

FIGURE 3-16a. *Relationship between muscle cross-sectional area and evoked twitch torque of the elbow flexors (n=46) in males from 9 to 18 y. Evoked twitch torque was measured on a custom-made dynomometer at an elbow joint angle of 80 degrees (180 degrees is full extension), using percutaneous electrical stimulation. Muscle cross-sectional area of the elbow flexors (biceps brachii and brachialis) was determined by computerized axial tomography taken at the mid-upper arm (right side) with the arm fully extended and relaxed. Previously unpublished data are from Blimkie et al.*

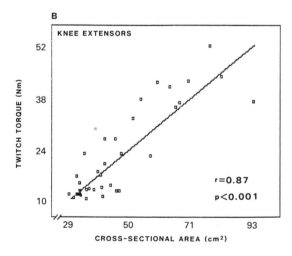

FIGURE 3-16b. *Relationship between muscle cross-sectional area and evoked twitch torque of the knee extensors (n=35) in males from 9 to 18 y. Evoked twitch torque was measured on a custom-made dynomometer at a knee joint angle of 90 degrees (180 degrees is full extension), using percutaneous electrical stimulation. Muscle cross-sectional area of the knee extensors (quadriceps) was determined by computerized axial tomography taken at the mid-thigh (right side) with the leg fully extended and relaxed. Previously unpublished data are from Blimkie et al.*

VARIATIONS IN STRENGTH **133**

ther differentiated into three sub-types, i.e., type IIa, IIb, and IIc fibers. It is generally accepted that the larger type II fibers are capable of producing greater absolute force than the typically smaller type I fibers (Close, 1972; Tesch & Karlsson, 1978). More controversial, however, is the issue of the relative (per cross-sectional area of muscle) strength of the individual muscle fiber types.

Previous reviews have dealt thoroughly with the topic of skeletal muscle development in general (Baldwin, 1984; Edgerton, 1978; Malina, 1969, 1978, 1986a) and human fiber type differentiation in particular (Colling-Saltin, 1980; Malina, 1986a). From about one year of age, the fiber type composition and distribution of the child has attained near adult proportions. Based on the few available studies, however, there appear to be higher proportions of type I and undifferentiated type IIc fibers during early and mid-childhood and even during adolescence when compared to adulthood for untrained people (Bell et al., 1980; Colling-Saltin, 1980; DuPlessis et al., 1985; Eriksson et al., 1974; Howald, 1982; Lundberg et al., 1979; MacDougall et al., 1981). Although males appear to have a more variable distribution of type I fibers than females, there does not seem to be any clear sex-associated variation in type I fiber distribution during the course of childhood (Hedberg and Jansson, 1976; Malina, 1986a).

The percent distribution of type II fibers is lower in early and mid-childhood compared with adulthood (Bell et al., 1980; Colling-Saltin, 1980) and attains adult proportions during late adolescence (Fournier et al., 1982; Hedberg & Jansson, 1976). In most (Colling-Saltin, 1980; Fournier et al., 1982; Hedberg & Jansson, 1976), but not all (Bell et al., 1980; MacDougall et al., 1981) studies, there was a greater prevalance of type IIa than type IIb fibers during childhood and adolescence. There is no clear evidence of an age- or sex-associated variation in the proportions of type IIa and b fibers beyond one year of age.

Muscle fibers undergo a tremendous increase in size during childhood and adolescence. Fiber diameters are approximately 30% and 50% of adult values at 1 and 5 years of age, respectively (Colling-Saltin, 1980). Muscle fiber diameter increases linearly with age from birth to adolescence, when adult values are attained (Aherne et al., 1971; Bowden & Goyer, 1960; Malina, 1986a). There is apparently no sex difference in fiber diameters during infancy and early childhood (Brooke & Engel, 1969). Whether a sex difference in fiber diameter exists during mid-childhood and adolescence is unknown. The pattern of fiber type differentiation and growth in fiber size seems to be similar for upper and lower extremities and for proximal and distal muscles (Colling-Saltin, 1980). However, it is possible that the biceps muscle of the arm may be differentiated earlier than other muscles (Colling-Saltin, 1980; Kamieniecka, 1968; Ringqvist et al., 1977).

There are only limited data on age-associated variation in muscle fiber area during childhood and adolescence. There is a strong positive relationship between fiber area and the logarithm of fiber diameter during gestation and early infancy (Colling-Saltin, 1980). There are no available data on fiber areas during the early or mid-childhood years. For females, fiber areas for the vastus lateralis and gastrocnemius muscles have been reported to be slightly smaller than males during adolescence (Costill et al., 1976; Hedberg and Jansson, 1976) but similar to young adult female values (Costill et al., 1976; Hedberg & Jansson, 1976; Saltin et al., 1977. At least for the vastus lateralis, fiber areas have been reported to increase from adolescence into adulthood for males (Costill et al., 1976; Hedberg & Jansson, 1976; Saltin et al., 1977). Little is known about changes in fiber areas with age for other muscle groups during childhood.

There is a paucity of data on skeletal muscle fiber type differentiation, distribution, and size during childhood, especially for the early and mid-childhood years. Furthermore, there are no available studies of the relationship between muscle fiber type distribution, fiber diameter or area, and either voluntary or evoked absolute strength or specific tension in children. The degree to which these factors account for sex- and age-associated variations in strength during childhood remains to be determined. Given the ethical considerations surrounding the use of the needle biopsy technique for muscle sampling with children, it may be some time before these specific issues are adequately addressed in the pediatric population.

E.   Muscle Contractile Characteristics

Skeletal muscle and muscle fiber sub-types have traditionally been differentiated on the basis of mechanical or contractile characteristics during either voluntary or evoked conditions (Buchthal & Schmalbruch, 1970; Komi, 1984). A summary is provided in Table 3-5 of the few studies that have investigated the relationship between muscle force and contractile properties of muscle during childhood and adolescence. Due to the considerable variability in techniques and procedures used in these studies, discussion will be restricted solely to the measurements of contraction time (elapsed time from the onset of force deflection following an electrical stimulation to attainment of peak force) and half-relaxation time (elapsed time from peak force to half the peak force during recovery) during evoked isometric contractions.

There appears to be a prolongation of contraction time for the triceps surae with advancing age during early childhood (Gatev et al., 1977, 1981). This age-associated variation may be influenced by the functional status of the child. There is little change during early infancy when the child is incapable of standing alone, a fairly marked

TABLE 3-5. *Isometric Strength and Contractile Characteristics of Muscle*

Author	Age	Sex	N	Muscle Group	Twitch Force (T.F.)	Tetanic Force (T.T.F.)	Max. Vol. Strength (M.V.C.)	T.F./MVC Ratio (%)	Contraction Time (ms)	Half-Relax Time (ms)
Blimkie et al, unpublished results	10y	M	25	Elbow Flexors	1.7 Nm		16.8 Nm	10.3	67.3	67.8
	11y	M	11	" "	1.8 Nm		24.5 Nm	7.2	59.3	61.0
	16y	M	10	" "	3.9 Nm		56.6 Nm	6.8	70.0	54.3
	10y	M	25	Knee Extensors	15.6 Nm		86.8 Nm	18.0	74.6	74.2
	16y	M	10	" "	39.1 Nm		203.8 Nm	19.2	70.5	56.4
Buchthal and Schmalbruch, 1970	16-63y	M+F	6	M. Adductor Pollicis						51.0
	16-63y	M+F	9	M. Biceps Brachii Cap. Long.	59 N*	343 N*	1275 N			51.4M 56.2F
Davies, 1985	9y	M	10	M. Triceps Surae	70 N		719 N	9.7	117.0	90.0
		F	11	"	71 N		717 N	9.9	118.0	97.0
	11y	M	14	"	85 N	765 N	877 N	9.7	123.0	96.0
		F	12	"	90 N	706 N	813 N	11.1	128.0	97.0
	14y	M	12	"	97 N	1054 N	1382 N	7.0	117.0	87.0
		F	14	"	126 N	1005 N	1292 N	9.7	123.0	95.0
	21y	M	12	"	120 N	1620 N	1932 N	6.2	118.0	82.0
		F	8	"	152 N	1256 N	1442 N	10.5	132.0	98.0
Edwards et al, 1973	?	?	9	M. Quadriceps						98.9**
Edwards et al, 1977	16-63y	M+F	81	M. Quadriceps						104.7*
	?	M+F	10	M. Quadriceps						103.3*
	?	M+F	10	M. Adductor Pollicis						95.8*
Gatev et al, 1977	2 wks	?	12	M. Triceps Surae					67.8	
	6 wks	?	12	"					66.5	
	3y	?	10	"					106.2	
	2 wks	?	12	M. Flexor Carpi Ulnaris					55.8	
	6 wks	?	12	"					46.2	
	3y	?	10	"					50.8	
Gatev et al, 1981	6 wks	?	12	M. Triceps Surae					66.5	
	11-12 Mth	?		"	11.2 N				88.8	110.1
	12-14 Mth	?		"	10.4 N				101.5	100.2
	3y	?		"					106.2	
	Adult	?	10	"					105.2	
Hosking et al, 1978	4-12y	?	16	M. Quadriceps						114.3*
	Adults	?	81	M. Quadriceps						104.7*
McComas and Thomas, 1968	5-15y	M	12	First Dorsal Interosseus					63.3	53.3
McComas et al, 1973	3-14y	M	13	Extensor Hallucis Brevis	1 N				66.2	65.1
	15-25y	M	24	"	3.1 N				65.3	57.5
	3-11y	M	8	"	0.8 N					
	12-14y	M	5	"	1.3 N					
	15-16y	M	6	"	2.9 N					
Newton and Yemm, 1986	10-19y	M	6	First Dorsal Interosseus					45.0	54.0
	70-79y	M	6	"					74.0	55.0
Slomic et al, 1968	18-57y	M+F	30	Adductor	4.6 N					
		"	29	Pollicis					65.0	
		"	23	Muscles		49.0 N				
		"	20	"			58.8 N			

Unless noted otherwise, all voluntary strength and evoked contractile properties were derived from indirect, external measurements.
Twitch force (T.F.), peak isometric force during a single evoked contraction;
Tetanic force (T.T.F.), peak isometric force during tetanic stimulation;
Maximal voluntary strength (M.V.C.), peak voluntary isometric contraction force;
T.F./M.V.C. ratio, ratio of evoked twitch force to maximal voluntary isometric force expressed as a percent;
Contraction time, elapsed time from the initial deflection in force production following electrical stimulation to the occurrence of peak twitch force;
Half-relaxation time, unless noted otherwise, the elapsed time from the occurrence of peak twitch force to the point of a 50% loss in the peak twitch force output.
* Measured as the elapsed time from the last stimulus at 30 Hz to a 50% loss in tetanic force.
** Measured as the elapsed time from the last stimulus at 40 Hz to a 50% loss in tetanic force.
* Measured in situ, as force at the muscle tendon.

increase during the period of assisted standing just prior to walking, and a further increase during the transition from the supported to unsupported walking stage. There is only a small increase (4–5 ms) in contraction time for the triceps surae from the onset of unassisted walking (12 to 14 months) to age 3 y, with a further 11–17 ms increase from early to mid-childhood (Davies, 1985; Gatev et al., 1977, 1981). There is no change in contraction time for the triceps surae in males from mid-childhood to adolescence or adulthood; contraction time for females increases with advancing age from mid-childhood to adulthood.

The age-associated variation in contractile properties for the elbow flexors and knee extensors of males aged 10 to 16 y are presented in Table 3-5. It is evident from these observations and from the relationships observed in our laboratory and depicted in Figures 3-17a,b that there is little change in contraction time for these muscle groups from mid-childhood to adolescence in males. This also seems to be the case for m. extensor hallucis brevis (McComas et al., 1973). Data for other muscle groups are less extensive, and interpretation of age-associated and developmental trends is often confounded by the pooling of data across ages, with no differentiation of children and adolescents (Buchthal & Schmalbruck, 1970; Gatev et al., 1977; Newton & Yemm, 1986; Slomic et al., 1968).

Compared with the data on contraction time, there is considerably less information on age-associated changes in half-relaxation time during childhood and adolescence (Table 3-5). For the triceps surae muscle group, half-relaxation time decreases only minimally from early to mid-childhood, with no further change during adolescence in females, but shortens progressively and substantially in males with increasing age from early childhood to adulthood (Davies, 1985; Gatev et al., 1981). The relationship between age and half-relaxation time for the elbow flexors and knee extensors are shown for males from 9 to 18 years of age in Figure 3-18a,b. Consistent with the trend for the triceps surae, age was significantly negatively correlated with both elbow flexor ($r = -0.346$) and knee extensor half-relaxation time ($r = -0.312$) in these subjects.

Although the gender is not specified, the data from Hosking et al. (1978) support our finding of a gradual reduction in knee extensor half-relaxation time with increasing age from childhood to adulthood. These observations conflict, however, with a report by Edwards et al. (1987) in which there was no difference in the mean relaxation rates (measured as % of force loss in 10 s following stimulation) between normal children and adults for the quadriceps muscle. On the other hand, there is also evidence of an age-associated decrease in half-relaxation time for the extensor hallucis brevis

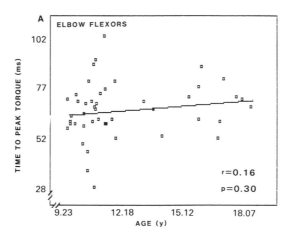

FIGURE 3-17a. *Relationship between elbow flexor contraction time and chronological age (n=46) in males. Contraction time was measured as time to peak torque during a single evoked isometric contraction (right arm) of the elbow flexors (biceps brachii and brachialis muscles) at a joint angle of 80 degrees (180 degrees is full extension), elicited by percutaneous electrical stimulation. Previously unpublished data are from Blimkie et al.*

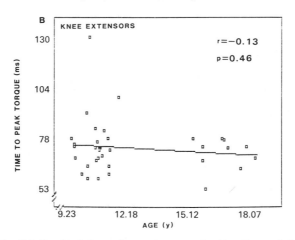

FIGURE 3-17b. *Relationship between knee extensor contraction time and chronological age (n=35) in males. Contraction time was measured as time to peak torque during a single evoked isometric contraction (right leg) of the knee extensors (quadriceps muscle) at a joint angle of 90 degrees 180 degrees is full extension), elicited by percutaneous electrical stimulation. Previously unpublished data are from Blimkie et al.*

muscle (McComas et al., 1973). Results from other studies provide no insight into the age-associated variation in half-relaxation time, either because they have not specified the age groups studied or because they have pooled children and adults together in their analysis (Edwards et al., 1977; Newton and Yemm, 1986).

138 *PERSPECTIVES IN EXERCISE*

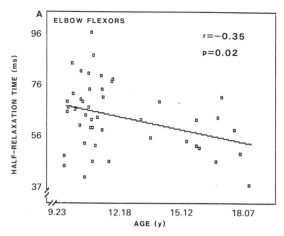

FIGURE 3-18a. *Relationship between elbow flexor half-relaxation time and chronological age (n=46) in males. Half-relaxation time was measured as the elapsed time from the occurrence of peak isometric twitch force (elicited by percutaneous electrical stimulation of elbow flexors at a joint angle of 80 degrees (180 degrees is full extension) to a 50 percent loss in force output. Previously unpublished data are from Blimkie et al.*

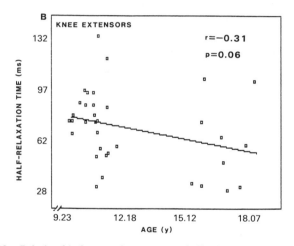

FIGURE 3-18b. *Relationship between knee extensor half-relaxation time and chronologiccal age (n=35) in males. Half-relaxation time was measured as the elapsed time from the occurrence of peak isometric twitch force (elicited by percutaneous electrical stimulation of knee extensors at a joint angle of 90 degrees (180 degrees is full extension) to a 50% loss in force output. Previously unpublished data are from Blimkie et al.*

There are no available reports of the interrelationship between skeletal muscle contractile properties and either voluntary or evoked strength characteristics in children. In unpublished result from our laboratory, time to peak torque (synonymous with contraction time) was insignificantly and weakly correlated ($-0.126 < r < 0.237$) with voluntary and evoked strength for the elbow flexors and knee extensors for males from 9 to 18 y. Although slightly higher, the correlations between half-relaxation time and either voluntary or evoked strength were also of a similar low magnitude ($-0.335 < r < -0.120$). These results suggest that these particular skeletal muscle contractile properties are not primary determinants of age-associated variation in either voluntary or evoked strength, at least for these two muscle groups in males. The degree to which these observations are generalizable to other muscle groups and to females requires further investigation.

F. Psycho- and Neurogenic Factors

Measurement of maximal voluntary strength is hampered by uncertainty regarding the degree to which subjects comprehend the attending task, the degree of compliance to instructions, and cooperation during the execution of the task, and the degree to which subjects are able to activate the motor unit pool of the particular muscle group being tested. Compared with adults, these factors may be even more limiting when testing children.

The degree of comprehension, compliance, and cooperation of subjects during voluntary strength assessments can be determined indirectly from statistical measures of reliability and reproducibility. Asmussen et al. (1959) reported test-retest (separated by about 2 h) variations in the range of 3.7% to 9.8% for maximal voluntary isometric strength of six muscle groups in a large sample of males ranging from 13 to 18 y. Hosking et al. (1976) reported that test-retest isometric strength measures (assessed with the Hammersmith Myometer) were reproducible (±15%) for six muscle groups in a pooled sample of boys and girls ranging from 4 to 13 y. Maximal voluntary isometric strength measured both by electromyometry and isometric dynomometry was also shown to be highly reliable in groups of boys with Duchenne Muscular Dystrophy (Scott et al., 1982). Edwards et al. (1987) reported average coefficients of variation (CV) of 6% and 7% for maximal voluntary strength of the quadriceps and adductor pollicis muscle groups, respectively, in pooled data that included results for normal children and adults. The coefficients of variation for maximal voluntary isometric elbow flexor and knee extensor strength measured for repeated trials on the same day and several days apart has recently been found to be from 4% to 11% in a group ($n = 6$) of 10-year-old boys (Blimkie et al., unpublished results).

The reliability and reproducibility of maximal voluntary isokinetic strength measures has also been assessed. Based on the Chi square statistic, Molnar and Alexander (1973) reported that isokinetic strength (30 deg/s) of the elbow and knee flexors and extensors measured a week apart was reproducible (no values reported) in a group of four children 7 to 14 y. In a later study involving considerably larger samples of boys and girls 7 to 15 y, Molnar et al. (1979) reported mean score deviations in maximal isokinetic strength (velocity of contraction unspecified) for within-trial and day-to-day variability (7 to 10 days apart) of 5.3% to 5.8%, and 7.9% to 9.8%, respectively, for eight muscle groups. In 10-year-old boys tested in our laboratory, the within-trial variation for maximal isokinetic elbow flexor and knee extensor strength has recently been found to be of about the same magnitude (5% to 11% CV) as for isometric strength measures for the same muscle groups. Day-to-day variability (CV) for these measures was considerably higher however, ranging from 10.8% to 16.2%.

Within-trial and day-to-day variability in strength can be attributed to both technical, physiological, and psychological influences inherent during testing. It is difficult to partition this variation into its component parts. Regardless, these observations indicate that children from 6 or 7 y and upwards are reasonably capable of reproducing relatively unskilled performances and maximal voluntary isometric strength efforts under controlled conditions. It is unlikely, therefore, that testing variability contributes significantly to the age- and sex-associated variations observed in maximal voluntary isometric strength during childhood.

Based on the few available studies, within-trial variability of isokinetic strength testing appears as good as for the isometric mode; however, there is more variability in isokinetic strength measurements separated by several days. Assuming that this variation is random, it, too, probably has little influence on the age- and sex-associated variations observed in maximal voluntary isokinetic strength at given angular velocities during childhood.

It is the author's opinion that the effects of age and sex on the reliability and reproductibility of voluntary isometric and isokinetic strength measures during childhood has not been satisfactorily investigated. Additionally, little is known about the effects of joint angle position or joint angular velocity on the reliability of isometric and isokinetic strength performances, respectively, in children or about the interaction of age and sex on these relationships.

There are no published reports of the reliability and reproductibility of evoked twitch forces in children. In unpublished data from our laboratory, within-trial and day-to-day variability in evoked (1 Hz) twitch torque for the elbow flexors and knee extensors is quite small, with coefficients of variation between 5.5% and 8.7% for 10 year-old-boys (Blimkie et al., unpublished results). Given the dearth of information in this area, it is difficult to determine the degree to which test variability contributes to age- and sex-associated variation in evoked strength measures during childhood. It appears however, that evoked strength, at least with the single twitch technique, can be reliably measured for the elbow flexors and knee extensors in children, and testing error associated with this technique probably contributes little to the age- and sex-associated variability observed in twitch strength during childhood. Whether this holds true for evoked tetanic contractions, for muscle groups other than the elbow flexors and knee extensors, and for females, remains to be determined.

Voluntary force development in muscle is highly dependent upon degree of motor unit activation (Komi, 1979; Komi, 1984; Belanger & McComas, 1981). The degree of motor unit activation is dependent upon both the level of voluntary neural drive (number of motor units recruited) and the level of activation (discharge frequency) of recruited motor units. Since motor unit activation is a normal antecedent of force development in muscle, it is possible that some of the observed variability in skeletal muscle strength during childhood may be attributed to age- and sex-associated differences in ability to activate muscle.

Based on dimensional theory, Asmussen and Heeboll-Nielsen (1956) reported that short, young girls and boys from their sample of children from 7 to 16 y were unable to produce the predicted muscle power that corresponded to height squared. They also indicated that young boys achieved their predicted strength capacity at an earlier age than girls. The authors suggested that the poorer-than-expected strength performances of the young and short boys and girls may have been caused by an inability to maximally activate their muscles during the voluntary strength test. The delay in attainment of predicted strength in girls compared with boys was loosely attributed to a sex difference. Although other interpretations are possible, e.g., the discrepancies may have been caused, at least partly, to differences in developmental status among subjects, these observations do lend some support to the possibility of age-, sex-, and size-associated variability in ability to activate the neuromuscular system during voluntary strength performance.

The more recent work by Davies (1985) provides further insight into this topic. Davies (1985) measured maximal, voluntary isometric, evoked twitch (1 Hz) and tetanic (50 Hz) twitch forces in the triceps surae muscle in groups of 9-, 11-, 14-, and 21-year-old males and females. Assuming that there is no age or sex variation in ability to activate muscle and that the twitch to tetanus strength ratio remains constant during childhood, then the ratio of evoked to maximal voluntary strength should be constant across ages and sex. In Davies' study (1985), the ratio of twitch torque (TT) (1 Hz) to maximal voluntary strength (MVC) for the triceps surae was similar for boys and girls at age 9, but decreased progressively for males from 9 to 21 y. This ratio did not change consistently with age for females. It is difficult to infer a greater degree of muscle activation in males from these data, however, because there was a concomitant change in the twitch to tetanus ratio from 11 to 21 y.

A somewhat different pattern emerged, however, for the ratio of tetanic (50 Hz) torque (PT) to maximal voluntary torque (Davies, 1985). For both males and females, the lowest ratio (indirectly implying greater relative voluntary activation) occurred at 14 and 15 y; ratios were similar at ages 11 through 21 y and between sexes at all ages. These data are difficult to interpret. On the one hand, the TT-MVC ratio results suggest that motor unit activation may vary with age and between sexes; on the other hand, the PT-MVC ratio results suggest that the ability to voluntarily activate muscle may vary with age, but not sex.

The degree of motor unit activation can be assessed more directly by means of the interpolated twitch technique (Belanger & McComas, 1981; Marton, 1954). With this technique, a supramaximal electrical stimulation is applied during the peak of a maximal voluntary isometric contraction. The increment in force output above that elicited by voluntary effort provides a measure of the degree of motor unit activation. This technique has been applied recently in our laboratory to both the elbow flexor and knee extensor muscle groups in 10- to 16-year-old males.

As shown in Figure 3-19a, there was no difference between age groups for percent motor unit activation of the elbow flexors (89.4% vs. 89.9%, for 10 to 16 year olds, respectively); however, there was a substantial age difference (Figure 3-19b) in degree of motor unit activation of knee extensors (77.7% vs. 95.3% for 10 and 16 year olds, respectively). Furthermore, there appears to be less variability in ability to activate motor units in the older boys. These results suggest that the ability to voluntarily activate muscle during isometric effort may vary with age for the knee extensors and across muscle groups. Whether there is a sex-associated variation in ability to voluntarily activate these or other muscle groups remains to be determined.

Based on these observations, it is possible that differences in ability to activate muscle contribute to the age- and sex-associated variation observed in human voluntary strength during childhood. The relative importance of this source of variability in differentiating

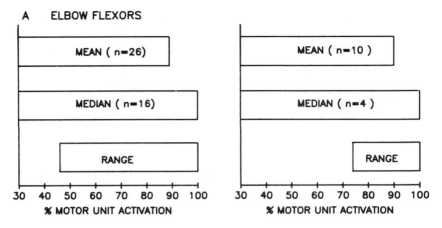

FIGURE 3-19a. *Relationship between percent motor unit activation and age in males for the elbow flexors.*

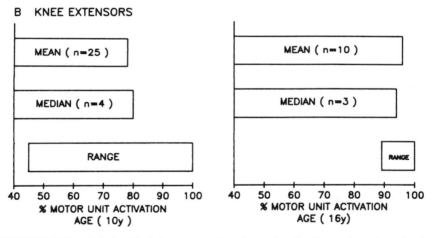

FIGURE 3-19b. *Relationship between percent motor unit activation and age in males for the knee extensors.*

Percent motor unit activation was determined using the interpolated twitch technique (Belanger and McComas, 1981; Merton, 1954), at joint angles of 100 degrees and 90 degrees for the elbow flexors and knee extensors, respectively. Previously unpublished data are from Blimkie et al.

strength performance of different muscle groups, across age, and between sexes needs further investigation.

G. Biomechanical Influences

In vivo muscle force has only rarely been measured directly in humans. Strength measurements, whether of an evoked or voluntary nature, involve the muscle acting across single or multiple joints. The mechanical advantage of the musculoskeletal system is variable across different muscle groups and is considered unfavorable because the measured force or torque is considerably smaller than the corresponding tension developed in the muscle tendon. Maughan (1984) reported on the influence of musculoskeletal mechanical advantage on the relationship between maximal voluntary isometric force and muscle cross-sectional area in adults. He reported a significant ($P < 0.05$) positive relationship between calculated mechanical advantage (determined from X-rays) and the measured maximal voluntary strength/cross-sectional area ratio (specific tension) for the quadriceps.

An approximation of this relationship has recently been investigated (Figures 3-20a,b) in males from 9 to 18 y, assuming that differences in mechanical advantage or muscle moment arm length vary in proportion to height (Sale et al., 1987). There were significant ($P < 0.001$), moderately strong, positive correlations between height and the ratio of maximal voluntary isometric torque to cross-sectional area, for the elbow flexors ($r = 0.670$; $n = 46$) and knee extensors ($r = 0.574$; $n = 35$). It is likely that part of the explained variability in these relationships is due to the shared variation of height with other undefined, non-biomechanical influences, e.g., neuromuscular maturation, that may occur concomitantly with growth. These data also suggest, however, that at least part of the age-associated variability in voluntary and evoked strength may be attributed to differences in mechanical advantage that occur in conjunction with growth.

Apparently, only Ikai and Fukunaga (1968) have investigated age-related differences in mechanical advantage of muscle between children and adults. Using X-rays to determine resistance arms (RA) and force arms (FA) for the elbow flexors, these authors found a slightly (insignificant) higher ratio of RA/FA in boys compared with adult men. However, this comparison was based on a very small sample of boys who were similar in age, and the relationship between mechanical advantage and strength per cross-sectional area was not determined. There are no published data on the relationship between strength per cross-sectional area and mechanical advantage covering different age groups, both sexes, and different muscle groups. Nevertheless, it seems prudent to correct strength scores for possible differences in mechanical advantage, especially when comparing children of vastly different sizes. Normalizing strength scores for height or limb-segment length may suffice as an indirect correction for differences in mechanical advantage among children.

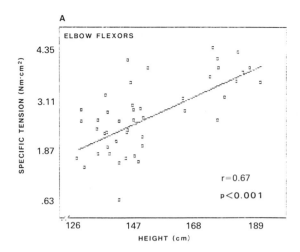

FIGURE 3-20a. *Relationship between height and maximal voluntary specific tension (maximal isometric torque normalized for muscle cross-sectional area) of elbow flexors in males (n=46) from 9 to 18 years of age. Maximal voluntary isometric torque was measured on a custom-made dynomometer at an elbow joint angle of 80 degrees (180 degrees is full extension). Elbow flexor (biceps brachii and brachialis muscles) cross-sectional area was determined by computerized axial tomography taken at the mid-upper arm (right side) with the arm fully extended and relaxed. Previously unpublished data are from Blimkie et al.*

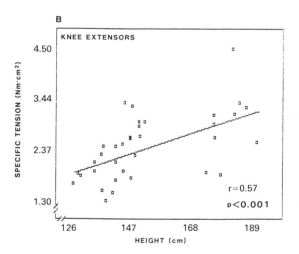

FIGURE 3-20b. *Relationship between height and maximal voluntary specific tension (maximal isometric torque normalized for muscle cross-sectional area) of knee extensors in males (n=35) from 9 to 18 y. Maximal voluntary isometric torque was measured on a custom-made dynomometer at a knee joint angle of 90 degrees (180 degrees is full extension). Knee extensor (quadriceps muscle) cross-sectional area was determined by computerized axial tomography taken at the mid-thigh (right side) with the leg fully extended and relaxed. Previously unpublished data are from Blimkie et al.*

The effects of architecture and angle of pennation of muscle on its functional characteristics has been described by Gans (1982) and Maughan (1984). Generally, the greater the angle of pennation, the smaller the proportion of force acting on the muscle tendon and the lower the measured external force. *Maughan (1984) suggests that increased muscle hypertrophy in adults contributes to an increase in absolute strength. However, because of the concomitant increase in pennation, this hypertrophy may result in a lower strength to muscle area ratio, at least in pennated muscles such as the quadriceps.* The age-associated relationships between muscle size, architecture, and function (in terms of strength) have not been investigated in children.

According to our unpublished data, from age 10 or 11 to 16 y, muscle cross-sectional area increases absolutely in males from 8 cm^2 to 15.8 cm^2 for elbow flexors, and 40 cm^2 to 70 cm^2 for knee extensors. The ratio of muscle cross-sectional area to height increased by 60% for elbow flexors, and 37% for knee extensors between the same ages. These data suggest that muscle size increases relatively more than height and possibly more than age-associated changes in mechanical advantage between mid-childhood and adolescence; also, the magnitude of this change may vary across different muscle groups. This should prove an advantage to the older, more fully developed boy (more so for the elbow flexors than for the knee extensors) by providing a relatively greater potential for absolute external force production.

However, some of this increased strength potential may be countered by a dissipation of effective strength due to the increased angle of tendon insertion and muscle pull that probably accompanies an increase in muscle size with growth, particularly during adolescence. This counterinfluence may be proportionately greater in pennated muscles like the quadriceps than in muscles like the elbow flexors where muscle fibers run parallel. The degree to which these biomechanical factors influence age-associated, sex-associated and muscle group variability in strength during childhood and adolescence requires more extensive investigation.

G. Endocrinological Influences

Differences in muscularity and in strength performance between the sexes, particularly during puberty and adolescence, have been associated with changes in endocrinological function during these stages of development. The changes in serum sex steroid concentrations, particularly testosterone, which is a potent anabolic agent, have been largely implicated in this sexual differentiation. As shown in Figure 3-21a, there is a dramatic increase in serum testosterone concentration in males during the course of pubertal development.

While there is also an increase in testosterone concentration in females (Figure 3-21b), it is of lower magnitude, and the peak level at the end of puberty (B5/PH5) is lower than that attained by boys at pubertal stage G2.

Besides testosterone, rather substantial changes also occur in other sex steroid concentrations, particularly in androstenedione, a weaker anabolic agent secreted primarily by the adrenal cortex. Compared with changes in testosterone secretion, the change in androstenedione secretion is smaller in males, but larger in females. Estradiol concentration changes vary little for males during puberty and increases in females only during the later stages of pubertal development.

Whereas the age- and developmentally associated variations in sex steroid concentrations have been adequately described, there have been no pediatric studies of concomitant changes in endocrinologic function and muscle size and strength. Differences in strength performance between the sexes and with advancing age before puberty are probably relatively independent of sex steroid influences, since the circulating levels increase only slightly during the early and mid-childhood years and are not different between the sexes (Winter, 1978).

An exhaustive review of hormonal control of muscle growth and strength performance is beyond the scope of this chapter. The reader is directed to two excellent reviews on the topic of hormonal control of muscle growth by Florini (1985; 1987). Testosterone is believed to be the most active stimulator of anabolic processes in muscle. It should be noted, however, that testosterone may influence other aspects of muscle development besides muscle growth. Testosterone has also been shown to regulate neurotransmitter release (Souccar et al., 1982) and to stimulate the conversion of muscle fiber types (Kelly et al., 1985) in experiments with rodents. Whether testosterone exerts similar non-anabolic effects on skeletal muscle in humans is an intriguing yet unresolved question.

The androgens (male sex steroids) are not the only hormones capable of influencing anabolic processes and muscle growth. Growth hormone, the somatomedins, insulin, and the thyroid hormones are all known to be important regulators of normal somatic and muscle tissue growth (Florini, 1987). Additionally, muscle growth and strength performance may be ultimately determined by the balance between hormonally regulated anabolic and catabolic processes. Cortisol in particular, and the glucocorticoids in general, are considered catabolic in nature and may have actions that oppose the anabolic hormone effects on muscle growth and strength performance. As was the case for the sex steroids, the relative importance

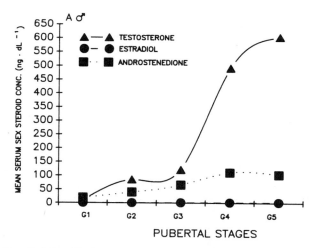

FIGURE 3-21a. *Relationship between serum sex steroid concentrations and pubertal stages for males.*

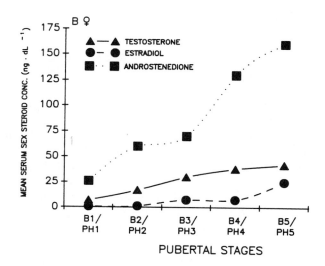

FIGURE 3-21b. *Relationship between serum sex steroid concentrations and pubertal stages for females.*

Data are from Winter (1978) and represent mean values. Pubertal staging (G₁, G₂, etc.) for males is based on development of external sex organs (scrotum and penis). Pubertal staging for females is based upon breast development (B1 to B5) for estradiol, and upon pubic hair growth (PH1 to PH5) for the androgens. For females, values for stage B5/PH5 represent mid-menstrual cycle levels.

of these hormones and of the balance between anabolic and catabolic hormones on the age- and sex-associated differentiation of muscle size and strength performance during childhood remains to be determined.

H. Genetic Influences

The importance of inheritance as a determinant of various types of human performance has been the topic of several reviews (Bouchard and Lortie, 1984; Bouchard and Malina, 1983; Klissouras, 1971; Komi and Karlsson, 1979; Malina, 1986b). Surprisingly few studies have investigated the relationship between inheritance and strength performance within the pediatric age range. A detailed summary of these studies is provided in the reviews by Bouchard and Malina (1983) and Malina (1986b). Results from these studies are difficult to interpret due to differences in population characteristics (sample sizes, age groups, and nationalities studied) and, more importantly, to the methods used to estimate the genetic effect.

Based on studies that used the twin model approach, there is a wide variability in the heritability estimates for isometric strength for the same muscle groups as well as for different muscles (Kovar, 1981; Malina, 1986b). Whereas some of the studies reported by these authors indicated a low to moderate degree of heritability for some isometric strength measures, results from other studies indicate little or no significant genetic effect for isometric strength performance during childhood (Kimura, 1956; Komi et al., 1973; Komi and Karlsson, 1979). In contrast, results from several studies (Engstrom and Fischbein, 1977; Mizuno, 1956; Sklad, 1973) indicate a moderate degree of heritability for absolute and normalized (height and weight corrected) composite isometric strength performance in children.

There are no available studies of the heritability of isokinetic strength. However, the studies by Kovar (1975) and Jones and Klissouras (1986) indicate a high genetic effect (heritability estimates of 85% to 97%) for dynamic strength or power of the elbow flexors in children. Likewise, Komi and Karlsson (1979) reported a high heritability estimate (98%) for leg muscle power (stair-running test) in a combined sample of children and young adults.

It is difficult, based on the existing literature, to provide an unequivocal statement about the importance of genetic influences on the differentiation of strength performance during childhood. There appears to be a low to moderate degree of heritability of isometric strength for some specific muscle groups, little or no genetic influence on others, and a moderate genetic effect for composite isometric strength. There is no available information regarding the heritability of either evoked isometric strength (twitch or tetanic tension) or maximal voluntary isokinetic strength in children. However, there appears to be a fairly strong genetic influence on dynamic strength and muscle power.

The heritability of strength performance, whatever its magnitude, could be mediated, at least in part, by genetic determination of muscle fiber composition and distribution within a muscle. Komi and Karlsson (1979), using the twin model approach, reported extremely high heritability estimates of 92.2% and 99.6% in females and males, respectively, (combined sample of children and young adults) for percent slow twitch fiber distribution in the vastus lateralis. A significant moderate negative correlation was also reported in this study between quadriceps isometric force and percent slow twitch fibers for males, but not females.

In a preliminary report, Bouchard and Lortie (1984) found a higher degree of resemblance in type 1 muscle fiber distribution in the vastus lateralis of monozygous twins rather than dizygous twins, inferring a genetic influence on muscle composition. In a more recent study, however, with larger twin samples (including some adolescent males and females), Bouchard et al. (1986) reported that there was no significant genetic effect for either the distribution of muscle fiber types I, IIa, or IIb or for muscle fiber areas for the vastus lateralis in either sex. The discrepancy between the findings of Komi and Karlsson (1979) and the more recent study by Bouchard et al. (1986) regarding heritability of muscle fiber composition may be explained by differences in conceptual and statistical approaches used in data analysis as well as by differences in sample sizes.

It appears from the more extensive study by Bouchard et al. (1986) that there is little genetic influence on the differentiation of muscle fiber composition and area, at least for the vastus lateralis. This conclusion remains to be confirmed, however, as does the generalizability of this conclusion to other muscle groups. Lastly, it should be noted that a genetic influence on strength performance may also be realized through genotypical regulation of factors other than muscle composition; for example, body size and limb-segment lengths have been previously identified as important correlates of strength performance during childhood.

I. Physical Activity Influences

The topic of resistance training and strength performance during childhood has been covered in Chapter 4 in this book. However, a brief discussion of the importance of habitual physical activity in the differentiation of strength performance during childhood is warranted.

Healthy children are generally considered to be habitually quite active, especially compared with adults. Physical activity, however, varies in kind and intensity and is an extremely difficult variable to quantify, especially in the pediatric population (Saris, 1986). While there is some limited information regarding levels and patterns of habitual physical activity for small samples and narrow age ranges of children, there is a dearth of information based on large samples covering both sexes and the entire childhood era.

Saris (1986) has recently summarized the results of studies on energy expenditure (based on heart rate records) and energy intake (based on food records) involving children ranging from 4 to 17 y. The only consistent trend was a higher energy expenditure and intake in boys compared with girls across all ages. In a recent survey of Canadian youth 10 to 19 y, there was only a slightly higher participation rate in physical activity (self reported) for boys compared with girls up to 13 y (Canada Fitness Survey, 1983). From 14 y, there was a progressive drop in participation rate for females with advancing age. The participation rate remained high and did not change for males until 19 y. Additionally, there were sex differences in the nature of preferred activities during participation, with boys preferring activities requiring a high degree of muscular strength and power (weight training and ice hockey).

While there appear to be differences in participation rates and in the nature and intensity of habitual physical activity between the sexes, the significance of these differences for explaining age- and sex-associated variation in strength performance during childhood remains to be determined.

VI. SUMMARY—CORRELATES AND DETERMINANTS OF STRENGTH

Numerous factors influence the expression of strength during childhood. Chronological age correlates moderately well with both voluntary and evoked strength; however, the relative importance of age itself in strength differentiation, independent of body size covariates such as height, weight and lean body mass, remains to be determined.

Strength is clearly influenced by body size and composition during childhood. Absolute strength increases with increasing body weight and lean body mass for males and females. Males are stronger than girls of the same height, and strength generally increases in a positive manner with increasing height for both sexes throughout childhood. The rate of increase in strength relative to height is similar for boys and girls until male puberty. Thereafter, strength increases at a much greater rate in relation to height in males.

There have been only a few studies of muscle size and strength during childhood. For specific age groups, correlations between muscle breadths and widths and strength have been only low to moderate. However, with wider age ranges, the correlations between muscle cross-sectional area and both voluntary and evoked strength are moderately high. There are only limited data on specific strength (strength per cross-sectional area of muscle) during childhood. Earlier studies suggest that there may be a gender difference in specific strength during mid-childhood, whereas more recent observations suggest that specific strength is constant across ages and between sexes from mid-childhood to adulthood.

Despite the increasing number of studies of muscle fiber composition and distribution in children, there are no studies to date of the relationship between muscle composition and either voluntary or evoked strength. The extent to which strength varies with muscle fiber type distribution and size throughout childhood remains to be determined.

There are several studies of contractile characteristics of a few specific muscle groups in children. Contraction time changes only minimally for the triceps surae, elbow flexors, and knee extensors in males from mid-childhood to adulthood, but increases with increasing age for the triceps surae in females. Half-relaxation time does not change considerably in the triceps surae for females during childhood and adolescence, but decreases substantially and progressively with age in males for the triceps surae, elbow flexors, and knee extensors. Despite these age-associated changes in contractile properties, there is no significant association between contractile properties and either voluntary or evoked strength for elbow flexors and knee extensors from mid-childhood to adolescence for males.

Within-trial and day-to-day variability in both voluntary and evoked strength is quite small and probably does not contribute substantially to the age- and sex-associated variability in strength performance. There is also some indirect, as well as direct, evidence suggesting that there may be age- and sex-related differences in ability to activate muscle and therefore to generate strength during maximal voluntary isometric efforts. There is also limited yet direct evidence to indicate that this ability may vary across muscle groups within the same individual.

Strength may also be influenced by biomechanical factors that influence mechanical advantage and the angle of muscle pull on the joint tendon. Evidence suggests that there is a positive association between height, an estimate of muscle moment arm length, and voluntary specific tension for the elbow flexors and knee extensors in males from 9 to 18 y. Additionally, it has been shown that the elbow flexor and knee extensor cross-sectional areas increase to a greater degree than the change in height (and possibly the change in mechanical advantage) between mid-childhood and adolescence in males. The effect of possible competing physiological and biomechanical influences, e.g., increased muscle size and potential for force production vs. increased angle of muscle pull and pennation (and potential force dissipation), on the age- and sex-associated variability in strength performance remains to be determined.

Muscle growth is clearly influenced by hormonal regulation. Testosterone, a potent anabolic agent has long been considered the key hormone responsible for the differentiation of muscle size and strength performance across age for males and between the sexes, especially during puberty and adolescence. However, the precise role of testosterone and other anabolic and catabolic hormones in the differentiation of muscle growth and strength performance during childhood remains to be elucidated.

The genetic influence on strength performance is equivocal. The heritability of strength performance varies from negligible to low to moderate for some individual isometric strength performances, and there is a moderate genetic effect on composite isometric strength. There is no information on the heritability of isokinetic strength for children, although dynamic strength and muscle power appear to be moderately influenced by genetics. There seems to be no significant genetic effect on muscle fiber type distribution or areas, at least for the vastus lateralis muscle.

Lastly, although there are differences in participation rates and in the nature and level of habitual physical activity between the sexes, the importance of these differences in explaining age- and sex-associated variation in strength performance during childhood remains to be determined.

VII. CONCLUSION

To date, much of the work that has been done regarding strength development during childhood has been descriptive in nature. Additional descriptive work is required to more completely characterize the age- and sex-associated variability in isometric voluntary and evoked strength for muscle groups besides those of the hand and wrist, and particularly for isokinetic strength of the major muscle groups.

It is also important, however, despite the technical and logistical constraints of working with children, to delve more deeply into the mechanisms underlying strength development during childhood. What happens to muscle quality (fiber type distribution, bio-

TABLE 3-6. *Future Research Directions—Strength Development During Childhood.*

*Description of isometric, isokinetic and evoked strength of more diverse and major muscle groups, particularly for females.

*Description of age- and sex-associated variation in strength for agonist, antagonist, and synergistic muscle groups.

*Description of age-and sex-associated variability in reliability and reproductibility of isometric, isokinetic, and evoked strength for major muscle groups.

*Description of age, sex, and muscle-group variability in ability to voluntarily activate muscle (motor unit activation).

*Description of age- and sex-associated variability in muscle fiber type, number and size, and the relationship between these changes and the differentiation of isometric, isokinetic, and evoked strength performance.

*Description of age, sex, and muscle-group variability in development of specific tension (strength per cross-sectional area) of major muscle groups.

*Description of age-, and sex-associated variability in mechanical advantage and architectural changes in the major groups, and the relationship between these changes and the differentiation of strength performance.

*Description of concomitant changes in the major anabolic and catabolic hormones with strength, as well as the relative importance of these hormones in the differentiation of strength performance.

*Clarification of the importance of genetic influences on various types of strength performance and confirmation of the apparent lack of genetic influence on fiber type composition and fiber size.

*Clarification of the importance of habitual physical activity in explaining the age- and sex-associated variability in strength performance.

chemistry, morphology, compliance) and neuromuscular and bio-mechanical function as the child matures to adulthood? How do these growth-related changes influence voluntary and evoked strength performance across ages and between sexes, both in normal healthy children and children with various pediatric diseases? Answers to these questions will require the application of relatively new tech-nological procedures, including computerized axial tomography and nuclear magnetic resonance imaging to determine muscle morphol-ogy, and the integration of biomechanical, electrophysiological, and biochemical techniques suitable for use with children.

As indicated in this review, more questions than answers have arisen from the work in this area. We have only begun to scratch the surface. These questions and others are summarized in Table 3-6 and need to be answered, but not at the expense of ethical and safety concerns for the child.

ACKNOWLEDGMENTS

I would like to thank Mr. Jean Ramsay and Ms. Joan Martin for their assistance in data collection and analysis, and my colleagues Dr. Digby Sale and Dr. Duncan MacDougall for their support and encouragement in this area of research. I would also like to thank Dr. George Brooks and Dr. Kenneth Baldwin, the reactors to this manuscript, for their insightful commentary and helpful suggestions. Appreciation is also extended to Mrs. Laura Diskin for her assistance in typing the manuscript.

The work in this paper was supported by grants from the Arts Research Board, McMaster University, and The Ministry of Tourism and Recreation, Ontario, Canada.

BIBLIOGRAPHY

1. Aherne, W., D.R. Ayyar, P.A. Clarke, and J.N. Walton. Muscle fiber size in normal infants, children and adolescents: an autopsy study. *Journal of the Neurological Sciences* 14:171–182, 1971.
2. Alexander, J., and G.E. Molnar. Muscular strength in children: preliminary report on objective standards. *Archives of Physical Medicine and Rehabilitation* 54:424–427, 1973.
3. Anderson, B., K. Froberg, and O. Lammert (personal communication). A longitudinal study on physical training of boys 10–16 years of age.
4. Asmussen, E. Growth in muscular strength and power. In G.L. Rarick (ed.). *Physical Activity Human Growth and Development.* New York: Academic Press. 1973, 60–79.
5. Asmussen, E., and K. Heeboll-Nielsen. A dimensional analysis of physical performance and growth in boys. *Journal of Applied Phsiology* 7:593–603, 1955.
6. Asmussen, E., and K. Heeboll-Nielsen. Physical performance and growth in children. Influence of sex, age and intelligence. *Journal of Applied Physiology* 8:371–380, 1956.
7. Asmussen, E., K. Heeboll-Nielsen, and S.V. Molbech. Methods for evaluation of muscle strength. Report No. 5, p. 3–13, 1959. Communication, Testing and Observation Institute, Danish National Association for Infantile Paralysis. Cited in Molnar et al., 1979.
8. Baldwin, K.M. Muscle development: neonatal to adult. *Exercise and Sport Sciences Reviews* 12:1–19, 1984.
9. Ball, T.E., S.B. Going, and T. Lohman. The relationship of muscle cross-sectional area to height in six to eighteen year old children. *Canadian Journal of Sport Sciences* 12:3P, 1987.
10. Belanger, A.Y., and A.J. McComas. Extent of motor unit activation during effort. *Journal of Applied Physiology* 51:1131–1135, 1981.
11. Bell, R.D., J.D. MacDougall, R. Billeter, and H. Howald. Muscle fiber types and morphometric analysis of skeletal muscle in 6-year-old children. *Medicine and Science in Sports and Exercise* 12:28–31, 1980.
12. Beunen, G., and R.M. Malina. Growth and physical performance relative to the timing of the adolescent spurt. *Exercise and Sport Sciences Reviews* 16:503–540, 1988.
13. Bookwalter, K.W., B. Bruce, C. Cameron, G.I. Fox, V.L. Hoffman, P. Newquist, D. Rains, and M. Rousey. Grip strength norms for males. *Research Quarterly* 21:249–273, 1950.
14. Bouchard, C., and G. Lortie. Heredity and endurance performance. *Sports Medicine* 1:38–64, 1984.
15. Bouchard, C., and R.M. Malina. Genetics of physiological fitness and motor performance. *Exercise and Sport Sciences Reviews* 11:306–339, 1983.
16. Bouchard, C., J.A. Simoneau, G. Lortie, M.R. Boulay, M. Marcotte, and M.C. Thibault. Genetic effects in human skeletal muscle fiber type distribution and enzyme activities. *Canadian Journal Of Physiology And Pharmacology* 64:1245–1251, 1986.
17. Bowden, D.H., and R.A. Goyer. The size of muscle fibers in infants and children. *Archives of Pathology* 69:188–189, 1960.
18. Brodie, D.A., J. Burnie, R.G. Eston, and J.A. Royce. Isokinetic strength and flexibility characteristics in preadolescent boys. In J.R. Rutenfranz, R. Mocellin, and F. Klimt (eds.). *Children and Exercise XII.* Champaign, IL: Human Kinetics, 1986, 309–319.
19. Brooke, M., and W. Engel. The histograph analysis of human muscle biopsies with regard to fiber types. *Neurology* 19:591–605, 1969.
20. Buchthal, F., and H. Schmalbruch. Contraction times and fiber types in intact human muscle. *Acta Physiologica Scandinavica* 79:435–452, 1970.
21. Buchthal, F. and H. Schmalbruch. Motor unit of mammalian muscle. *Physiological Reviews* 60:90–142, 1980.
22. Burke, R.E., and V.R. Edgerton. Motor unit properties and selective involvement in movement. *Exercise and Sport Sciences Reviews* 3:31–81, 1975.
23. Burnie, J., and D.A. Brodie. Isokinetic measurement in preadolescent males. *International Journal of Sports Medicine* 7:205–209, 1986.
24. Canada Fitness Survey. *Canadian youth and physical activity.* Ottawa: Fitness and Amateur Sport, 1983.
25. Canada Fitness Survey. *Physical fitness and Canadian youth.* Ottawa: Fitness and Amateur Sport, 1985.

26. Carron, A.V., E.J. Aitken, and D.A. Bailey. No title. In H. Lavallee, and R.J. Shephard (eds.). *Frontiers of Activity and Child Health.* Ottawa: Editions Du Pelican. 1977, 139–143.
27. Carron, A.V., and D.A. Bailey. Strength Development In Boys From 10 Through 16 Years. Monograph. *Society For Research In Child Development* 39(4):1–37, 1974.
28. Chapman, S.J., S.R. Grindrod, and D.A. Jones. Cross-sectional area and force production of the quadriceps muscle. *Journal of Physiology* 353:53P, 1984.
29. Cheek, D.B. Growth and body composition. In D.B. Cheek (ed.). *Fetal and Postnatal Cellular Growth: Hormones and Nutrition.* New York: Wiley, 1975, pp. 389–408.
30. Clarke, H.H. *Physical And Motor Tests In The Medford Boy's Growth Study.* Englewood Cliffs, N.J.: Prentice-Hall, 1971.
31. Clarke, H.H., and E.W. Degutis. Comparison of skeletal age and various physical and motor factors with the pubescent development of 10-, 13-, and 16-year-old boys. *Research Quarterly* 33:356–368, 1962.
32. Close, R.I. Dynamic properties of mammalian skeletal muscle. *Physiological Reviews* 52:129–197, 1972.
33. Colling-Saltin, A-S. Skeletal muscle development in the human fetus and during childhood. In K. Berg and B.O. Eriksson (eds.). *Children and Exercise. IX.* Baltimore: University Park Press, 1980, 193–207.
34. Costill, D.L., J. Daniels, W. Evans, W. Fink, G. Krahenbuhl, and B. Saltin. Skeletal muscle enzymes and fiber composition in male and female track athletes. *Journal of Applied Physiology* 40:149–154, 1976.
35. Davies, C.T.M. Strength and mechanical properties of muscle in children and young adults. *Scandinavian Journal of Sports Science* 7:11–15, 1985.
36. Davies, C.T.M., D.O. Thomas, and M.J. White. Mechanical properties of young and elderly human muscle. *Acta Medica Scandinavica* Supplement 711:219–226, 1986.
37. Davies, C.T.M., M.J. White, and K. Young. Muscle function in children. *European Journal of Applied Physiology* 52:111–114, 1983.
38. DeKoning, F.L., M.A. Van'tHof, R.A. Binkhorst, and J.A. Vos. Parameters of the force-velocity curve of human muscle in relation to body dimensions. *Human Biology* 58:221–238, 1986.
39. Dempsey, Y. The relationship between the strength of the elbow flexors and muscle size of the upper arm in children. Unpublished Master's Thesis. University of Wisconsin, Madison, 1955.
40. DuPlessis, M.P., P.J. Smit, L.A.S. DuPlessis, H.J. Geyer, G. Mathews, and H.N.J. Louw. The composition of muscle fibers in a group of adolescents. In R.A. Binkhorst, H.C.G. Kemper, and W.H.M. Saris (eds.). *Children and Exercise. XI.* Champaign, Il.: Human Kinetics, 1985, 323–328.
41. Edgerton, V.R. Exercise and the growth and development of muscle tissue. In G.L. Rarick (ed.). *Physical Activity, Human Growth and Development.* New York: Academic Press, 1973, 1–31.
42. Edwards, R.H.T., S.J. Chapman, D.J. Newham, and D.A. Jones. Practical analysis of variability of muscle function measurements in Duchenne Muscular Dystrophy. *Muscle and Nerve* 10:6–14, 1987.
43. Edwards, R.H.T., A. Young, G.P. Hosking, and D.A. Jones. Human skeletal muscle function: description of tests and normal values. *Clinical Science and Molecular Medicine* 52:283–290, 1977.
44. Engstrom, L.M., and S. Fischbein. Physical capacity in twins. *Acta Geneticae Medicae et Gemellologiae* 26:159–165, 1977.
45. Eriksson, B.O., P.D. Gollnick, and B. Saltin. The effect of physical training on muscle enyzme activities and fiber composition in 11-year-old boys. *Acta Paediatrica Belgica* Supplement 28:245–252, 1974.
46. Faust, M.S. Somatic Development Of Adolescent Girls. Monograph. *Society For Research In Child Development* 42(1):1–90, 1977.
47. Fisher, M.B., and J.E. Birren. Age and strength. *Journal of Applied Psychology* 31:490–497, 1947.
48. Florini, J.R. Hormonal control of muscle cell growth (review). *Journal of Animal Sciences* 61:21–38, 1985.
49. Florini, J.R. Hormonal control of muscle growth. *Muscle And Nerve* 10:577–598, 1987.
50. Forbes, G.B. Toward a new dimension in human growth. *Pediatrics* 36:825–835, 1965.
51. Fournier, M., J. Ricca, A.W. Taylor, R.J. Ferguson, R.R. Montpetit, and B.R. Chaitman. Skeletal muscle adaptation in adolescent boys: sprint and endurance training and detraining. *Medicine and Science in Sports and Exercise* 14:453–456, 1982.
52. Fowler, W.M., and G.W. Gardner. Quantitative strength measurements in muscular dystrophy. *Archives of Physical Medicine and Rehabilitation* 48:629–644, 1967.
53. Funato, K., T. Fukunaga, T. Asami, and S. Ikeda. Strength training for prepubescent boys

and girls. In *The Proceedings Of The Department of Sport Sciences, College Of Arts and Sciences. University of Tokyo.* 21:9–19, 1987.

54. Gans, C. Fiber architecture and muscle function. *Exercise and Sport Sciences Reviews* 10:160–207, 1982.
55. Gatev, V., L. Stamatova, and B. Angelova. Contraction time in skeletal muscles of normal children. *Electromyography and Clinical Neurophysiology* 17:441–451, 1977.
56. Gatev, V., M. Stefanova-Uzunova, and L. Stamatova. Influence of vertical posture development on the velocity properties of triceps surae muscle in normal children. *Journal of Neurological Sciences* 52:85–90, 1981.
57. Gilliam, T.B., S.P. Sady, P.S. Freedson, and J. Villanacci. Isokinetic torque levels for high school football players. *Archives of Physical Medicine and Rehabilitation* 60:110–114, 1979a.
58. Gilliam, T.B., J.F. Villanacci, P.S. Freedson, and S.P. Sady. Isokinetic torque in boys and girls ages 7 to 13: effect of age, height, and weight. *Research Quarterly* 50:599–609, 1979b.
59. Gollnick, P.D., and D.R. Hodgson. The identification of fiber types in skeletal muscle: a continual dilemma. *Exercise and Sport Sciences Reviews* 14:81–104, 1986.
60. Grace, T.G., E.R. Sweetser, M.A. Nelson, L.R. Ydens, and B.J. Skipper. Isokinetic muscle imbalance and knee-joint injuries. *The Journal of Bone and Joint Surgery* 66-A:734–740, 1984.
61. Hedberg, G., and E. Jansson, (1976). Skelettmuskelfiber-komposition. Kapacitet och intresse for olika fysiska aktiviteter bland elever: gymnasieskolan. Rapport 54, *Pedagogiska Institute* Umea. Cited in Malina, 1986a.
62. Holmes, J.R., and G.J. Alderink. Isokinetic strength characteristics of the quadriceps femoris and hamstring muscles in high school students. *Physical Therapy* 64:914–918, 1984.
63. Hosking, G.P., U.S. Bhat, V. Dubowitz, and R.H.T. Edwards. Measurement of muscle strength and performance in children with normal and diseased muscles. *Archives of Disease in Childhood* 51:957–963, 1976.
64. Housh, T.J., W.G. Thorland, G.D. Tharp, G.D. Johnson, and C.J. Cisar. Isokinetic leg flexion and extension strength of elite adolescent female track and field athletes. *Research Quarterly* 55:347–350, 1984.
65. Howald, H. Training-induced morphological and functional changes in skeletal muscle. *International Journal of Sports Medicine* 3:1–12, 1982.
66. Ikai, M., and T. Fukunaga. Calculations of muscle strength per unit cross-sectional area of human muscle by means of ultrasonic measurement. *International Zeitschrift fur angewandte Physiologie einschliesslich Arbeitsphysiologie* 26:26–32, 1968.
67. Jones, H.E. The relationship of strength to physique. *American Journal of Physical Anthropology* 5:29–39, 1947.
68. Jones, H.E. *Motor Performance And Growth.* Berkley: University of California Press, 1949.
69. Jones, B., and V. Klissouras. Genetic variation in the force-velocity relation of human muscle. In R.M. Malina and C. Bouchard (eds.). *Sports And Human Genetics.* Champaign Il.:Human Kinetics, 1986, 155–163.
70. Kamieniecka, Z. The studies of development of human fetal muscles with reference to some muscular diseases. *Journal of the Neurological Sciences* 7:319–329, 1968.
71. Kelly, A., G. Lyons, B. Gambki, and N. Rubinstein. Influences of testosterone on contractile proteins of the guinea pig temporalis muscle. *Advances In Experimental And Biological Medicine* 182:155–168, 1985.
72. Kemper, H.C.G. Health and fitness of Dutch teenagers: a review. In J.A.P. Day (ed.). *Perspectives In Kinanthropometry.* Champaign, Il: Human Kinetics, 1986, 61–80.
73. Kimura, K. The study on physical ability of children and youths: on twins in Osaka City. *Jinrui Idengaku Zasshi* 64:172–196, 1956. Cited in Bouchard and Malina, 1983.
74. Klissouras, V. Heritability of adaptive variation. *Journal of Applied Physiology* 31:338–344, 1971.
75. Knuttgen, H.G., and W.J. Kraemer. Terminology and measurement in exercise performance. *Journal of Applied Sport Science Research* 1:1–10, 1987.
76. Komi, P.V. Neuromuscular performance: factors influencing force and speed production. *Scandinavian Journal of Sport Sciences* 1:2–15, 1979.
77. Komi, P.V. Physiological and biomechanical correlates of muscle function: effects of muscle structure and stretch-shortening cycle on force and speed. *Exercise and Sport Sciences Reviews* 12:81–121, 1984.
78. Komi, P.V., and J. Karlsson. Physical performance, skeletal muscle enzyme activities, and fiber types in monozygous and dizygous twins of both sexes. *Acta Physiologica Scandinavica* Supplement 462:1–28, 1979.
79. Komi, P.V., V. Klissouras, and E. Karvinen. Genetic variation in neuromuscular performance. *International Zeitschrift fur angewandte Physiologie einschliesslich Arbeitsphysiologie* 31:289–304, 1973.
80. Kovar, R. Motor performance in twins. *Acta Geneticae Medicae et Geme Illologiae* 24:174, 1975. Cited in Bouchard and Malina, 1983.

158 *PERSPECTIVES IN EXERCISE*

81. Kovar, R. *Human variation in motor abilities and its genetic analysis,* 1981. Prague: Charles University. Cited in Bouchard and Malina, 1983.
82. Kulig, K., J.G. Andrews, and J.G. Hay. Human strength curves. *Exercise and Sport Sciences Reviews* 12:417–466, 1984.
83. Lohman, T.G., M.H. Slaughter, R.G. Boileau, J. Bunt, and L. Lussier. Bone mineral measurements and their relation to body density in children, youth and adults. *Human Biology* 56:667–679, 1984.
84. Lundberg, A., B.O. Ericksson, and G. Mellgren. Metabolic substrates, muscle fiber composition and fiber size in late walking and normal children. *European Journal of Pediatrics* 130:79–92, 1979.
85. MacDougall, J.D., R.D. Bell, and H. Howald. Skeletal muscle ultrastructure and fiber types in prepubescent children. In F.J. Nagle, and H.J. Montoye (eds.). *Exercise In Health And Disease.* Springfield, Il.: Charles C. Thomas Publisher, 1981, 113–117.
86. Maglischo, C.W. Bases of norms for cable-tension strength tests for upper elementary, junior high and senior high school girls. *Research Quarterly* 39:595–603, 1968.
87. Malina, R.M. Quantification of fat muscle and bone in man. *Clinical Orthopaedics and Related Research* 65:9–38, 1969.
88. Malina, R.M. Anthropometric correlates of performance. *Exercise and Sport Sciences Reviews* 3:249–274, 1975.
89. Malina, R.M. Growth of muscle tissue and muscle mass. In F. Falkner, and J.M. Tanner (eds.). *Human Growth. Vol. 2. Postnatal Growth.* New York: Plenum Press, 1978, 273–294.
90. Malina, R.M. Growth of muscle tissue and muscle mass. In F. Falkner, and J.M. Tanner (eds.). *Human Growth. A Comprehensive Treatise. Vol. 2, Postnatal Growth Neurobiology.* New York:Plenum Press, 1986a, 77–99.
91. Malina, R.M. Genetics of motor development and performance. In R.M. Malina and C. Bouchard (eds.). *Sport And Human Genetics.* Champaign, Il.:Human Kinetics, 1986b, pp. 23–58.
92. Malina, R.M. (in press). Growth and maturation: normal variation and the effects of training. In C.V. Gisolfi and D.R. Lamb (eds.). *Perspectives In Exercise Science And Sports Medicine: Volume II Youth Exercise And Sport.* Indianapolis: Benchmark Press.
93. Malina, R.M., and F.E. Johnston. Relations between bone, muscle and fat widths in the upper arms and calves of boys and girls studied cross-sectionally at ages 6 to 16 years. *Human Biology* 39:211–223, 1967.
94. Maresh, M.M. Measurements from roentgenograms, heart size, long bone lengths, bone muscle and fat widths, skeletal maturation. In R.W. McCammon (ed.). *Human Growth and Development.* Springfield, Il.: Charles C. Thomas, 1970, 155–200.
95. Maughan, R.J. Relationship between muscle strength and muscle cross-sectional area. Implications for training. *Sports Medicine* 1:263–269, 1984.
96. Maughan, R.J., J.S. Watson, and J. Weir. Strength and cross-sectional area of human skeletal muscle. *Journal of Physiology* 338:37–49, 1983.
97. McComas, A.J., R.E.P. Sica, and P. Petito. Muscle strength in boys of different ages. *Journal of Neurology, Neurosurgery, and Psychiatry* 36:171–173, 1973.
98. McComas, A.J., and H.C. Thomas. Fast and slow twitch muscle in man. *Journal of the Neurological Sciences* 7:301–307, 1968a.
99. McComas, A.J., and H.C. Thomas. A study of the muscle twitch in the Duchenne type Muscular Dystrophy. *Journal of the Neurological Sciences* 7:309–312, 1986b.
100. Meredith, H.V. The rhythm of physical growth: a study of eighteen anthropometric measurements on Iowa City white males ranging in age between birth and eighteen years. *University of Iowa Study. Studies In Child Welfare.* II:3. 128, 1935. Cited in Metheny, 1941.
101. Merton, P.A. Voluntary strength and fatigue. *Journal of Physiology* (London) 123:553–564, 1954.
102. Matheny, E. The present status of strength testing for children of elementary school and preschool age. *Research Quarterly* 12:115–130, 1941.
103. Miyashita, M., and H. Kanehisa. Dynamic peak torque related to age, sex and performance. *Research Quarterly* 50:249–255, 1979.
104. Mizuno, T. Similarity of physique, muscular strength and motor ability in identical twins. *Bulletin Of The Faculty Of Education. Tokyo University* 1:190–191, 1956. Cited in Bouchard and Malina, 1983.
105. Molnar, G.E., and J. Alexander. Objective, quantitative muscle testing in children: a pilot study. *Archives of Physical Medicine and Rehabilitation* 54:224–228, 1973.
106. Molnar, G.E., J. Alexander, and N. Gutfeld. Reliability of quantitative strength measurements in children. *Archives of Physical Medicine and Rehabilitation* 60:218–221, 1979.
107. Montoye, H.J., and D.E. Lamphier. Grip and arm strength in males and females, age 10 to 69. *Research Quarterly* 48:109–120, 1977.

108. Morris, C.B. The measurement of the strength of muscle relative to the cross-section. *Research Quarterly* 19:295–303, 1948.
109. Nemoto, I., H. Kanehisa, and M. Miyashita. Submitted for publication. The effects of sports training on the age-related changes of body composition and isokinetic peak torque in knee extensors of junior speed skaters.
110. Newton, J.P. and R. Yemm. Changes in the contractile properties of the human first dorsal interosseous muscle with age. *Gerontology* 32:98–104, 1986.
111. Osternig, L.R. Isokinetic dynamometry: implications for muscle testing and rehabilitation. *Exercise and Sport Sciences Reviews* 14:45–80, 1986.
112. Parker, M.G., D. Holt, E. Bauman, M. Drayna, and R.O. Ruhling. Descriptive analysis of bilateral quadriceps and hamstrings muscle torque in high school football players. *Medicine and Science in Sports and Exercise* 14:152, 1982.
113. Rarick, G.L., and J.A.J. Thompson. Roentgenographic measures of leg muscle size and ankle extensor strength of 7-year-old children. *Research Quarterly* 27:321–332, 1956.
114. Rich, G.Q. Muscular fatigue curves of boys and girls. *Research Quarterly* 31:485–498, 1959.
115. Ringqvist, M., I. Ringqvist, and L.-E. Thornelh. Differentiation of fibers in human masseter, temporal and biceps brachii muscles. A histochemical study. *Journal of the Neurological Sciences* 32:265–273, 1977.
116. Royce, J. Use of body components as reference standards for basal metabolic rate. *Research Quarterly* 29:60–73, 1958.
117. Sale, D.G. (in press). Strength training in children. In C.V. Gisolfi and D.R. Lamb (eds.). *Perspective In Exercise Science And Sports Medicine: Volume II Youth Exercise and Sport.* Indianapolis: Benchmark Press.
118. Sale, D.G., J.D. MacDougall, S.E. Alway, and J.R. Sutton. Voluntary strength and muscle characteristics in untrained men and women and male bodybuilders. *Journal of Applied Physiology* 62:1786–1793, 1987.
119. Sale, D.G., and R.W. Norman. Testing strength and power. In J.A. MacDougall, H.A. Wenger, and H.J. Green (eds.). *Physiological Testing of The Elite Athlete.* Ottawa: Mutual Press, 1982, 7–37.
120. Saltin, B., J. Henriksson, E. Nygaard, P. Anderson, and E. Jansson. Fiber types and metabolic potentials of skeletal muscles in sedentary man and endurance runners. *Annals of the New York Academy of Science* 301:3–29, 1977.
121. Saris, W.H.M. Habitual physical activity in children: methodology and findings in health and disease. *Medicine And Science In Sports And Exercise* 18:253–263, 1986.
122. Saris, W.H.M., J.W.H. Elvers, M.A. Van'tHof, and R.A. Binkhorst. Changes in physical activity of children aged 6 to 12 years. In J. Rutenfranz, R. Mocellin, and F. Klimt (eds.). *Children and Exercise. XII.* Champaign, Il.: Human Kinetics, 1986, 121–130.
123. Schlinkman, B. Norms for high school football players derived from Cybex data reduction computor. *The Journal of Orthopaedic and Sports Physical Therapy* 5:243–245, 1984.
124. Scott, O.M., S.A. Hyde, C. Goddard, and V. Dubowitz. Quantitation of muscle function in children: a prospective study in Duchenne Muscular Dystrophy. *Muscle and Nerve* 5:291–301, 1982.
125. Shephard, R.J. *Physical Activity and Growth.* Chicago: Year Book Medical Publishers, 1982.
126. Sklad, M. Rozwoj fizyczny: motorycznosc blizniat. *Materialy i Prace Antropologiczne* 85:3–102, 1973. Cited in Bouchard and Malina, 1983.
127. Slomic, A., A. Rosenfalck, and F. Buchthal. Electrical and mechanical responses of normal and myasthenic muscle. *Brain Research* 10:1–75, 1968.
128. Smedley, F.W. Report of Director of Department of Child-Study and Pedagogic Investigation. *Forty-Sixth Annual Report of the Board of Education. Public Schools of the City of Chicago,* 1900, 280. Cited in Metheny, 1941.
129. Souccar, C., A.J. Lapa, and J.R. do Valle. The influence of testosterone on neuromuscular transmission in hormone sensitive mammalian skeletal muscles. *Muscle And Nerve* 5:232–237, 1982.
130. Stolz, H.R., and L.M. Stolz. *Somatic Development Of Adolescent Boys.* New York: The Macmillan Company, 1951.
131. Tabin, G.C., J.R. Gregg, and T. Bonci. Predictive leg strength values in immediately prepubescent and postpubescent athletes. *The American Journal of Sports Medicine* 13:387–389, 1985.
132. Tanner, J.M. Radiographic studies of body composition in children and adults. *Symposium Of The Society Of Human Biology* 7:211, 1962.
133. Tesch, P., and J. Karlsson. Isometric strength performance and muscle fiber type distribution in man. *Acta Physiologica Scandinavica* 103:47–51, 1978.
134. Thorland, W.G., G.O. Johnson, C.J. Cisar, T.J. Housh, and G.D. Tharp. Strength and anaerobic responses of elite young female sprint and distance runners. *Medicine and Science in Sports and Exercise* 19:56–61, 1987.

160 *PERSPECTIVES IN EXERCISE*

135. Tsunoda, N., S. Ikegawa, H. Yata, M. Kondo, H. Kanehisa, T. Fukunaga, and T. Asami. Structural and functional characteristics of thigh muscle in athletes. In D.A. Winter, R.W. Norman, R.P. Wells, K.C. Hays, and A.E. Patla (eds.). *Biomechanics. International Series on Biomechanics, Vol. 5A.* Champaign, IL.:Human Kinetics, 1985, 15–20.
136. Vos, J.A., W. Geurts, T. Brandon, and R.A. Binkhorst. A longitudinal study of muscular strength and cardiorespiratory fitness in girls (13 to 18 years). In J. Rutenfranz, R. Mocellin, and F. Klimt (eds.). *Children and Exercise. XII.* Champaign, Il.: Human Kinetics, 1986, 233–243.
137. Winter, J.S.D. Prepubertal and pubertal endocrinology. In F. Falkner and J.M. Tanner (eds.). *Human Growth. Vol. 2. Postnatal Growth.* New York: Plenum Press, 1978, 183–213.

DISCUSSION

GONYEA: In measuring specific tension as tension per unit cross-sectional area of the muscle, did you normalize to eliminate connective tissue? It seems like you had a lot of scatter in the data, and I was wondering if the percent of connective tissue or other non-contractile tissues is similar in different age groups of children. If not, such differences certainly would influence the specific tensions.

BLIMKIE: We separated subcutaneous fat and bone from our measurement of lean area, but no, we did not attempt to separate the contractile and noncontractile elements of the lean tissue. All we did here is CAT measurements of the muscle girth, and we didn't attempt to differentiate muscle from connective tissue. This is a very interesting topic to pursue, i.e., how muscle varies in proportion to some of the connective tissues as a child develops and matures to a young adult. It hasn't been done as far as I know on either a cross-sectional or longitudinal basis in children.

GONYEA: It appeared that the young children were not able to activate 100 percent of their motor units. Do you get any feeling that that's a learning process in motor skill development?

BLIMKIE: I am tempted to say yes, but the task which we were utilizing for the assessment of motor unit activation was a fairly nonskilled task. We just asked them to do an isometric maximal voluntary contraction with the elbow flexors and knee extensors. There is not a high level of skill involved in that activity, but it is possible there may have been some learning or skill development phenomena influencing those results.

ROGOL: Peak height velocity is a nice variable to use, but one needs many height measurements because it occurs over such a short period of time. It's very easy to miss; if its slope changes, peak height velocity can change remarkably.

Also we need to remember that some of the androstenedione and other hormones you didn't mention may be precursors to still other hormones. There are complex interrelationships among these hormones.

Finally, CT scanning a group of well children is very difficult, and rightly so, should require approval by institutional human subjects review boards because of the radiation involved. Magnetic resonance imaging should open many avenues of research to use because no radiation is involved. But unfortunately, this technique is very expensive.

BLIMKIE: Peak height velocity is a biological marker I have used to normalize some of the developmental curves, and you do require longitudinal data to make those measurements. What I presented here was simply a summary of information in the literature. In terms of the sex steroid hormones and their possible influence on strength, I just did not have time to address this issue thoroughly in my oral presentation. This issue is discussed, however, in my written chapter. Besides sex steroid hormones though, I think, we should also look at the interplay between sex hormones and the glucocorticoids and the possible antagonism here between anabolic and catabolic states of muscle of the developing child. There are other hormones to consider as well, e.g., growth hormones, somatomedins, etc.

BOUCHARD: Would you comment on the role of genotype in determining differences in muscular strength?

BLIMKIE: You pointed out in some of your work that genotype may influence strength performance. This effect may be totally independent of the quantitative influence of gross muscle size; genotype may also influence strength performance by altering the expression of other traits that are correlated with strength performance, such as size, height, or perhaps lever arms and segmental growth. So there are many different ways in which the genotype may influence strength performance. I think one can certainly see where genotype would influence individual differences, but the precise role of genetic variability in accounting for the population-based the age- and sex-associated variability seen in some of these performance measures remain to be determined.

BLIMKIE: Is there any information, Claude, about the genetic effect on muscle fiber number?

BOUCHARD: Only in animal studies, which show differences for the various strains of rats.

GONYEA: If one looks at the single fiber data in the few studies of animals where specific tension in motor units was recorded, it appears that there is tremendous uniformity. On the other hand, for your data, in which you were recording specific tension per cross-sectional area of muscle, there is tremendous scatter. We need to know the biology behind that scatter.

BLIMKIE: There are technical and ethical constraints which limit our ability to answer this question in children. Do we use invasive, possibly non-ethical, techniques, or do we wait for the development of more sophisticated non-invasive and more ethically acceptable procedures to look at that issue?.

TIPTON: What is the latest information on gender differences in specific strength?

BLIMKIE: There has been some limited work done in that area. Mervin Davies from Nottingham looked at the development of both voluntary and evoked force of the triceps surae muscle groups in relation to muscle cross-sectional area in boys and girls between 9 and 18 to 19 years of age. The boys and girls generally fall on the same line. Obviously, the males will exceed the girls in overall absolute strength because they end up having larger muscles following puberty. I think the early work by Ikai and Fukanawa, which includes boys and girls from the age of 12 or so, showed a similar type of relationship. So per cross-sectional area of the muscle, there appears to be a fairly tight association between the two genders.

4

Strength Training in Children

DIGBY G. SALE, PH.D.

SUMMARY
ACKNOWLEDGEMENTS
BIBLIOGRAPHY
DISCUSSIONS

INTRODUCTION

Training for improved strength by repeatedly overcoming heavy resistance is known as resistance strength training (RST) and is a part of the overall training regimen of most athletes. The term "resistance strength training" refers to common forms of strength training such as weight training (with "free" weights or machines), and calisthenics (using all or some portion of body weight as resistance), as well as training with equipment providing pneumatic (air pressure), hydraulic (oil pressure), and electromechanical resistance. There is evidence that RST can enhance athletic performance and may prevent injuries. Resistance strength training has also become a popular component of recreational fitness programs and has been used successfully to preserve lean body mass during body weight reduction programs. Finally, RST is often used in the rehabilitation of skeletomuscular injuries.

In contrast to the wide age range of people currently involved in all of the above activities, research into the effects of RST has focussed almost entirely on young adults. Prepubescent and pubescent children are involved in all the activities to which RST is applied; therefore, they presumably should derive the same benefits from RST as adults, i.e., increased strength to enhance performance in sport and recreational activities, increased protection against sport injuries, and more rapid recovery and rehabilitation from sport injuries. However, children have been the subject of few studies. Indeed, the practice of RST by children (particularly prepubescent children) is controversial. The controversy is over whether 1) children can make significant gains in strength and muscle mass from RST, 2) the gains improve athletic performance, and 3) children are particularly susceptible to skeletomuscular injuries and other medical problems if they participate in RST.

Resistance strength training is critical for two competitive weightlifting sports: Olympic lifting, which includes the snatch and the clean and jerk lifts, and "power" lifting, which includes the dead lift, squat, and bench press. Training and competition in these sports includes what would be termed high risk movements, i.e., single maximal lifts, overhead lifts, and ballistic efforts against high inertia. These movements carry risk of injury in any age group that does them, but there is controversy about whether children are particularly susceptible to these risks. The American Academy of Pediatrics (1983) and the National Strength and Conditioning Association (1985) have published position statements on RST in children that address the points of controversy.

The purpose of the first part of this chapter is to review the evidence about the effects of RST in prepubescent and pubescent children. Prepubescent children include girls up to the age of 11–12 y and boys up to the age of 13–14 y. Pubescent (adolescent) children are girls aged 12–18 y and boys aged 14–18 y. It will be shown that children can increase voluntary strength after RST and that the increase is similar to that observed in older age groups. ("Voluntary strength" refers to the peak force or torque produced by a single maximal voluntary contraction, measured either on the training equipment or on a strength testing dynamometer. "Power" is the force developed multiplied by the velocity at which it acts.) The issue of whether the increased voluntary strength enhances athletic performance will also be addressed.

Part I will also consider the mechanisms responsible for the increase in voluntary strength after RST; namely, adaptive changes within the muscles and nervous system. The effect of RST on cardiac function and on connective tissue and bone will also be briefly treated (see related chapters in this volume). Part II of the chapter will present guidelines for RST in children and discuss strength training injuries. It will be argued that if the guidelines are followed, the benefit/risk ratio of RST in children is about the same as that in adults. Part III will provide a general summary of the chapter. All three parts of the chapter will address the points of controversy in RST.

I. EFFECTS OF RESISTANCE STRENGTH TRAINING

A. Voluntary Strength

1. Prepubescent Children. Most studies of the effects of RST on voluntary strength in prepubescent children have used weight training as the training mode (McGovern, 1984; Pfeiffer & Francis, 1986; Servedio et al., 1985; Sewall & Micheli, 1986; Vrijens, 1978); however, studies using isometric contractions (Nielsen et al., 1980; Rohmert, 1968), wrestling drills (Clarke et al., 1984), pneumatic machines (Sewall & Micheli, 1986), calisthenics (Siegel et al., 1988), and hydraulic machines (Weltman et al., 1986) have been done also. Control groups are important in training studies with growing children, and most studies have included them. Studies with both girls and boys have been done. To be effective and safe, RST in children must be carefully supervised; several of the studies have emphasized this point. Various methods of measuring voluntary strength have been used, including the training exercises themselves, performance in calisthenics, isometric tests, and isokinetic tests. The training periods have ranged from five to 14 wks. A summary of the results of these studies is given in Table 4-1, and more details of some of the studies are given in Figures 4.1 to 4.5. The general finding of these studies is that prepubescent children increase voluntary strength significantly after RST.

Asmussen (1973) and Vrijens (1978) referred to studies, published in German, showing significant increases in voluntary strength after isometric (Rohmert, 1968) and "dynamic" (Grimm & Raede, 1967) RST in prepubescents. These studies are not included in the table. In the first study (Vrijens, 1978) in Table 4-1, prepubescent children failed to show a significant increase in most of the measures of strength used. This prompted many to question whether prepubescent children were trainable at all. The subsequent studies in Table 4-1 clearly demonstrated that this age group could increase strength. An additional example is the recently completed study at McMaster Univeresity (Ramsay, Blimkie, Sale, MacDougall, & Gardner, unpublished observations), in which 13 prepubescent boys aged 9–11 y weight trained 3 d/wk for 20 wks and increased their voluntary strength significantly (Figure 4.6).

2. Pubescent Children. There is less controversy over whether pubescent children can make significant increases in strength with RST. Several studies have demonstrated increases in voluntary strength in pubescent children after isometric training (De Koning et al., 1984; Nielsen et al., 1980; Rarick & Larsen, 1958; Wolbers & Sills, 1956), weight training (Delorme et al., 1952; Gallagher et al., 1949; Gilliam, 1981; Kusinitz & Keeney, 1958; Pfeiffer & Francis, 1986; Sailors & Berg, 1987; Vrijens, 1978), and stretch-shortening cycle ("plyometric") training (Steben & Steben, 1981). The results of three of these studies have already been presented (see Figures 4.1, 4.2, & 4.3). As further examples, three additional studies are presented in Figures 4.7 to 4.9.

3. Effect of Strength Training on Athletic Performance. Only two studies have examined the effects of RST on athletic performance in prepubescent children. Nevertheless, both isometric (Nielsen et al., 1980; see Figure 4.2) and hydraulic (Weltman et al., 1986; see Figure 4.5) resistance training increased vertical jump performance. In the study by Nielsen et al. (1980) the specificity in strength training observed in adults (Sale & MacDougall, 1981) was also apparent in young girls. Although the girls that did isometric training increased vertical jump performance significantly, an even greater

TABLE 4-1. *Strength Training Studies in Prepubescent Children*

Reference	Training mode	Age y	Sex	Duration wks	Control group?	Strength increase?
Vrijens (1978)[1] (Fig. 4.1)[2]	weights	10.4	M	8	No	No
Nielsen et al. (1980) (Fig. 4.2)	isometric	7–19	F	5	Yes	Yes
Clarke et al. (1984)	wrestling	7–9	M	12	Yes	Yes
McGovern (1984)*	weights	grades 4–6	F, M	12	Yes	Yes
Servedio et al. (1985)*	weights	11.9	M	8	Yes	Yes
Pfeiffer & Francis (1986) (Fig. 4.3)	weights	8–11	M	8	Yes	Yes
Sewall & Micheli (1986) (Fig. 4.4)	weights; pneumatic	10–11	F, M	9	Yes	Yes
Weltman et al. (1986) (Fig. 4.5)	hydraulic	6–11	M	14	Yes	Yes
Siegel et al. (1988)	weights	8.4	F, M	12	Yes	Yes

[1]Studies listed chronologically. [2]Indicates figure in chapter with more details. *abstract.

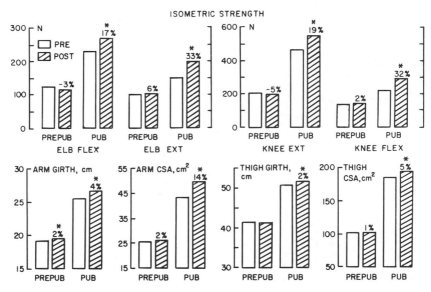

FIGURE 4-1. *Effects of weight training in prepubescent (PREPUB) and pubescent (PUB) boys. Sixteen boys with a mean age of 10.4 y and 12 boys with a mean age of 16.7 y did an "isotonic" (assumed to be weight training) circuit of eight exercises 3 d/wk for 8 wks. Eight to 12 repetitions were done with each exercise with a load corresponding to 75% of the 1 RM (one repetition maximum; i.e., the greatest load that can be used for one repetition). Top: isometric strength of elbow (ELB) and knee flexion (FLEX) and extension (EXT) increased significantly (*) only in the pubescent boys. Bottom: Arm and thigh girth and muscle cross-sectional area (CSA) increased significantly only in the pubescent boys. Percent changes are also indicated. See text for further discussion. Based on Vrijens (1978).*

increase was obtained in a group of girls that trained with jumping drills (specificity in training is discussed in Part II of the chapter). More research is needed on the effects of RST on athletic performance in children. (For a review of the effects of strength training on athletic performance in young adults, see Fleck & Kraemer, 1987.)

4. Comparative Trainability of Children. Some of the studies reviewed above compared the training response in different age groups. The results have varied. Vrijens (1978; Figure 4.1) found that pubescent boys made greater absolute and percentage increases in (voluntary) strength than prepubescent boys. In contrast, Pfeiffer & Francis (1986; Figure 4.3) found that prepubescent boys made greater percentage increases in strength than pubescent boys. Nielsen et al. (1980; Figure 4.2) observed that the youngest of girls aged 7–19 y made percentage strength increases similar to those of the oldest girls. Pubescent males made percentage increases in strength greater than (Pfeiffer & Francis, 1986; Figure 4.3) and similar to (Sail-

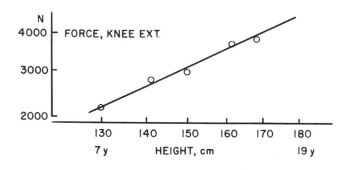

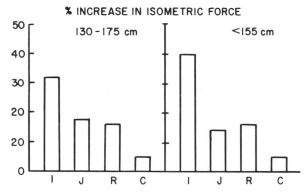

FIGURE 4-2. *Effects of isometric, jump, and sprint training on isometric knee extension strength. Girls aged 7–19 y and ranging in height from 130–175 cm trained either by isometric knee extension contractions (n = 50, 24 contractions per session), jumping (n = 80, 80 jumps per session), or sprinting (n = 75, 10 starts of 100 steps per session). Training sessions occurred 3 d/wk for 5 wks. Top: correlation between height (age) and pretraining isometric knee extension strength. Bottom: the effects of isometric (I, n = 50), jump (J, n = 80), sprint (S, n = 75), and no (C, n = 36) training on isometric knee extension strength (expressed as percentage increases). The results are given for all ages combined (left panel, height range: 130–175 cm) and for the youngest girls (right panel, height <155 cm). All three training groups made greater increases than the control group; however, the group that specifically trained with isometric contractions made the greatest increase, conforming to the often observed specificity in strength training (Sale & MacDougall, 1981). Based on Nielsen et al. (1980).*

ors & Berg, 1987; Figure 4.9) postpubescent males. Figure 4.10 shows the results of recent studies conducted at McMaster University (Hamilton, Ontario), in which prepubescent boys (10 y), young men and women (21 y), and older men (63 y) trained the elbow flexors. All groups trained 3 d/wk. The training lasted 20 wks in the boys and young adults and 12 wks in the older men. The boys and young adults did five sets of 5–12 and 8–12 RM, respectively. The older men did four sets of 10 RM. The young adults and older men trained

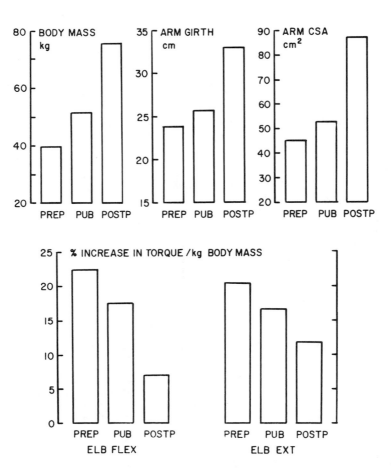

FIGURE 4-3. *Strength training responses in prepubescent (PREP, n = 15, mean [SD] age, 10.3 [1.2] y), pubescent (PUB, n = 15, 13.1 [1.0] y), and postpubescent (POSTP, n = 10, 19.8 [1.2] y) males. Weight training, using free weights and weight stack machines, was done 3 d/wk for 8 wks. Nine exercises were done in three sets at 50, 75, and 100% of the 10 RM. Four of the exercises (knee extension and flexion, bench press, arm curl) were designated primary because they were most specific to the strength tests; namely, knee and elbow flexion and extension strength measured on an isokinetic dynamometer. Strength was measured as the peak torque of concentric contractions done at joint angular velocities of 30 and 120°/s. Top: pretraining values for body mass, arm girth, and arm cross-sectional area (the latter calculated by the author from the reported girth values). Bottom: increases in isokinetic elbow flexion and extension strength after training are shown, averaged across two velocities. The increases were expressed as percentage increases in torque per kilogram body mass. The absolute (N.m) or relative (N.m/kg) pre- and post-training strength values were not reported. Overall, the three training groups made significant increases in strength relative to the corresponding control groups. The results in the training groups are shown in the figure (bottom panel). Elbow flexion and extension only are shown (knee extension and flexion showed the same pattern of results), and the increases at the two velocities have been averaged. Based on Pfeiffer & Francis (1986).*

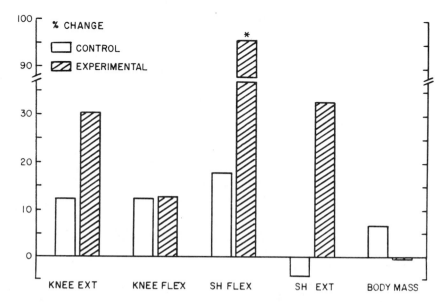

FIGURE 4-4. *Effects of weight and pneumatic resistance training on isometric strength in eight boys and two girls (seven boys and one girl served as a control group), aged 10–11 years. Training was done on a weight machine (knee extension) and two pneumatic machines (chest press, rowing) 3 d/wk for 9 wks. Three sets of 10 repetitions at 50, 80, and 100% of the 10 RM of each exercise were done. The experimental (trained) group made a significantly (*) greater increase in shoulder flexion strength than the control group. The actual absolute pre- and posttraining strength values in the groups were not reported. See text for discussion. Based on Sewall & Micheli (1986).*

on the same weight stack machines, whereas the boys trained on a different machine suitable to their smaller size. Thus, the training programs for the groups were similar, except for the eight-week shorter training period in the older men. Figure 4.10 shows the strength results as measured on the training device (left) and on an isokinetic (middle) and isometric (right) dynamometer. Expressing the training-induced increase in strength on an absolute basis (middle panels) tended to favor the young men, who had the greatest absolute strength. In contrast, expressing the increase as a percentage (bottom panels) tended to favor the boys, who had the smallest absolute strength (see also the comparison between pubescent and postpubescent males in Figure 4.9). Regardless of how the increases are expressed, however, the prepubescent boys were "competitive" in their training response.

There is an issue concerning the "fairest" way (absolute vs. percentage) to express and compare training-induced increases in strength. On the one hand, a given absolute increase in strength

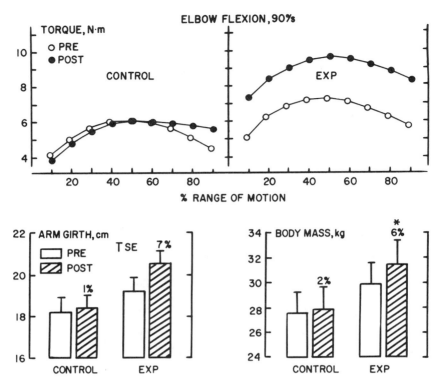

FIGURE 4-5. *Effects of hydraulic resistance training in prepubescent boys, aged 6–11 y. The exercises done, 3 d/wk for 14 wks, included elbow flexion/extension, bench press, hip adduction/abduction, shoulder horizontal flexion ("butterfly"), forearm conditioner, and jump squat. The exercises were arranged in a circuit that was done three times in a 45 min session. Each exercise consisted of doing as many repetitions as possible in 30 s. Sit-ups and stationary cycling were also included in the circuit. Two distinguishing features of hydraulic RST—in comparison to weight training, calisthenics, and pneumatic RST—are the absence of eccentric contractions and the feasibility of doing alternate, reciprocal contractions of opposing (agonist/antagonist) muscle groups at a joint. Strength was measured on an isokinetic dynamometer as the average torque and work output at two velocities (30 and 90°/s) in knee and elbow flexion/extension. Top: the trained (EXP) group increased isokinetic strength significantly (right panel) through the range of movement, whereas the control group did not (left panel). Pre- (unfilled symbols) and posttraining (filled symbols) values are shown. Bottom: the trend for a greater increase in arm girth in the trained group was not significant (left), but this group did gain significantly (*) more body mass. Based on Weltman et al. (1986).*

represents a smaller percentage increase in an older age group with greater initial absolute strength, and therefore a comparison of percentage increases favors the younger age group. On the other hand, it may not be fair to expect a younger age group, that may have less than half the absolute strength of an older age group, to make an absolute increase similar to that of an older age group. The issue is not easily resolved.

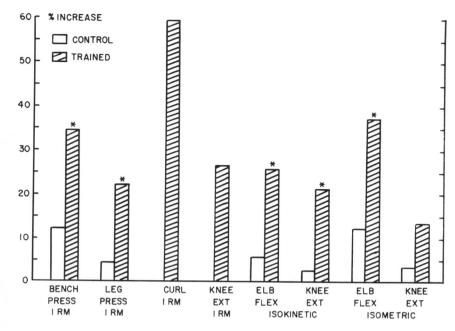

FIGURE 4-6. *Effects of weight training (3 d/wk for 20 wks) on weightlifting strength (1 RM) and or isokinetic and isometric strength in 13 prepubescent boys (9–11 y). The exercises, using weight stack machines, included primary exercises (arm curl, knee extension) done for five sets of 10–12 RM for 10 wks and five sets of 5–7 RM for 10 wks, and secondary exercises (leg press, bench press, lat pulldown, and sit-ups) done for three sets of 10–12 RM for 10 weeks and three sets of 5–7 RM for 10 wks. Percent increases in strength in the control and trained groups are shown. The control group was not tested for arm curl and knee extension 1 RM. In the other measurements, the trained group made significantly (*) greater increases except for isometric knee extension. Based on unpublished observations by Ramsay et al., Human Performance Laboratory, Department of Physical Education, McMaster University.*

A final issue is whether it is possible to give children and adults the same training stimulus in order to compare the training response. It is not difficult to equate training frequency and duration, or the number of sets and repetitions. However, equating "intensity" of training might be considered a problem. Intensity of effort can be equated by asking all groups to make maximal efforts in training. If it can be assumed that children can achieve the same degree of motor unit activation as adults during maximal effort (see next section), then the training stimulus would be equated for muscle activation. Tension development within the muscle would also have to be equated. Children, because of their smaller muscle size and absolute strength (Figure 4.11, top and middle panels), must use a much smaller absolute training resistance or load than adults. With all other factors equivalent, it is not possible to equate absolute

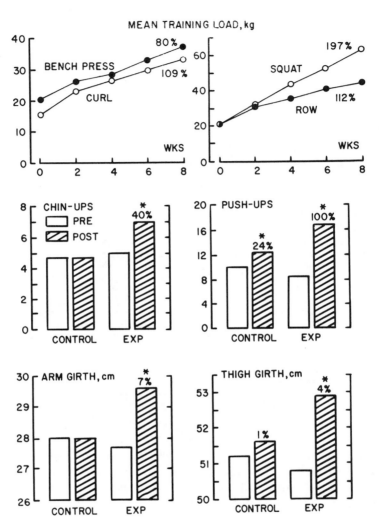

FIGURE 4-7. *Effects of weight training in 22 adolescent (12–17 y) boys. Weight training was done 3 d/wk for 8 wks. The squat, shoulder press, curl, pullover, and sit-up free weight exercises were done for one to three sets of 8–12 repetitions in each training session. Top: the training group (EXP) made progressive increases in training load in the training exercises (filled symbols, bench press and row; unfilled symbols, curl and squat) during the 8 wk training period. Middle: the trained group made significantly greater increases in chin-ups (left) and push-ups (right), although the control group also made a significant (*) increase in push-ups. Bottom: only the trained group increased arm and thigh girth. Based on Kusinitz & Keeney (1958).*

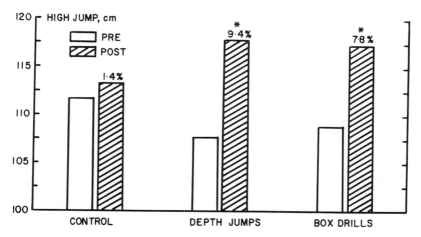

FIGURE 4-8. *Effect of "plyometric" (depth jumps, box drills) training on high jump performance in 7th and 8th grade boys and girls. One hundred and sixty girls and boys were placed into the following groups (20 girls and 20 boys in each): 1) control; 2) trained by depth jumps from a 25.4 cm platform; 3) trained with box drills, i.e., jumping over and on and off 25.4 cm high boxes; 4) trained with hopping, bounding, and high knee action movements. Training was done 10 min/d, 5 d/wk for 7 wks. Before and after the training period, all subjects were tested in the high, long, and triple jump. The figure shows the pre- and posttest high jump results in the control group (left) and in groups that trained with depth jumps (middle) and box drills (right). The two training groups made significant (*) increases in high jump performance. Based on Steben & Steben (1981).*

tension development. It may not matter, however, because the stimulus to the muscle is probably more related to tension developed per unit muscle cross-sectional area. It can be seen in the bottom panel of Figure 4.11 that children can develop, during maximal voluntary contractions, about the same force per unit muscle cross-sectional area as adults, despite large differences in absolute strength and muscle size. Thus, it seems possible to equate the training stimulus in children and adults.

5. Mechanisms of Increase in Voluntary Strength. Voluntary strength is determined by the cross-sectional area and "specific tension" of the involved muscles, and by the ability of the central nervous system to fully activate the muscles. Further, expression of voluntary strength can be likened to a skilled act, i.e., prime mover muscles must be fully activated and synergists and antagonists appropriately activated to coordinate the movement. It follows that increases in voluntary strength after RST could be the result of a combination of "neural" adaptations, i.e., an increased ability to activate and coordinate the relevant muscles, and "muscular" adaptations, i.e., an increase in muscle size and specific tension (force

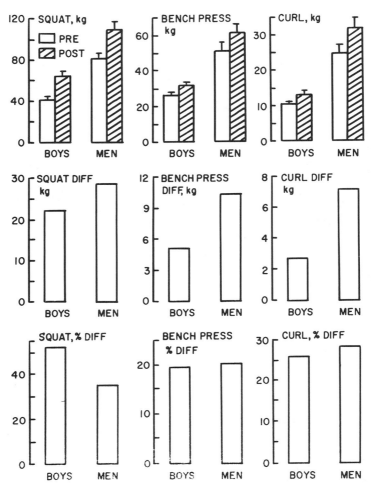

FIGURE 4-9. *Effects of weight training in five adolescent boys (12.6 y) and five young men (24 y). Three sets (65, 85, and 100% of the 5 RM) of the squat, bench press, and arm curl free weight exercises were done 3 d/wk for 8 wks. Strength/endurance was measured as the 5 RM in the training exercises. There were no significant changes in these measures in the six boys and six men who served as control subjects. Top: pre- and posttraining values for the 5 RM in the squat, bench press, and arm curl exercises are shown. Both groups made significant increases in all exercises. Middle: the absolute increases in the 5 RM are shown. Bottom: the percent increases in the 5 RM are shown. Note that the men tended to make greater absolute increases than the boys, but the boys made similar percent increases. Based on Sailors & Berg (1987).*

per unit muscle cross-sectional area). A suggested scheme for the relative roles of neural and muscular adaptation during the course of training is presented in Figure 4.12 (for a review of the relative roles of neural and muscular adaptation, see Komi, 1986, and Sale,

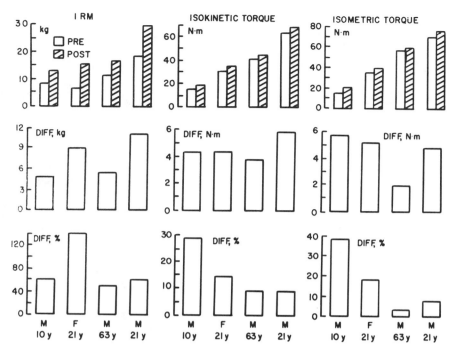

FIGURE 4-10. *Effects of weight training on elbow flexion 1 RM (weight training exercise), isokinetic torque, and isometric torque in prepubescent boys (M, 10 y), young women (F, 21 y), older men (M, 63 y), and young men (M, 21 y). Top: pre- and post-measurements are shown. In the 1 RM test the boys used a different machine than the adults; consequently, the boys' 1 RM values are higher than would be expected. All groups were tested on the same isokinetic and isometric dynamometers. Middle: the absolute increases in strength after training are shown. Bottom: the percent increases in strength after training are shown. The boys were "competitive" in their training response, compared with the older age groups, particularly when the results are expressed as percent increases. See text for further discussion. Based on unpublished observations from the Human Performance Laboratory, department of physical education, McMaster University.*

1986, 1987). In the early stage of training, which is the stage that most training studies have focussed on, neural adaptation or perhaps some qualitative change in muscle predominates. After several weeks, obvious muscular adaptation, in the form of hypertrophy, begins to occur. In the advanced stages of training, muscular adaptation predominates, and progress is limited to the extent to which the muscles can be made to hypertrophy.

Is the relative importance of neural and muscular adaptation the same in children (particularly prepubescent children) and adults? It is possible, for example, that prepubescent children cannot activate their muscles as well as adults in the untrained state and, therefore,

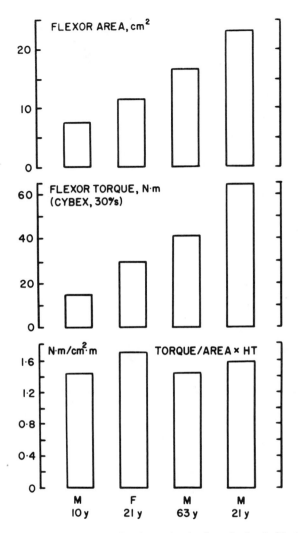

FIGURE 4-11. *Elbow flexor cross-sectional area (top), elbow flexion isokinetic torque (30°/s) (middle), and elbow flexion torque expressed per unit of the product of flexor cross-sectional area and body height (expressed in meters) (bottom) in prepubescent boys (M, 10 y), young women (F, 21 y), older men (M, 63 y), and young men (M, 21 y). There are large differences among the groups in absolute flexor area and flexor torque, and the correlation between flexor area and torque is evident. An estimate of "specific tension" (i.e., force per unit muscle cross-sectional area) can be made by dividing the absolute torque by the product of muscle cross-sectional area and an estimate of muscle lever arm length (assumed to be proportional to body height). Although the boys have a relatively small muscle size and absolute strength, their voluntary "specific tension" is similar to the older age groups. Based on unpublished observations from the Human Performance Laboratory, department of physical education, McMaster University.*

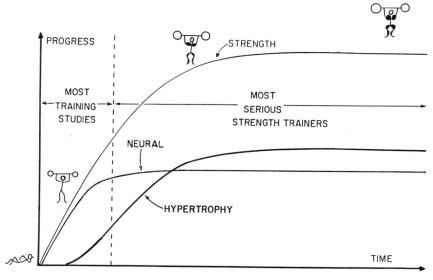

FIGURE 4-12. *Relative roles of neural and muscular adaptation in strength training. In the early phase of training, which may cover a period of several weeks, neural adaptation plays its biggest role. This is also the period covered by most published training studies. Later on, muscular adaptation predominates, and progress is largely limited to the extent to which the muscles can be made to hypertrophy.*

have more potential for strength increases due to neural adaptation. On the other hand, adults may have more potential for increasing muscle size. On the issue of whether children can activate their muscles as fully as adults, Figure 4.13 shows the results of a technique called the interpolated twitch (Belanger & McComas, 1981) that is used to determine the extent of motor unit activation during maximal voluntary contractions. The method consists of superimposing, during a maximal voluntary contraction, a single supramaximal electrical stimulus to the nerves supplying the involved muscles. Motor units not activated by voluntary effort will respond to the stimulus by producing an increment on the force recording. The smaller the increment, the greater the degree of activation by voluntary effort. In isometric knee extension, a group of prepubescent (10 y) boys had about 10% less motor unit activation than a group of young men and women, but about 10% more activation than a group of middle-aged women. In elbow flexion, the difference between the boys and a group of older men was only 5% in favor of the men, whereas the boys were a few percentage points higher than the middle-aged women. In two other muscle groups,

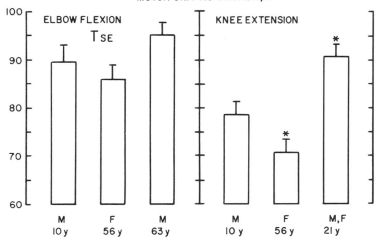

FIGURE 4-13. *Extent of motor unit activation in boys (M, 10 y), middle aged women (F, 56 y), older men (M, 63 y), and young men and women (M, F, 21 y), as estimated by the interpolated twitch technique. In elbow flexion (left), the boys have the same level of activation as the older men and women. In knee extension, the boys have significantly less activation than the young adults but significantly greater activation than the older women. See text for discussion. Based on unpublished observations from the Human Performance Laboratory, department of physical education, McMaster University.*

older men and women have demonstrated the same motor unit activation as younger adults (Vandervoort & McComas, 1986). More data on this issue are needed; however, the data in Figure 4.13 indicate that children have close to the same motor unit activation ability as adults.

The issue of whether prepubescent children can increase muscle mass is raised more often. One argument is that a sufficient level of male sex hormone is necessary for training-induced increases in muscle mass. Up to the age of puberty in the male, the level of androgens is too low to promote muscle hypertrophy (Figure 4.14). Trainability increases rapidly during puberty as the serum androgen levels increase markedly. During this period, strength increases rapidly in the male in comparison with the female, even without training (top panel in Figure 4.14). Throughout life, females face difficulty in achieving the same absolute values as males for muscle mass and strength because of low levels of male sex hormones.

The extent of muscular and neural adaptation in prepubescent and pubescent children will be addressed in the next three sections.

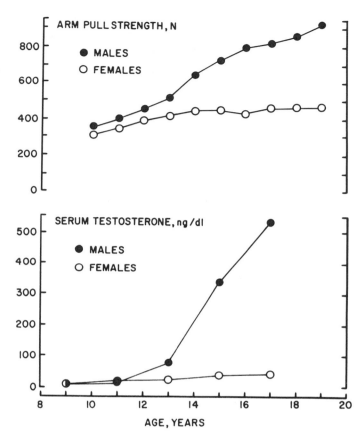

FIGURE 4-14. *Changes in arm pull strength (based on Montoye & Lamphiear, 1977) and serum testosterone (based on Winter, 1978) with age in males and females. Upper limb strength appears to increase markedly in the males, relative to the females, at the same time (i.e., age range) as the serum testosterone increases markedly in the males. See text for discussion in relation to trainability.*

B. Evoked Contraction Strength

One measure of muscular adaptation is evoked contraction strength; that is, the contraction force produced by electrical stimulation of muscle rather than by voluntary effort. Any increase in evoked contraction strength observed after RST could be attributed to adaptive changes in the muscles. By comparison, increases in voluntary strength could be due wholly or partly to neural adaptation.

The best measure of evoked contraction strength would be the force produced by maximal tetanic stimulation at the optimal frequency for force generation. This procedure is quite painful, however, and its use is therefore limited, particularly in children. In contrast, a single maximal stimulus is acceptable to most subjects, including children, and the maximal twitch contraction evoked by the single stimulus can thus be used as a measure of evoked contraction strength.

In Figure 4.15, peak twitch torque of elbow flexion and knee extension is shown before and after 20 wks of weight training in

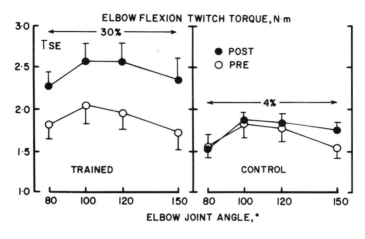

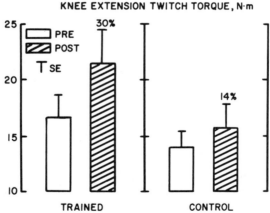

FIGURE 4-15. *Effects of weight training on evoked isometric twitch contraction torque in prepubescent boys (9–11 y). Top: elbow flexion twitch torque increased by an average of 30% (significant) over the joint angles tested in the training group (left), whereas twitch torque did not increase significantly in the control group. Bottom: knee extension twitch torque (measured at one joint angle, 90°) increased significantly (30%) only in the trained group. Based on unpublished observations from the Human Performance Laboratory, department of physical education, McMaster University.*

the prepubescent boys described earlier in connection with Figure 4.6. Peak twitch torque increased significantly. In Figure 4.16 the results for elbow flexion in the boys are compared with those for young men and women (described earlier in connection with Figure

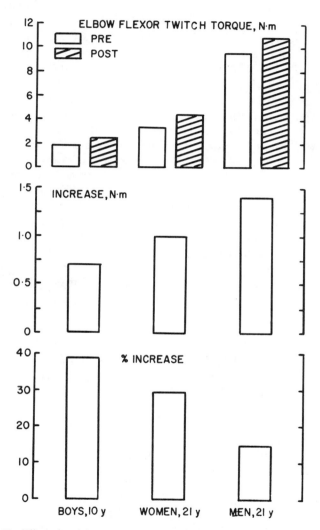

FIGURE 4-16. *Effect of weight training on elbow flexor evoked isometric twitch torque in prepubescent boys and young men and women. Top: absolute pre- and posttraining values. Middle: absolute increases in twitch torque. Bottom: percent increases in twitch torque. The boys made the smallest absolute but largest percent increases in torque. See text for further discussion. Based on unpublished observations from the Human Performance Laboratory, department of physical education, McMaster University.*

4.10) who did a similar training program. All three groups made significant increases in twitch torque. The young men, who had the greatest absolute torque, made the largest absolute increase in torque, whereas the boys, who had the smallest absolute torque, made the largest percentage increase in torque. When both absolute and percentage increases are weighed, the boys responded similarly to the young adults. To the author's knowledge, these are the only evoked contraction data in children before and after strength training.

An increase in twitch torque might be interpreted as an increase in contractile force of the involved muscles. This is not the only possible interpretation, however. A single stimulus (in comparison to a train of stimuli at high frequency) does not fully activate the contractile elements; therefore, a twitch contraction is not a true representation of maximal contraction strength. It is possible that twitch torque could increase after training without a corresponding increase in tetanic torque, the latter a true representation of contraction strength. This result could occur, for example, if training caused a change in excitation-contraction coupling such that the "active state" was more intense or prolonged in response to a single stimulus. Such a change would increase twitch but not tetanic force; the twitch/tetanus ratio would increase. Therefore, an increase in twitch torque is an equivocal indication of increased contractile force. Nevertheless, an increase in twitch torque as observed in Figures 4.15 & 4.16 indicates some form of adaptation within the muscles in response to training.

C. Muscle Size

Only two published studies have examined the effect of RST on muscle size in prepubescent boys (Vrijens, 1978; Weltman et al., 1986). The details of these studies were given above in the section on voluntary strength. Vrijens (1978; see also Figure 4.1) found no increase in arm or leg girth and cross-sectional area (soft tissue X-ray) after eight wks of weight training. Weltman et al. (1986; see also Figure 4.5) found only a trend of an increase in arm girth after 14 wks of hydraulic resistance training; however, there was a significant increase in body mass in the trained group.

In a recent study done at McMaster University, prepubescent boys trained with weights for 20 wks (the same study described in previous sections and depicted in Figures 4.6, 4.10, 4.11, 4.13, 4.15, and 4.16). Elbow flexor and knee extensor cross-sectional area (computerized tomography scanning method) did not increase significantly (Figure 4.17). In one other study published in abstract form (McGovern, 1984), 12 wks of weight training failed to cause an increase in limb girth.

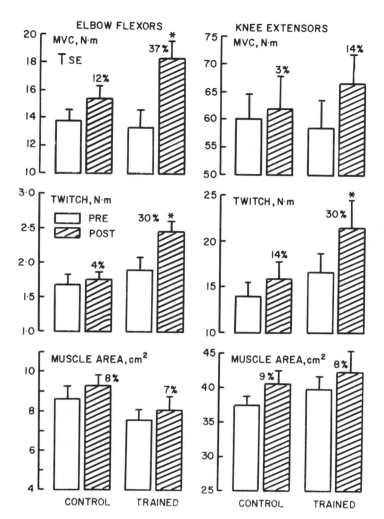

FIGURE 4-17. *Effect of weight training on elbow flexor (left) and knee extensor (right) voluntary isometric strength (top), evoked isometric twitch contraction strength (middle), and muscle cross-sectional area (bottom) in prepubescent boys (9–11 y). The trained group did not increase muscle cross-sectional area significantly, relative to the control group, despite significantly greater increases in voluntary and evoked contraction strength. See text for further discussion. Based on unpublished observations from the Human Performance Laboratory, department of physical education, McMaster University.*

The lack of increase in muscle size found by Vrijens (1978) was also associated with no significant increase in isometric voluntary strength (Figure 4.1). In contrast, Weltman et al. (1986; Figure 4.5) and the McMaster study (Figure 4.17) found a lack of muscle size increase associated with a significant increase in voluntary strength. This latter finding is not unique to prepubescent boys in short-term training experiments; for example, in the study depicted in Figure 4.9, pubescent and postpubescent males increased voluntary strength but not limb girth. Finally, the McMaster study (Figure 4.17) found no increase in muscle cross-sectional area despite a significant increase in evoked twitch contraction strength.

In relation to increases in muscle size, only one published study has compared the training response in prepubescent boys and older age groups. Vrijens (1978; Figure 4.1) found that whereas prepubescent boys failed to increase isometric strength and muscle size, pubescent boys increased in both (as has been shown in studies of pubescent boys alone; e.g., Delorme et al., 1952; Kusinitz & Keeney, 1958 [see Figure 4.7]). In Figure 4.18 the effects of a weight training program similar to that employed by Vrijens are compared in prepubescent boys (10 y), young men and women (21 y), and older men (63 y). The striking finding is the boys' relatively poor increase in muscle size in comparison to the other groups. On the other hand, the boys did relatively well on increases in voluntary and even evoked twitch contraction strength. More studies are needed, but it would appear on the basis of the presently available evidence that prepubescent boys (and perhaps girls) have more difficulty increasing muscle mass by RST than older age groups.

The reason for the difficulty that prepubescent boys have in gaining muscle mass by RST is not clear. The possible impediment of low serum androgen levels in this age group has been discussed above (see also Figure 4.14). If this was the only problem, females of all ages might be expected to share the difficulty in increasing muscle mass. It is clear in Figure 4.18, however, that young adult women at least are quite capable of increasing muscle mass. The possibility that children cannot activate their muscles as well as older adults was also discussed above; children can activate their muscles as well as or almost as well as older age groups (Figure 4.13). If the stimulus to muscle hypertrophy is related to specific tension (force per unit cross-sectional area) developed during contraction, then again children are similar to older adults (Figure 4.11). This topic requires further study, both to confirm the apparent impairment of muscle mass increases in prepubescent children, and to discover the reason, or reasons, for the impairment if it does in fact exist.

A puzzling finding in the study shown in Figure 4.17 is the significant increase in evoked twitch contraction strength without a corresponding increase in muscle cross-sectional area. Two interpretations are possible. One is that specific tension increased as a result of training. This would contribute to the increased voluntary

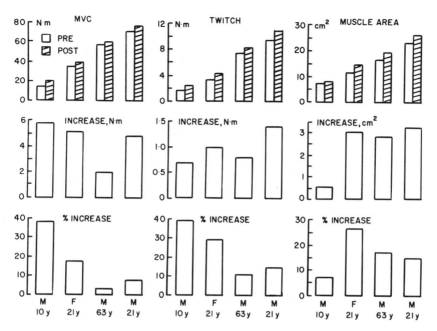

FIGURE 4-18. *Effect of weight training on elbow flexor voluntary isometric strength (left), evoked isometric twitch contraction strength (center), and muscle cross-sectional area (right) in prepubescent boys (M, 10 y), young women (F, 21 y), older men (M, 63 y), and young men (M, 21 y). Pre/post values (top), absolute increases (middle), and percent increases (bottom) are shown. The boys were quite "competitive" with the older age groups in making increases in voluntary and evoked contraction strength. In contrast, the boys alone were unable to increase muscle cross-sectional area significantly. See text for further discussion. Based on unpublished observations from the Human Performance Laboratory, department of physical education, McMaster University.*

strength observed. A second interpretation is that maximal contractile force (as would be revealed by tetanic stimulation) did not increase; rather, the twitch/tetanus ratio increased secondary to an adaptation in excitation-contraction coupling. Further studies are needed to evaluate these interpretations.

D. Neural Adaptation

Training-induced neural adaptation refers to increased ability to activate prime mover muscles and/or improved coordination of synergists and antagonists. The result is increased force in the intended direction of movement. Increased activation of prime movers has received the most attention in training studies. Electromyographic techniques have been used to monitor increases in motor unit activation. Some, but not all, studies using these techniques in adults have shown an increase in motor unit activation (for reviews, see Komi, 1986, & Sale, 1986, 1987). There are no comparable studies in children.

Another method of determining motor unit activation, the interpolated twitch technique, was illustrated in Figure 4.13 (see also the section above on Mechanisms of Increase in Voluntary Strength). This technique was applied in the McMaster boys training study (Figure 4.19). There was a trend for motor unit activation to increase in the trained group, but this was not a significant increase. It will be recalled that these boys made significant increases in voluntary strength and evoked twitch contraction strength, but not in muscle size (Figure 4.18). The technique was also used on the older men shown in Figure 4.18; they did not increase their already high level of motor unit activation (see also Figure 4.13).

There is other indirect evidence of neural adaptation in response to RST. The evidence in adults includes increases in voluntary strength without increases in muscle size (although an increase in specific tension cannot always be ruled out) and evoked

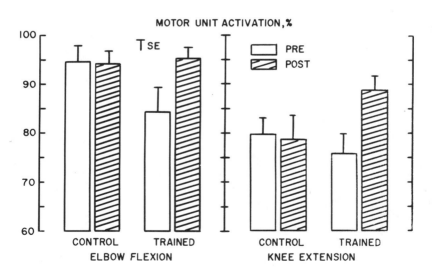

FIGURE 4-19. *Effect of weight training on extent of motor unit activation during maximal voluntary isometric contractions of elbow flexion (left) and knee extension (right). Motor unit activation was estimated by the interpolated twitch method. The trend of increases in the trained group was not significant. See text for further discussion. Based on unpublished observations from the Human Performance Laboratory, department of physical education, McMaster University.*

contraction strength, and specificity in the voluntary strength increases, including movement pattern, contraction type, and contraction velocity (for a review, see Sale, 1986, 1987).

There is similar evidence in the studies done with children. One example of specificity is in Figure 4.2. The girls were trained with isometric contractions and, in accordance with specificity, made their greatest strength increase in the isometric test. Another group of girls (not shown) who trained by jumping made their greatest increase in the jump test. A second example of specificity is in Figure 4.6. The boys made the greatest increase in elbow flexion strength in the test corresponding to the training mode, the 1 RM on the training machine. Smaller increases occurred in the less specific isometric and isokinetic tests. It should be noted that, although specificity is evident in these two examples, the specificity is not absolute. There is some transfer to related movements. (The interpretation that transfer has occurred assumes that there has been no increase in muscle sizes or specific tension.) Therefore, an increase in nonspecifically measured voluntary strength does not necessarily indicate "true strength gains" exclusive of neural adaptation, as some have argued (Sewall & Micheli, 1986). An example of an increase in voluntary strength in children without an increase in muscle size is shown in Figure 4.17.

At present, there is no evidence that children behave differently than older age groups in neural adaptation to RST.

E.   Cardiac Function and Dimensions

Blood pressure increases to much higher levels during high resistance exercise (MacDougall et al., 1985) than during "aerobic" exercise (Robinson et al., 1988). It is not known if similarly high blood pressures occur in children during resistance exercise, although one recent report (Nau et al., 1988) suggests that the pressures may not be as high. It might be expected that cardiac muscle would respond to a regularly imposed high resistance (pressure) load in the same way as skeletal muscle often does—by undergoing hypertrophy. Although the results have not been uniformly consistent, cross-sectional data (Brown et al., 1983; Keul et al., 1981; Longhurst et al., 1980; Menapace et al., 1982; Morganroth et al., 1975; Salke et al., 1985) and longitudinal studies (Knakis & Hickson, 1980; Ricci et al., 1982) in adults indicate that cardiac hypertrophy may occur in response to RST. No corresponding studies in children have been published; however, one abstract reported that eight wks of Olympic weightlifting did not cause cardiac hypertrophy in six prepubescent boys (Servedio et al., 1985). In the McMaster boys training study (e.g., Figure 4.17), cardiac hypertrophy did not occur after 20 wks of weight training. By late adolescence (18 y) cardiac hypertrophy seems to be possible, as indicated by a preliminary report of a cross-sectional study involving Junior Olympic weight lifters (Fleck et al., 1988). Further studies are needed, but an interesting question is whether prepubescent boys have the same difficulty in inducing cardiac hypertrophy as they seem to have in inducing skeletal muscle hypertrophy (e.g., Figure 4.18).

Although blood pressure reaches high levels during resistance exercise, this form of exercise does not cause chronically elevated resting blood pressure. Some early cross-sectional studies showed borderline hypertension in bodybuilders (Spitler et al., 1980) and a powerlifter (Staron et al., 1981). However, many of the athletes tested in these studies were consuming anabolic steroids, which are associated with elevated blood pressure (Colliander & Tesch, 1988). Other studies have shown normal resting blood pressure in strength-trained athletes (Colliander & Tesch, 1988; Longhurst et al., 1980; MacDougall et al., 1985). Longitudinal strength training studies have shown no effect (Allen et al., 1976) or a small but significant decrease in resting blood pressure in normotensive men (Fahey et al., 1975; Hurley et al., 1988; Stone et al., 1983). Hydraulic resistance training caused no change in resting blood pressure in prepubescent children (Rians et al., 1987), and weight training caused a decreased resting blood pressure in borderline hypertensive adolescent boys (Hagberg et al., 1984).

A favorable effect of exercise on blood cholesterol levels is usually associated with low resistance aerobic training that causes an increase in maximal aerobic power and a decrease in body fat. Nevertheless, weight training itself will cause a decrease in total and LDL cholesterol and an increase in HDL cholesterol, without causing an increase in aerobic power or a decrease in body fat (Hurley et al., 1988). Other longitudinal studies have shown a beneficial effect of RST on the blood cholesterol profile (Goldberg et al., 1984; Johnson et al., 1982), including one study in prepubescent boys (Weltman et al., 1987). The high volume RST (many sets and repetitions with short rest periods) done by bodybuilders seems to be more beneficial for the blood profile than the low volume RST (few sets and repetitions with long rest periods) done by weightlifters (Hurley et al., 1984). On the other hand, the use of anabolic steroids can reverse the effect of training and cause a poor blood profile (Hurley et al., 1984), and may be responsible for the poor profiles that have been observed in other weight-trained athletes (Clarkson et al., 1981; Farrell et al., 1982). Additional studies of the effects of RST on the blood profile of children are needed.

F. Tendons, Ligaments, and Bone

There are no studies in humans on tendon and ligament adaptation to RST. Animal research (see the brief review by Fleck & Kraemer, 1987, pp. 172–173) does suggest that tendons and ligaments become stronger in response to increased mechanical loading. For example, a recent study showed that increased mechanical loading caused more rapid maturation of growing tendon (Curwin et al., 1988).

There are also few studies of the effects of RST on bone in children. Larson (1973) cited Ivanitsky (1962), who found the radius in (11–13 y) tennis players to be larger than that of swimmers and gymnasts. The tennis players also had a larger right than left radius (see also studies in adult tennis players, e.g., Montoye et al., 1980; Pirnay et al., 1987). In adults, there is evidence that bone density is greater in strength-trained than in endurance-trained athletes (Lane et al., 1988; Nilsson & Westlin, 1971; Westfall et al., 1988). A recent longitudinal study has indicated the effectiveness of RST for increasing bone density in adult women (Chow et al., 1987; for a recent review on exercise and bone, see Smith & Gilligan, 1987). Now that safe measurement of bone density is readily available, future studies will no doubt examine the effects of RST and other forms of training on bone density in children.

G. Summary

There is increasing interest in the effects of RST on children and especially on prepubescent children, because children are increasingly involved in activities to which RST has been applied. To date, the number of studies on the topic is small. The available evidence indicates that prepubescent children are quite capable of increasing voluntary strength in response to RST. In comparison with pubescent children and older age groups, however, prepubescent children experience more difficulty in increasing skeletal muscle mass. On the other hand, there is evidence of some form of adaptation in the muscles of children, based on measurements of evoked contractile properties. Current evidence shows that children exhibit the same types of neural adaptation as adults.

Even fewer studies have addressed cardiac and connective tissue adaptation to RST in prepubescent and older children. More studies are needed to determine whether the adaptations seen in adults also occur in children. In particular, it will be interesting to learn if children share with adults the beneficial effects of RST on blood pressure and blood "profile," benefits that until recently were only associated with aerobic exercise.

Based on the conclusion that children can adapt and derive benefit from RST, Part II of the chapter will present guidelines for RST in children.

II. STRENGTH TRAINING FOR CHILDREN

The focus of this part of the chapter will be training guidelines for prepubescent children, because strength training in this age group is a subject of controversy and concern. Some consideration will be given to pubescent (mid- and late adolescent) children; however, this group can for the most part be treated the same way as young adults. The principles of training will be presented first, followed by various aspects of program design. Finally, a section will be devoted to strength training injuries and their prevention.

A. Principles of Training

1. Overload. The term "overload" (Hellebrandt & Houtz, 1956) refers to an exercise task that requires considerable voluntary effort to complete. A maximal overload requires maximal voluntary effort. In strength training, two goals are 1) to learn to activate prime mover muscles fully and to coordinate antagonists and synergists, and 2) to induce hypertrophy in all of the muscle fibers that can contribute force in the intended direction of movement. Maximal overload achieves the first goal by repeated maximal or near maximal efforts in the training. The second goal is achieved only when all the appropriate muscle fibers are active in the exercise, as occurs in the full motor unit activation associated with maximal overload.

Maximal overload can be achieved in two ways: 1) by doing brief maximal contractions, or 2) by doing submaximal contractions to fatigue failure (i.e., until no more repetitions can be done with a given load, or until a given force of contraction can be maintained no longer). In the second way, full motor unit activation does not occur at the beginning of exercise; rather, activation increases as fatigue develops and may be complete at the point of fatigue failure.

The two methods of overload can be applied with the common resistance training modes. Thus, in isometric strength training, the trainee can do a series of brief maximal contractions, a sustained submaximal contraction, or a series of submaximal (e.g., at 50% of maximal force) contractions to failure. In weight training (or using pneumatic resistance machines), the trainee can do single maximal repetitions or lifts (each called a "one repetition maximum", 1 RM) or as many repetitions as possible with a fraction of the 1 RM (e.g., 80% 1 RM). A comparatively recent training mode is the "accommodating resistance" device (e.g., Cybex, Orthotron, Hydra-Gym, Kin/Com, Biodex, Ariel, Merrac). These devices have a mechanism (e.g., hydraulic) that provides resistance that precisely matches the force applied by the trainee. Some devices limit velocity of movement to a more or less constant preset value, hence the term "isokinetic" (Perrine, 1968). These devices allow both methods of overload to be applied, but training usually consists of a series of maximal contractions at a preset speed. The two ways of applying maximal overload with the different training modes are shown in Figure 4.20.

One difference between weight (and pneumatic resistance) training and isometric or isokinetic training is that the former most commonly uses the second method of overload (submaximal contractions to fatigue), whereas the latter two most commonly use the first method (series of maximal contractions). In weight training, therefore, the percentage of maximal strength (% 1 RM) to be used in training must be determined. Figure 4.21 shows, for two common weight training exercises, the number of repetitions that can be done with various percentages of 1 RM. The bottom panel shows, on an expanded scale, an arbitrarily defined strength training "zone" (60–100% of the 1 RM). Bodybuilders prefer to train at 70–90% 1 RM, depending on the exercise. Competitive weightlifters prefer to do at least a significant portion of their training at 90–100% 1 RM. The optimum number of repetitions (to failure) for increasing strength has been the subject of many short-term training studies (for a recent review, see Fleck & Kraemer, 1987). The results have not been consistent. A wide variety of schemes is effective, provided that the overload principle is applied.

Where in the strength training zone of Figure 4.21 should children train? There is general agreement that training with single maximal repetitions (100% 1 RM) should be avoided in prepubescent children (Duda, 1986, citing recommendations from the American Orthopaedic Society for Sports Medicine in 1985; Fleck & Kraemer, 1987; National Strength and Conditioning Association, 1985; Totten, 1986). The concern is the greater risk of injury associated with single maximal lifts. This would rule out Olympic and powerlift training involving single maximal repetitions (see also discussion below under 3. Specificity). Indeed, single maximal lifts are used with discretion even by advanced adult strength trainers. It is recommended that children perform about 8 to 12 repetitions to concentric contraction failure (i.e., 8–12 RM) in upper limb exercises and 15–20 RM in lower limb exercises. The greater number of repetitions in lower limb exercises is suggested because more repetitions can be done with a given percentage of the 1 RM (see Figure 4.21). These recommendations are similar to those given elsewhere (6–15 RM, Duda, 1986; minimum of 10 RM, Fleck & Kraemer, 1987; 7–11 RM, Micheli, 1988; 6–15 RM, National Strength and Condi-

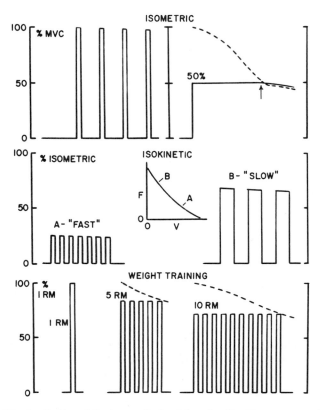

FIGURE 4-20. *Application of the two methods of "overload" with common training modes. Top: in isometric training, the trainee may do a series of brief maximal contractions (left), or a submaximal contraction to "fatigue failure" (right). In the submaximal contraction example, a force equal to 50% of maximum was sustained as long as a possible. The dashed line indicates the decline in force-generating capacity due to fatigue. When the force-generating capacity drops below the required level (in this case 50% of the maximum when not fatigued), fatigue failure occurs. It is notable that the fatigue process begins almost immediately after the start of exercise, and there is a compensatory progressive increase in motor unit activation. The time point of fatigue failure depends on the force level (% maximum force) selected. The same discussion applies to weight/pneumatic training (bottom). Middle: maximal overload in isokinetic training consists of a series of maximal effort contractions at selected velocities. At the left, a series of contractions at a relatively high velocity is shown. Because of the force-velocity relationship for concentric contractions (center: F, force; V, velocity), the actual force produced by the contractions will be small relative to maximal isometric force (vertical axis), despite maximal voluntary effort. A greater resistance "load" can be achieved by selecting a lower velocity (B); the lower velocity allows a greater force to be developed during the contractions (right). Bottom: in weight/pneumatic training, the trainee may do a series of single maximal lifts (1 RM's) (left), or sets of repetitions to "failure" with a resistance corresponding to some percentage of the 1 RM. In the example of the 5 RM (center), the resistance was 90% of the 1 RM (repetition maximum). Force-generating capacity (dashed line) declined rapidly due to fatigue and only five repetitions were possible (i.e., 5 RM). With the lighter resistance of 80% 1 RM, the decline in force-generating capacity occurred at a slower rate and had further to decline before "terminating" performance; thus, more repetitions (10, 10 RM) could be done. See text for further discussion.*

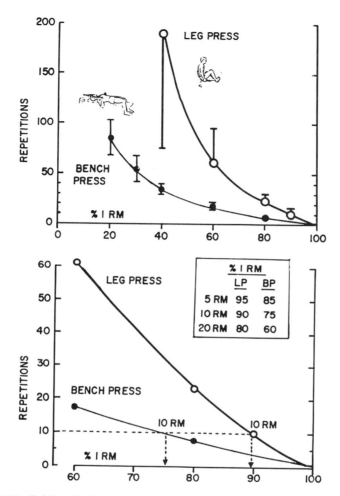

FIGURE 4-21. *Relationship between percentage of 1 RM used and the number of repetitions that can be done in the leg press and bench press exercises. The exercises were done by young men on weight training machines. Top: For a given percentage of the 1 RM, more repetitions could be done on the leg press than the bench press. Note the large intersubject variability, particularly at the lighter loads (values are means and standard errors). Bottom: A portion of the horizontal axis from the top panel (% 1 RM) is expanded into an arbitrarily defined strength training "zone" (60–100% 1 RM). The inset also shows the difference between the two exercises in the number of repetitions done (i.e., RM) with a given percent of the 1 RM. See text for further discussion. Based on unpublished observations from the Human Performance Laboratory, department of physical education, McMaster University.*

tioning Association, 1985; 8–12 RM, Smith, 1984; 12–15 RM, Totten, 1986).

In practice, the simplest way to determine the training load for a given exercise is to decide the repetition range to be used (e.g.,

8–12) and then, by trial and error, to find the maximum resistance that can be handled for the repetition range (i.e., 8–12 RM). A second approach is to test the trainee's 1 RM in an exercise and then, using a table (e.g., Landers, 1985) that shows the number of repetitions that can be done with a given percentage of the 1 RM, to select the percentage of 1 RM that causes the repetitions to fall within the desired range. There are two limitations to this second approach. The first is that a 1 RM test must be done for each exercise, with the attendant risk of injury. The second limitation is the assumption that the relationship between % 1 RM and the number of repetitions that can be done is the same for all trainees and exercises. This limitation is revealed in Figure 4.21, which shows a striking difference between the bench press and leg press exercises in the number of repetitions that can be done with a given % 1 RM (other exercises vary within and possibly outside the extremes depicted in the figure). For a given exercise, there is also considerable interindividual variability. Finally, gender (Maughan et al., 1986) and training (Anderson & Kearney, 1982; Sale et al., 1988) affect the number of repetitions done with a given % 1 RM. Therefore, the first method is recommended because it is safer, faster, and more convenient.

2. Progression. As strength increases during training, an absolute resistance that initially represented a maximal overload for a designated number of repetitions or duration of contraction no longer does so. To maintain maximal overload, the resistance and/or number of repetitions must be increased. In isometric and isokinetic training, there is no need to increase the number of repetitions because the resistance automatically increases to match the increased strength of the trainee. Thus, progression is automatically "built in" for isometric and isokinetic training. However, another form of progression in isokinetic training should be mentioned. A trainee may begin training at a moderately high velocity that prevents high force development because of the force-velocity relationship for concentric contractions (Figure 4.20). After a period of training at this velocity, the "load" can be increased by selecting a lower velocity on the isokinetic device. The lower velocity will allow the trainee to develop more force and therefore encounter more resistance. This method was used in one of the strength training studies in prepubescent children (Weltman et al., 1986).

In weight training it is not practical to progress just by increasing the resistance. The common approach is to progress through a range of repetitions, then increase the resistance by a small amount to bring the repetitions back down to the lower limit of the repetition range. For example, Micheli (1988) recommended the "7–11" program. The 7 RM is determined for each exercise. When the child can do 11 repetitions with the initial 7 RM resistance (now reduced to an 11 RM), a small (5–10%) increase in resistance is made to bring the repetitions back down to 7 (i.e., the "new" 7 RM). The same approach can be used with any designated range of repetitions.

Progression in strength training can also be achieved by increasing the "volume" of training, i.e., by increasing the number of sets and exercises and by increasing the training frequency. Progression by a volume increase is limited, however, because only so much time can and should be devoted to training. In contrast, progression by increased "intensity" does not increase the time cost of training.

3. Specificity. Specificity of movement pattern, contraction type, and contraction velocity in strength training is well-established (for recent reviews see Fleck & Kraemer, 1987; Sale, 1986, 1987). Although the evidence comes from studies with adults, specificity probably applies equally in children. Three issues about specificity in children have been raised. First, it has been recommended that although training should be specific to the sport, it should be superimposed on a "base" of strength training for all body parts (American Academy of Pediatrics, 1983). The "base" is to ensure balanced development (Totten, 1986).

A second issue is whether "explosive" high velocity training should be done, even if it is specific to sport performance. The concern is the risk of injury from sudden, ballistic movements against inertial resistance, as in lifting weights (Jesse, 1977; Smith, 1984). The same concern could be raised about "plyometric" exercises, which involve very strong eccentric contractions under high stretch loads (Komi, 1986). Consequently, it has been recommended that weight training be done with relatively slow, controlled movements rather than with sudden, jerking movements (Jesse, 1977; Micheli, 1988; Smith, 1984). The issue has not been raised generally with isokinetic type training, and this kind of high velocity training has been used in children without ill effects (Rians et al., 1987). However, the use of one particular isokinetic device that was designed to increase vertical jump performance has been associated with injuries (Brady et al., 1982).

The third issue combines the first two. Olympic weightlifting movements are "explosive" actions requiring synchronous, coordinated activity of many joints involving a large proportion of the body's skeletal muscle mass. In the field of strength training, there are many who believe that the Olympic lifts confer special benefits to athletes in many sports other than weightlifting. It is claimed that the "explosive power" developed by training with these lifts is transferred to many sport movements (e.g., O'Shea, 1982; Totten, 1986). Totten (1986) recommends their use for the 10–13 y age group, albeit with very light resistance and an emphasis on technique. O'Shea (1982) recommends these lifts for high school age athletes after they have developed a strength "base", and refers to studies (without citing them) that Olympic lifting movements "tend to develop a superior level of full range body power". On the other hand, these claims have been vigorously challenged (Jesse, 1977, 1979). Concern has also been raised about the risk of injury in doing these lifts, in particular the sudden, jerking action (Jesse, 1977; Micheli, 1988; Smith, 1984) and the overhead lifting phase (Fleck & Kraemer, 1987; Mason, 1970; National Strength and Conditioning Association, 1985). The American Academy of Pediatrics (1983) has recommended against the use of Olympic lifts for children.

Even if some of the beneficial claims for these lifts are proved true, the benefits will have to be weighed against the risks of injury and the considerable amount of time spent learning the techniques. In the meantime, it is recomended that Olympic lifts not be used in prepubescent strength training programs designed for general training and athletic enhancement. They might be introduced with some caution in mid- to late adolescence if future studies support the claims made for them. On the other hand, children who have been specially selected for training in the Olympic lifts and who are carefully coached and supervised may well be able to train with these lifts with a risk of injury no greater (or perhaps smaller) than that associated with participation in many other sports. One of the strength training studies (Servedio et al., 1985) with prepubescent children used Olympic lifts as the training mode.

4. Volume. Volume refers to the number of exercises done in each training session, the number of sets of each exercise, and the frequency (d/wk) of training. A typical training session consists of one exercise for each major muscle group (about 6 to 10 exercises). One to three sets of each exercise is recommended (Micheli, 1988; Smith, 1984; Totten, 1986). A training session should last about 30–60 min (Fleck & Kraemer, 1987). Two to three sessions per week, with at least one day's rest between sessions, are recommended (Duda, 1986; Fleck & Kraemer, 1987; Micheli, 1988; National Strength and Conditioning Association, 1985; Totten, 1986). The optimum number of sets per exercise and the optimum training frequency have been the subjects of short-term training experiments (see review by Fleck & Kraemer, 1987). The results (mainly in young adults) are not consistent and do not seriously challenge the "field" experience indicating that a few sets of each exercise, done 2–3 d/wk, is optimal. Future studies may determine if children have a different recovery ability than adults, thereby necessitating an adjustment in training volume.

5. **Summary.** The foregoing discussion of training principles can be summarized as the following guidelines:

1. In weight/pneumatic training, one to three sets of 8–12 RM in upper limb and 15–20 RM in lower limb exercises should be performed. In isokinetic training, one to three sets of 10–30 repetitions, depending on the velocity setting, of each exercise are appropriate.

2. In weight/pneumatic training, progression is achieved by increasing repetitions to the upper limit of the specified range, then increasing resistance by a small amount so the repetitions fall to the lower limit of the specified range. In isokinetic training, progression in overload is automatic, provided that the trainee continues to make maximal or near-maximal efforts in training. Additional progression in overload can be achieved by selecting a lower velocity setting, which requires stronger contractions against greater resistance.

3. A general "base" program involving all major muscle groups is recommended. Exercises specific to a particular sport can be superimposed on this base.

4. Specificity of velocity in training should be approached with extreme caution. Ballistic efforts against high resistance carry a high risk of injury and are not recommended. Instead, exercises should be done in a relatively slow manner through a full range of movement. Caution should also be applied in "plyometric" training. Moderately high velocity movements done on isokinetic machines carry much less risk and are acceptable.

5. A general program consists of six to 10 exercises in training sessions lasting 30–60 min, performed two or three days per week. There should be at least one day's rest between successive training sessions.

B. Program Design

The first step in the design of a strength training program is to apply the principles of training that have been discussed in the previous section. Additional items must be considered, however, and some of them will be briefly covered here. A more complete and comprehensive treatment of program design has recently been published, and includes a section on training for children (Fleck & Kraemer, 1987).

1. Selection of Equipment. Weight training is still the most common form of strength training, and there is a vast array of weight training equipment to choose from. In addition to the time honored "free" weights (barbells and dumbbells) and related accessories (e.g., benches, "power racks"), there are many types of weight training machines, whose common feature is the "weight stack." There are a few manufacturers of isokinetic or quasi-isokinetic equipment suitable for a training facility. There is one brand of pneumatic resistance equipment that is similar in principle to weight resistance, but with the distinguishing feature of providing high resistance with low inertia. No doubt some types of equipment have not been included here, and a detailed critical evaluation of the different types of equipment is beyond the scope of this chapter. Nevertheless, some evaluative comments will be made.

The three most important criteria for selecting equipment (assuming availability and no responsibility for purchase and maintenance) are 1) effectiveness, 2) safety, and 3) convenience and ease of use. All of the equipment listed above is effective in applying the principles of overload and progression. Depending on the goal of the training, any one of the types of equipment may provide the best application of specificity.

In weight training circles, the relative merits of free weights and weight machines have been hotly debated. Some argue that the greater skill and balance required to handle free weights are developed and transferred to athletic performance (e.g., O'Shea, 1982; Totten, 1986). A counterargument would be that while there is no doubt that the skill and balance acquired from lifting free weights enhances the ability to lift free weights, there is no evidence that this skill and balance is useful in many sports. For example, a paddler should gain as much from a pullover machine as the barbell pullover exercise. An undeniable advantage of free weights is the almost unlimited number of exercises that can be done. By comparison, weight machines are limited, although most of the common exercises are covered, and hand pulley machines allow a diversity of movements. Some weight machines are designed to provide a pattern of resistance that approximates the "strength curve" (i.e., variation in strength through a range of movement) of a given movement, thereby giving optimal loading through the range of movement. Many free weight exercises fail to do this. These are but samples of the arguments that abound in this debate. There is no easy resolution.

The relative merits of isokinetic training versus weight training are also debated. Isokinetic machines allow exercise to be done at various controlled velocities, provide "matching variable resistance" through a range of movement, and allow reciprocal exercise of opposing muscle groups (i.e., alternating concentric contractions of agonists and antagonists at a joint). On the other hand, sport movements are rarely done at constant velocity; therefore, isokinetic machines lose marks on specificity. Finally, the proponents of pneumatic machines point to its feature of high resistance with low inertia. This feature obviates the problem of "run-away" momentum that occurs when ballistic movements are done with free weights or weight machines. These machines also provide the acceleration-deceleration pattern common to many sport movements.

The second criterion is safety. With proper instruction, supervision, and exercise selection, all types of training equipment can be used safely with minimal risk. Use of free weights requires the most care because of the skill and balance required to handle them (the same feature claimed as a virtue above). The greater the skill required, the smaller the margin for error and the greater the risk of accident. The risk can be minimized by "spotting" and by the use of safety stops on benches and racks. Nevertheless, well-designed and well-maintained weight machines (and pneumatic machines) afford an added measure of safety. There is little chance of losing balance or being crushed. Isokinetic machines have the unique feature of "vanishing resistance." In these machines, resistance load exists only as a reaction to the voluntary contraction applied. If the voluntary effort ceases (for example in response to sudden pain), the resistance disappears. This safety feature is particularly useful in resistive rehabilitation exercise.

The third criterion is convenience and ease of use. Weight machines are popular because of the quickness with which resistance can be changed (if the weight stack pin can be found!). Convenient, rapid-moving circuit weight training with groups of trainees depends on weight machines. There is no need for spotters. These advantages over free weights are also enjoyed by pneumatic and isokinetic machines. On the other hand, many advanced strength trainers do not use circuit training (see below), prefer to have training partners who can act as spotters, and have plenty of time during rest periods between sets to change the weight. Some of these advanced lifters are too big to fit into the machines and are too strong for the weight stack. These trainees find free weights to be the most convenient. Prepubescent children may be too small to fit into some machines, and the gradations in resistance may be too coarse. The mismatch between the size of a child and a machine might in some instances put undue stress on joints. On the whole, however, most equipment can be used by children, so the considerations above regarding the advantages of machines apply to them.

Then what equipment is best for children to use? The best answer may be that all of it is appropriate from time to time; others have also suggested this (National Strength and Conditioning Association, 1985; Totten, 1986). A variety of equipment will maintain interest and will provide children with a broad training background on which to make their own future decisions about training modes.

2. Set Systems. The traditional method in weight training is to do all sets of an exercise together in a series before moving to another exercise. One to three minutes of rest are taken between sets. This method could be called the "standard set" system. The standard set system is still preferred by advanced strength trainers and bodybuilders. They prefer to concentrate on one exercise at a time. The standard set system is also most suitable when doing a "split" routine (see below), a common intermediate and advanced training practice. Finally, bodybuilders believe that the temporary congestion and swelling of muscles (the "pump") that occurs when all sets of an exercise are done together (and all exercises for a muscle group) is a necessary stimulus to muscle growth. (It also produces a satisfying sensation.)

At the opposite extreme is the "circuit set" system in which, one set of each exercise is done in succession. Then the series may be repeated for a second or more times, hence the term "circuit." One or two exercises for each muscle group are included in the circuit. The exercises are arranged so that exercises for the same muscle group do not immediately follow each other; thus, while one muscle group is exercising, the other muscle groups can be recovering. This arrangement of exercises in a circuit allows the rest periods between successive sets to be brief (30 s or less) in comparison to the standard set system (1–3 min.). Therefore, one advantage of the circuit system is the time saved to complete a given number of exercises and sets. If a cardiovascular stimulus is sought, the circuit system's shorter rest periods maintain a higher heart rate during the training session, in comparison with the standard system. The advent of weight machines with individually selected weight stacks made circuit training with groups fast and convenient. Pneumatic and isokinetic machines are also suitable for circuit training. The disadvantages of the circuit system are the reasons advanced strength trainers tend not to use it: the impairment of concentration when moving from one exercise to the next in rapid succession; the difficulty in including several exercises for one muscle group in the same session; its unsuitability for "split" routines; and the lack of sufficient "pump."

A set system that is a compromise between the standard and circuit systems is called the "alternate" set or "superset" system. In this system, the exercises are organized into pairs. To be most effective, the two exercises in a pair should be for two different muscle groups (usually opposing muscle groups at a joint). The trainee alternates between the two exercises until the required number of sets has been done. In one variation, one set of each exercise is done in succession with no rest between (hence the term "superset"), followed by a short rest (30–60 s), then the next two sets, and so on. In the second variation, sets of the two exercises are alternated with short rest periods between. Both variations save time in comparison with the standard system, allow a level of intermediate concentration between that of the standard and circuit systems, and are suitable for "split" routines. The system is occasionally used by advanced strength trainers.

Which system should children use? Again, the best answer may be all of them from time to time. The variety will help maintain interest. However, the circuit system allows groups of children to be moved quickly through a training session, a feature that is attractive when leading a group with a shorter attention span. The relatively long rest periods of the standard system may invite boredom and distraction.

3. Order of Exercises. In the circuit system, it is important to order the exercises so the same muscle group is not used in two successive sets. This allows short rest periods between successive sets without compromising recovery in any muscle group. In the standard system, large muscle group, multi-joint exercises should be done before small muscle group, single joint exercises involving the same muscle group. The rationale is that if a small muscle group exercise (e.g., elbow extension) is done first, it will be difficult to do justice with a subsequent large muscle group exercise (e.g., bench press) that requires force production by the small muscle group (e.g., elbow extensors). (Some advanced trainers occasionally do the opposite, called the "pre-exhaust" technique, for a claimed benefit [see Fleck & Kraemer, 1987].) In a basic program with the standard system, it is helpful to separate exercises for the same muscle group. For example, the order: bench press, lat pulldown, shoulder press, and arm curl, is preferred over the order: bench press, shoulder press, lat pulldown, and arm curl. The former order allows some recovery of a muscle group before it is engaged in another exercise.

4. Split Routine. A basic, beginning strength training program consists of one or two exercises for each target muscle group. These exercises are performed in single sessions two or three days per week. This approach can be used indefinitely for many trainees and is probably the best for children. In serious advanced training, however, the prescribed volume of sets and exercises may be too much (and too long) to fit practically into one training session. The solution is to divide the volume into two or more parts and do the parts in different sessions, usually on different days. Hence, the term "split routine." One example is to perform the upper body exercises 2 d/wk and lower body exercises two other days per week. There are many different kinds of split routines (see Fleck & Kraemer, 1987). Note that in split routines, training may occur 4–6 d/wk, but each muscle group is trained only 2–3 d/wk. Split routines are probably not appropriate for children, because it is difficult to justify so many weekly training sessions for a group that should be engaged in a variety of activities. Split routines may be appropriate in adolescence for those at the intermediate level (arbitrarily defined here as one year of regular training experience).

5. Warm-up. The primary purpose of warm-up before a strength training session is to minimize the risk of injury. Although general activities such as jogging, calisthenics, and stretching can be done as part of the warm-up, the most effective warm-up is to do one or more submaximal sets of each exercise before doing the "working" sets; that is, the sets with overload. For example, if the 10 RM in an exercise is 40 kg warm-up sets of 10 repetitions with 20 kg (50% 10 RM) and 30 kg (75% 10 RM) could be done before the first set with the 10 RM. The more advanced (and stronger) the trainee, the greater the number of warm-up sets that should be done. One or two warm-up sets are sufficient for children.

6. "Breaking In". In the very first training sessions, the overload principle should not be applied. Instead, the trainee should do sets of repetitions with light resistance. The emphasis should be on learning the technique of the exercises (particularly important with free weight exercises). The second purpose of the "break-in" period is to minimize the muscle soreness that occurs when unfamiliar activities are introduced. Muscle soreness is more likely to occur in weight and pneumatic resistance exercise, because of the eccentric contraction component, than in isokinetic exercise, which usually has no eccentric component. In successive sessions in weight training, the resistance can be gradually increased until the RM for the designated repetition range has been established. Overload can then be applied without ill effects.

7. Periodization. The basic training principles of overload (intensity), progression, and volume can be applied in a straightforward manner for the first several weeks or even months of training. Progression is achieved primarily by increasing resistance (intensity); sets of exercises may increase moderately (e.g., from one to three to three to five), and frequency of training remains the same. Eventually, however, progression will slow or even stop. A state of "overtraining" (Fleck & Kraemer, 1982) or "staleness" may develop if there is a continuing attempt to apply maximal overloading and there are no other variations in the program from time to time. The problem can be avoided by "periodization," which consists of varying the intensity and volume of training according to various schemes and time periods. The various schemes are often organized into "cycles," some designed for specific purposes as well as to prevent overtraining and to provide variety (for a detailed discussion of periodization, see Stone et al., 1981, 1982). Presumably, periodization may also be helpful to children involved in long-term training programs.

8. Integration. Many athletes must train for aerobic and anaerobic power as well as strength. Since strength and endurance training stimulate different and sometimes opposite adaptations in skeletal muscle, there is the possibility that concurrent strength and endurance training are antagonistic to each other. Indeed, the two published studies of this phenomenon have shown that concurrent strength and endurance training impairs increases in strength but not increases in aerobic power (Dudley & Djamil, 1985; Hickson, 1980). Additional studies, published as abstracts, have shown no impairment of the development of endurance (Demment et al., 1985; Hickson et al., 1988; MacDougall et al., 1987) or strength (Demment et al., 1985; Volpe et al., 1988) by concurrent strength and endurance training. Several factors could affect the existence and extent of antagonism between concurrent strength training, including the intensity and volume of training and the distribution of the two forms of training. A study of the latter factor indicated that training strength and endurance on separate days was preferable to same-day training for strength development (Sale et al., 1988). Although the available evidence indicates that strength and endurance training of moderate volume and intensity can be done concurrently without antagonism, it should be recognized that children will be (or should be) involved in a variety of activities, and their recovery ability in comparison to adults is not known. Therefore, increases in the volume of strength training in this group should be made with discretion.

C.   Strength Training Injuries

Participation in any strenuous physical activity carries the risk of injury, and strength training is no exception. The types, incidence, causes, and prevention of strength training injuries will be reviewed in this section, with particular reference to children. The possible role of strength training in preventing other sport injuries will also be discussed.

1. Types of Injury. The back is the most common site of strength training injuries (Brady et al., 1982; Brown & Kimball, 1983; Jackson, 1979; Jackson et al., 1982; Jesse, 1977; Kulund et al., 1978; Micheli, 1988). As one example, Brady et al. (1982) reported that back injuries (lumbosacral pain) amounted to 67% of the strength training injuries that occurred in a large group of junior and senior high school athletes. As a second example, 50% of the training injuries in a group of adolescent powerlifters were to the lower back (Brown & Kimball, 1983). The causes of the back injuries are considered to be the performance of single maximum lifts, particularly overhead lifts (Jackson, 1979; Jackson et al., 1982; Jesse, 1977; Mason, 1970; National Strength and Conditioning Association, 1985), and sudden, ballistic movements (Brady et al., 1982; Jesse, 1977; Sewall & Micheli, 1986). The Olympic lifts (Jesse, 1977), any overhead lifts, the dead lift (Brady et al., 1982), and explosive squat movements on an isokinetic training device (Brady et al., 1982) have been associated with back injuries.

Knee injuries are apparently the next most common strength training injury (Brady et al., 1982). Strength training also has its share of muscle pulls, tendonitis, and sprains (Brown & Kimball, 1983). In adults, there are a few case reports of nerve injury from lifting weights (Braddom & Wolfe, 1978; Dangles & Bilos, 1980).

Of particular concern in children is the risk of injuries to bone growth plates that can cause growth arrest and deformity (Wilkins, 1980). The peak incidence of epiphyseal fractures occurs in 12–13 y olds, and the most common site is the distal radial epiphysis (Wilkins, 1980). In relation to sport participation, the injury is more likely to occur in bigger, stronger children, i.e., in adolescent rather than prepubescent children (Wilkins, 1980). It is also of interest that the growth plates are actually stronger in prepubescent than adolescent children (Micheli, 1988).

Growth plate injuries have occurred in adolescents while strength training (Benton, 1983; Brady et al., 1982; Cahill & Griffith, 1978; Gumbs et al., 1982; Ryan & Salciccioli, 1976); however, the incidence is rare (Brady et al., 1982; Gumbs et al., 1982; Ryan & Salciccioli, 1976). The injury has occurred at the wrist during excessive overhead lifts (Gumbs et al., 1982; Ryan & Salciccioli, 1976). Sudden, ballistic lifts carry greater risk because of the associated greater shear-type forces at the joints (Micheli, 1988).

In Part I of the chapter it was noted that blood pressure is markedly elevated during strength training exercise. The elevation is similar whether doing single maximal contractions or doing sets of repetitions to "failure" (MacDougall et al., 1985). During the same conditions, there is also a large increase in intra-thoracic and intra-abdominal pressure caused by the Valsalva maneuver (forced expiration against a closed glottis). The Valsalva maneuver contributes to, but is not totally responsible for, the elevation in blood pressure during strength training exercise (MacDougall et al., 1985). Hyperventilation prior to a lift and a prolonged Valsalva during a maximal lift can cause blackout and fainting (Compton et al., 1973). Even a brief (few seconds) Valsalva, by transiently restricting venous return, causes veins to swell and the face to turn red. The Valsalva maneuver might then be judged as hazardous and something to be avoided in strength exercise. However, the Valsalva has a beneficial function. The forced expiration against a closed glottis turns the trunk into a rigid cylinder, which stabilizes the spine (Harmon et al., 1988) and provides a firm base upon which the muscles of the limbs can act. The increased intra-thoracic pressure caused by the Valsalva increases cerebro-spinal fluid pressure, which may actually reduce the pressure difference across cerebral blood vessel walls (see discussion by MacDougall et al., 1985). Regardless of the differing opinions on the advisability of using the Valsalva maneuver in strength exercise, the Valsalva is virtually a reflex response to maximal or near-maximal efforts, whether they occur in a single lift or at the end of a set of repetitions. The only way to prevent the Valsalva is not to apply the overload principle in training. It is recommended that children be allowed to breath naturally during strength exercise. The Valsalva will nearly always occur at the appropriate time, without instruction. The natural pattern in weight training exercise is to inhale on the "easy" eccentric phase of a repetition and, depending on the degree of effort required, to exhale (preceded by brief Valsalva during maximal and near-maximal efforts) on the more difficult concentric contraction phase. One instruction that should be given is not to maintain a prolonged Valsalva during a sustained maximal effort.

2. Injuries in Training Studies. None of the training studies reviewed in Part I showed injurious effects of short-term strength training in prepubescent or adolescent children. For example, musculoskeletal scintigraphy revealed no evidence of damage to epiphyses, bone or muscle after 14 weeks of hydraulic resistance training by prepubescent boys (Rians et al., 1987). Similarly, weight training caused no obvious injurious effects in prepubescent (Sewall & Micheli, 1986) and adolescent (Kusinitz & Keeney, 1958) boys.

3. Prevention of Injuries. The following recommendations for preventing injuries are based on the above review of strength training injuries and a review of recommendations of others.

1. Medical Examination. Children should have a medical examination prior to participating in a strength training program (National Strength and Conditioning Association, 1985).

2. *Instruction and Supervision.* Thorough instruction should be given in the execution of exercises, particularly free weight exercises. This should be part of the "break-in" period of a new program. Competent and close supervision is required at all times, particularly with prepubescent children (Hejna et al., 1982; Mannis, 1983; Rians et al., 1987).

3. *Equipment Maintenance and Safe Environment.* Training equipment should be regularly serviced to avoid hazards (e.g., frayed cables, loose collars). Strength training "etiquette" should be taught (e.g., returning weights and equipment to proper place after use) to provide a safe, clear environment.

4. *Maximal Lifts.* Single maximal lifts, particularly overhead lifts, carry a substantial risk of injury and should be avoided (American Academy of Pediatrics, 1983; Brady et al., 1982; Gumbs et al., 1982; Jackson, 1979; Jackson et al., 1982; Jesse, 1977, 1979; Mason, 1970; Micheli, 1988; National Strength and Conditioning Association, 1985).

5. *"Explosive" Lifts.* Sudden, explosive movements against high resistance should be avoided in children (Brady et al., 1982; Micheli, 1988; Sewall & Micheli, 1986), even though such movements may be deemed specific to sport requirements. Such movements may be introduced with caution in late adolescence. The same considerations apply to high load "plyometric" training. Moderately high velocity isokinetic training against relatively low resistance can be done safely (Weltman et al., 1986).

6. *Breathing Pattern.* Generally, proper breathing, including the Valsalva maneuver, will occur by "instinct" in strength exercise; however, trainees should be taught to avoid a prolonged Valsalva (breath hold) in the last repetition (i.e., at "failure") of a set, because blackout or fainting could result (Compton et al., 1973).

4. Prevention of Sport Injuries by Strength Training. A properly conducted strength training program should not only avoid causing injury, it may also prevent injuries during participation in various sports (see review by Fleck & Falkel, 1986). For example, male and female high school athletes who trained with weights had a lower injury rate (26%) than those who did not (72%, Hejna et al., 1982). In adolescents, the increased muscle mass and perhaps increased bone density (see Part I) resulting from strength training may provide the increased resistance to injury, particularly in contact sports (Micheli, 1988). Strength training may also prevent overuse injuries (Dominguez, 1978).

SUMMARY

This chapter addressed the following questions: 1) Can children increase strength by strength training? 2) Does any increase in strength enhance athletic performance? 3) Can children increase strength as much as older age groups, and are the adaptations to training similar? 4) Should children train differently than older age groups? 5) Are children particularly susceptible to training injuries, and how can the risk of injury be minimized? 6) Can strength training help prevent sport injuries in children?

On the basis of the few studies that have been done, it is clear that children can significantly increase voluntary strength and athletic performance by strength training. Children have less absolute strength and muscle mass than older age groups; therefore, it is difficult for children to make the same absolute increases in strength by training as adults. However, children make similar or even greater relative (percentage) increases in strength than adults.

Training-induced increases in voluntary strength are due to adaptations within the muscles (e.g., increase in muscle size) and within the nervous system (e.g., increased ability to fully activate the muscles). The present evidence indicates that children may have more difficulty than older age groups in increasing muscle mass. On the other hand, adaptations within the nervous system are similar to or even greater in children than in older groups.

There is at present no evidence to indicate that the basic principles of strength training should be applied differently in children than in adults. Strength training programs for children should be distinguished, however, by careful and competent instruction and supervision at all times.

Certain strength training practices carry a relatively high risk of injury for any age group that uses them. These practices include single maximal lifts, overhead lifts, and ballistic efforts against high inertia. While it is not known if children are more or less susceptible to training injuries than older groups, it would be prudent to err on the side of caution and minimize the use of these practices by children. This recommendation implies that competitive weightlifting would be ruled out for children, because this activity involves the high risk practices. The possibility cannot be excluded that selected children, under the supervision of expert coaches, can participate in this sport with a risk no greater than that associated with training and competition in many other sports.

In adolescents and adults, strength training helps to prevent the occurrence of sport injuries. Future research with prepubescent children may show a similar favorable effect.

In conclusion, children can derive most, if not all of, the benefits of strength training that adults can, and with no greater risk of injury, provided that the program is well-designed and that the supervision is competent.

ACKNOWLEDGMENTS

The author gratefully acknowledges the assistance of Dr. C. J. Blimkie and Mr. J. Ramsay in assembling the literature reviewed in this manuscript. The McMaster Boys Strength Training Study, the unpublished results of which were frequently cited and illustrated in the manuscript, was conducted under the direction of Dr. C. J. Blimkie, department of physical education, McMaster University. Mrs. L. Diskin provided secretarial assistance.

The preparation of the manuscript was supported in part by the Natural Sciences and Engineering Research Council of Canada.

BIBLIOGRAPHY

1. Allen, T.E., R. Byrd, and D. Smith. Hemodynamic consequences of circuit weight training. *Research Quarterly* 47:299–306, 1976.
2. American Academy of Pediatrics. Weight training and weightlifting: Information for the pediatrician. *The Physician and Sportsmedicine* 11(3):157–161, 1983.
3. Anderson, T. and J.T. Kearney. Muscular strength and absolute and relative muscular endurance. *Research Quarterly for Exercise and Sport* 53:1–7, 1982.
4. Asmussen, E. Growth in muscular strength and power. In L.G. Rarick, (ed.). *Physical Activity, Human Growth, and Development.* (60–79). New York: Academic Press, 1973.
5. Belanger, A.Y. and A.J. McComas. Extent of motor unit activation during effort. *Journal of Applied Physiology: Respiratory, Environmental and Exercise Physiology* 51:750–754, 1981.
6. Benton, J.W. Epiphyseal fracture in sports. *The Physician and Sportsmedicine* 10:63–71, 1983.
7. Braddom, R.L. and C. Wolfe. Musculocutaneous nerve injury after heavy exercise. *Archives of Physical Medicine and Rehabilitation* 59:290–293, 1978.
8. Brady, T.A., B.R. Cahill, and L. Bodnar. Weight training-related injuries. *American Journal of Sports Medicine* 10:1–5, 1982.
9. Brown, E.W. and R. Kimball. Medical history association with adolescent powerlifting. *Pediatrics* 72:636–644, 1983.
10. Brown, S., R. Byrd, M.O. Jayasinghe, and D. Jones. Echocardiographic characteristics of competitive and recreational weight lifters. *Journal of Cardiovascular Ultrasonography* 2:163–165, 1983.
11. Cahill, B.R. and E.H. Griffith. Effect of pre-season conditioning on the incidence and severity of high school football knee injuries. *American Journal of Sports Medicine* 6:180–184, 1978.
12. Chow, K., J.E. Harrison, and C. Notarius. Effect of two randomized exercise programmes on bone mass of healthy postmenopausal women. *British Medical Journal* 295:1441–1444, 1987.
13. Clarke, D.H., P. Vaccaro, and N.M. Andresen. Physiological alterations in 7- to 9-year-old boys following a season of competitive wrestling. *Research Quarterly for Exercise and Sport* 55:318–322, 1984.
14. Clarkson, P.M., R. Hintermister, M. Fillyaw, and L. Stylos. High density lipoprotein cholesterol in young adult weight lifters. *Human Biology* 53:251–257, 1981.
15. Colliander, E.B. and P.A. Tesch. Blood pressure in resistance-trained athletes. *Canadian Journal of Sport Sciences* 13:31–34, 1988.
16. Compton, D., P.M. Hill, and H. Sinclair. Weight lifters black out. *Lancet* 2:1234–1237, 1973.
17. Curwin, S., A.C. Vailas, and R.R. Roy. Response of immature chicken tendon to increased mechanical loading. *Medicine and Science in Sports and Exercise* 20(2, Supplement):S57, 1988.
18. Dangles, C. and J. Bilos. Ulnar nerve neuritis in a world champion weightlifter. A case report. *American Journal of Sports Medicine* 8:443–445, 1980.
19. DeKoning, F.L., R.A. Binkhorst, A.C.A. Vissers, and J.A. Vos. The influence of static strength training on the force-velocity relationship of the arm flexors of 16-year-old boys.

In J. Ilmarinen and I. Valimaki, (eds.). *Children and Sport Peadiatric Work Physiology.* (201–205). New York:Springer-Verlag, 1984.
20. Delorme, T.L., B.G. Ferris, and J.R. Gallagher. Effect of progressive resistance exercise on muscle contraction time. *Archives of Physical Medicine and Rehabilitation* 33:86–92, 1952.
21. Demment, R., G. Hunter, and D. Miller. Strength and endurance training in previously untrained and endurance-trained subjects. *National Strength and Conditioning Association Journal* 6:56–57, 1985.
22. Dominguez, R. H. Shoulder pain in age group swimmers. In B.O. Eriksson and S. Furlong (eds.). *Swimming Medicine IV* (105–109). Baltimore: University Park Press, 1978.
23. Duda, M. Prepubescent strength training gains support. *The Physician and Sportsmedicine* 14(2):157–161, 1986.
24. Dudley, G.A., and R. Djamil. Incompatibility of endurance- and strength-training modes of exercise. *Journal of Applied Physiology* 59:1446–1451, 1985.
25. Fahey, T.D., L. Akka, and R. Rolph. Body composition and VO_2 max of exceptional weight trained athletes. *Journal of Applied Physiology* 39:559–561, 1975.
26. Farrell, P.A., M.B. Maksud, M.L. Pollock, C. Foster, J. Anholm, J. Hare, and A.S. Leon. A comparison of plasma cholesterol, triglycerides, and high density lipoprotein-cholesterol in speed skaters, weightlifters and nonathletes. *European Journal of Applied Physiology* 48:77–82, 1982.
27. Fleck, S.J. and J.E. Falkel. Value of resistance training for the reduction of sports injuries. *Sports Medicine* 3:61–68, 1986.
28. Fleck, S.J., C. Heinke, and W. Wilson. Cardiac MRI of elite Junior Olympic weight lifters. *Medicine and Science in Sports and Exercise* 20 (2, Supplement):S54, 1988.
29. Fleck, S.J. and W.J. Kraemer. The overtraining syndrome. *National Strength and Conditioning Association Journal* 4(4):50–51, 1982.
30. Fleck, S.J. and W.J. Kraemer. *Designing Resistance Training Programs.* Champaign, IL: Human Kinetics Books, 1987.
31. Gallagher, J.R., M.T. Andover, and T.L. Delorme. The use of progressive resistance exercise in adolescence. *Journal of Bone and Joint Surgery* 31-A:847–858, 1949.
32. Gilliam, G.M. Effects of frequency of weight training on muscle strength enhancement. *Journal of Sports Medicine* 21:432–435, 1981.
33. Goldberg, L., D.L. Elliott, R.W. Schutz, and F.E. Kloster. Changes in lipid and lipoprotein levels after weight training. *Journal of the American Medical Association* 252:504–506, 1984.
34. Grimm, D. and H. Raede. Erfolgreiche Anwendung des Kreisbetriebs in einer 3. Klasse. *Theor. Prax. Korperkult* 16:333–342, 1967.
35. Gumbs, V.L., D. Segal, J.B. Halligan, and G. Lower. Bilateral distal radius and ulnar fracture in weightlifting. *American Journal of Sports Medicine* 10:375–379, 1982.
36. Hagberg, J.M., A.A. Ehsani, D. Goldring, A. Hernandez, D.R. Sinacore, and J.O. Holloszy. Effect of weight training on blood pressure and hemodynamics in hypertensive adolescents. *Journal of Pediatrics* 104:147–151, 1984.
37. Harmon, E.A., P.N. Frykman, E.R. Clagett, and W.J. Kraemer. Intra-abdominal and intra-thoracic pressure during lifting and jumping. *Medicine and Science in Sports and Exercise* 20:195–201, 1988.
38. Hejna, W.F., A. Rosenberg, D.J. Buturusis, and A. Krieger. Prevention of sports injuries in high school students through strength training. *National Strength and Conditioning Association Journal* 4:28–31, 1982.
39. Hellebrandt, F.A. and S.J. Houtz. Mechanisms of muscle training in man: Experimental demonstration of the overload principle. *Physical Therapy Review* 36:371–383, 1956.
40. Hickson, R.C. Interference of strength development by simultaneously training for strength and endurance. *European Journal of Applied Physiology* 45:255–263, 1980.
41. Hickson, R.C., B.A. Dvorak, E.M. Corostiaga, T.T. Kurowski, and C. Foster. Strength training and performance in endurance-trained subjects. *Medicine and Science in Sports and Exercise* 20(2, Supplement):S86, 1988.
42. Hurley, B.F., J.M. Hagberg, A.P. Goldberg, D.R. Seals, A.A Ehsani, R.E. Brennan, and J.O. Holloszy. Resistive training can reduce coronary risk factors without altering VO_2 max or percent body fat. *Medicine and Science in Sports and Exercise* 20:150–154, 1988.
43. Hurley, B.F., D.R. Seals, J.M. Hagberg, A.C. Goldberg, S.M. Ostrove, J.O. Holloszy, W.G. Wiest, and A.P. Goldberg. High-density-lipoprotein cholesterol in bodybuilders vs. power lifters: negative effects of androgen use. *Journal of the American Medical Association* 252:507–513, 1984.
44. Ivanitsky, M.F. *Medical Tribune* 3:34, 1962.
45. Jackson, D.W. Low back pain in young athletes: Evaluations of stress reaction and discogenic problems. *American Journal of Sports Medicine* 7:364–366, 1979.
46. Jackson, D.W., H. Wiltse, R.D. Dingeman, and M. Hayes. Stress reactions involving the pars interarticularis in young athletes. *American Journal of Sports Medicine* 9:304–312, 1982.

47. Jesse, J.P. Olympic weightlifting movements endanger adolescent weightlifters. *The Physician and Sportsmedicine* 5(9):61–67, 1977.
48. Jesse, J.P. Misuse of strength development programs in athletic training. *The Physician and Sportsmedicine* 7(10):46–52, 1979.
49. Johnson, C.C., M.H. Stone, S.A. Lopez, L.A. Herbert, L.T. Kilgore, and R.J. Byrd. Diet and exercise and middle-aged men. *Journal of the American Dietetic Association* 81:695–701, 1982.
50. Keul, J., H. Dickhuth, G. Simon, and M. Lehman. Effect of static and dynamic exercise on heart volume, contractility and left ventricular dimensions. *Circulation Research* I:(Supplement) 162–170, 1981.
51. Knakis, C., and R. Hickson. Left ventricular response to a program of lower-limb strength training. *Chest* 78:618–621, 1980.
52. Komi, P.V. Training of muscle strength and power: Interaction of neuromotoric, hypertrophic and mechanical factors. *International Journal of Sports Medicine* 7(Supplement):10–15, 1986.
53. Kulund, D.N., J.B. Dewey, C.E. Brubaker, and J.R. Roberts. Olympic weightlifting injuries. *The Physician and Sportsmedicine* 6(11):111–119, 1978.
54. Kusinitz, I. and C.E. Keeney. Effects of progressive weight training on health and physical fitness of adolescent boys. *Research Quarterly* 29:294–301, 1958.
55. Landers, J. Maximum based on reps. *National Strength and Conditioning Association Journal* 6(6):60–61, 1985.
56. Lane, N., W. Bevier, M. Bouxsein, R. Wiswell, and R. Marcus. Effect of exercise intensity on bone mineral. *Medicine and Science in Sports and Exercise* 20(2, Supplement):S51, 1988.
57. Larson, R.L. Physical activity and the growth and development of bone and joint structures. In G.L. Rarick, (ed.). *Physical Activity, Human Growth and Development.* (32–59). New York: Academic Press, 1973.
58. Longhurst, J.C., A.R Kelly, W.J. Gonyea, and J.H. Mitchell. Echocardiographic left ventricular masses in distance runners and weight-lifters. *Journal of Applied Physiology: Respiratory, Environmental and Exercise Physiology* 48:154–162, 1980.
59. MacDougall, J.D., D. Sale, I. Jacobs, S. Garner, D. Moroz, and D. Dittmer. Concurrent strength and endurance training do not impede gains in VO₂ max. *Medicine and Science in Sports and Exercise* 19(2):S88, 1987.
60. MacDougall, J.D., D. Tuxen, D.G. Sale, J.R. Moroz, and J.R. Sutton. Arterial blood pressure response to heavy resistance exercise. *Journal of Applied Physiology* 58:785–790, 1985.
61. Mannis, C.I. Transchondral fracture of the dome of the talus sustained during weight training. *American Journal of Sports Medicine* 11:354–356, 1983.
62. Mason, T.A. Is weight lifting deleterious to the spines of young people? *British Journal of Sports Medicine* 5:54–56, 1970.
63. Maughan, R.J., M. Harmon, J.B. Leiper, D. Sale, and A. Delman. Endurance capacity of untrained males and females in isometric and dynamic muscular contractions. *European Journal of Applied Physiology* 55:395–400, 1986.
64. McGovern, M.B. Effects of circuit weight training on the physical fitness of prepubescent children. *Dissertation Abstracts International* 45(2):452A–453A, 1984.
65. Menapace, F.J., W.J. Hammer, T.F. Ritzer, K.M. Kessler, H.F. Warner, J.F. Spann, and A.A. Bove. Left ventricular size in competitive weight-lifters: An echocardiographic study. *Medicine and Science in Sports and Exercise* 14:72–75, 1982.
66. Micheli, L.J. Strength training in the young athlete. In E.W. Brown, and C.E. Branta, (eds.). *Competitive Sports for Children and Youth.* (99–105). Champaign, IL.:Human Kinietics Books, 1988.
67. Montoye, H.J. and D.E. Lamphiear. Grip and arm strength in males and females, age 10 to 69. *Research Quarterly* 48:109–120, 1977.
68. Montoye, H.J., E.L. Smith, D.F. Fardon, and E.T. Howley. Bone mineral in senior tennis players. *Scandinavian Journal of Sports Science* 2:26–32, 1980.
69. Morganroth, J., B.J. Maron, W.L. Henry, and J.E. Epstein. Comparative left ventricular dimensions in trained athletes. *Annals of Internal Medicine* 82:521–524, 1975.
70. National Strength and Conditioning Association. Position paper on prepubescent strength training. *National Strength and Conditioning Association Journal* 7(4):27–31, 1985.
71. Nau, K., R. Beekman, and V. Katch. Acute blood pressure response to weightlifting in children. *Medicine and Science in Sports and Exercise* 20(2, Supplement):S31, 1988.
72. Nielsen, B., K. Nielsen, M. Behrendt-Hansen, and A. Asmussen. Training of functional muscular strength in girls 7–19 years old. In K. Berg and B.O. Eriksson (eds.) *Children and Exercise IX.* (69–78). Champaign, IL.: Human Kinetics Books, 1980.
73. Nilsson, B.E. and N.E. Westlin. Bone density in athletes. *Clinical Orthopedics and Related Research* 7:179–182, 1971.
74. O'Shea, J.P. Strength fitness training for the high school athlete. *Canadian Athletic Trainers*

Association Journal Summer:11–13, 1982.

75. Perrine, J.J. Isokinetic exercise and the mechanical energy potential of muscle. *Journal for Health, Physical Education and Recreation* 39:40–48, 1968.

76. Pfeiffer, R.D., and R.S. Francis. Effects of strength training on muscle development in prepubescent, pubescent, and postpubescent males. *The Physician and Sportsmedicine* 14(9):134–143, 1986.

77. Pirnay, F., M. Bodeux, J.M. Crielaard, and P. Franchimont. Bone mineral content and physical activity. *International Journal of Sports Medicine* 8:331–335, 1987.

78. Rarick, G.L. and G.L. Larsen. Observations on frequency and intensity of isometric muscular effort in developing static muscular strength in postpubescent males. *Research Quarterly* 29:333–341, 1958.

79. Rians, C.B., A. Weltman, B.R. Cahill, C.A. Janney, S.R. Tippett, and F.I. Katch. Strength training for prepubescent males: Is it safe? *American Journal of Sports Medicine* 15:483–489, 1987.

80. Ricci, G., D. LaJoie, R. Petitcure, F. Peronnet, R.J. Ferguson, M. Fournier, and A.W. Taylor. Left ventricular size following endurance, sprint, and strength training. *Medicine and Science in Sports and Exercise* 14:344–347, 1982.

81. Robinson, T.E., D.Y. Sue, A. Huzczuk, D. Weiler-Ravell, and J.E. Hansen. Intra-arterial and cuff blood pressure responses during incremental exercise. *Medicine and Science in Sports and Exercise* 20:142–149, 1988.

82. Rohmert, W. Rechts-Links-Vergleich bei sometrischem Armuskeltraining mit vershiedenum Trainingsreiz bei achtjahrigen Kindern. Internationale angew. *Physiologie* 26:363–393, 1968.

83. Ryan, J.R. and G.G. Salciccioli. Fracture of the distal radial epiphysis in adolescent weightlifters. *American Journal of Sports Medicine* 4:26–27, 1976.

84. Sailors, M. and K. Berg. Comparison of responses to weight training in pubescent boys and men. *Journal of Sports Medicine* 27:30–37, 1987.

85. Sale, D.G. Neural adaptation in strength and power training. In N.L. Jones, N. McCartney, and A.J. McComas, (eds.). *Human Muscle Power*. (281–305). Champaign, IL.: Human Kinetics, 1986.

86. Sale, D.G. Influence of exercise and training on motor unit activation. In K.B. Pandolf, (ed.). *Exercise and Sport Sciences Reviews, Vol. 15* (95–151). New York: MacMillan, 1987.

87. Sale, D., I. Jacobs, D. Moroz, J.D. MacDougall, and S. Garner. Comparison of two regimens of combined strength and endurance training. *Medicine and Science in Sports and Exercise* 20(2, Supplement):S9, 1988.

88. Sale, D. and D. MacDougall. Specificity in strength training: A review for the coach and athlete. *Canadian Journal of Applied Sport Sciences* 6:87–92, 1981.

89. Salke, R.C., T.W. Rowland, and E.J. Burke. Left ventricular size and function in body builders using anabolic steroids. *Medicine and Science in Sports and Exercise* 17:701–704, 1985.

90. Servedio, F.J., R.L. Bartels, and R.L. Hamlin. The effects of weight training using Olympic style lifts on various physiological variables in pre-pubescent boys. *Medicine and Science in Sports and Exercise* 17:288 (abstract), 1985.

91. Sewall, L., and L.J. Micheli. Strength training for children. *Journal of Pediatric Orthopedics* 6:143–146, 1986.

92. Siegel, J.A., D.N. Camaione, and T.G. Manfredi. Upper body strength training and prepubescent children. *Medicine and Science in Sports and Exercise* 20(2, Supplement):S53, 1988.

93. Smith, E.L., and C. Gilligan. Effects of inactivity and exercise on bone. *The Physician and Sportsmedicine* 15(11):91–102, 1987.

94. Smith, T.K. Preadolescent strength training. Some considerations. *Journal of Physical Education, Recreation, and Dance* 55:43–44, 80, 1984.

95. Spitler, D.L., F.J. Diaz, S.M. Horvath, and J.E. Wright. Body composition and maximal aerobic capacity of body builders. *Journal of Sports Medicine* 10:181–188, 1980.

96. Staron, R.S., F.C. Hagerman, and R.S. Hikida. The effects of detraining of an elite power lifter: A case study. *Journal of Neurological Sciences* 51:247–257, 1981.

97. Steben, R.E. and A.H. Steben. The validity of the strength shortening cycle in selected jumping events. *Journal of Sports Medicine and Physical Fitness* 21:28–37, 1981.

98. Stone, M.H., H. O'Bryant, and J. Garhammer. A hypothetical model for strength training. *Journal of Sports Medicine and Physical Fitness* 21:342–351, 1981.

99. Stone, M.H., H. O'Bryant, J. Garhammer, J. McMillan, R. Rozeneck. A theoretical model of strength training. *National Strength and Conditioning Association Journal* 4(4):36–39, 1982.

100. Stone, M.H., G.D. Wilson, D. Blessing, and R. Rozeneck. Cardiovascular responses to short-term Olympic style weight training in young men. *Canadian Journal of Applied Sport Sciences* 8:134–139, 1983.

101. Totten, L. Practical considerations in strengthening the prepubescent athlete. *National Strength and Conditioning Association Journal* 8(2):38–40, 1986.

102. Vandervoort, A.A. and A.J. McComas. Contractile changes in opposing muscles of the human ankle joint with aging. *Journal of Applied Physiology* 61:361–367, 1986.
103. Volpe, S., K. Webb, J. Walberg, and D. Hinkle. Influence of aerobic exercise on strength training. *Medicine and Science in Sports and Exercise* 20(2, Supplement):S86, 1988.
104. Vrijens, J. Muscle strength development in the pre- and post-pubescent age. *Medicine and Sport* 11:152–158, 1978.
105. Weltman, A., C. Janney, C.B. Rians, K. Strand, B. Berg, S. Tippett, J. Wise, B.R. Cahill, and F.I. Katch. The effects of hydraulic resistance strength training in pre-pubescent males. *Medicine and Science in Sports and Exercise* 18:629–638, 1986.
106. Weltman, A., C. Janney, C.B. Rians, K. Strand, and F.I. Katch. The effects of hydraulic-resistance strength training on serum lipid levels in prepubertal boys. *American Journal of Diseases in Children* 141:777–780, 1987.
107. Westfall, C., S. Going, R. Parmenter, C. Perry, T. Boyden, and T. Lohman. Femur and spine bone mineral of eumenorrheic female body builders, swimmers, runners, and controls. *Medicine and Science in Sports and Exercise* 20(2, Supplement):S60, 1988.
108. Wilkins, K.E. The uniqueness of the young athlete: Musculoskeletal injuries. *American Journal of Sports Medicine* 8:377–382, 1980.
109. Winter, J.S.D. Prepubertal and pubertal endocrinology. In F. Falkner, and J.M. Tanner, (eds.). *Human Growth 2. Postnatal Growth* (183–213). New York: Plenum Press, 1978.
110. Wolbers, C.P. and F.S. Sills. Development of strength in high school boys by static muscle contractions. *Research Quarterly* 27:446–450, 1956.

DISCUSSION

SALE: The point was raised as to whether or not children can increase muscle size by strength training during puberty when they are growing rapidly anyway. I know little about growth and development, but my colleague Dr. Joe Blimkie has told me that the peak height velocity and the normal large increase in muscle mass occurs as puberty is taking effect. This is the period in which many claim that trainability starts to increase. So the rate of muscular growth in response to training may actually be greater during puberty than at the earlier ages.

Another question was asked about creatine kinase (CK) responses and muscle soreness in children. Joe Blimkie did some CK studies on his McMaster boys.

BLIMKIE: We studied the creatine kinase response to exercise both on an acute basis in response to an individual exercise session and chronically over 20 weeks of training. Of course, we didn't have any background information concerning the time course of the CK response in young children. We thought, however, that we would see the response within a 24-hour period. So we looked at CK before the exercise session, three hours immediately after the exercise session, and then 24 hours later. We saw a slight increment in the CK level at the three-hour time, but a reduction at 24 hours. This was surprising to us because we thought we'd see a more substantial increase. However, there were no reports of muscle soreness from these young children either. We haven't really analyzed the data yet on the chronic time course to see whether there is any chronic effect of training on CK levels.

CLARKSON: Did you use eccentric contractions in your study?

BLIMKIE: Yes. This training model included both concentric and eccentric contractions. That's why we were a bit surprised not to see an increase in CK levels.

CLARKSON: We're finding that the delay in the CK response after eccentric exercise is 2 d.

BLIMKIE: But the exercise wasn't solely confined to eccentric exercise. It was primarily concentric lifting that they performed.

SALE: My concern about Olympic lifting isn't so much with children who have the required physical traits. Some children are born with physical traits that will make them good athletes in a particular sport and will make them resistant to injury. If they are handled with care and supervision, I don't see a problem. I have more quarrel with people who say that athletes in every sport are going to be magically transformed by doing Olympic lifts. I can't see how a paddler is going to benefit in particular by doing these explosive lifts. There is no question that for some types of training, you have to take this risk to excel. But there are other types of strength training that will give athletes in many sports the maximum possible response without having to take the risks associated with Olympic lifting. I think it just requires some experience and knowledge to be able to make that discrimination. I agree with Bill Gonyea that there shouldn't be an overriding fear of Olympic lifts that suppresses investigation and exploration.

STRONG: Does anybody have long-term experience concerning the morbidity and mortality of powerlifters? It seems from the literature that the super heavyweights have a greatly shortened lifespan. This may not be related to the lifting as much as it is to some of the unusual supplements that they may ingest as well as to their weight and other activities.

SALE: In regard to the morbidity, my opinion is that the most significant factor would be the chronic use of anabolic steroids and the deleterious effects that they have on the blood lipid profile, an effect that is fairly well documented. There are very few serious lifters who don't carry chronic injuries into retirement. I don't think that's going to make one die prematurely, but there's no doubt that we all will carry our adolescent excesses with us into middle age, regardless of the sport in which we participate.

STRONG: Did Alexseev not die of a stroke before 40? And did Paul Anderson not have two kidney transplants by age 50? These are the kinds of problems that I was thinking of in addition to the steroids. It may be the high protein content of the diet or simply the large body size that's involved.

BLIMKIE: Or it may be the body type that selects itself out to be good at this.

GONYEA: The other aspect is the high lean muscle mass to body fat ratio in these lifters. The older super heavyweight was very fat, and that's changed dramatically. Now we have power lifters that are lifting competitively in their sixth and seventh decades. I think nutrition has become an important issue, and training without steroids has become an important issue. Winning for any sake in any athletic endeavor carries some health risks that may be fatal, and strength training is no different than any of the other sports.

BALDWIN: Is there translation of strength training effects to various tasks on the athletic scene? Are there some indices that we can use to show that strength is paying off in terms of performance? For example, if I could get Larry Bird to go into a strength training program for his legs, could he begin to start slam dunking the basketball for the Celtics so they might return to the glory years?

SALE: Two studies on prepubescent children, one by Weltman et al. and the other by Nielson, did show that strength training with isometric contractions or with hydraulic resistance did increase vertical jump ability, which could be considered a type of athletic performance. If the sport performance doesn't require a lot of strategy, and if strength is recognized as an important factor in that sport, one observes a large transfer of an increase in strength to an increase in performance. But when the skill is "open" and more complex, it becomes more difficult to detect this relationship. For example, at one time we worked with the national ski team in Canada; we became discouraged because we often got negative correlations; that is, the skiers that were the strongest and had the greatest anaerobic power were slowest getting down the hill. Factors other than our physiological measurements were obviously more important. Now we work with rowers. Theirs is a closed skill, and we get a nice transfer of increases in strength to increases in speed over the race course. Thus, with some less complex skills, one can justify the use of strength training in children in the same ways one would with adolescents or adults.

HOLLOSZY: Is there any evidence that children who train strenuously end up with a larger number of muscle fibers and as a result have a greater potential for developing large muscles later in life?

SALE: I am not aware of that in human muscle. Bill Gonyea may have done some studies with young cats in training, but I'm not sure.

GONYEA: No. As far as I know, there hasn't been a study done with exercise using young animals or young humans.

SALE: We do have some estimated muscle fiber numbers in adult men and women in one upper limb muscle. We have found that in the biceps, males had significantly more muscle fibers than females.

The most obvious interpretation is that they were born that way, and this may give the edge to the male in upper body strength that has been pointed out so many times. Whether or not that has occurred from birth or whether it suddenly manifests itself at puberty, I don't know.

SHEPHARD: I would endorse what other people have said about the need to look at the risks versus the benefits of strength training in young people as a group, but I wonder whether we would be wise to include an endorsement of the idea that an examination of a symptom-free young person is essential before he or she begins any strength training. I don't think there is any evidence that this has a positive influence in terms of benefits versus the cost of such an examination. In fact, it may be making exercise seem a medical procedure rather than a natural behavior for the child.

BROOKS: Do we have any evidence that the increases in strength that you have shown in children are permanent? Are there any data on twins, where one twin trains and gets ahead and the other then catches up in strength later on?

SALE: I don't know about the twin studies. Claude Bouchard may have something on that, but Joe Blimkie actually had a detraining phase as part of his study.

BLIMKIE: Obviously we were limited in the numbers of subjects that we began with. We had a control group of six boys and had 13 boys in the training group. We followed them for a two-month period subsequent to the cessation of the training program to see whether or not the strength gains were permanent. We divided the group of 19 boys into thirds. One group trained once per week for two months, one group did no training at all but had belonged to the initial training group, and another group of six boys had belonged to the initial control group. What we saw in that particular two-month period was that the boys who had initially made significant strength gains lost those strength gains by the end of two months, even the group that continued to perform one training session on a weekly basis. So we can say that one training session per week was not a sufficient stimulus to sustain the strength gain that was achieved earlier.

BOUCHARD: I think it is pretty difficult to determine whether or not there are differences between the various age groups in trainability, because within a given age, the range in the training response is quite considerable. We find almost a 100 percent difference in the training response among individuals of the same gender and age class. So if you want to show that there are differences with age in trainability, you have to have, first of all, a fairly large sample size to have a good group mean for the training response. In other words, you have to have high responders and low responders and average responders in large enough quantities in the group. Second, if one wants to show there are differences across ages, one must be sure that the maximal training response has occurred. On the basis of our data, I suspect that there is no difference in trainability across age at all, not even before puberty. We have a similar training response across ages. The variation that we find among individuals is much greater than the variation we find with age.

SALE: We certainly agree that there is great individual variation. For some reason, the prepubescent boys had more difficulty increasing muscle size than the adults, even though they were comparable in everything else. I accept your point, however.

BLIMKIE: One doesn't know until after the fact whether or not the groups are matched comparably in terms of training sensitivity. I guess we assume that the selection of subjects into the training studies ensures that we get equal proportions of highly sensitive and lesser sensitive responders to training in the different age groups. But that may not always be the case.

MALINA: Bill Gonyea made the statement that the maximal growth rate occurs in prepubescent children. In most studies of growth, estimated either from size or estimated diameters of muscles from X-rays, growth rate in prepubescent children is very, very slow compared to that in infants, in early childhood, and in adolescence; so what do you mean by maximal growth rate, Bill?

GONYEA: I was thinking of caloric utilization per unit body mass, which seems to be quite high in prepubescent children. If you do a linear measurement or an estimate of mass increase, you're right. I think it's a matter of how we measure it, but certainly the caloric utilization per unit of mass is very high in the prepubescent.

MALINA: That doesn't really refer to growth. That's energy expenditure. Growth rate at that stage is quite slow, and the energy intake that is used for growth at this stage of life is less than 1%.

MICHELI: I would like to comment on the injury question. There have been two studies of Olympic-type lifts in younger athletes, both of which show a very high incidence of low-back injuries, i.e., spondylolysis. Therefore, I would like to echo concerns of certain presenters here that strength training may indeed have benefits for certain children in certain situations if well supervised, but Olympic strength training has to be watched very carefully because of maneuvers that involve hyperlordosis of the low back. They may not die from it, but they have a very high incidence of low-back injury.

SUTTON: Do we know anything about the blood pressure responses to weightlifting in children, even by indirect measurements of blood pressure? Have there been reports of children having strokes or other cerebrovascular incidents of any kind while performing these weightlifting maneuvers?

SALE: I don't have real answers to that. However, I believe Frank Katch's group has made direct blood pressure measurements in children and found that the blood pressure response in these children was somewhat less than what we have seen in young adults. Whether or not this was due to any inhibition or anxiety the children had during the study, I don't know.

The relative force production is related to the blood pressure response in our adults. In other words, a 250 lb. football player, will exhibit the same blood pressure as a 150 lb. man if both make maximal contractions and achieve the same degree of motor unit activation. Children can achieve about the same force per unit cross-sectional area of muscle as can adults. If the pressor response is related to that, then these children may in fact be developing, in maximal training, the same types of blood pressures as we see in adults. Whether or not they are more resistant to any cerebrovascular accidents, I don't know.

VAILAS: There is a recent study that has shown that strength training with prepubescent children is associated with a decrease in the incidence of myotendinous injury. That is one isolated situation. However, there is also evidence of a greater incidence of scoliosis in female swimmers who are undergoing strength training. Whether this is caused by the swimming or the strength training is unclear, but some people feel that the scoliosis incidence is somewhat elevated in this population.

We need to follow these athletes over a longer period of time to see what has happened to them beyond the point of skeletal maturity. For example, Mandelbaum et al. recently studied collegiate gymnasts and showed that the gymnasts who had the greatest wrist pain had a very large positive ulnar variance. It was suggested that this ulnar variance was caused by some of the mechanical factors that had been imposed upon bone and was related either to the sport or to the strength training of these athletes that was started very early in childhood and continued into the college years. So I think these are the kinds of things that we have to be very careful about.

SALE: Some years ago we did electrophysiological studies on young gymnasts and found evidence of nerve damage, such as reduced motor unit counts and reduced compound action potentials. As a former gymnast, I am well aware of what was happening in this case; i.e., chronic trauma to the wrists and ankles.

One point I want to make is that in strength training done in the normal way, the amount of time actually spent doing contractions isn't very long. I think a child is more likely to get injured by practicing a particular sport several hours a day than if he or she comes in for 30 min, two or three times per week and does a few sets of weight training exercises with each muscle group. That type of strength training is probably benign in comparison to some of the overuse situations that young children are exposed to in other sports.

5

Growth and Maturation: Normal Variation and Effect of Training

ROBERT M. MALINA, PH.D.

INTRODUCTION
 I. GROWTH AND MATURATION
 II. SOMATIC GROWTH
   A. Body Size
   B. Physique
   C. Body Composition
   D. Fat Distribution
 III. BIOLOGICAL MATURATION
   A. Skeletal Maturation
   B. Somatic Maturation—Age at Peak Height Velocity
     1. Timing of Growth Spurts in Other Dimensions
   C. Sexual Maturation
 IV. MATURITY-ASSOCIATION VARIATION IN GROWTH
   A. Early and Late Maturers
   B. Variation Relative to Age at Peak Height Velocity
 V. TRAINING, GROWTH, AND MATURATION
   A. A Biosocial Model
   B. Physical Activity and Training
   C. Training and Stature
   D. Training, Body Weight, and Composition
   E. Training and Fat Distribution
   F. Training and Physique
   G. Training and Maturation
     1. Age at Peak Height Velocity
     2. Skeletal Maturation
     3. Sexual Maturation
 VI. TRAINING, MATURATION, AND HORMONES
 SUMMARY
 BIBLIOGRAPHY
 DISCUSSION

INTRODUCTION

The integrated nature of growth and maturation is maintained, to a large extent, by the actions of genes, hormones, nutrients and energy, which interact with the environments in which the child lives. Potential environmental sources of variation in growth and maturation include socioeconomic status of the family, illness history, family size, dietary changes, climate, physical activity, psychosocial conditions, and others.

Regular physical activity is often viewed as a favorable influence on the processes of growth and maturation. Activity, of course, takes many forms, and that associated with regular training for sport is of primary interest to this discussion. The task of partitioning activity-induced changes from those associated with normal growth and maturation, however, is complex. Age- and sex-associated variation in several measures of growth and maturation, and maturity-associated variation in growth are thus first considered. The influence of regular training on growth and maturation is then evaluated.

I. GROWTH AND MATURATION

The terms "growth" and "maturation" may have different meanings to professionals working with children and adolescents. Growth refers to an increase in size, either of the body as a whole or of its parts. Aerobic power, muscular strength, and endurance are largely related to body size and have growth patterns that are generally similar to those for stature and weight. Maturity implies a time component marking the rate of progress toward the mature state, which varies among systems of the body. Skeletal age, age at appearance of secondary sex characteristics, and age at peak height velocity (PHV) are the most commonly used indicators of biological maturity.

Growth and maturation are processes that begin prenatally and continue postnatally into the third decade of life. Studies of growth and maturation do not ordinarily focus on the processes per se, but on the outcomes of these processes, i.e., size and maturity status attained rather than cellular hyperplasia and hypertrophy and accretion of intercellular materials.

II. SOMATIC GROWTH

A. Body Size

Stature and weight are the two most commonly used indicators of growth status. Both follow a four-phased or double sigmoid pattern: rapid gain in infancy and early childhood, slower, relatively constant gain in middle childhood, rapid gain during the adolescent spurt, and slow increase and eventual cessation of growth at the attainment of adult size. Body weight, of course, continues to increase after statural growth has ceased. Sex differences in stature and weight are negligible during childhood. During the early part of adolescence, girls are, on average, taller and heavier because they enter the adolescent spurt earlier than boys. Girls soon lose the size advantage as the male adolescent spurt occurs. Boys catch up and eventually surpass girls in stature and weight.

Most external body dimensions, e.g., leg length, biacromial and bicristal breadths, and limb circumferences; estimates of body composition, e.g., fat-free mass, muscle, and skeletal mass; and dimensions of the viscera, e.g., heart and lung volume, follow growth patterns similar to those for stature and weight. The timing and magnitude of the adolescent spurt in specific dimensions and tissues vary. Sex differences are minor during childhood, i.e., there is much overlap between boys and girls. The basic pattern of sexual dimorphism in size, physique, and body composition is established during adolescence. Descriptive statistics for age- and sex-associated variation in a variety of measures of somatic growth of North American children from birth to young adulthood have been summarized elsewhere (Malina & Roche, 1983; Roche & Malina, 1983).

B. Physique

Physique refers to the general configuration of the body as opposed to emphasis on specific features. The concept of somatotype developed by Sheldon is often used to describe changes in physique during growth. The somatotype is a composite based on differential contributions of endomorphy, mesomorphy, and ectomorphy. Endomorphy refers to the relative preponderance of the digestive organs and of softness and roundness of contour throughout the body. Mesomorphy refers to a predominance of muscle, bone, and connective tissue so that muscularity has very clear definition. Ectomorphy refers to a general linearity of build, predominance of surface area over body mass, and weak definition of musculature.

The method of somatotyping as described by Sheldon is based on anthroposcopic ratings of standardized photographs in combination with a stature/weight ratio (Sheldon et al., 1940, 1954). The method has a degree of subjectivity, but in the hands of trained raters, it is quite reliable. More recently, the anthropometric method of Heath and Carter (Carter, 1980), has received relatively wide use. The method relies on the basic principles of Sheldon, but uses several anthropometric dimensions to estimate the three components of the somatotype. Endomorphy, for example, is based on the sum of three skinfold thicknesses; mesomorphy is based on arm and calf circumferences corrected for the triceps and medial calf skinfolds, respectively, and biepicondylar and bicondylar breadths corrected for stature; and ectomorphy is based on a stature/weight ratio as in Sheldon's method.

Somatotype ratings range from 1 through 7, although in the Heath-Carter method ratings higher than 7 can be assigned. A rating of 1 represents the least expression of the somatotype component. The higher the rating, the greater the expression of the somatotype component. Ratings of each component comprise the individual's somatotype. For example, if a somatotype is 263, the first number (2) refers to endomorphy, the second (6) to mesomorphy, and the third (3) to ectomorphy. Thus, this individual is low in endomorphy, high in mesomorphy, and moderate in ectomorphy.

Mean somatotypes for several longitudinal samples of boys seen at different ages from early childhood to young adulthood are summarized in Table 5-1. Standard deviations for most means are about 1.0 and are not shown in the table. Mean somatotypes change little with age in boys. If there is a trend, it is toward an increase in mesomorphy after about 13 y. Somatotypes in the Belgian series, shown in Table 5-1, were rated with a slight modification of Sheldon's original procedures and with the Heath-Carter anthropometric method. The two methods give different estimates. Heath-Carter anthropometric somatotypes are generally lower in endomorphy and higher in mesomorphy at most ages.

Two of the samples of boys were somatotyped in adulthood. Mesomorphy increases and ectomorphy declines between late adolescence and adulthood. Endomorphy is more variable.

In contrast to the relative wealth of data for boys, there is a dearth of longitudinal somatotype data for girls (Table 5-2). With growth and maturation, girls gain primarily in endomorphy and decline somewhat in ectomorphy. From 17 to 33, endomorphy and mesomorphy continue to increase, while ectomorphy declines.

C. Body Composition

Changes in body composition during growth are reasonably well-documented. However, recent discussions of the chemical immaturity of children emphasize limitations in applying adult-based constants and formulae, which quite often yield spuriously high or low estimates of body composition in growing individuals. Several investigators have used both direct and indirect estimates of body composition from a variety of sources to derive estimates of the body composition of reference children and adolescents. Fomon and col-

TABLE 5-1. Mean Somatotypes* of Boys in Several North American and European Longitudinal Studies

Age	Connecticut (Walker, 1978) Anthroposcopic			California (Zuk, 1958) Anthroposcopic			Oregon (Clarke, 1971) Anthroposcopic			England (Walker & Tanner, 1980) Anthroposcopic			Belgium (Claessens et al., 1986) Anthroposcopic			Belgium (Claessens et al., 1986) Anthropometric			Czechoslovakia (Parizkova & Carter, 1976) Anthropometric		
	Endo	Meso	Ecto	Endo	Meso	Ecto	Endo	Meso	Ecto	Endo	Meso	Ecto	Endo	Meso	Ecto	Endo	Meso	Ecto	Endo	Meso	Ecto
2-5	3.7	4.2	4.1																		
5										3.5	3.8	3.8									
8										3.5	3.9	4.0									
9							3.4	4.2	2.9												
10							3.5	4.1	2.9												
11							3.4	4.2	3.2	3.5	3.8	4.0							2.1	4.1	3.4
12				3.2	3.3	3.9	3.5	4.1	3.2										2.1	3.9	3.6
13							3.5	4.0	3.2				3.5	3.5	3.7	2.2	4.1	3.6	1.9	4.0	3.6
14							3.3	4.1	3.3	3.5	3.8	4.2	3.5	3.7	3.5	2.3	4.1	3.7	2.3	4.0	3.8
15							3.3	4.1	3.5				3.5	3.6	3.6	2.6	3.8	3.7	1.5	3.8	3.8
16							3.4	4.2	3.4				3.4	3.7	3.8	2.7	4.1	3.8	1.6	3.8	3.7
17													3.4	3.9	3.6	2.5	4.0	3.5	1.8	3.8	3.5
18	4.1	4.3	3.6[a]	2.9	4.1	4.3							3.5	4.0	3.4	2.6	3.9	3.4	2.3	4.3	3.3
Adult				3.0	4.7	3.7[b]				3.5	4.0	3.9							2.7	5.4	2.5[c]

*Somatotypes: Endo = endomorphy, Meso = mesomorphy, Ecto = ectomorphy
[a]Late adolescent somatotype
[b]Somatotype at 33 years of age
[c]Somatotype at 24 years of age (Carter & Parizkova, 1978)

TABLE 5-2. *Mean Somatotypes of Girls in Two Longitudinal Studies*

Age (yrs)	Endomorphy	Mesomorphy	Ectomorphy	Reference
2–5	4.4	4.5	3.8	Connecticut
Late adolescent	5.1	3.3	3.4	(Walker, 1978)
12	2.9	3.3	3.5	California
17	4.3	3.5	3.3	(Zuk, 1958)
33	4.7	3.9	2.8	

leagues (1982) reported such estimates for children between birth and 10 y. Haschke (1983) did the same for boys from 10 to 18 y, while Lohman (1986) made similar estimates for boys and girls from about 7 y to young adulthood. In these analyses, the basic issue is the chemical composition of the developing individual compared with the adult, and the need to adjust formulae for estimating body composition to account for the chemical immaturity of children.

Densitometry and hydrometry are two of the more commonly used methods of estimating gross body composition in children. Measurements of body density (BD) were compiled from 32 studies (Malina et al., 1988), while measurements of total body water (TBW) were compiled from eight studies of children, youth, and young adults (Boileau et al., 1984; Cheek, 1968; Edelman et al., 1952; Haschke, 1983; Novak, 1966; Schutte, 1980; Schutte et al., 1984; Young et al., 1968). Subjects were primarily white, but several samples of American blacks are included. The total sample for BD included 3,667 subjects, (2,110 males, 1,557 females) from 8 through 20 y, while that for TBW included 924 subjects (540 males and 384 females) 6 through 23 y. Reported means for BD and TBW were adjusted for sample size in each study, and the data were then consolidated by age and sex to describe growth curves for these body composition parameters from middle childhood to young adulthood.

Growth curves for BD and TBW are shown in Figure 5-1. Although the data base is heterogeneous and cross-sectional, the means provide an indication of the growth pattern and sex difference in these basic parameters of body composition. BD declines in males from about 8 through 10 y and then increases gradually through about 16 to 17 y. In females, BD declines from about 8 through 11 y and subsequently shows only a slight increase, which reaches a plateau by about 14 y. BD declines slightly in both sexes in late adolescence and young adulthood. TBW, on the other hand, shows a growth pattern similar to stature and weight. While sex differences in BD are consistent through childhood and adolescence, they become apparent for TBW only with the male adolescent spurt.

BD and TBW values were subsequently converted to estimates

of fat-free mass (FFM) and fat mass (FM). To allow for the changing chemical composition of the FFM during growth, estimated density and water content of the FFM at different ages reported by Lohman (1986) were used to derive percentage fat and FFM respectively. Relative fatness was subsequently converted to absolute FM, which was then subtracted from body weight to derive FFM in the BD sample,

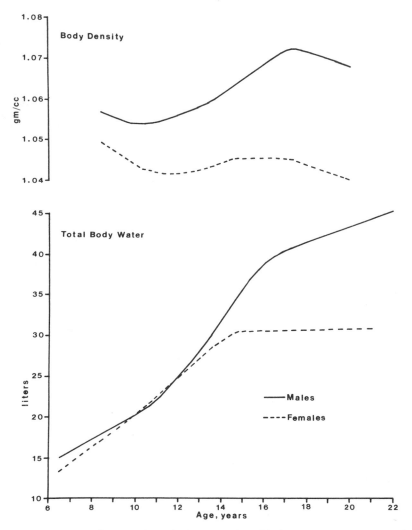

FIGURE 5-1. *Growth curves for body density and total body water. Data points are based on moving averages and smoothed.*

while FFM was subtracted from body weight to derive FM in the TBW sample.

Since body weight is needed to derive FM and FFM, weights and statures of the two body composition samples were compared to each other (Figure 5-2) and to reference data for American children (Hamill et al., 1977). The composite curves for stature and weight

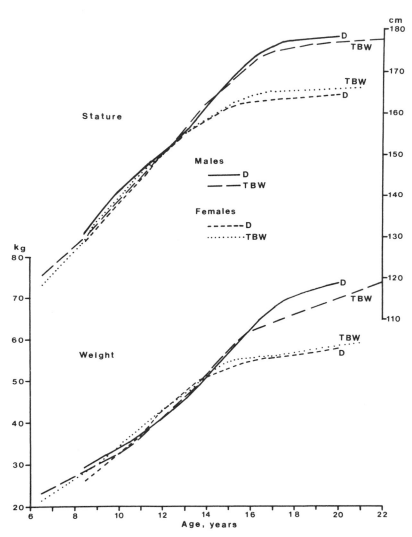

FIGURE 5-2. *Statures and weights of the samples upon which estimates of body composition are based. Data points are based on moving averages and smoothed.*

are similar to the reference data in both sexes, but males in the BD series tend to be slightly taller and heavier than males in the TBW series from 16 y into young adulthood. Hence, the estimates of FFM and FM for the composite samples should provide a reasonably adequate indication of the growth pattern in FFM and FM (Figure 5-3).

FFM follows a growth pattern similar to stature and weight, and the sex difference become clearly established during the adolescent

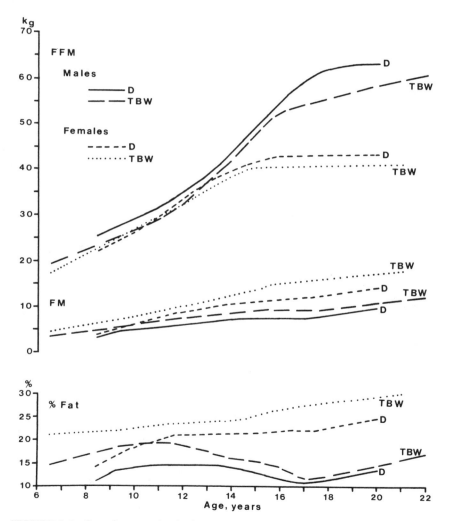

FIGURE 5-3. *Growth curves for fat-free mass (FFM), fat mass (FM) and relative fatness (percent fat). Data oionts are based on moving averages and smoothed.*

growth spurt. It appears that BD provides a slightly greater estimate of FFM from middle childhood through adolescence in both sexes, although the magnitude of the difference in late adolescent males is influenced in part by the stature and weight differences between the samples. Young adult values of FFM are reached earlier in females, about 15 to 16 y, compared with 19 to 20 y in males. In late adolescence and young adulthood, males have, on average, a FFM that is about 1.5 times larger than that of females. The difference reflects the male adolescent spurt in muscle mass and the sex difference in stature in young adults. For example, the sex difference in densitometric estimates of FFM per unit stature prior to the male adolescent spurt is negligible, i.e., 0.26 kg $FFM \cdot cm^{-1}$ and 0.25 kg $FFM \cdot cm^{-1}$ at 13 y in males and females, respectively. Subsequently, FFM increases at a greater rate than stature in males so that by young adulthood males have about 0.36 kg $FFM \cdot cm^{-1}$ stature while females have only about 0.26 kg $FFM \cdot cm^{-1}$ stature.

Estimated FM increases, on the average, at a slightly greater rate from childhood through adolescence in girls. It appears to reach a plateau near the time of the adolescent spurt in boys. Estimates of FM derived from TBW tend to be higher than those derived from BD in both sexes, but the difference appears to increase with age through adolescence in girls. In contrast to FFM, females have, on average, about 1.5 to 2.0 times the FM of males in late adolescence and young adulthood.

Females have a greater percentage of body fat than males from childhood into young adulthood. Relative fatness of females increases gradually through adolescence in the same manner as FM. Relative fatness appears to be rather stable in males until just before the adolescent spurt (about 12 y), when it gradually declines. Percentage fat reaches its lowest point at about 16 to 17 y, then gradually rises into young adulthood. Rapid growth of FFM while fat accumulation is rather slow accounts for the decline in relative fatness during male adolescence, i.e., fat contributes a lesser percentage to body weight at this time.

Estimates of relative fatness that allow for the changing chemical composition of the FFM in children and youth are lower than those reported in the original studies that used adult-based formulae. Thus, by adjusting for the chemical immaturity of children and youth, estimates of fatness are reduced and perhaps more realistic. Nevertheless, those based on TBW are consistently higher.

The impact of adolescence on body composition is marked. Using the densitometric estimates, boys gain about 32.5 kg of FFM and 3.2 kg of FM from about 10 to 18 y, but decline in relative fatness by about 2.7%. Girls gain about 17.3 kg of FFM, 7.1 kg of FM, and

5.0% in relative fatness over the same span. This reduces to about 4.1 kg FFM·y^{-1}, 0.4 kg FM·y^{-1}, and −0.3% fat·y^{-1} in boys, and 2.2 kg FFM·y^{-1}, 0.9 kg FM·y^{-1}, and +0.6% fat·y^{-1} in girls from 10 to 18 y. These estimates are reasonably similar to those of Chumlea et al. (1983) for 30 boys and 39 girls measured for two or three consecutive years from 10 to 18 y, i.e., 4.4 kg FFM·y^{-1}, 0.1 kg FM·y^{-1}, and −1.1% fat·y^{-1} in boys and 2.3 kg FFM·y^{-1}, 1.1 kg FM·y^{-1}, and +0.2% fat·y^{-1} in girls.

D. Fat Distribution

Regional variation in amount of adipose tissue is currently of interest because fat distribution, adipose tissue metabolism, abnormalities in lipid and carbohydrate metabolism, and several chronic diseases are associated in adults (Bjorntorp, 1986). Fat distribution refers to location of fat and not to the absolute or relative amount of fat. Adults with a more central distribution of fat, e.g., relatively more on the abdomen than on the extremities, are apparently more at risk for cardiovascular disease and non-insulin dependent diabetes. Changes in fat distribution during growth thus merit closer examination.

The distribution of subcutaneous fat is commonly viewed in terms of the ratio of skinfold thicknesses measured on the trunk to those measured on the extremities. Changes in the ratio of the sum of three trunk skinfolds (subscapular, suprailiac and abdominal) to the sum of three extremity skinfolds (triceps, biceps, and medial calf) during growth are shown in Figure 5-4. The proportional distribution of trunk and extremity subcutaneous fat is rather stable during childhood and similar in boys and girls. Subsequently, sex differences in subcutaneous fat distribution occur. Females appear to gain relatively more subcutaneous fat on the trunk during early adolescence, but later they gain fat on the trunk and extremities at a similar rate. Males, on the other hand, accumulate relatively more fat on the trunk during adolescence, which is accentuated by a reduction in subcutaneous fat on the extremities at this time (Malina & Bouchard, 1988).

There is, at present, no effective means of distinguishing between subcutaneous and internal fat in children. Assuming that the ratio of the sum of skinfolds taken at several trunk and extremity sites (the six skinfolds indicated above) to a densitometric estimate of FM provides an estimate of the contribution of subcutaneous fat to FM, FM increases at a faster rate than subcutaneous fat during childhood in both sexes (Figure 5-5). The trend continues through adolescence in girls, but the relationship between subcutaneous fat

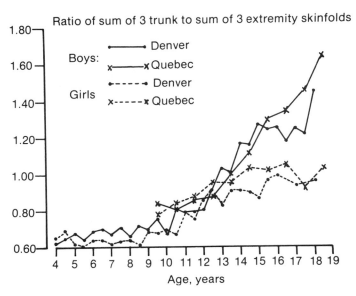

FIGURE 5-4. *Ratios of the sum of three trunk (subscapular, suprailiac, abdominal) to the sum of three extremity (triceps, biceps, medial calf) skinfold thicknesses in Denver and Quebec children and youth. Medians, drawn after Malina and Bouchard (1988).*

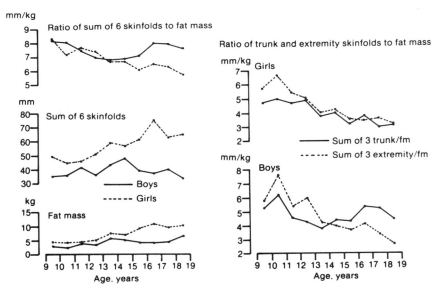

FIGURE 5-5. *Changes in fat mass, subcutaneous fat, and ratios of subcutaneous fat to fat mass in Quebec children and youth. Fat mass is densitometrically estimated, and subcutaneous fat is based on the sum of the six skinfolds indicated in Figure 5-4. Medians, drawn after Malina and Bouchard (1988).*

and FM changes during male adolescence. Relative to FM, males have proportionally more subcutaneous fat on the trunk and less on the extremities.

III. BIOLOGICAL MATURATION

The concept of maturation refers to the individual's "biological clock," which regulates progress toward the mature state. Individuals vary in level of maturity attained at a given point in time, i.e., maturity status at a given age, and in tempo or rate of maturation over time, i.e., maturity progress. The concept of maturation thus relates biological time to calendar time, and the two do not necessarily proceed in concert.

Maturation varies to some extent with the biological system used. The more commonly used maturity indicators in growth studies are skeletal, somatic, and sexual maturation. Indicators of somatic and sexual maturation are limited to the adolescent or pubertal phase of growth and thus have limited applicability. Skeletal maturation, on the other hand, can be monitored from infancy through young adulthood, but estimation of skeletal maturation requires that children be exposed to radiation (X-rays).

A. Skeletal Maturation

Since all children start with a prenatal skeleton of cartilage and have a fully ossified skeleton in early adulthood, the maturation of the skeleton is one of the more effective methods for assessing biological maturation. Monitoring the progress of individual bones from cartilage model to adult morphology provides the basis for assessing skeletal maturity.

The maturity progress of the skeleton is easily monitored with the careful and judicious used of standardized X-rays, and the bones of the hand and wrist provide the primary basis for assessing skeletal maturity in growth studies. The Greulich-Pyle (Greulich & Pyle, 1959) and Tanner-Whitehouse (Tanner et al., 1983) methods are most commonly used.

The Greulich-Pyle method is sometimes called the atlas or inspectional method. It entails the matching of a hand-wrist X-ray of a specific child as closely as possible with a series of standard X-ray plates, which correspond to successive levels of skeletal maturation at specific chronological ages. The method should be applied by rating the skeletal maturity of each individual bone. Each bone is matched to the standard plates in the atlas, and the one with which the individual bone most closely coincides is noted. The skeletal age of the standard plate is the assigned skeletal age of the bone in question. The process is repeated for all bones that are present in the hand and wrist, and the child's skeletal age is the median of the skeletal ages of each individually rated bone. In practice, however, the Greulich-Pyle method is applied most often in a more global manner, i.e., the bones of the hand-wrist are compared as a group to the standard plates in the atlas. The age of the standard plate with which a given child's film most closely matches is assigned as the child's skeletal age. Thus, if the hand-wrist X-ray of a 7-year-old child matches the standard plate for 8-year-old children, the child's skeletal age is 8 years.

The Tanner-Whitehouse method entails matching the features of individual bones on a given film to a series of written criteria for the stages through which 20 bones of the hand-wrist pass as they progress from initial appearance to the mature state. Each stage for the 20 bones that are rated has a specific point score. The scores of the 20 bones are then totaled to give a skeletal maturity score, which can be converted to a skeletal age.

A new method for assessing the skeletal maturity of the hand and wrist, the Fels Method (Roche et al., 1988) has been recently described. As for the other methods, matching is the basis of the technique. However, the authors defined and verified the presence of maturity indicators for each bone of the hand-wrist for consistency and reliability. Redundant indicators were deleted and/or combined to reduce the number. Grades are assigned to the maturity indicators of each bone and subsequently entered into a microcomputer that, with the appropriate program, calculates a skeletal age and a standard error for the film under evaluation. The latter feature, i.e., the standard error, is not available with the Greulich-Pyle and Tanner-Whitehouse methods.

All methods provide an estimate of skeletal age, which corresponds to the level of skeletal maturity attained by children in the reference sample at a specific chronological age. Skeletal ages determined by the methods, however, are not equivalent.

Girls are advanced in skeletal maturity compared to boys at all ages and reach skeletal maturity earlier. Skeletal maturity of the hand and wrist is attained, on average, by girls at about 16 to 17 y and by boys at about 18 to 19 y, depending on the method used.

B. Somatic Maturation—Age at Peak Height Velocity (PHV)

The timing of the adolescent growth spurt in specific body dimensions can be used as an indicator of somatic maturity. The most commonly used measurement is stature, and the maturity indicator is the age at peak height velocity, i.e., the age of maximal growth in stature during the spurt. Longitudinal data are required to estimate the age at PHV. Growth curves are fit either mathematically or graphically to individual records to extract age at PHV, the velocity of statural growth at this time, and occasionally the age at initiation of the spurt.

Ages at PHV and peak height velocities for samples of North American and European children have been recently summarized (Beunen & Malina, 1988; Malina et al., 1988). The distributions of the reported mean/median ages at PHV and standard deviations are shown in Table 5-3. Allowing for methodological differences in estimating these parameters, the data show a reasonable degree of uniformity among samples of North American and European children. The uniformity is of interest given the period of time over which the longitudinal observations have been made. Studies of

TABLE 5-3. *Frequency Distributions of Mean/Median Ages at Peak Height Velocity and Standard Deviations Reported for North American and European Girls and Boys**

Age	Girls	Boys
Ages at PHV		
(yrs)		
11.4	2	
11.5	1	
11.6	3	
11.7	4	
11.8	1	
11.9	5	
12.0	4	
12.1	2	
12.2	4	
13.4		1
13.5		
13.6		
13.7		1
13.8		2
13.9		6
14.0		3
14.1		5
14.2		3
14.3		1
14.4		1
Standard Deviations		
(yrs)		
0.7	3	
0.8	2	2
0.9	8	7
1.0	6	6
1.1	5	4
1.2	1	1

*Based on data reported in Beunen and Malina (1988) and Malina et al. (1988). Standard deviations were not reported for some samples.

United States children were begun in the late 1920s, a number of the European studies were begun in the mid-1950s, and others were done in the 1960s and 1970s.

Girls are advanced, on average, about two years in the timing of the initiation of the growth spurt and PHV. PHV occurs close to 12 y in girls and 14 y in boys, with standard deviations of one year or a bit more in most studies (Table 5-3). In contrast, the magnitude of the spurt, PHV, is generally greater in males, although there is considerable overlap compared with that for mean ages at PHV.

These trends are only sample estimates, and there is considerable variation within samples. For example, in 112 boys of the Zurich study, estimates for individual boys range from 7.8 to 13.5 y for age at initiation of the spurt, from 12.0 to 15.8 y for age at PHV, and 6.7 to 12.4 $cm \cdot y^{-1}$ for PHV. Corresponding data for 110 Swiss girls are 6.6 to 12.9 y for age at initiation of the spurt, 9.3 to 15.0 y for age at PHV, and 5.0 to 10.1 $cm \cdot y^{-1}$ for PHV (Largo et al., 1978).

1. **Timing of Growth Spurts in Other Dimensions.** Ages at peak velocity and peak velocities of adolescent growth in other dimensions provide information on the differential timing of growth spurts. Estimated ages at peak velocity and peak velocities for stature, body weight, estimated leg length, and sitting height in several longitudinal studies are thus summarized in Table 5-4. Maximum growth in leg length generally occurs, on average, before PHV, while maximum growth in weight and sitting height occur after PHV.

The timing of maximum velocities of several anthropometric dimensions relative to PHV and peak weight velocity (PWV) in Belgian boys is indicated in Table 5-5. Corresponding data are not available for girls. Maximum velocities for lower limb dimensions

TABLE 5-4. *Mean Ages (Years) at Peak Velocity for Stature, Body Weight, Estimated Leg Length, and Sitting Height in Several Samples of North American and European Youth**

	Leg Length	Stature	Sitting Height	Weight
Girls				
California	11.0	11.7	11.8	12.2
England	11.6	11.9	12.2	12.9
Poland	11.2	11.7	12.2	12.4
Boys				
California	13.6	14.1	14.5	14.5
Belgium	14.0	14.2	14.3	14.6
England	13.6	13.9	14.3	14.3
Poland	13.6	14.0	14.4	14.2

*Based on Malina et al. (1988), which includes same sizes, methods of estimating ages, and standard deviations. Most standard deviations are approximately ±1 year.

TABLE 5-5. *Timing of Maximum Observed Velocities of Anthropometric Dimensions Relative to Peak Height Velocity and Peak Weight Velocity in Belgian Boys**

Dimension	Peak Height Velocity			Peak Weight Velocity		
	Before	At	After	Before	At	After
Height			X			
Weight		X				
Sitting height		X	X			
Leg length	X		X			
Biacromial breadth		X		X		
Chest breadth		X		X		
Biepicondylar breadth, humerus		X	X			
Bicondylar breadth, femur	X		X			
Chest circumference, inspiration		X	X			
Flexed arm circumference		X		X		
Thigh circumference	X			X		
Calf circumference	X		X			

*Adapted from Beunen et al. (1988).

precede PHV, but maximum velocities for body weight, sitting height, and skeletal breadths and circumferences of the trunk and upper extremity follow PHV. In contrast, no dimensions show their maximum velocity after PWV. Rather, all dimensions experience their spurts prior to or coincident with PWV. Of those that occur coincident with PWV, two are skeletal breadths of the trunk, biacromial and chest breadths. The timing of adolescent spurts in limb circumferences is, of course, confounded in part by loss of subcutaneous fat on the extremities during male adolescence.

C. Sexual Maturation

The assessment of sexual maturation is based upon the development of the secondary sex characteristics, i.e., breast development and menarche in girls, penis and testes (genital) development in boys, and pubic hair in both sexes. Menarche is the most commonly reported maturity indicator of female adolescence. The most commonly used criteria for pubic hair, breast and genital maturation are the five-stage scales described by Tanner (1962), which are based in part upon criteria of earlier studies. Stage 1 indicates the absence of development of the particular characteristic, and Stage 2 indicates the initial development. Stages 3 and 4 indicate intermediate stages of development, while Stage 5 indicates the mature state.

The development of these characteristics is, of course, a continuous process upon which the stages are superimposed. Thus, the rating scales are somewhat arbitrary. For example, a boy just entering Stage G 3 of genital development is rated the same as a boy nearing the end of G 3, i.e., they are both rated as being in G 3. The latter boy is really more advanced in maturation than the former, but given the limitations of the procedure, both are rated as being in G 3.

The most common sequences for the development of secondary sex characteristics in girls and boys based on the mean/median ages for several samples of European and North American youth are summarized in Table 5-6. Age at PHV is also included so that the timing of secondary sex characteristic development relative to age at maximum growth can be noted. Allowing for the range of mean/median ages for each stage/event, several trends are apparent. First, in most samples, the budding of the breasts in girls (B 2) and the initial enlargement of male genitalia (G 2) are, on average, the first overt signs of sexual maturation. In three samples of girls the average age at PH 2 is equal to or in advance of B 2, and in only one sample of boys the average age of PH 2 is in advance of G 2. Although methodological variation is a factor, i.e., ratings made from standardized photographs as in the Harpenden Growth Study vs. ratings made upon clinical examination, there are some children in

TABLE 5-6. *Sequence of Pubertal Events in North American and European Girls and Boys*[*]

	Girls			Boys	
n[1]	Event[2]	Range[3]	n	Event	Range
12	B 2	10.6–11.4	12	G 2	11.0–12.4
10	PH 2	10.4–12.1	9	PH 2	12.2–13.4
12	B 3	11.2–12.6	11	G 3	12.7–13.4
10	PH 3	11.9–13.1	8	PH 3	13.1–13.9
8	PHV	11.5–12.1	12	G 4	13.4–14.7
10	PH 4	12.5–13.5	6	PHV	13.8–14.1
11	B 4	12.2–13.8	9	PH 4	13.9–15.1
12	M	12.8–13.5	11	G 5	14.6–17.3
8	PH 5	13.9–15.2	8	PH 5	14.9–16.1
11	B 5	13.7–15.6			

*Based on data reported in Malina (1978), supplemented by the following: Bielicki et al. (1984), Billewicz et al., (1981), Filipsson and Hall (1976), Harlan et al. (1979, 1980), Largo and Prader (1983a, 1983b), MacMahon (1973), Roede and Van Wieringen (1985).

[1]n refers to the number of studies reporting a mean or median age for the particular pubertal event.

[2]Pubertal events are as follows: B 2–B 5, G 2–G 5, and PH 2–PH 5 refer to breast, genital and pubic hair stages 2 through 5 respectively; PHV refers to peak height velocity; M refers to menarche.

[3]Range refers to the range of reported mean or median ages (years) for each pubertal event.

whom pubic hair development coincides with or precedes breast or genital development.

Second, girls mature, on average, in advance of boys. Stages of breast and genital development, however, are not directly comparable, so comparison of ages is not warranted. Third, PHV tends to occur earlier in the pubertal sequence of events in girls than in boys. And fourth, menarche is a rather late maturational event that occurs, on average, more than a year after PHV and when girls have passed through or are in breast and pubic hair stages B 4 and PH 4.

Variation in the sequence of events at puberty is partly genuine and partly methodological. One of the major sources of variation is the interval between observations in longitudinal studies. For example, if the interval between observations is six months, it is possible that a girl might be near the end of B 2 at the first examination and at B 4 one year later. Hence, no stage B 3 is recorded for her.

The preceding is based primarily on longitudinal data, with the exception of national surveys of Dutch and American children. Sample sizes in longitudinal studies, however, are not ordinarily large enough to derive estimates for the population. Population estimates of secondary sex characteristic development in a national sample of Dutch children, based on the *status quo* method, are thus given in Table 5-7.

TABLE 5-7. *Selected Percentiles for Ages (Years) at Which Stages of Secondary Sex Characteristics are Attained in a National Sample of Dutch Youth**[*]

		Percentiles		
		P 10	P 50	P 90
Girls				
Breast	B 2	9.1	10.5	12.3
	B 3	10.2	11.7	13.1
			12.9	
	B 4	11.4	14.5	
	B 5	12.5	14.2	—
Pubic hair	PH 2	9.0	10.8	12.6
	PH 3	10.2	11.7	13.1
	PH 4	11.3	12.6	14.0
	PH 5	12.2	14.0	16.4
Menarche		11.7	13.3	14.9
Boys				
Genital	G 2	9.3	11.3	13.3
	G 3	11.6	13.1	14.5
	G 4	12.7	14.0	15.6
	G 5	13.5	15.3	18.6
Pubic hair	PH 2	9.0	11.7	13.5
	PH 3	11.7	13.1	14.5
	PH 4	12.9	14.0	15.5
	PH 5	13.5	15.0	18.4

*Adapted from Roede and Van Wieringen (1985).

IV. MATURITY-ASSOCIATED VARIATION IN GROWTH

Maturity-associated variation in growth is considered from two perspectives: first, the growth status of children of contrasting maturity status, and second, variation in growth status relative to the timing of the adolescent growth spurt. The latter is especially important, given individual variation in the timing of the spurt.

A. Early and Late Maturers

The impact of variation in rate of maturation on growth has been traditionally viewed in comparisons of children of contrasting maturity status, i.e., early versus late maturers. Within a given chronological age group, children advanced in biological maturity status are, on average, taller and heavier, and have a larger FFM and FM than those who are delayed. Early maturing boys tend to have relatively more subcutaneous fat on the trunk than on the extremities compared with late maturers, while early and late maturing girls differ only in overall fatness and not in the distribution of subcutaneous fat. Maturity-associated differences are most pronounced during midadolescence. Late maturing children generally catch up in stature, but differences in body weight and composition tend to persist into adulthood. These trends reflect, in part, physique differences between early and late maturers. Endomorphy and mesomorphy are generally associated with advanced maturation, but ectomorphy is associated with delayed maturation (Tanner, 1962; Deutsch et al., 1985; Malina & Bouchard, 1988, 1989).

Variation in maturity status also influences physical performance, but does so differentially in boys and girls. Among boys, those advanced in maturity status within a given age group tend to be stronger and to perform better on tests of motor performance, especially in mid-adolescence (14 to 15 y). The difference relates to the size advantage of early maturing boys. Among girls, early maturers tend to be slightly stronger in early adolescence, but as adolescence continues, the differences between maturity groups are reduced considerably. In contrast, there is little consistent difference in the motor performance of early and late maturing girls (Malina & Bouchard, 1989).

B. Variation Relative to Age at PHV

There is, of course, considerable variation among individuals in the chronological age at which the adolescent growth spurt occurs. To reduce the time spread across the age axis in studies of adolescent growth, PHV is often used as the reference, and years before and after PHV are used as the time axis, rather than chronological age. Hence, adolescent changes in various dimensions and functions can be expressed relative to the timing of the growth spurt in stature. This approach is subsequently used to consider changes in body composition during adolescent spurt.

Changes in bone, muscle, and subcutaneous fat widths measured on standardized radiographs of the arm and calf relative to PHV are illustrated in Figure 5-6. Maximal gains or peak velocities in humerus and tibia widths occur coincidentally with PHV in boys, but in girls, maximal gains in humerus width appear to occur about six months after PHV while maximum gains in the tibia width appear to occur just before PHV. Maximal gains in bone widths are greater in boys.

Peak velocities of arm and calf muscle widths occur after PHV in both sexes. In the arm, peak velocity occurs about three to four months after PHV in boys and about six months after PHV in girls. For the calf, peak gain in muscle tissue occurs at PHV in boys with no clear peak in girls. Boys have a spurt in arm muscle that is approximately twice the magnitude of that for girls, but the peak in calf muscle is only slightly greater in boys.

Changes in subcutaneous fat on the arm and calf show a different pattern relative to PHV. Both boys and girls show negative velocities, i.e., a fat loss, on the arm coincident with PHV, but the loss in boys is greater than in girls. It appears that gains in the width

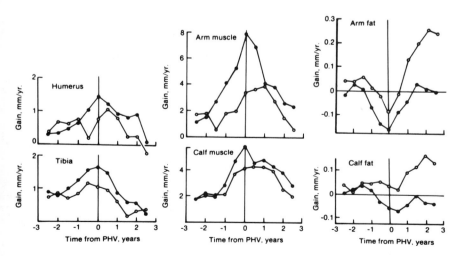

FIGURE 5-6. *Biyearly gains in widths of bone, muscle, and fat on the arm and calf aligned on peak height velocity in children of the Harpenden Growth Study. Filled circles are males; open circles are females. Redrawn and modified with permission after Tanner et al. (1981).*

of fat tissue on the arm begin to decline about one year before PHV, reach their lowest point coincident with PHV, then rise systematically after PHV in both sexes. The increase in fatness after PHV is greater in girls than in boys. In the calf, on the other hand, girls show no loss of subcutaneous fat. Rather, the rate of fat accumulation slows down at PHV, reaches it lowest point about six months after PHV, then rises sharply. Boys begin to lose fat on the calf during the year before PHV, and the loss continues to about six months after PHV. The velocities for fat, however, tend to remain negative in boys for almost three years after PHV.

Differential changes in specific skinfolds relative to PHV contribute to the variation in fat distribution at this time. In a large longitudinal sample of Belgian boys (Beunen et al., 1988), for example, estimated velocities for the subscapular skinfold remained positive throughout the growth spurt and did not vary relative to PHV. On the other hand, velocities of the suprailiac skinfold peaked about one year before PHV, then declined around the time of PHV. The velocities of this lower trunk skinfold, though declining, were positive at PHV, but became negative about two years after PHV. Thus, upper and lower trunk skinfolds appeared to behave differently during the adolescent spurt.

The timing of the adolescent loss of subcutaneous fat on the extremities also varies between the upper and lower extremities. Velocities of the triceps skinfold are positive until one year before PHV, then become negative, reaching a maximum negative velocity about 1.5 y after PHV. Velocities subsequently increase and eventually become positive. In contrast, velocities of the calf skinfold, though declining piror to PHV, approach zero at PHV, then become negative, reaching a maximum negative velocity about three years after PHV (Beunen et al., 1988).

The apparent differences between radiographic (Tanner et al., 1981) and skinfold data (Beunen et al., 1988) for the arm and calf reflect methodological variation. Fat widths measured on radiographs represent the sum of anterior and posterior widths on the arm and medial and lateral fat widths on the calf, while skinfolds represent a double fold of skin and underlying subcutaneous tissue at the specific site. Methods of estimating velocities also differed in the two studies.

Data for changes in FFM and FM relative to PHV are limited. Longitudinal data for Czechoslovak boys (Parizkova, 1976) indicate a gain of about 7.5 kg FFM $\cdot$ y^{-1} and of 0.8 kg FM $\cdot$ y^{-1} at PHV, but a decline in relative fatness of about -0.4% fat $\cdot$ y^{-1} at PHV. When densitometric estimates of FFM and FM collated from the literature are viewed for the years around the time of PHV, i.e., about 11 to

13 years in girls and 13 to 15 years in boys, changes in body composition at the time of the growth spurt may be estimated. The estimated annual increases in FFM are 7.2 $kg \cdot y^{-1}$ for boys and 3.5 $kg \cdot y^{-1}$ for girls during the interval near PHV. Corresponding estimates for changes in absolute fat mass at this time are about 0.7 $kg \cdot y^{-1}$ in boys and 1.4 $kg \cdot y^{-1}$ in girls, and estimates for relative fatness are about $-0.5\% \cdot y^{-1}$ in boys and $+0.9\% \cdot y^{-1}$ in girls.

Data on physical performance during the adolescent spurt have also been related to PHV. Maximal oxygen uptake shows a maximal gain near the time of PHV in boys, but data are not sufficient to offer a generalization for girls. Maximal gains in measures of static, explosive, and functional strength reach their peaks after PHV, but measures of running speed and speed of limb movement apparently reach their peaks prior to PHV in boys. Static strength data for girls are not consistent when expressed relative to PHV; one study showed a peak after PHV, and another study showed no clear peak. Data relating other performance tasks to PHV are not available, but when expressed relative to age at menarche, there is no tendency for performance to peak before, at, or after menarche (Beunen & Malina, 1988).

V. TRAINING, GROWTH AND MATURATION

Age-, sex-, and maturity-associated variation in size, physique, and body composition is reasonably well-documented. Growth and maturation are highly individualized processes in adequately nourished children. Thus, can the physical activity of regular training influence growth and maturation? Can regular training, on one hand, alter growth in size, physique, and body composition, and on the other hand, influence the tempo of skeletal maturation and the timing and tempo of the adolescent growth spurt and sexual maturation? These issues are addressed subsequently. The influence of regular physical activity on specific tissues, i.e., skeletal, muscular, and adipose tissues, during growth are considered in other papers in this volume.

A. A Biosocial Perspective

Although the focus of this discussion is on the role of regular training as an influence on physical growth and maturation, training is only one of many factors that may modify these biological processes. Other important factors are either in or mediated through the social environments of the developing individual. Hence, growth and maturation, though they are biological processes, should not be approached in a solely biological manner. A biosocial perspective is warranted. To this end, a biosocial model is offered in Figure 5-7.

When environmental conditions are optimal, growth and maturation are regulated primarily by the genotype. The processes of growth (size attained) and maturation (rate) are probably under separate genetic control (Malina & Bouchard, 1989; Bailey & Garn, 1986; Mueller, 1986). The same may also apply to the prepubertal and pubertal phases of growth.

Genotype-environment interactions mediate the responsiveness of individuals to various stresses. Furthermore, many stresses that can affect growth and maturation are either directly or indirectly influenced by social environments. Energy and nutrient intake, for example, are to a large extent directed by the family, especially the mother; family size is related to the age at menarche but the mechanism of this relationship is not known; habits of physical activity and sport participation are influenced by home, school, and community environments. Growth and maturation are thus outcomes of mutiple interactions between the individual and his/her environments that occur between conception and maturity. *Given the complexity of environmental sources of stress and genotype-environment interactions, a single stress, e.g., the physical activity of regular training, operating throughout the growth period or at a single phase of the period will not, by itself, determine a child's growth and maturation.*

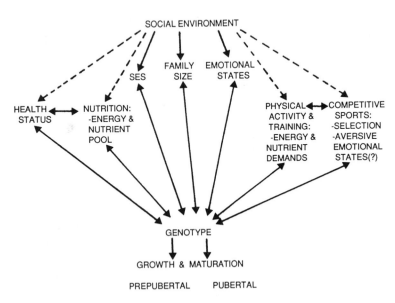

FIGURE 5-7. *A biosocial model of factors affecting growth and maturation.*

B. Physical Activity and Training

Physical activity is not necessarily the same as regular training, especially during childhood and youth. Although an individual may participate regularly in physical activity, this may not qualify as training. Training ordinarily refers to regular, systematic practice of physical activities such as calisthenics, weightlifting, running, and games or sports at specific intensities and for specific periods of time, often with competition as the objective. Training programs vary in kind, e.g., training for endurance, strength, and sports skill, but may include a variety of training stimuli, e.g., both strength and endurance training in swimming, or endurance and skill training in soccer, or perhaps, strength, endurance, and skill training in basketball. Training is not a single entity; rather, it can be viewed as a continuum from relatively mild to severely stressing exertion. Programs, however, need to be defined more specifically in terms of intensity, duration, and volume if the role of training as a factor that influences growth and maturation is to be identified and partitioned from other factors known to affect these processes.

In studies of children and youth, programs are generally short term, i.e., several weeks to several months. Rarely is the training stimulus monitored over several years. An exception, of course, is young athletes. Outstanding young athletes in a number of sports often begin systematic training at an early age. Swimmers and gymnasts, for example, often begin regular training in these sports as early as 6 and 7 y. On the other hand, young athletes in other sports often begin regular training in the early or mid-teens. Although studies of young athletes provide significant information on the influence of regular physical training on growth and maturation, it must be emphasized that elite young athletes are often members of a highly select group, and in many sports young athletes differ in size, physique, and maturity status relative to the general population of children. It cannot be assumed, therefore, that differences in growth and maturation between young athletes and non-athletes can be attributed simply to regular training. The growth and maturity characteristics of young athletes have been summarized elsewhere (Malina, 1983b; 1988a; 1988b; 1988c).

C. Training and Stature

Regular training has no apparent effect on statural growth. Although some early data suggested an increase in stature with regular physical activity (Beyer, 1896; Schwartz et al., 1928; Adams, 1938), the studies are generally limited to the late teens, and the observed changes are usually quite small. Further, the comparisons do not control for subject selection and maturity status. For example, the boys who volunteered for the training program in the study of Schwartz et al. (1928) were generally delayed in sexual maturation relative to the control subjects. Hence, many control subjects were dropped from the comparison to yield a "revised" control group.

The limitations of studies of young athletes in making inferences about training and statural growth is especially clear in observations on young swimmers and gymnasts (Astrand et al., 1963; Peltenburg et al., 1984a). These are sports in which girls begin training at an early age. By late childhood and early adolescence, swimmers are generally taller and heavier than gymnasts, although both groups have been training for several years. Analysis of the growth records of these young athletes indicates that the swimmers were already taller than average prior to the start of swim training, and the gymnasts were already shorter than average prior to the start of gymnastics training. Further, midparent statures of the parents of swimmers were, on the average, greater than the midparent statures of parents of gymnasts. Clearly, there are more important factors than training in the size differences between swimmers and gymnasts. There is undoubtedly a genetic component, as suggested by midparental statures, as well as a selection factor. In addition to selection for skill, there is probably selection for smaller body size in gymnastics and for larger body size in swimming, given the power demands of the sport. Selection is made by the young athlete, parents, and coaches, and quite often not in the order listed.

Given current concern for possible effects of running training on children and youth, an examination of several studies of runners is warranted. Three earlier studies of endurance running in boys (Daniels & Oldridge, 1971; Ekblom, 1969; Eriksson, 1972) give inconclusive results. After 32 months of training, five boys, 11 y at initiation of the program, showed a somewhat accelerated growth rate relative to four control subjects and Swedish reference data (Ekblom, 1969), and 12 boys between 11 and 13 y increased an average of 3.5 cm after 16 wks of endurance training (Eriksson, 1972). It is not justified to conclude that the accelerated growth was caused by training since maturity status was not controlled, and the boys could have experienced all or part of their adolescent spurts during the training interval. For example, an average gain of 3.5 cm over four months would correspond to an annual gain of about 10 cm, which would seem to suggest an adolescent spurt. In the third study, six boys, 10 to 15 y, had statures that equaled reference data at the start of a 22-month endurance program. However, at the end of the program, their statures were slightly below the reference data.

More recent comparisons of young distance runners are generally consistent with the earlier studies. Eight elite male cross-country runners 8 through 11 y described by Mayers and Gutin (1979) were taller and heavier than eight normally active nonrunners. Although the boys were classified as prepubertal, their pubertal status was not assessed; rather, it was assumed to be prepubertal because all boys were under 11.8 y (see Tables 5.6 and 5.7 for variation in pubertal development of boys). It is of interest that the statures of the runners were all at or above the median for United States reference data (Hamill et al., 1977), while those of the non-runners were distributed above and below the median. The size differences between the groups could well represent maturity-associated variation between the runners and non-runners at these ages.

Perhaps the most comprehensive analysis of the growth of elite distance runners (18 males, 14 females) 9 to 15 y is that of Seefeldt et al. (1986, 1988). Although the runners were, on average, slightly shorter than normally active nonrunners, growth rates did not differ between the samples. The shorter stature of the runners is more likely related to their delayed skeletal maturation (Seefeldt et al., 1988).

The studies of young gymnasts, swimmers, and runners thus indicate that regular training does not have a negative influence on statural growth. This is relevant to a frequently misquoted early study of adolescent athletes (Rowe, 1933). In a comparison of the growth of male athletes and non-athletes about 14 to 16 y, the athletes were taller but grew at a slower rate over the two years of observation. Some have accepted this observation at face value and concluded that training for athletic competition may slow down growth in stature (Lopez & Pruett, 1982; Parizkova, 1974; Rarick, 1978). However, a critical observation of Rowe was apparently overlooked. The observed differences in the growth rates of athletes and non-athletes could reflect variation in maturity status: ". . . since the athletic group is composed of boys who have matured earlier, age considered, than the group of non-athletic boys, the athletic boy is not going to grow as much as the non-athletic boy over the period studied" (Rowe, 1933, p. 115).

The preceding discussion is based largely on relatively small samples of youngsters training in sports. Comparisons of larger samples of youth grouped by degree of physical activity gives similar results (Rensen et al., no date; Ruffer, 1965).

D. Training, Body Weight, and Composition

Physical activity is an important factor in the regulation of body weight. Regular training often results in a decrease in fatness and an increase in FFM, quite often with an increase in body weight.

The early studies of youth in the late teens, for example, consistently indicate an increase in body weight in association with regular training (Beyer, 1896; Adams, 1938; Jokl et al., 1941). The weight gain probably reflects continued growth of FFM and muscle mass in late adolescence and early 20s, and the beneficial effect of regular activity. An increase in FFM, however, is not consistent across more recent studies of late adolescents and young adults (Forbes, 1978). The differences might reflect the status of subjects in the early and more recent studies. Concern for undernutrition was an issue in the early studies, but concern for overnutrition is central in many of the more recent studies.

Data that consider the effects of regular training on body composition across several years during childhood and adolescence are limited to boys. Changes in FFM and relative fatness of small samples of boys engaged in different levels of sports training and participation over a seven-year period from 11 to 18 y are shown in Figure 5-8. Three levels of training were compared: (a) regularly trained (n = 8)—intensive, 6 h·wk^{-1}; (b) trained on an irregular basis (n = 18)—in sports schools with about 4 h of organized activities per wk; and (c) untrained (n = 13)—about 2.5 h of activity per wk, including school physical education (Parizkova, 1974). Specific intensities of the training programs, however, were not indicated. The groups differed somewhat in body composition at the beginning of the study, but during the course of the study and at its end, the most active boys had significantly more FFM and less FM than the moderately and least active. The latter two groups differed only slightly in FFM, but the untrained boys had greater relative fatness. Given the negligible differences in FFM between the moderately trained and untrained boys, the need for a more intense training stimulus to produce changes in FFM during growth is obvious. These trends must be viewed with a degree of caution. The timing of the adolescent spurts varied among the three groups. The most active boys reached PHV earliest, followed by the moderately active and then the least active (Sprynarova, 1987). These trends are consistent with differences in skeletal maturity among the three activity groups at 14 and 15 y (Parizkova, 1974). The differences in FFM among the three groups may thus reflect, in part, maturity-associated variation.

During a 16-week endurance training program, nine boys 11 to 13 y gained, on the average, 0.5 kg in weight and 12 g of potassium as measured with potassium^{40} (Von Dobeln & Eriksson, 1972). A 12 g increase in potassium corresponds to a gain of about 4 kg of muscle mass, which would indicate that the 0.5 kg gain in body weight was accompanied by a loss of about 3 kg of fat during the endurance training program. Relative to growth in stature, the in-

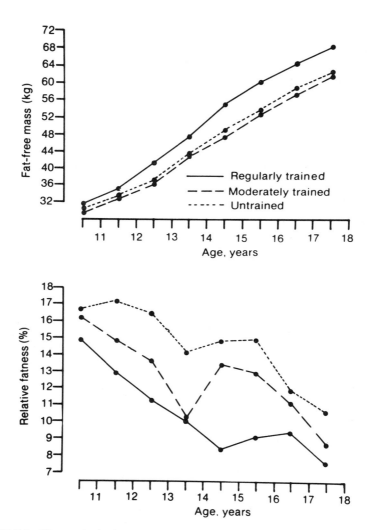

FIGURE 5-8. *Changes in fat-free mass and relative fatness of boys followed longitudinally from 10 through 17 y and exposed to different levels of training. Redrawn after Parizkova (1974).*

crease in potassium was about 6% greater than expected, while the gain in weight was about 5% less than expected. These changes are probably the result of both training and growth. The boys gained, on the average, 3.5 cm in stature over the 16-week program. Such a gain over a relatively short period of time may be indicative of the adolescent spurt with a concomitant gain in FFM.

The results of these two studies summarize reasonably well the information on training and body composition during growth of males. Youngsters regularly engaged in physical activity programs, be they formal training for sport or recreational activities, generally have more FFM and less FM than those who are not regularly active. Are the changes in body composition associated with regular training greater than those associated with normal growth and maturation? The increase in FFM observed in youth regularly trained over a several year period would seem to suggest an increase greater than that expected with normal growth and maturation. However, persistence of changes in body composition associated with training are not ordinarily considered. On the other hand, a good deal of the variation in body composition associated with regular physical activity or inactivity is associated with fatness, which fluctuates inversely with the training stimulus. Fatness tends to decrease during periods of regular training and to increase during periods of inactivity. Thus, changes in response to short-term training programs often reflect fluctuating levels of fatness with minimal or no changes in FFM.

Short-term observations on girls, which are limited to gymnasts and swimmers (Parizkova, 1977), suggest similar trends. The question of sex differences in the responses of FFM and FM to training during growth, however, may merit consideration. After 15 wks of high intensity training, young adult males, for example, experienced a significant decline in relative fatness and subcutaneous fat, but females did not. Males also had a significant gain in FFM while females did not (Tremblay et al., 1988).

E. Training and Fat Distribution

Information on the possible influence of training on fat distribution during growth is not available. Evidence from young adult males, however, suggests greater reductions in trunk than in extremity skinfold thicknesses after 20 wks of aerobic training (Despres et al., 1985). Similar results are apparent in young adult males, but not in females, after 15 wks of high intensity training (Tremblay et al., 1988). The non-significant loss of subcutaneous fat in females appeared evenly distributed between the extremity (−11%) and trunk (−8%) skinfolds, while the significant loss of subcutaneous fat in males occurred more in trunk (−27%) than in extremity (−15%) skinfolds.

F. Training and Physique

Methodological variation in physique assessment and individual variation in somatotype stability during adolescence confounds the evaluation of training-associated changes. In three groups of boys with different training programs from 11 to 18 years of age, distributions of somatotypes did not differ among the groups, suggesting no effect of training on somatotype. The boys changed considerably in somatotype during adolescence, but the changes occurred in a random manner (Parizkova & Carter, 1976). Thus, there does not appear to be a significant effect of regular training on somatotype during growth.

Some forms of the training may result in muscular hypertrophy of the body parts specifically exercised, for example, thoracic and arm measurements in male gymnasts, shoulder musculature in young swimmers, or muscular responses to weight training programs. Such changes may, at times, be rather extreme, and give the impression of altered physique. However, the changes are rather localized and do not markedly alter an individual's somatotype (Malina, 1979; 1983a).

G. Training and Maturation

It is difficult to quantify the effects of regular training on maturity indicators commonly used in growth studies. The available data are limited to adolescence, and the processes underlying somatic, skeletal, and sexual maturation at this time are regulated to a large extent by the same hormones. Studies of the interrelationships among indicators of sexual, skeletal, and somatic maturity in boys and girls followed longitudinally through adolescence indicate a general maturity factor that underlies the tempo of growth and maturation during adolescence. However, there is sufficient variation among individuals that no single maturity rating system provides a complete description of the tempo of growth and maturation of an individual boy or girl during adolescence (Malina, 1988a). The apparent "disharmony" among maturity indicators reflects to some extent real biological variation, e.g., there is no consistent relationship between the age at which a secondary sex characteristic begins to develop and the rate of progress through the maturational stages. It also reflects to some extent methodological concerns, e.g., intervals between observations during adolescence. There is also variation in the nature of hormonal regulation of the prepubertal and pubertal phases of growth and maturation.

1. **Age at PHV.** Age at PHV does not appear to be affected by regular training (Table 5-8). Small samples of boys classified as physically active and inactive for the years prior to and during the adolescent growth spurt do not differ in estimated ages at PHV. It may be of interest that the small group of inactive Canadian boys had a slightly greater estimated PHV than the active boys, 9.9 vs.

TABLE 5-8. *Ages (Years) at Peak Height Velocity in Boys Classified by Level of Habitual Physical Activity*

		Ages at Peak Height Velocity		
		n	M	SD
Canadian[1]				
	Active	14	14.26	1.17
	Inactive	11	14.14	0.73
Japanese[2]				
	Athletes	4	12.56	
	Active	7	13.30	
	Normal activity	43	13.31	

[1]After Mirwald and Bailey (1986). Boys were rated as active or inactive on the basis of questionnaires, sports participation, and teacher ratings over a five-year period.
[2]After Kobayashi et al. (1978). Athletes were "highly trained boys, who were winners of the Japan junior championship . . . for middle-long distance running events." They engaged in regular running training and competitive running. Active boys trained for 1.0 to 1.5 hrs/day, 4–5 days/week over 5 years, while boys with normal activity were a control group of junior high school students.

8.8 cm $\cdot$ y^{-1} (Mirwald & Bailey, 1986). Corresponding data are not available for girls.

   2. Skeletal Maturation. Although regular activity functions to enhance mineralization of bone tissue (Bailey et al., 1986; Malina, 1979, 1983a), it does not accelerate or delay skeletal maturation of the hand and wrist. Data for teenage female athletes in several sports indicate corresponding gains in chronological and skeletal ages over periods of three to four years from 12 to 17 y (Table 5-9). Within each sport, the athletes were also grouped as having advanced, average, or delayed skeletal ages. There is little variation in category changes within each sport: 19 (21%) girls changed maturity categories, while 70 (79%) remained in the same category. Of the small number who changed categories, 11 shifted from advanced to average or from average to delayed, while eight shifted from delayed to average or from average to advanced.

   Similar results are apparent in adolescent boys exposed to several years of regular training (Cerny, 1970; Kotulan et al., 1980). Given variation in the assessment of skeletal maturity, in addition to normal variation in adolescent growth and sexual maturation, it is reasonable to conclude that regular training has no apparent effect on skeletal maturation of the hand and wrist in boys and girls 11 through 17 y.

   3. Sexual Maturation. Longitudinal data on the sexual maturation of either girls or boys undergoing regular training are not extensive. Discussions of training and sexual maturation most often focus on later mean ages at menarche in athletes, and intensive training is suggested as the factor that delays menarche (Malina,

TABLE 5-9. *Changes During Adolescence in Chronological and Skeletal Ages of Female Athletes 12–17 years of age.*[*]

Sport	n	Gain[1] in CA (y)	Gain[1] in SA (y)	Change in Skeletal Age Category[2] None	(+)	(−)
Gymnastics	24	4.2	4.1	17	3	4
Figure skating	16	3.5	4.0	10	3	3
Tennis	14	2.8	2.5	12	0	2
Volleyball	12	2.8	2.5	10	0	2
Football	23	3.3	3.3	21	2	0

[*]Adapted from Novotny (1981).
[1]Gains are differences between mean chronological ages (CA) and skeletal ages (SA), respectively, at the beginning and completion of the study, i.e., gymnasts gained 4.2 years in chronological age and 4.1 years in skeletal age during the study.
[2]The athletes were grouped as average, advanced, or delayed in skeletal age. (+) indicates that skeletal age shifted from delayed to average or from average to advanced, while (−) indicates that skeletal age shifted from advanced to average or from average to delayed.

1983b; 1988a; 1988b). Data dealing with the inferred relationship between training and delayed menarche are, however, associational and retrospective. Other factors, such as dietary restriction, lack of sleep, and family size, all of which are known to influence menarche, are ordinarily not considered.

The menarcheal data are generally consistent with observations of breast and pubic hair development of young gymnasts and ballet dancers, though not of age-group swimmers (Malina, 1988b). Surprisingly, secondary sex characteristic development of young runners has not been reported, but observations on skeletal maturation indicate a trend toward a delay (Malina, 1988b; Seefeldt et al., 1988). In contrast, sexual and skeletal maturity status of young male athletes in several team and individual sports tends, with few exceptions, to be advanced. Young ice hockey players (under 13 y), gymnasts, figure skaters (Malina, 1988b), and distance runners (Seefeldt et al., 1988) tend to be somewhat delayed in maturation. Given the nature of these data, which are largely cross-sectional, and selection practices in youth sports, especially as competitive levels increase, it is difficult to make inferences about regular training and the sexual maturation of young athletes.

A corollary of the suggestion that training delays menarche is that changes in body weight or composition associated with intensive training may function to delay menarche. This is related to the critical weight or critical fatness hypothesis that a certain level of weight (about 48 kg) or fatness (about 17%) is necessary for menarche to occur (Frisch, 1976; 1988). Focus on relative fatness implies a role for the ratio of FFM to FM. Accordingly, intensive training supposedly functions to reduce and maintain relative fatness below the hypothesized minimal level, or to increase FFM and thus raise the ratio of FFM to FM, thereby delaying menarche, i.e., maturation of young girls may be delayed by keeping them lean through regular training. This procedure, incidentally, has been suggested as a means of reducing the rate of teenage pregnancy (Frisch, 1981). As noted earlier, data on the effects of regular training on the FFM of girls are lacking; data on relative fatness are more extensive. The hypothesis, however, may not apply to individuals experiencing emotional stress and to extremely muscular girls (Frisch, 1988).

The critical weight or fatness hypothesis has been discussed at length by many (Garn et al., 1983; Johnston et al., 1975; Malina, 1978; Scott & Johnston, 1982; 1985; Trussell, 1980), and the evidence does not support the specificity of weight or fatness, or of a threshold level for weight or fatness, as the critical variable for menarche.

VI. ACTIVITY, MATURATION, AND HORMONES

The suggested mechanism for the association between training and delayed menarche is hormonal. It is suggested that intensive training, and perhaps an associated energy drain, alter circulating levels of gonadotrophic and ovarian hormones, and in turn delay menarche. The hormonal data, however, are derived largely from studies of post-menarcheal women, both athletes and non-athletes (Malina, 1983b; 1988a; 1988b). Veldhuis et al. (1985), for example, suggested that exercise-associated amenorrhea in adult distance runners is due to a decreased pulsatile release of luteinizing hormone (LH). However, it is not certain whether intensive training alters the pulsatile release of LH in premenarcheal girls.

Prepubertal growth and maturation are principally dependent upon the stimulation of growth hormone (GH), while pubertal growth and maturation are chiefly under the influence of steroid hormones, among others. For example, the increased GH secretion during puberty is apparently mediated by gonadal steroids (Link et al., 1986; Mauras et al., 1987). With regard to possible effects of training on maturation, several questions arise. Are there differential responses of the neuroendocrine system to training in the prepubertal and pubertal phases of growth and maturation? Can regular, intensive prepubertal training alter the hypothalamic gonadostat or neuroendocrine circuits, and in turn delay the adolescent spurt and sexual maturation? Are there possible cumulative effects of hormonal responses to regular training? On the other hand, can regular, intensive training during the pubertal phase of growth alter the progress of the growth spurt and sexual maturation? It should be noted that the majority of hormonal data do not deal with chronic changes associated with regular, intensive training.

The first sign of the onset of puberty is an increase in LH secretion during sleep late in childhood. The pulsatile release of LH is correlated with the number of sleep cycles in late prepubertal or early pubertal children and precedes the initial overt signs of puberty. The development of the nocturnal pulsatile pattern is apparently a critical aspect of sexual maturation. It is suggested that once this central nervous system mediated mechanism is initiated, it is resistant to change and is ". . . susceptible only to the most severe of influences, such as malnutrition or sleep deprivation" (Wall & Cumming, 1985, p. 76). As puberty progresses, the pulsatile release of LH gradually extends into the waking part of the day, and the day-night differences in gonadotrophin pulses become progressively less. With sexual maturity, LH secretion occurs equally during the day and night in males, and develops a cyclical pattern in females. Deep sleep also markedly affects the release of GH. The largest increase in GH concentration usually follows the first episode of deep sleep.

Given the apparent role of sleep in the maturation process, the effects of training and competition on sleep in young athletes merit closer scrutiny. The effects of daytime exercise on sleep are presumably beneficial, i.e., longer sleep, more slow-wave sleep, and more growth hormone production during sleep (Oswald, 1980; Weitzman, 1980). On the other hand, stress is associated with both increased and decreased LH concentrations in the waking state (Shangold, 1984). The effects of pre- and post-competition anxiety on sleep and hormonal production might thus be a seemingly contradictory factor in late prepubertal or early pubertal athletes.

The pattern of LH production has been considered in small samples of female athletes. Bonen et al. (1978), for example, noted a short luteal phase in four post-menarcheal swimmers. This same pattern is also characteristic of teenage girls and may be a normal age-associated trend during sexual maturation. Veldhuis et al. (1985) reported a decrease in pulsatile LH secretion in six of nine amenorrheic distance runners, i.e., not all women experience altered hormonal function with training (Table 5-10). Two of the nine runners began regular exercise before menarche and had delayed menarche, 16.5 and 17 y, respectively, while the seven other runners attained menarche from 12 to 14 y. It is of interest that one of the two runners with early onset of training and delayed menarche had a LH pulse frequency within the range of control subjects, while the other had a LH pulse frequency just below the control range. The

TABLE 5-10. *LH Pulse Frequency in Adult Controls and Adult Runners, with Information on Age at Menarche (M) and Training History (TH) for the Runners, Subject Identifies are Shown Under ID.**

LH Pulse Frequency (pulses/24 hrs)	Adult Controls	Adult Runners ID	M	TH
15	X	V	13 yrs	4 yrs
14				
13		VI	17	10
12		IV	14	5
11	XXXX			
10	XX			
9	XX			
8	X			
7				
6		IX	16.5	15
5		VII	13	1.5
4		VIII	12	3
3		II	14	2
2		I	13	6
1		III	14	5
Group M ± SEM	10.5 ± 0.6	6.8 ± 1.7		

*Adapted from Velduis et al. (1985).

five other runners with reduced LH pulses had ages at menarche from 12 to 14 y.

It is hazardous to make inferences from post-menarcheal athletes to those in the process of sexual maturation. Growing and maturing individuals are not miniature adults and do not necessarily respond to environmental conditions, including acute or chronic exercise, in a similar manner as adults.

Hormonal data for active prepubertal or pubertal girls are limited, the results are not consistent across studies, and the data base can be characterized as weak. The results are often based on single samples of hormones whose temporal sequence is markedly pulsatile. Low gonadotrophin secretion in association with "mild growth stunting," for example, have been reported in premenarcheal ballet dancers (Warren, 1980). The dancers were delayed in breast development, menarche, and skeletal maturation, which would suggest a prolonged prepubertal state. They were not, however, delayed in pubic hair development.

Lower plasma levels of estrone, testosterone, and androstenedione have been observed in gymnasts compared with swimmers of the same age and prepubertal status (Peltenburg et al., 1984b). However, plasma gonadotrophins and dehydroepiandrosterone-sulphate (DHEAS) levels did not differ between the two groups. On the other hand, plasma levels of estrone, testosterone, and androstenedione did not differ between early pubertal (Stage B 2 of breast development) gymnasts and swimmers, although the swimmers were, on average, older by about one-half of a year (Peltenburg et al., 1984b). Both the prepubertal and early pubertal gymnasts had been training regularly for a longer period than the swimmers, since 4.8 and 5.0 y, respectively, compared to 7.2 and 8.0 y, respectively. The similar levels of DHEAS in the prepubertal gymnasts and swimmers suggests a similar stage of adrenarche. Considering the difference in the duration of training in the two groups, this observation does not support the suggestion that training delays adrenarche and prolongs the prepubertal state (Brisson et al., 1982). Moreover, more recent evidence does not support the view that secretion of adrenal androgens triggers sexual maturation (Wierman & Crowley, 1986).

The effects of regular training on basal levels of hormones in children and adolescents are not certain. Evidence for small samples of female swimmers 13 to 18 y indicates no differences in basal plasma concentrations of estradiol at the start and after 24 wks of training in pre-menarcheal girls, but a lower basal level of estradiol in post-menarcheal swimmers after training for 24 wks. Both groups experienced a decline in basal estradiol concentrations in plasma during the first 12 wks of training, followed by a rise at 24 wks. The pre- and post-menarcheal swimmers also had similar basal plasma concentrations of ACTH, cortisol, prolactin, and testosterone during the 24 week-training season (Carli et al., 1983a). In the combined group, circulating ACTH gradually increased, prolactin tended to increase, testosterone decreased, and cortisol showed a variable pattern during the season.

A role for beta-endorphins in amenorrhea of runners and, in turn, delayed menarche in athletes has also been postulated (McArthur et al., 1980). The effect of naloxone, an opiate receptor antagonist, under conditions of exercise in adults, for example, results in a marked increase in LH. However, responses of normal prepubertal and early pubertal (stages 1 and 2 respectively of secondary sex characteristic development) girls and boys to naloxone under basal conditions are different from those of adults (Fraioli et al., 1984). Naloxone did not have an effect on LH secretion in the children, even those in whom an LH response to exogenous LHRH was recorded. It has been recently suggested, however, that fundamental changes in the opiate neuroendocrine system are associated with, and perhaps cause, the onset of puberty (Mauras et al., 1986).

Given the available information on the hormonal profiles of young athletes and the responses of young girls to training, it is difficult to implicate regular training as the critical factor in the delay of sexual maturation observed in many athletes. Other factors must be considered. Constitutional delay is one of these factors, as it is apparently the most common cause of delayed menarche in athletes (Shangold, 1988).

Corresponding data on the hormonal responses of young males to acute or chronic exercise are not extensive. Emphasis is usually on testosterone and growth hormone with lack of data on LH. Evidence for adults suggests that endurance running is associated with reduced testosterone levels (Wheeler et al., 1984). Among swimmers 12 to 16 y (presumably pubertal), basal plasma levels of testosterone showed no change after 4 wks of training, increased significantly after 12 wks, remained rather stable from 12 to 24 wks, and decreased below preseason values after 43 wks (Carli et al., 1983b). In contrast, basal gonadotrophin and growth hormone levels were not altered with swim training. Most of the changes during the course of the season were variable and within the physiological range.

Hormonal responses to maximal exercise bouts are also variable among boys. For example, five young marathon runners, 13 y, experienced an increase in plasma testosterone relative to pre-race values, while 17- and 40-year-old runners experienced a significant depression in plasma testosterone after the race (Schmitt et al., 1983). In contrast, postmaximal exercise (cycle ergometry) concentrations of serum testosterone did not differ in boys grouped by stage of pubertal development (Fahey et al., 1979). On the other hand, relative increases in plasma testosterone after incremental treadmill exercise to $\dot{V}O_2$ max were greater in a longitudinal study of prepubertal and late-pubertal boys, but responses of mid- and post-pubertal boys were more variable (Wall & Cumming, 1985).

Studies of the hormonal responses of young athletes of both sexes are variable and not conclusive. *Acute changes in response to exercise and chronic changes associated with regular, intensive training must be distinguished.* Many studies are based on single serum samples, but virtually all hormones are episodically secreted. Studies in which 24-h levels of hormones are monitored or in which actual pulses of hormones are sampled every 20 min or so are needed. Further, the simple presence of a hormone does not necessarily imply that it is physiologically active. There may be variation in the responsiveness of hormone receptors at the tissue level. It is possible that training may have an influence on hormonal receptors at different stages of pubertal development, but this issue has not yet been addressed.

SUMMARY

Responses of the developing individual to the physical activity of regular training are probably not sufficient to alter genotypically programmed growth and maturation processes. Thus, training has no apparent effect on stature and on maturation as ordinarily assessed in growth studies. If it does have an influence on these measures, it is most likely through interactions with other environmental factors. On the other hand, training can be an important factor in the regulation of body weight and composition.

Physical activity is presumably important in growth and maturation, but it is not known how much activity is necessary or how much may be excessive. The day-to-day activities of childhood and adolescence are apparently adequate to maintain the integrity of growth and maturation processes, with the possible exception of adipose tissue growth. Relative physical inactivity in combination with a chronic excess of energy intake over energy expenditure is associated with greater levels of fatness.

There is need for longitudinal studies of young athletes in the context of sport-specific training programs, e.g., weight training, swim training, or combinations of programs, and in the context of training and nutritional influences on body composition. Longitudinal studies are essential, for they can contribute significantly to a better explanation of the variability noted in cross-sectional studies of young athletes.

BIBLIOGRAPHY

1. Adams, F.H. A comparative anthropometric study of hard labor during youth as a stimulator of physical growth of young colored women. *Research Quarterly* 9:102–108, 1938.
2. Åstrand, P.O., L. Engstrom, B.O. Eriksson, P. Karlberg, I. Nylander, B. Saltin, and C. Thoren. Girl swimmers. *Acta Paediatrica* Supplement 147, 1963.
3. Bailey, D.A., R.M. Malina and R.L. Mirwald. Physical activity and growth of the child. In F. Falkner and J.M. Tanner (eds.), *Human Growth*. Volume 2. New York:Plenum. 147–170, 1986.
4. Bailey, S.M., and S.M. Garn. The genetics of maturation. In F. Falkner and F.M. Tanner (eds.), *Human Growth*. Volume 3. New York:Plenum. 169–195, 1986.
5. Beunen, G., and R.M. Malina. Growth and physical performance relative to the timing of the adolescent spurt. *Exercise and Sport Sciences Reviews* 16:503–540, 1988.
6. Beunen, G., R.M. Malina, M.A. Van't Hof, J. Simons, M. Ostyn, R. Renson, and Van D. Gerven, *Adolescent Growth and Motor Performance: A Longitudinal Study of Belgian Boys*. Champaign, Il.: Human Kinetics, 1988.
7. Beyer, H.G. The influence of exercise on growth. *Journal of Experimental Medicine* 1:546–558, 1896.
8. Bielicki, T., J. Koniarek, and R.M. Malina. Interrelationships among certain measures of growth and maturation rate in boys during adolescence. *Annals of Human Biology* 11:201–210, 1984.
9. Billewicz, W.L., H.M. Fellowes, and A.M. Thomson. Pubertal changes in boys and girls in Newcastle upon Tyne. *Annals of Human Biology* 8:211–219, 1981.
10. Bjorntorp, P. Fat patterning and disease: a review. In N.G. Norgan (ed.), *Human Body Composition and Fat Distribution*. Wageningen:Stichting Nederlands Instituut voor de Voeding. 201–209, 1986.
11. Boileau, R.A., T.G. Lohman, M.H. Slaughter, T.E. Ball, S.B. Going, and M.K. Hendrix. Hydration of the fat-free body in children during maturation. *Human Biology* 56:651–666, 1984.
12. Bonen, A., A.N. Belcastro, A.A. Simpson, and W. Ling. Comparison of LH and FSH concentrations in age group swimmers, moderately active girls, and adult women. In B. Eriksson and B. Furberg (eds.), *Swimming Medicine IV*. Baltimore:University Park Press. 70–78, 1978.

13. Brisson, G.R., S. Dulac, F. Peronnet, and M. Ledoux. The onset of menarche: A late event in pubertal progression to be affected by physical training. *Canadian Journal of Applied Sport Sciences* 7:61–67, 1982.
14. Carli, G., G. Martelli, A. Viti, L. Baldi, M. Bonifazi, and Lupo di Prisco, C. The effect of swimming training on hormone levels in girls. *Journal of Sports Medicine and Physical Fitness* 23:45–51, 1983a.
15. Carli, G., G. Martelli, A. Viti, L. Baldi, M. Bonifazi, and Lupo di Prisco, C. Modulation of hormone levels in male swimmers during training. In A.P. Hollander, P.A. Huijing and G. de Groot (eds.), *Biomechanics and Medicine in Swimming.* Champaign, Il.:Human Kinetics. 33–40, 1983b.
16. Carter, J.E.L. *The Heath-Carter Somatotype Method* (3rd ed.). San Diego, Ca.:San Diego State University Syllabus Service, 1980.
17. Carter, J.E.L., and J. Parizkova. Changes in somatotypes of European males between 17 and 24 years. *American Journal of Physical Anthropology,* 48:251–254, 1978.
18. Cerny, L. The results of an evaluation of skeletal age of boys 11–15 years old with different regime of physical activity. In J. Kral and V. Novotny (eds.), *Physical Fitness and Its Laboratory Assessment.* Prague:Charles University. 56–59, 1970.
19. Cheek, D.B. *Human Growth.* Philadelphia:Lea and Febiger, 1968.
20. Chumlea, W.C., R.M. Siervogel, A.F. Roche, P. Webb, and E. Rogers. Increments across age in body composition for children 10 to 18 years of age. *Human Biology* 55:845–852, 1983.
21. Claessens, A., G. Beunen, and J. Simons. Stability of anthroposcopic and anthropometric estimates of physique in Belgian boys followed longitudinally from 13 to 18 years of age. *Annals of Human Biology* 13:235–244, 1986.
22. Clarke, H.H. *Physical and Motor Tests in the Medford Boys' Growth Study.* Englewood Cliffs, N.J.:Prentice-Hall, 1971.
23. Daniels, J., and N. Oldridge. Changes in oxygen consumption of young boys during growth and running training. *Medicine and Science in Sports* 3:161–165, 1971.
24. Despres, J.P., C. Bouchard, A. Tremblay, R. Savard, and M. Marcotte. Effects of aerobic training on fat distribution in male subjects. *Medicine and Science in Sports and Exercise* 17:113–118, 1985.
25. Deutsch, M.I., W.H. Mueller, and R.M. Malina. Androgyny in fat patterning is associated with obesity in adolescents. *Annals of Human Biology* 12:275–286, 1985.
26. Edelman, I.S., H.B. Haley, P.R. Schloerb, D.B. Sheldon, B.J. Friis-Hansen, G. Stoll, and F.D. Moore. Further observations on total body water. I. Normal values throughout the life span. *Surgery, Gynecology and Obstetrics* 95:1–12, 1952.
27. Ekblom, B. Effect of physical training on oxygen transport system in man. *Acta Physiologica Scandinavica* Supplement 328, 1969.
28. Eriksson, B.O. Physical training, oxygen supply and muscle metabolism in 11–13 year old boys. *Acta Physiologica Scandinavica* Supplement 384, 1972.
29. Fahey, T.D., A. del Valle-Zuris, G. Oehlsen, M. Trieb, and J. Seymour. Pubertal stage differences in hormonal and hematological responses to maximal exercise in males. *Journal of Applied Physiology* 46:823–827, 1979.
30. Filipsson, R., and K. Hall. Correlation between dental maturity, height development and sexual maturation in normal girls. *Annals of Human Biology* 3:205–210, 1976.
31. Fomon, S.J., F. Haschke, E.E. Ziegler, and S.E. Nelson. Body composition of reference children from birth to age 10 years. *American Journal of Clinical Nutrition* 35:1169–1175, 1982.
32. Forbes, G.B. Body composition in adoelscence. In F. Falkner and J.M. Tanner (eds.), *Human Growth.* Volume 2. New York:Plenum. 239–272, 1978.
33. Fraioli, F., M. Cappa, A. Fabbri, L. Gnessi, C. Moretti, P. Borrelli, and A. Isidori. Lack of endogenous opioid inhibitory tone on LH secretion in early puberty. *Clinical Endocrinology* 20:299–305, 1984.
34. Frisch, R.E. Fatness of girls from menarche to age 18 years, with a nomogram. *Human Biology* 48:353–359, 1976.
35. Frisch, R.E. Athletics can combat teen-age pregnancy. *New York Times,* 16 July (letter), 1981.
36. Frisch, R.E. Fatness and fertility. *Scientific American* 258 (3):88–95, 1988.
37. Garn, S.M., M. LaVelle, and J.J. Pilkington. Comparisons of fatness in premenarcheal and postmenarcheal girls of the same age. *Journal of Pediatrics* 103:328–331, 1983.
38. Greulich, W.W., and S.I. Pyle. *Radiographic Atlas of Skeletal Development of the Hand and Wrist* (2nd ed.). Stanford: Stanford University Press, 1959.
39. Hamill, P.V.V., T.A. Drizd, C.L. Johnson, R.B. Reed, and A.F. Roche. NCHS growth curves for children birth-18 years, United States. *Vital and Health Statistics* Series 11 No. 165, 1977.
40. Harlan, W.R., G.P. Grillo, J. Cornoni-Huntley, and P.E. Leaverton. Secondary sex char-

acteristics of boys 12 to 17 years of age: The U.S. Health Examination Survey. *Journal of Pediatrics* 95:293–297, 1979.

41. Harlan, W.R., E.A. Harlan, and G.P. Grillo. Secondary sex characteristics of girls 12 to 17 years of age: The U.S. Health Examination Survey. *Journal of Pediatrics* 96:1074–1078, 1980.

42. Haschke, F. Body composition of adolescent males. *Acta Paediatrica Scandinavica* Supplement 307, 1983.

43. Jokl, E., E.H. Cluver, C. Goedvolk, and T.W. de Jongh. *Training and efficiency.* South African Institute for Medical Research, Report No. 303, 1941.

44. Johnston, F.E., A.F. Roche, L.M. Schell, and N.B. Wettenhall. Critical weight at menarche: A critique of a hypothesis. *American Journal of Diseases of Children* 129:19–23, 1975.

45. Kobayashi, K., K. Kitamura, M. Miura, H. Sodeyama, Y. Murase, M. Miyashita, and H. Matsui. Aerobic power as related to body growth and training in Japanese boys: A longitudinal study. *Journal of Applied Physiology* 44:666–672, 1978.

46. Kotulan, J., M. Reznickova, and Z. Placheta. Exercise and growth. In Z. Placheta (ed.), *Youth and Physical Activity.* Brno:J.E. Purkyne University Medical Faculty:61–117, 1980.

47. Largo, R.H., T. Gasser, A. Prader, W. Stuetzle, and P.J. Huber. Analysis of the adolescent growth spurt using smoothing spline functions. *Annals of Human Biology* 5:421–434, 1978.

48. Largo, R.H., and A. Prader. Pubertal development in Swiss boys. *Helvetica Paediatrica Acta* 38:211–228, 1983a.

49. Largo, R.H., and A. Prader. Pubertal development in Swiss girls. *Helvetica Paediatrica Acta* 38:229–243, 1983b.

50. Link, K., R.M. Blizzard, W.S. Evans, D.L. Kaiser, M.W. Parker, and A.D. Rogol. The effort of androgens on the pulsatile release and the twenty-four-hour mean concentration of growth hormone in peripubertal males. *Journal of Clinical Endocrinology and Metabolism* 62:159–164, 1986.

51. Lohman, T.G. Applicability of body composition techniques and constants for children and youths. *Exercise and Sports Sciences Reviews* 14:325–357, 1986.

52. Lopez, R., and D.M. Pruett. The child runner. *Journal of Physical Education, Recreation and Dance* 53:78–81, 1982.

53. MacMahon, B. Age of menarche, United States. *Vital and Health Statistics* Series 11 No. 133, 1973.

54. Malina, R.M. Adolescent growth and maturation: Selected aspects of current research. *Yearbook of Physical Anthropology* 21:63–94, 1978.

55. Malina, R.M. The effects of exercise on specific tissues, dimensions, and functions during growth. *Studies in Physical Anthropology* 5:21–52, 1979.

56. Malina, R.M. Human growth, maturation, and regular physical activity. *Acta Medica Auxologica* 15:5–27, 1983a.

57. Malina, R.M. Menarche in athletes: A synthesis and hypothesis. *Annals of Human Biology* 10:1–24, 1983b.

58. Malina, R.M. Competitive youth sports and biological maturation. In E.W. Brown and C.F. Branta (eds.), *Competitive Sports for Children and Youth.* Champaign, Il.:Human Kinetics. 227–245, 1988a.

59. Malina, R.M. Biological maturity status of young athletes. In R.M. Malina (ed.), *Young Athletes: Biological, Psychological, and Educational Perspectives.* Champaign, Il: Human Kinetics. 121–140, 1988b.

60. Malina, R.M. Growth and maturation of young athletes: Biological and social considerations. In F.L. Smoll, R.A. Magill and M.J. Ash (eds.), *Children in Sport.* Champaign, Il.: Human Kinetics, In press, 83–101.

61. Malina, R.M., and C. Bouchard. Subcutaneous fat distribution during growth. In C. Bouchard and F.E. Johnston (eds.), *Fat Distribution during Growth and Later Health Outcomes.* New York: Liss. 63–84 in press.

62. Malina, R.M., and C. Bouchard. *Growth and Physical Activity.* Champaign, Il.: Human Kinetics, in press, 1989.

63. Malina, R.M., C. Bouchard, and G. Beunen. Human growth: Selected aspects of current research on well-nourished children. *Annual Review of Anthropology* 17:187–219, 1988.

64. Malina, R.M., and A.F. Roche. *Manual of Physical Status and Performance in Childhood.* Volume 2. Physical Performance. New York:Plenum, 1983.

65. Mauras, N., R.M. Blizzard, K. Link, M.L. Johnson, A.D. Rogol, and J.D. Veldhuis. Augmentation of growth hormone secretion during puberty: Evidence for a pulse amplitude-modulated phenomenon. *Journal of Clinical Endocrinology and Metabolism* 64:596–601, 1987.

66. Mauras, N., J.D. Veldhuis, and A.D. Rogol. Role of endogenous opiates in pubertal maturation: Opposing actions of naltrexone in prepubertal and late pubertal boys. *Journal of Clinical Endocrinology and Metabolism* 62:1256–1263, 1986.

67. Mayers, N., and B. Gutin. Physiological characteristics of elite prepubertal cross-country

runners. *Medicine and Science in Sports* 11:172–176, 1979.
68. McArthur, J.W., B.A. Bullen, I.Z. Beitins, M. Pagano, T.M. Badger, and A. Klibanski. Hypothalamic amenorrhea in runners of normal body composition. *Endocrine Research Communications* 7:13–25, 1980.
69. Mirwald, R.L., and D.A. Bailey. *Maximal Aerobic Power.* London, Ontario:Sport Dynamics, 1986.
70. Mueller, W.H. The genetics of size and shape. In F. Falkner and J.M. Tanner (eds.), *Human Growth.* Volume 3. New York: Plenum. 145–168, 1986.
71. Novak, L.P. Total body water and solids in six- to seven-year-old children: Differences between the sexes. *Pediatrics* 38:483–489, 1966.
72. Novotny, V. Veranderungen des Knochenalters im Verlauf einer mehrjahrigen sportlichen Belastung. *Medizin und Sport* 21:44–47, 1981.
73. Oswald, J. Sleep as a restorative process: Human clues. In P.S. McConnell, G.J. Boer, H.J. Romijn, N.E. van de Poll and M.A. Corner (eds.), *Adaptive Capabilities of the Nervous System.* New York:Elsevier:279–288, 1980.
74. Parizkova, J. Particularities of lean body mass and fat development in growing boys as related to their motor activity. *Acta Paediatrica Belgica,* Supplement 28:233–242, 1974.
75. Parizkova, J. Growth and growth velocity of lean body mass and fat in adolescent boys. *Pediatric Research* 10:647–650, 1976.
76. Parizkova, J. *Body Fat and Physical Fitness.* The Hague: Martinus Nijhoff, 1977.
77. Parizkova, J., and J.E.L. Carter. Influence of physical activity on stability of somatotypes in boys. *American Journal of Physical Anthropology* 44:327–339, 1976.
78. Peltenburg, A.L., W.B.M. Erich, M.L. Zonderland, M.J.E. Bernink, J.L. van den Brande, and I.A. Huisveld. A retrospective growth study of female gymnasts and girl swimmers. *International Journal of Sports Medicine* 5:262–267, 1984a.
79. Peltenburg, A.L., W.B.M. Erich, J.J.H. Thijssen, W. Veeman, M. Jansen, M.J.E. Bernink, M.L. Zonderland, J.L. van den Brande, and I.A. Huisveld. Sex hormone profiles of premenarcheal athletes. *European Journal of Applied Physiology* 52:385–392, 1984b.
80. Rarick, G.L. Competitive sports in childhood and early adolescence. In R.A. Magill, M.J. Ash and F.L. Smoll (eds.), *Children in Sport.* Champaign, Il.: Human Kinetics. 113–128, 1978.
81. Renson, R., R.M. Malina, G. Beunen, M. Ostyn, J. Simons, J. Uytterbrouck, D. Van Gerven, and B. Van Reusel, (no date). Sports participation and the growth, maturity and motor fitness of Belgian boys 12–18 years of age. Unpublished report.
82. Roche, A.F., W.C. Chumlea, and D. Thissen. *Assessing the Skeletal Maturity of the Hand-Wrist: Fels Method.* Springfield, Ill.:Thomas, 1988.
83. Roche, A.F., and R.M. Malina. *Manual of Physical Status and Peformance in Childhood. Volume 1. Physical Status.* New York:Plenum, 1983.
84. Roede, M.J., and J.C. van Wieringen. Growth diagrams 1980: Netherlands third nationwide survey. *Tijdschrift voor Sociale Gezondheidszorg,* Supplement 63, 1985.
85. Rogol, A.D. Pubertal development in endurance-trained female athletes. In E.W. Brown and C.F. Branta (eds.), *Competitive Sports for Children and Youth.* Champaign, Il.: Human Kinetics:173–193, 1988.
86. Rowe, F.A. Growth comparisons of athletes and non-athletes. *Research Quarterly* 4:108–116, 1933.
87. Ruffer, W.A. A study of extreme physical activity groups of young men. *Research Quarterly* 36:183–196, 1965.
88. Schmitt, W.M., A. Schnabel, and W. Kindermann. Hormonal responses to marathon running in children and adolescents. *International Journal of Sports Medicine* 4:68 (abstract), 1983.
89. Schutte, J.E. Prediction of total body water in adolescents. *Human Biology* 52:381–391, 1980.
90. Schutte, J.E., E.J. Townsend, J. Hugg, R.F. Shoup, R.M. Malina, and C.G. Blomqvist. Density of lean body mass is greater in blacks than in whites. *Journal of Applied Physiology* 56:1647–1649, 1984.
91. Schwartz, L., E.H. Britten, and L.R. Thompson. Studies in physical development and posture. 1. The effect of exercise in the physical condition and development of adolescent boys. *Public Health Bulletin* No. 179:1–38, 1928.
92. Scott, E.C., and F.E. Johnston. Critical fat, menarche, and the maintenance of menstrual cycles: A critical review. *Journal of Adolescent Health Care* 2:249–260, 1982.
93. Scott, E.C., and F.E. Johnston. Science, nutrition, fat, and policy: Tests of the critical-fat hypothesis. *Current Anthropology* 26:463–473, 1985.
94. Seefeldt, V., J. Haubenstricker, C. Branta, and D. McKeag. Anthropometric assessment of body size and shape of young runners and control subjects. In M.R. Weiss and D. Gould (eds.), *Sport for Children and Youths.* Champaign, Il.:Human Kinetics. 247–254, 1986.
95. Seefeldt, V., J. Haubenstricker, C. Branta, and S. Evans. Physical characteristics of elite young distance runners. In E.W. Brown and C.F. Branta (eds.), *Competitive Sports for Chil-*

dren and Youth. Champaign, Il.:Human Kinetics. 247–258, 1988.

96. Shangold, M.M. Exercise and the adult female: Hormonal and endocrine effects. *Exercise and Sport Sciences Reviews* 12:53–79, 1984.

97. Shangold, M.M. Menstruation. In M.M. Shangold and G. Mirkin (eds.), *Women and Exercise: Physiology and Sports Medicine.* Philadelphia:F.A. Davis. 129–144, 1988.

98. Sheldon, W.H., C.W. Dupertuis, and E. McDermott. *Atlas of Men.* New York:Harper and Brothers, 1954.

99. Sheldon, W.H., S.S. Stevens, and W.B. Tucker. *The Varieties of Human Physique.* New York:Harper and Brothers, 1940.

100. Sprynarova, S. The influence of training on physical and functional growth before, during and after puberty. *European Journal of Applied Physiology* 56:719–724, 1987.

101. Tanner, J.M. *Growth at Adolescence.* Oxford:Blackwell Scientific Publications, 1962.

102. Tanner, J.M., P.C.R. Hughes, and R.H. Whitehouse. Radiographically determined widths of bone, muscle and fat in the upper arm and calf from 3–18 years. *Annals of Human Biology* 8:495–517, 1981.

103. Tanner, J.M., R.H. Whitehouse, N. Cameron, W.A. Marshall, M.J.R. Healy, and H. Goldstein. *Assessment of Skeletal Maturity and Prediction of Adult Height* (TW2 Method) (2nd ed.). New York:Academic Press, 1983.

104. Tremblay, A., J.P. Despres, and C. Bouchard. Alteration in body fat and fat distribution with exercise. In C. Bouchard and F.E. Johnston (eds.), *Fat Distribution during Growth and Later Health Outcomes.* New York: Liss. 297–312, 1988.

105. Trussell, J. Statistical flaws in evidence for the Frisch hypothesis that fatness triggers menarche. *Human Biology* 52:711–720, 1980.

106. Velduis, J.D., W.S. Evans, L.M. Demers, M.O. Thorner, D. Wakat, and A.D. Rogol. Altered neuroendocrine regulation of gonodotropin secretion in women distance runners. *Journal of Clinical Endocrinology and Metabolism* 61:557–563, 1985.

107. Von Dobeln, W., and B.O. Eriksson. Physical training, maximal oxygen uptake and dimensions of the oxygen transporting and metabolizing organs in boys 11–13 years of age. *Acta Paediatrica Scandinavica* 61:653–660, 1972.

108. Walker, R.N. Pre-school physique and late-adolescent somatotype. *Annals of Human Biology* 5:113–129, 1978.

109. Walker, R.N., and J.M. Tanner. Prediction of adult Sheldon somatotypes I and II from ratings and measurements at childhood ages. *Annals of Human Biology* 7:213–224, 1980.

110. Wall, S.R., and D.C. Cumming. Effects of physical activity on reproductive function and development in males. *Seminars in Reproductive Endocrinology* 3:65–80, 1985.

111. Warren, M.P. The effects of exercise on pubertal progression and reproductive function in girls. *Journal of Clinical Endocrinology and Metabolism* 51:1150–1157, 1980.

112. Weitzman, E.D. Biological rhythms and hormone secretion patterns. In D.T. Krieger and J.C. Hughes (eds.), *Neuroendocrinology.* Sunderland, Ma.:Sinauer Associates. 85–92, 1980.

113. Wheeler, G.D., S.R. Wall, A.N. Belcastro, and D.C. Cumming. Reduced serum testosterone and prolactin levels in male distance runners. *Journal of the American Medical Association* 252:514–516, 1984.

114. Wierman, M.E., and W.F. Crowley Jr. Neuroendocrine control of the onset of puberty. In F. Falkner and J.M. Tanner (eds.), *Human Growth. Volume 2. Postnatal Growth, Neurobiology.* New York:Plenum. 225–241, 1986.

115. Young, C.M., A.D. Bogan, D.A. Roe, and L. Lutwak. Body composition of pre-adolescent and adolescent girls. IV. Total body water and creatinine excretion. *Journal of the American Dietetic Association* 53:579–587, 1968.

116. Zuk, G.H. The plasticity of the physique from early-adolescence through adulthood. *Journal of Genetic Psychology* 92:205–214, 1958.

DISCUSSION

SHEPHARD: I'd like to discuss the influence of exercise upon the growth process and your mentioning Don Bailey's study as perhaps the best proof that there wasn't any effect upon growth.

MALINA: No, if I may, his data were probably the best analyzed.

SHEPHARD: I noticed in the data that there were 14 subjects in one group and 11 in the other, and I think this was out of an original sample of 160. These subjects were not randomly allocated to start with, so I think that sort of data can really never answer the question. The only study I know where there has been an allocation to regimens independent of the volition of the child is the one we did at Trois Rivières. There we did see a retardation of the radiographic age in a sample of 562 children of about three to four months in those who were involved in the exercise program. We were only able to follow these children through to the age of about 12, and during this period there wasn't any substantial impact on their size; but, in terms of the maturation of the wrist, there definitely were differences between the active and inactive children.

MALINA: With regard to Bailey's data, he also has the average group. These were the extremes of activity/inactivity, and the average group is equal to them. So there are really no differences per se in that sample. With regard to the Trois Rivières study, I don't recall the specific differences in skeletal maturity between the groups at the start. That's the only data set I know, and those youngsters were by no means overly taxed physically, in which case you might see that so-called slight retardation of skeletal maturity. All of the other data on more heavily trained children, mostly athletes, mostly from Czechoslovakia, show virtually no effect on skeletal maturity.

SHEPHARD: Yes, but those children were not randomly allocated, were they?

MALINA: Yes, that's true, but the focus in this chapter was not the athlete per se. In the general population, I would expect a three- or four-month variation because of the method of assessing skeletal maturity.

SHEPHARD: The Trois Rivières subjects were all assessed by the same individuals, so I don't think that this could have been a factor.

BLIMKIE: Bob, you spoke about the different timing of the upper and lower body growth in segment lengths. This morning I was talking about the possible influence of biomechanical changes on lever arms and the impact that it might have on strength performance, and I suggested that standardization of strength data by dividing by body height might be one way of normalizing this type of data. Given the variability that you see between upper and lower body timing of segment lengths, would it be more accurate during a certain pubertal period to standardize for a specific segment length rather than for body height?

MALINA: I think that would make more sense, but people have height data, and measuring body segments is a lot more difficult than measuring stature. For example, there is no way to measure lower extremity length. The way it's ordinarily done is stature minus sitting height. There is no way to determine the head of the femur on an anthropometric basis. So most of what we call leg length is actually subischial length, i.e., stature minus sitting height.

LOUCKS: Over the last 150 years, a drop in the age of menarche has been noted. In the early 1800s it was around 17 years of age, and now you're showing 12 or 13. Has there been a similar drop in peak height velocity or in any of these other maturational events? If not, does that mean that these events are not linked together?

MALINA: There are no good longitudinal data. In the U.S., the longitudinal studies were begun in the 1920s and conducted mostly in the 1930s and 40s. They were basically middle- to upper-class children, and there are no major differences in the U.S. studies and the more recent studies in Europe. However, the secular trend toward larger body size in well-off American children stopped in the 1930s. The secular trend to larger size in all American children basically stopped in the mid-1950s. But we have no data that could take this back to the historical perspective. It looks like the age of menarche has leveled off over the last 20 years at about 12.8 years in the U.S. and at a little over 13 in northwest European countries.

LOUCKS: In light of the resurgence of the body composition hypothesis, do you have any remarks you would like to make about that?

MALINA: In terms of the so-called critical weight or critical fatness hypotheses, the best I could tell from the literature and the work that some of my colleagues and myself have done, there does not seem to be anything that we would call a critical weight or a critical level of fatness. There is considerable variation in fatness at the time of menarche. If there was a critical weight or fatness, you would expect variations to be reduced at menarche. In fact, variability expands at this time. Secondly, the hypothesis is based on estimates of fatness predicted from weight and height, and the prediction equation has nearly a 9 kg error band if you start taking it out to its extremes. Thirdly, the hypothesis does not apply to extremely thin girls or to extremely muscular girls. So the hypothesis has undergone numerous revisions.

TIPTON: Animal data suggest that performing strenuous exercise soon after weaning ultimately produces shorter bones. This has been demonstrated by numerous investigators and has been shown in normal animals, in hypophysectomized animals, and in thyroidectomized animals. How are we going to reconcile the animal and human data? What are we going to do about this concept, supported by animal data, that there is an attenuation of the growth process in long bones?

MALINA: Good point, Charlie. I'm fully aware of your work and that of others suggesting that extremely strenuous exercise might impair longitudinal growth of bones in animals. I accept the data, and I go back to the observation made by Steinhouse in 1933 that, apparently with regard to bone growth, a certain amount of stress and strain is necessary. Perhaps if we exceed that certain amount of stress, it has negative effects. The only example of a negative effect of strenuous activity on long bone growth in humans is one isolated study published as an abstract from Japan. The investigators observed that six youngsters out of about 3,000 experienced a premature closure of the proximal tibial and distal femoral epiphyses, and this was attributed to carrying heavy loads on their shoulders. However, what most people overlooked in that study was the fact that those youngsters were from an economically underprivileged and undernourished area of Japan. I suspect that heavy activity perhaps may have an effect on youngsters who are already nutritionally stressed and perhaps may interfere with their growth processes. I have trouble reconciling the animal and the human data, and I don't really know the answer. On the other hand, there are some more clinical data, like those from a study that Buskirk did on tennis players, showing that the preferred arm was longer than the unpreferred arm. They attributed this to exercise during puberty as stimulating growth in length.

BOUCHARD: It may be, Charlie, that this is one area for which the human is not a good model for the rodent. My understanding of the literature is that the data are mixed, that you have the animal studies showing a negative effect of intense exercise on bone length, but also a whole series of studies showing no effect at all, in mice, particularly.

HOLLOSZY: I don't think we should be using the word "animal." That's rather all encompassing. I think what Charlie is referring to is male rats, and male rats are very different from most other animals in that they markedly decrease their food intake when they are exercised vigorously. I think what you are seeing is a factor of food deprivation, not an effect of exercise. Female rats, which increase their food intake with exercise, actually are bigger than female rats that do not exercise, and I can't think of any other species of animal in which there is any evidence that exercise slows bone growth. The question that I had was why doesn't exercise accelerate growth in view of the fact that it stimulates growth hormone secretion?

MALINA: I would suspect that most of the hormonal responses are to meet the acute requirements of the exercise stress, and really there is little evidence on the long-term effects of chronic bouts of exercise on basal hormonal levels that might be of possible significance down the road. But most of the data are based on acute exercise bouts, and very few of them are from children.

VAILAS: We just finished a study using chickens, a bipedal animal that experiences a precise time of epiphyseal closure. The results indicate that under strenuous conditions of treadmill running, there is a delay in the onset of the growth spurt. However, much to our surprise, we expected early closure and that wasn't the case. At the time of epiphyseal closure, there were no differences between the strenuously trained birds and the sedentary animals. The two groups did not vary in body weight. This might support some of the studies done in humans, but exercise produced a significant delay in the period of accelerated growth in these animals.

BAR-OR: I have a question for Roy Shephard. If I remember correctly, your Trois Rivières highly active group had five hours a week of physical education compared with one or none for the other group. Do you have any information about what these children did the other 142$^{1}/_{2}$ hours of the week?

SHEPHARD: Yes, we did check that, and there was not, any significant evidence that there was a compensatory decrease in their leisure time.

BAR-OR: It's quite amazing that this group showed quite a marked difference of three months delay in their bone age. One other comment is that when we deal with studies where we are increasing habitual activity of children by some training, we really ought to look at what they are doing when they are not taking part in training. They may be increasing their activity. We don't really know what the overall caloric expenditure is or what other stimuli of training may be taking place during the rest of the week.

SHEPHARD: I think that is very important to check.

MORGAN: I'd like to come back to Charlie's question in terms of the discrepancy that may or may not exist. It seems to me that a major distinction between the rat model and the human model is the case of volunteerism on the part of the human for experimentation in a democratic society and then the selection issue in the cross-sectional and non-intervention type of studies with the human. In the case of the rat model, I presume you just get the rats from the rat farm and randomly assign them to conditions. I think Roy was getting at this question earlier when he said, "Oh yes, but they weren't randomly assigned." Well, in a democratic society, it's pretty hard to randomly assign people without getting their informed consent, whereas with the rats you can, of course, do that. So I think there is one possible explanation.

BLIMKIE: This concept about the influence of physical activity on growth raises a number of issues. There was an hypothesis a number of years ago that there may be a critical period for the implementation of exercise for the enhancement of growth, and that critical period was thought to be during the pubertal growth spurt. I think the hypothesis was that exercise normally elicits an acute growth hormone response and that if you superimpose that upon the normal pubertal surge in growth hormone, it may have an enhancing effect on growth outcome. There was an interesting study done on the growth hormone response of boys at different stages of pubertal development (stages 1 to 5). There was a growth hormone response to cycling exercise at each stage of puberty; however, the proportional change from resting levels to post-exercise levels did not differ across that developmental status. This is just one particular exercise mode and looking at one hormone.

MALINA: That was Tom Fahey's study, mostly Mexican-American boys. Some of the data from Steve Walt and Dave Cummings' lab also showed that you don't see differences between prepubertal, pubertal, and postpubertal boys in hormonal responses to acute treadmill exercise.

BROOKS: I would like to change the focus a bit and talk about apparent sex differences in adiposity. In your talk you brought up the influence of familial and sociological effects. Do you think the difference in adiposity is behavioral, and are cultural or cross-cultural data of any benefit in assessing this large difference in adiposity?

MALINA: I think sex differences in adiposity are a fact of nature, and cross-cultural data are perfectly consistent with the trends you see in well-nourished North American and European children.

SUTTON: What we don't really have is the 24-hour secretion rates of any of the anabolic hormones. The differences between fit and unfit people are not dramatic, if one considers maximal exercise in terms of the peak growth hormone response, although the untrained do appear to have a prolonged elevation of growth hormone for some time post-exercise. What we don't know, with the exception of one study, is what actually happens subsequently if you put these people through a training program. The key issues are surely related to things like the production of somatomedin and other anabolic hormones. The only additional piece of information I think is particularly curious, although we must be guarded in our interpretation, is that in certain individuals (both male and female) there is evidence that prolonged severe exercise may suppress the hypothalamic-pituitary axis with suppression of both testosterone in the male and estradiol in the female. But I think it's terribly important to be guarded about those studies because all of them, to my knowledge, have been cross-sectional in nature. We really have very little information, except for one study by Boyden, looking at the influence longitudinally of a training program where people have been randomly assigned to groups.

MALINA: I remember reading one abstract looking at hormonal responses before and after a marathon race. In this study, 13-year-old boys had all-together different responses than late adolescent boys and adult men and there was no effect on testosterone, whereas the late adolescent boys and adult men had a significantly depressed testosterone. There were no differences among the three groups in growth hormone level after the race.

ROGOL: Can I speak to the point that John Sutton made? We agree with you 100%. We have been doing a prospective study of 18 months using essentially the same exercise protocol as the Arizona group. We are looking at secretion of growth hormone and gonadotropins every 10 minutes for 24 hours. The data are very preliminary. We do not see any changes in growth hormone, but from 12 to 18 months there may be some loss of diurnal variation in gonadotropin secretion with the pattern, in a few women only, being much more like the pubertal pattern, i.e. very few pulses of LH during the daytime, but after the attainment of sleep, the pulses occur at that time, which is the recapitulation of the pubertal pattern.

MALINA: That's a very good point. Not all women respond the same way. This is part of the problem with generalizing from some of Frisch's writing from the Harvard study, suggesting that for every year a girl trains she is going to delay her maturation by X number of months. Not all people respond to the training stimulus the same way. I'm glad your results are showing that.

SUTTON: If one looks at the importance of intensity vs. the fitness of the individual, one gets much better information from studies done in a more carefully controlled manner. If you exercise persons at 50% of their $\dot{V}O_2$ max, you probably won't get much of a change in testosterone or in growth hormone. However, if the exercise intensity is increased, this will occur. Also, in very prolonged exercise, you may get a peak which decreases with continued exercise. If you've sampled a person running a marathon, the peak may well have occurred and, by the time you've actually sampled him, the hormone level has already returned to the baseline. And of course you then need to qualify whether or not the persons actually ran at the same percentage of $\dot{V}O_2$ max throughout the marathon. Field studies are exciting both to do and to possibly get some initial glimpse at what perturbation may be occurring, but they do not really help in unraveling mechanisms.

SCANLON: Bob, something very much excited me back there when you said we need to take the family into consideration. Would you just hone that point a minute, and then I would like to add to it. Were you relating this to girls being delayed in menarche?

MALINA: No, I'm just speaking about children and sport in general. Most studies focus on children alone, and they rarely consider teammates or peers or other activities the children do. From my experience coaching three children in Little League, I really think youth sports is a family operation. A good deal of stress in youth sports is not sport-generated, but family-generated. When we were drafting boys for Little League baseball not too long ago, it was said for one boy, "If you draft him, you draft his mother." And what I'm saying is we need to look at other factors that influence children and other sources of stress. Youngsters get more strokes from older siblings than from their parents and vice versa. If you focus exclusively, for example, on firstborns, they're an experiment, an experiment in rearing. They're under a lot more stress probably than subsequent born. What I'm suggesting is that when we look at the youngster at sport, we broaden our horizon and look at the whole social and family matrix within which sport operates. That's my main message for both sexes.

SCANLON: We've been looking recently at sources of stress by significant others and sources of enjoyment and how significant others function in that kind of role. Just a discouraging word, it looks like if stress is experienced, it's because of mom, dad, and coach. If enjoyment is experienced, the child owns that and the others don't have much of a role in it. But, I thought you were talking in terms of kids selecting into sport. I would refer anyone who's interested to the work of Benjamin Bloom on developing talent in young people. Bloom has looked across talent domains. These are people who excel in sport, music, art, neuroscience, etc. He studied the role of the family, the first teacher, the second teacher, and the coach in this development of talent. One thing that Bloom has found, and we have subsequently found with elite skaters, is that the initial involvement is terribly casual. It isn't that you have Tchaikovsky on your hands and you take him in to get piano lessons. It's almost a freak thing that you go to the skating rink or you sit down at the piano or whatever, and often it's that first teacher or coach that makes it such an enjoyable experience that the child gets involved, and then it escalates from there.

MALINA: But in Bloom's work he emphasizes throughout that it was the parents who reinforced whether it's math, music, or sports.

SCANLON: Correct! His point is more of a nurture than a nature argument.

6

Exercise and Obesity: Emphasis on Animal Models

LAWRENCE B. OSCAI, PH.D.

INTRODUCTION

Obesity in children and adolescents is common. However, there is considerable variation in the incidence of obesity from group to group (Johnson et al., 1956b; Stunkard et al., 1972; Forbes, 1975; Lohman et al., 1989). In one large scale study of 6,346 school children in Boston, Johnson et al. (1956b) estimated that 9% of the boys and 12.5% of the girls were obese. Stunkard et al. (1972) reported the prevalence of obesity to be as high as 40% in a group of 6-year-old boys. The variation has been attributed, in part, to differences in age, sex, socioeconomic status, and methods used to assess obes-

273

ity. There is evidence that the incidence of obesity in children is increasing (Gortmaker et al., 1987).

In considering factors responsible for obesity in children, one must consider factors affecting energy balance, i.e., factors regulating energy intake and expenditure (including growth) and storage. In this review, both human data and animal work are presented in an attempt to focus on issues related to the energy balance equation. Further, adipose tissue lipoprotein lipase (LPL) is discussed in some detail because it plays a key role in the storage of lipid in the fat cell. Finally, since there is relatively little direct experimental evidence regarding the role of exercise in the prevention of obesity in youth, an attempt has been made to point out possible directions for future research.

I. CONSEQUENCES OF OBESITY IN CHILDREN

Obese children are at greater risk for diabetes (Drash, 1973), coronary heart disease (Lauer et al., 1975), hypertension (Rames et al., 1978), as well as a number of other disorders (Johnston, 1985). Recently, it has been suggested that the distribution of fat deposits, particularly abdominal fat, is an important predictor of risk of overall mortality, stroke, heart disease, and diabetes (Bray & Bouchard, 1988). Aside from the metabolic abnormalities, there are severe social and psychological consequences of obesity. In terms of suffering, the psychological burden may be the greatest adverse effect of obesity (Consensus conference statement, 1985). The strong prejudice in this country against obese people is evident in children as young as 6 years of age (Wadden & Stunkard, 1985).

II. TRACKING OF BODY FAT IN CHILDREN

Interest in tracking body fat during growth stems from the fact that the long-term treatment of adult obesity is usually unsuccessful (Stunkard & McLaren-Hume, 1959). Because the treatment of adult obesity is difficult, early intervention treatment for those children who are likely to become obese adults may prove effective. In this context, there is evidence that adult body fatness can be predicted with reasonable accuracy in extreme cases, i.e., for very lean individuals or for very obese individuals (Abraham et al., 1971; Fisch et al., 1975; Rimm & Rimm, 1976; Johnston & Mack, 1978; Zack et al., 1979; Stark et al., 1981; Freedman et al., 1987). For example, Abraham et al. (1971) reported that 84% of markedly overweight children remained overweight as adults. In another study, Freedman et al. (1987) reported that 72% of the children who were very overweight at year one remained above the 85th percentile in year nine. In contrast, obese children who are not at the extreme end of the distribution do not necessarily become obese adults (Mullins, 1958; Weil, 1977). In a study by Mullins (1958), about one-third of a group of 101 patients were obese and, of these, only about one-third were found to be cases of persistent juvenile obesity.

It should be pointed out that there are problems inherent in assessing body composition in growing individuals that may hamper the tracking of body fat. For example, several commonly used methods for estimating body composition (i.e., densitometry, hydrometry, and potassium[40] spectroscopy) are based on the assumption that fat-free weight (FFW) is relatively constant. However, recent evidence indicates that FFW is labile during growth (Boileau et al., 1985). Specifically, water and mineral contents of the FFW are not constant as the child matures. This problem has been discussed in detail (Boileau et al., 1985).

III. ACTIVITY PATTERNS OF OBESE AND NONOBESE CHILDREN

Whether or not obese children exercise less than nonobese children is controversial. In an early report, Bruch (1940) collected data provided by parents and children on 160 obese children. The obese children were found to be inactive. Rose and Mayer (1968) measured limb movement taken from 24-hour actometer readings on 29 infants and reported that obese babies were hypoactive. More recently, Roberts et al. (1988) used the double-labeled water method to calculate energy expenditure in babies born to overweight mothers. Energy expenditure at three months of age was 20.7% lower in the infants who became overweight than in the other infants (256 $\pm$ 27 kJ $\cdot$ kg^{-1} $\cdot$ day^{-1} and 323 $\pm$ 12 kJ $\cdot$ kg^{-1} $\cdot$ day^{-1}, respectively; P < 0.05). This difference could account for the mean difference in weight gain. These data suggest that reduced energy expenditure can be an important factor contributing to rapid weight gain during the first year of life. The same pattern has been reported in adolescents. Using the recall method, Johnson et al. (1956a) reported that 28 obese high school girls were significantly less active than 28 nonobese girls of similar age, height, and socioeconomic status. Stefanik et al. (1959) obtained activity schedules by recall for 14 obese and 51 nonobese adolescent boys. The degree of participation in exercise tended to be less for the obese than for nonobese subjects. Bullen et al. (1964) used time-lapse photography to show that adolescent obese girls were far less active than nonobese girls, even during periods of supervised sport. In their study, a total of 27,211 individual observations were made.

In contrast to the above results, there is evidence that physical activity in obese children is similar to that in nonobese children. Stunkard and Pestka (1962) as well as Wilkinson et al. (1977) monitored physical activity in 12-year-old boys and girls. They found the exercise patterns of the obese to be similar to those of the nonobese. Bradfield et al. (1971) calculated energy expenditure from continuous monitoring of heart rate and found no difference in expenditure between obese and nonobese high school girls.

The above data indicate that obese children are either less active or just as active as comparable nonobese controls. It should be pointed out that evidence is also available to show that obese boys may expend more energy than nonobese controls. Waxman and Stunkard (1980) converted physical activity assessments into caloric expenditure values by measuring oxygen consumption. They reported that four obese boys expended more calories than four nonobese controls.

IV. RELATIONSHIP BETWEEN CALORIC INTAKE AND ADIPOSITY

A. Children

Traditionally, it has been thought that a major cause of obesity is overeating. While hyperphagia may contribute to obesity under certain conditions, there is a growing body of evidence to show that other factors may play an even more important role in the etiology of obesity. Nearly 45 years ago, Wallgren (1945) reported that there was no relation between caloric intake and body weight in 363 infants living in Sweden. Since this early study, other investigators have failed to establish a correlation between food intake and adiposity in infants (Rose & Mayer, 1968; Vobecky et al., 1983; Roberts et al., 1988) and in adolescents (Stefanik et al., 1959; Rolland-Cachera & Bellisle, 1986; Johnson et al., 1956a; Hampton et al., 1967). These results are important because they suggest that factors other than caloric intake may play an important role in the overall development of obesity.

B. Animals

Recently, it has been shown that a lack of relationship between caloric intake and adiposity also exists in the laboratory rat. The finding that rats exhibit a similar lack of relationship between caloric intake and adiposity indicates that the rat can be used as a model to investigate the mechanisms that allow such a phenomenon to occur. In this context, we noticed that body fat content varied widely within a group of rats eating the same diet and raised under similar conditions. As a first step in an effort to investigate this problem, experiments were undertaken to determine if this difference in body fat content was due to a difference in caloric intake (Scotellaro et al., submitted). Rats were raised in litters of four. After weaning, they were provided unrestricted access to a diet of Purina chow. At the end of the study, the results showed that the five fattest rats had nearly twice as much fat as the five leanest rats. Surprisingly, the five fattest rats consumed 32,927 ± 2115 calories over 55 wks, which was essentially the same as the value of 32,940 ± 2256 calories per 55 wks for the five leanest rats. The relationship between total calories consumed per 55 wks vs. total body fat expressed in grams was calculated for the entire group. A correlation coefficient of $r = 0.02$ was obtained. These results provide evidence that the difference in fat content (145 g fat for the leanest rat and 355 g fat for the fattest rat) within a group of 27 adult rats raised under similar conditions was not due to differences in caloric intake.

The possibility exists that metabolic factors may be responsible for the 2.5-fold difference in adiposity in rats raised under similar conditions. It is well recognized that brown adipose tissue (BAT) plays an important thermogenic role in rats. BAT mitochondria contain a unique protein (Henningfield & Swick, 1987; Nicholls & Locke, 1984), which is thought to regulate the uncoupling of substrate oxidation from ATP production (Klingenberg, 1984). A defect in the uncoupling protein would prevent the rats from wasting extra calories, resulting in obesity. The concentration of uncoupling protein in BAT mitochondria, as well as the total amount of uncoupling protein present in the animal, is thought to be the best marker of thermogenic capacity (Henningfield & Swick, 1987). Therefore, the possibility exists that the concentration of uncoupling protein in BAT mitochondria of the leaner animals might have been greater than that of the fatter animals. It is of interest that infants are thought to have BAT; however, it is controversial as to whether significant amounts of BAT exists in adult humans.

It is also possible that a difference in spontaneous physical activity may contribute to the differences in body fat among the rats. For example, Ravussin et al. (1986) used a walk-in respiratory chamber to determine energy expenditure in 177 humans. Although fat-free body mass accounted for 81% of the variance in caloric expenditure between individuals, a large portion of the variability was attributed to spontaneous activity.

A third explanation for the difference in body fat is a difference in basal metabolic rate among the rats. Ravussin et al. (1988) reported that in 126 subjects, resting metabolic rate at the initial visit predicted the gain in body weight over a four-year follow-up period. When the 15 subjects who gained more than 10 kg were compared with the remaining 111 subjects, the initial resting metabolic rate was lower in those who gained the weight (1694 ± 103 vs 1764 ± 109 kcal/day).

A fourth explanation is a difference in the caloric cost of digesting, absorbing, and processing a meal. Thus, the difference in adiposity could reflect the cumulative effect of greater efficiency in handling food.

V. EARLY FEEDING EXPERIENCE

Pediatricians have long suspected that overeating in infants may affect food habits and regulation of energy intake in later life (Breast feeding, 1978). However, evidence describing the nature of such a link in humans is missing. In this context, there is evidence in the laboratory rat that voluntary food intake can be fixed simply by controlling the amount of food consumed in the first 21 days of life (Oscai & McGarr, 1978). In that study, rats suckled in litters of 22 (low caloric intake) had a permanently smaller body size as they aged. This was due to a habitually lower voluntary food intake (Oscai & McGarr, 1978). In contrast, rats suckled in litters of four (high caloric intake) had a permanently larger body size as adults because of a higher voluntary food intake. The carcasses of the smaller animals contained about 18% fat, whereas the carcasses of the larger animals contained 30% fat (Oscai, 1982). These results are of interest because they show that body fat content can be increased by dietary manipulation in the early stages of life. The results are also of interest because they might apply to humans.

VI. DIETARY-INDUCED SEVERE OBESITY: EXERCISE IMPLICATIONS

Dietary fat has long been recognized as an obesity-promotion agent (Mickelsen et al., 1955). But, only recently has it been determined that dietary sugar can also cause the severe form of obesity in rats (Oscai et al., 1987). The data indicate that sugar is just as potent as fat in producing severe obesity, and when the two agents are present in the same diet, they have a mild additive effect. For example, carcass fat averaged about 45% after the long-term ingestion of either a sugar-rich diet or a fat-rich diet (Oscai et al., 1987). However, when the two agents were present in the same diet, carcass fat was increased to 51% (Oscai et al., 1987). Severe obesity developed in the rats eating the sugar-rich and/or fat-rich diets even though they did not overeat. These results provide evidence that severe obesity can develop in the absence of hyperphagia in animals eating excessive amounts of sugar and/or fat.

Sugar and fat are the only agents known to produce severe obesity under normal conditions. It would appear important, therefore, to have a clear understanding of the role of exercise in preventing obesity in animals and in humans eating diets rich in sugar and fat. Unfortunately, there is only a limited amount of information available regarding this point. Pitts (1984) examined the impact of exercise on body composition in young, growing rats eating an exaggerated amount of fat (60% Crisco g/100 g). In this study, the fat-fed rats that were exposed to voluntary exercise wheels had carcasses that contained 114 ± 28 g of fat at 260 days of age. This value was essentially the same as that of 119 ± 10 g of carcass fat for sedentary, control animals eating a low-fat diet of Purina chow, and markedly lower than that of 303 ± 53 g of carcass fat for the second group of sedentary, control rats eating the same fat-rich diet. These results suggest that exercise may play an important role in the prevention of obesity in the early stages of life.

VII. ADIPOSE TISSUE LIPOPROTEIN LIPASE

Lipoprotein lipase is the rate-limiting enzyme in the clearing of triglycerides from circulation in adipose tissue (Robinson, 1970). Since adipose tissue LPL hydrolyzes circulating chylomicrons (i.e., dietary fat) and very low density lipoproteins, the possibility exists that this enzyme may play a regulatory role in the development of obesity. Unfortunately, the effects of consuming diets high in fat and sugar on adipose tissue LPL are controversial. With respect to animals eating a diet high in fat, there are four studies that indicate that adipose tissue LPL is increased (Cryer et al., 1978; De Gasquet et al., 1981; Hülsmann et al., 1979; Weisenburg-Delorme & Harris, 1975) and, conversely, four studies demonstrate that enzyme activity is decreased (De Gasquet et al., 1981; Childs et al., 1981; Lawson et al., 1981; Leveille & Hanson, 1966). One obvious problem with these studies is that the results were expressed on a per gram tissue basis. It is well-known that a fat-rich diet will markedly increase the size of the fat cell.

Because of the uncertainty regarding the effect of dietary fat on adipose tissue LPL, we performed preliminary experiments. Young, male rats were force-fed 5 ml of corn oil (Wesson) to determine its effect on LPL activity in adipose tissue of fasted animals. Control animals received an equivalent volume of saline. Assays were performed on fresh tissue homogenates as described by Borensztajn et al. (1972). Figure 6-1 shows that LPL activity in adipose tissue increased from 27.7 ± 0.6 U/g fresh tissue to 68.3 ± 4.7 U/g fresh tissue 3 h after fat feeding. These results provide evidence that di-

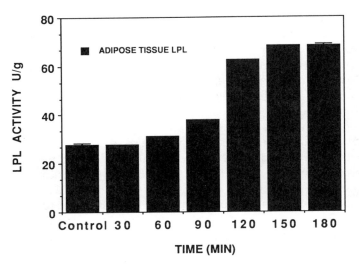

FIGURE 6-1. *Effect of force-feeding corn oil on whole homogenates of rat adipose tissue. Values are means ± SE. Each value is the mean for six animals in the control group and in the 180 min group. All other values are means for two animals per group.*

etary fat is capable of increasing LPL activity in adipose tissue of rats.

Relatively little information is available regarding the long-term ingestion of a sugar-rich diet on adipose tissue LPL activity. In one of the few studies, Granneman and Wade (1983) reported that LPL activity increased more than two fold in adipose tissue of rats fed Purina chow plus a 32% sucrose solution in the drinking bottles for a period of 8 wks versus comparable animals eating Purina chow with no sugar in their water. The role of adipose tissue LPL in the development of obesity, and how exercise impacts on this development is a fertile area for future research.

VIII. INHERITANCE OF BODY FAT

A. Humans

It is uncertain if obesity in humans is genetically determined. Obesity is known to run in families; however, the problem has been to determine the relative importance of genetic influence versus family environment in the development of obesity (Van Itallie, 1986). Stunkard et al. (1986), using the Danish Adoption Register, obtained information on 3,580 male and female adoptees (mean age, 42 years). Body mass index (weight in kilograms divided by the square of the height in meters) was used as a measure of fatness. They concluded that genetic influences were important determinants of the body mass index. However, as pointed out by Bouchard et al. (1988), measurements such as body mass index, weight-for-height, or percentage deviation from ideal weight mainly reflect heaviness, not necessarily fatness. Further, these workers showed that the biological inheritance component varies considerably with the type of body composition measurements. In this context, fat distribution is receiving increasing attention (Bray & Bouchard, 1988). For example, biological inheritance accounted for only 5% of the variance for the body mass index and subcutaneous fat, but 20% to 30% for the percentage of body fat, fat mass, and the distribution of body fat. The amount of internal fat appears to be influenced more by heredity than does the amount of subcutaneous fat (Bouchard et al. 1988).

Bogardus et al. (1986) provided evidence that metabolic rates at rest are similar within families. Further, Ravussin et al. (1988) suggested that a low resting metabolic rate predicts subsequent weight gain. In this context, Fontaine et al. (1985) suggest that resting metabolic rate is, to some extent, genetically determined. If true, the above results could have interesting implications regarding human energy balance and body fat content.

B. The Genetically Obese Zucker Rat: A Model For Early Onset Obesity

The Zucker obese rat (fa/fa) (Zucker & Zucker, 1961) has been used extensively over the past decade as a rodent model for studying the early onset of obesity. Boulangé et al. (1979) as well as Dugail et al. (1988) have reported that adipose tissue LPL activity is elevated at 1 wk of age in the obese Zucker rat. The increase in LPL enzyme activity occurs in parallel with an increase in adiposity (Boulangé et al., 1979; Dugail et al., 1988), and occurs before the detection of hyperphagia (Boulangé et al., 1979). Surprisingly, the increase in adipose tissue LPL activity also occurs before the detection of hyperinsulinemia in the obese animals (Zucker & Antoniades, 1972). This is an unexpected finding because there is considerable evidence that insulin regulates LPL in adipose tissue (Eckel, 1987). The increase in adipose tissue LPL activity that occurs in the first week of life in the obese Zucker rat (Boulangé et al., 1979; Dugail et al., 1988), remains elevated well into adulthood (Gruen et al., 1978; Cleary et al., 1980). The above observations have led Greenwood et al. (1981) to postulate that abnormal regulation of adipose tissue LPL in the obese Zucker rat results in enlargement of fat cells and is important in the etiology of obesity.

The above data on the obese Zucker rat may, indeed, reflect

what is happening to total tissue LPL activity. However, there is a technical flaw that compromises the interpretation of the results. It has long been recognized that LPL activity exists in two distinct fractions in adipose tissue (i.e., a capillary-bound fraction and an intracellular fraction) (Robinson, 1970), a fact that has not been consistently accounted for in LPL assays.

IX. DIRECTION OF FUTURE WORK ON PREVENTING OBESITY IN YOUTH

Nearly 35 years ago, Kennedy (1953) hypothesized that depot fat is regulated. More recently, Hirsch and his group (Faust et al., 1977) extended this hypothesis by suggesting that fat cell size is an important element in the regulation of energy storage and the control of food intake. If such a concept is true, then the fat cell should generate a "signal" to communicate its status or current requirements (Faust, 1981). Thus, a signal between the fat cell and the appetite centers in the brain would participate in the regulation of food intake and body fat mass. However, such a signal has never been identified. In this context, adipsin is a new and potentially important gene product of the adipocyte (Cook et al., 1987). It has been identified by isolating complementary DNA (cDNA) clones corresponding to messenger RNAs (mRNA) that are specifically induced during adipocyte differentiation. Adipsin is a serine protease homolog. It is synthesized and secreted by adipose cells and is found in the bloodstream (Cook et al., 1987; Flier et al., 1987). Adipsin mRNA is increased in adipose tissue under conditions of fuel mobilization (i.e., fasting). In contrast, adipsin mRNA is decreased under conditions that promote fat storage in adipose tissue (i.e., continuous infusion of glucose) (Flier et al., 1987).

A vigorous program of treadmill running (2 h daily) suppresses the appetite of male rats (Crews et al., 1969). In contrast to heavy work of short duration, light work of extended duration (6 h of daily swimming) stimulates the appetite of female rats, but the same swimming program has no effect on voluntary food intake of male rats (Oscai et al., 1971). Thus, three experimental conditions have been established in which exercise promotes fuel mobilization from adipose tissue resulting in a smaller fat cell, yet voluntary food intake is increased, decreased, or remains the same. A change in adipsin expression under the different levels of voluntary food intake would provide evidence for a link between the fat cell and the brain, with implications for appetite control. We plan to examine the expression of adipsin mRNA in adipose tissue of exercise-trained male and female rats, under the different levels of voluntary food intake. Our goal is to provide a more basic understanding of the relationship between appetite and body fat mass as they relate to exercise.

SUMMARY

Obesity is a prevalent disorder among children and adolescents. Obese children are at greater risk for coronary heart disease, diabetes, hypertension, and a number of other disorders. Recent evidence suggests that fat distribution, particularly abdominal fat, may be an important and independent predictor of future health. Contrary to popular belief, obese children do not necessarily consume more calories than comparable nonobese children. Results from animal studies are presented showing a lack of relationship between caloric intake and adiposity. Since this finding has been demonstrated repeatedly in humans, it is our plan to use the rat as a model to determine mechanisms responsible for this phenomenon.

It has been hypothesized that lipoprotein lipase in adipose tissue plays a regulatory role in the etiology of obesity. In our sugar-induced obesity model, sugar might increase adipose tissue LPL by increasing circulating insulin, resulting in an increased capacity to clear very low density lipoprotein (VLDL) from blood. Evidence is presented to show that dietary fat also increases LPL in adipose tissue, suggesting that it may play a central role in both dietary-induced obesity models.

ACKNOWLEDGMENTS

This work was supported by the United States Public Health Service Grant AM-17357.

BIBLIOGRAPHY

1. Abraham, S., G. Collins, and M. Nordsieck. Relationship of childhood weight status to morbidity in adults. *HSMHA Health Reports* 86:273–284, 1971.
2. Bogardus, C., S. Lillioja, E. Ravussin, W. Abbott, J.K. Zawadzki, A. Young, W.C. Knowler, R. Jacobowitz, and P.P. Moll. Familial dependence of the resting metabolic rate. *New England Journal of Medicine* 315:96–100, 1986.
3. Boileau, R.A., T.G. Lohman, and M.H. Slaughter. Exercise and body composition of children and youth. *Scandinavian Journal of Sports Sciences* 7:17–27 1985.
4. Borensztajn, J., D.R. Samols, and A.H. Rubenstein. Effects of insulin on lipoprotein lipase activity in the rat heart and adipose tissue. *American Journal of Physiology* 223:1271–1275, 1972.
5. Bouchard, C., L. Pérusse, C. LeBlanc, A. Tremblay, and G. Thériault. Inheritance of the amount and distribution of human body fat. *International Journal of Obesity* 12:205–215, 1988.
6. Boulangé, A., E. Planche, and P. de Gasquet. Onset of genetic obesity in the absence of hyperphagia during the first week of life in the Zucker rat (fa/fa). *Journal of Lipid Research* 20:857–864, 1979.
7. Bradfield, R.B., J. Paulos, and L. Grossman. Energy expenditure and heart rate of obese high school girls. *American Journal of Clinical Nutrition* 24:1482–1488, 1971.
8. Bray, G.A., and C. Bouchard. Role of fat distribution during growth and its relationship to health. *American Journal of Clinical Nutrition* 47:551–552, 1988.
9. Breast-feeding. *Pediatrics* 62:591–601, 1978.

10. Bruch, H. Obesity in childhood. IV. Energy expenditure of obese children. *American Journal of Diseases of Children* 60:1082–1109, 1940.
11. Bullen, B.A., R.B. Reed, and J. Mayer. Physical activity of obese and nonobese adolescent girls appraised by motion picture sampling. *American Journal of Clinical Nutrition* 14:211–223, 1964.
12. Childs, M.T., J. Tollefson, R.H. Knopp, and D.A. Bowden. Lipid metabolism in pregnancy. VIII. Effects of dietary fat versus carbohydrate on lipoprotein and hepatic lipids and tissue triglyceride lipases. *Metabolism* 30:27–35, 1981.
13. Cleary, M.P., J.R. Vasselli, and M.R.C. Greenwood. Development of obesity in Zucker obese (fa/fa) rat in absence of hyperphagia. *American Journal of Physiology* 238:E284–E292, 1980.
14. Consensus conference statement. Health implications of obesity. *Annals of Internal Medicine* 103:1073–1077, 1985.
15. Cook, K.S., H.Y. Min, D. Johnson, R.J. Chaplinsky, J.S. Flier, C.R. Hunt, and B.M. Spiegelman. Adipsin: a circulating serine protease homolog secreted by adipose tissue and sciatic nerve. *Science* 237:402–404, 1987.
16. Crews, E.L., K.W. Fuge, L.B. Oscai, J.O. Holloszy, and R.E. Shank. Weight, food intake, and body composition: effects of exercise and of protein deficiency. *American Journal of Physiology* 216:359–363, 1969.
17. Cryer, A., J. Kirtland, H.M. Jones, and M.I. Gurr. Lipoprotein lipase activity in the tissues of guinea pigs exposed to different dietary fats from conception to three months of age. *Biochemical Journal* 170:169–172, 1978.
18. DeGasquet, P., E. Planche, and A. Boulangé. Lipoprotein lipase at onset of obesity induced in rats by a high-fat diet. *International Journal of Obesity* 5:701–705, 1981.
19. Drash, A. Relationship between diabetes mellitus and obesity in the child. *Metabolism* 22:337–344, 1973.
20. Dugail, I., A. Quignard-Boulange, L. Brigant, J. Etienne, L. Noe, and M. Lavau. Increased lipoprotein lipase content in the adipose tissue of suckling and weaning obese Zucker rats. *Biochemical Journal* 249:45–49, 1988.
21. Eckel, R.H. Adipose tissue lipoprotein lipase. In J. Borensztajn (ed.). *Lipoprotein Lipase*. Chicago: Evener Publishers, 1988.
22. Faust, I.M. Signals from adipose tissue. In L.A. Cioffi, W.P.T. James, and T.B. Van Itallie (eds.). *The Body Weight Regulatory System: Normal and Disturbed Mechanisms*. New York: Raven Press, 1981.
23. Faust, I.M., P.R. Johnson, and J. Hirsch. Surgical removal of adipose tissue alters feeding behavior and the development of obesity in rats. *Science* 197:393–396, 1977.
24. Fisch, R.O., M.K. Bilek, and R. Ulstrom. Obesity and leanness at birth and their relationship to body habits in later childhood. *Pediatrics* 56:521–528, 1975.
25. Flier, J.S., K.S. Cook, P. Usher, and B.M. Spiegelman. Severely impaired adipsin expression in genetic and acquired obesity. *Science* 237:405–408, 1987.
26. Fontaine, E., R. Savard, A. Tremblay, J.P. Després, E. Poehlman, and C. Bouchard. Resting metabolic rate in monozygotic and dizygotic twins. *Acta Geneticae Medicae et Gemellologiae* 34:41–47, 1985.
27. Forbes, G.B. Prevalence of obesity in childhood. In G.A. Bray (ed.). *Obesity in Perspective*. Bethesda, MD: DHEW Publication No. (NIH) 75:708, 1975.
28. Freedman, D.S., C.L. Shear, G.L. Burke, S.R. Srinivasan, L.S. Webber, D.W. Harsha, and G.S. Berenson. Persistence of juvenile-onset obesity over eight years: the Bogalusa heart study. *American Journal of Public Health* 77:588–592, 1987.
29. Gortmaker, S.L., W.H. Dietz, A.M. Sobol, and C.A. Wehler. Increasing pediatric obesity in the United States. *American Journal of Disease of Children* 141:535–540, 1987.
30. Granneman, J.G., and G.N. Wade. Effect of sucrose overfeeding on brown adipose tissue lipogenesis and lipoprotein lipase activity in rats. *Metabolism* 32:202–207, 1983.
31. Greenwood, M.R.C., M. Cleary, L. Steingrimsdottir, and J.R. Vasselli. Adipose tissue metabolism and genetic obesity: the LPL hypothesis. In P. Björntorp, M. Cairella, and A.N. Howard (eds.). *Recent Advances in Obesity Research: III*. London: John Libbey, 1981.
32. Gruen, R., E. Hietanen, and M.C. Greenwood. Increased adipose tissue lipoprotein lipase activity during the development of the genetically obese rat (fa/fa). *Metabolism* 27:1955–1966, 1987.
33. Hampton, M.C., R.L. Huenemann, L.R. Shapiro, and B.W. Mitchell. Caloric and nutrient intakes of teen-agers. *Journal of the American Dietetic Association* 50:385–396, 1967.
34. Henningfield, M.F., and R.W. Swick. Immunochemical detection and quantitation of brown adipose tissue uncoupling protein. *Biochemical Cell Biology* 65:245–251, 1987.
35. Hülsmann, W.C., M.M. Geelhoed-Mieras, H. Jansen, and U.M.T. Houtsmuller. Alteration of the lipase activities of muscle, adipose tissue and liver by rapeseed oil feeding of rats. *Biochimica et Biophysica Acta* 572:183–187, 1979.

36. Johnston, F.E. Health implications of childhood obesity. *Annals of Internal Medicine* 103:1068–1072, 1985.
37. Johnston, F.E., and R.W. Mack. Obesity in urban black adolescents of high and low relative weight at 1 year of age. *American Journal of Disease of Children* 132:862–864, 1978.
38. Johnson, M.L., B.S. Burke, and J. Mayer. Relative importance of inactivity and overeating in the energy balance of obese high school girls. *American Journal of Clinical Nutrition* 4:37–44, 1956a.
39. Johnson, M.L., B.S. Burke, and J. Mayer. The prevalence and incidence of obesity in a cross-section of elementary and secondary school children. *American Journal of Clinical Nutrition* 4:231–238, 1956b.
40. Kennedy, G.C. The role of depot fat in the hypothalamic control of food intake in the rat. *Proceedings of the Royal Society of London B*, 140:578–592, 1953.
41. Klingenberg, M. Characteristics of the uncoupling protein from brown-fat mitochondria. *Biochemical Society Transactions* 12:390–393, 1984.
42. Lauer, R.M., W.E. Connor, P.E. Leaverton, M.A. Reiter, and W.R. Clarke. Coronary heart disease risk factors in school children: the Muscatine study. *Journal of Pediatrics* 86:697–706, 1975.
43. Lawson, N., A.D. Pollard, R.J. Jennings, M.I. Gurr, and D.N. Brindley. The activities of lipoprotein lipase and of enzymes involved in triacylglycerol synthesis in rat adipose tissue. *Biochemical Journal* 200:285–294, 1981.
44. Leveille, G.A., and R.W. Hanson. Adaptive changes in enzyme activity and metabolic pathways in adipose tissue from meal-fed rats. *Journal of Lipid Research* 7:46–55, 1966.
45. Lohman, T.G., S.B. Going, M.H. Slaughter, and R.A. Boileau. Concept of chemical development in children and youth. Implications for estimating obesity in childhood. *Human Biology*, (In press, 1989).
46. Mickelsen, O., S. Takahashi, and C. Craig. Experimental obesity. I. Production of obesity in rats by feeding high-fat diets. *Journal of Nutrition* 57:541–554, 1955.
47. Mullins, A.G. The prognosis in juvenile obesity. *Archives of Disease in Childhood* 33:307–314, 1958.
48. Nicholls, D.G., and R.M.Locke. Thermogenic mechanisms in brown fat. *Physiological Reviews* 64:1–64, 1984.
49. Oscai, L.B. Dietary-induced severe obesity: a rat model. *American Journal of Physiology* 242:R212–R215, 1982.
50. Oscai, L.B., M.M. Brown, and W.C. Miller. Effect of dietary fat on food intake, growth and body composition in rats. *Growth* 48:415–424, 1984.
51. Oscai, L.B., and J.A. McGarr. Evidence that the amount of food consumed in early life fixes appetite in the rat. *American Journal of Physiology* 235:R141–R144, 1978.
52. Oscai, L.B., W.C. Miller, and D.A. Arnall. Effects of dietary sugar and of dietary fat on food intake and body fat content in rats. *Growth* 51:64–73, 1987.
53. Oscai, L.B., P.A. Mole, and J.O. Holloszy. Effects of exercise on cardiac weight and mitochondria in male and female rats. *American Journal of Physiology* 220:1944–1948, 1971.
54. Pitts, G.C. Body composition in the rat: interactions of exercise, age, sex, and diet. *American Journal of Physiology* 246:R495–R501, 1984.
55. Rames, L.K., W.R. Clarke, W.E. Connor, M.A. Reiter, and R.M. Lauer. Normal blood pressures and the evaluation of sustained blood pressure elevation in childhood: the Muscatine study. *Pediatrics* 61:245–251, 1978.
56. Ravussin, E., S. Lillioja, T.E. Anderson, L. Christin, and C. Bogardus. Determinants of 24-hour energy expenditure in man. *Journal of Clinical Investigation* 78:1568–1578, 1986.
57. Ravussin, E., S. Lillioja, W.C. Knowler, L. Christin, D. Freymond, W.G.H. Abbott, V. Boyce, B.V. Howard, and C. Bogardus. Reduced rate of energy expenditure as a risk factor for body-weight gain. *New England Journal of Medicine* 318:467–472, 1988.
58. Rimm, I.J., and A.A. Rimm. Association between juvenile onset obesity and severe adult obesity in 73,532 women. *American Journal of Public Health* 66:479–481, 1976.
59. Roberts, S.B., J. Savage, W.A. Coward, B. Chew, and A. Lucas. Energy expenditure and intake in infants born to lean and overweight mothers. *New England Journal of Medicine* 318:461–466, 1988.
60. Robinson, D.S. The function of the plasma triglycerides in fatty acid transport. In M. Florkin & E.H. Stotz (eds.). *Comprehensive Biochemistry*. Amsterdam:Elsevier, 1970.
61. Rolland-Cachera, M.-F., and F. Bellisle. No correlation between adiposity and food intake: why are working class children fatter? *American Journal of Clinical Nutrition* 44:779–787, 1986.
62. Rose, H.E., and J. Mayer. Activity, calorie intake, fat storage, and the energy balance of infants. *Pediatrics* 41:18–29,is 1968.
63. Scotellaro, P.C., J. Gorski, and L.B. Oscai. (Submitted for publication). Lack of relationship between caloric intake and body fat content in rats.
64. Stark, O., E. Atkins, O.H. Wolff, and J.W.B. Douglas. Longitudinal study of obesity in the

national survey of health and development. *British Medical Journal* 283:13–17, 1981.

65. Stefanik, P.A., F.P. Heald, and J. Mayer. Caloric intake in relation to energy output of obese and non-obese adolescent boys. *American Journal of Clinical Nutrition* 7:55–62, 1959.
66. Stunkard, A., E. d'Aquili, S. Fox, and R.D.L. Filion. Influence of social class on obesity and thinness in children. *Journal of American Medical Association* 221:579–584, 1972.
67. Stunkard, A., and M. McLaren-Hume. The results of treatment for obesity. A review of the literature and report of a series. *A.M.A. Archives of Internal Medicine* 103:79–85, 1959.
68. Stunkard, A., and J. Pestka. The physical activity of obese girls. *American Journal of Diseases of Children* 103:812–817, 1962.
69. Stunkard, A.J., T.I.A. Sorensen, C. Hanis, T.W. Teasdale, R. Chakraborty, W.J. Schull, and F. Schulsinger. An adoption study of human obesity. *New England Journal of Medicine* 314:193–198, 1986.
70. Van Itallie, T.B. Bad news and good news about obesity. *New England Journal of Medicine* 314:239–240, 1986.
71. Vobecky, J.S., J. Vobecky, D. Shapcott, and P.P. Demers. Nutrient intake patterns and nutritional status with regard to relative weight in early infancy. *American Journal of Clinical Nutrition* 38:730–738, 1983.
72. Wadden, T.A., and A.J. Stunkard. Social and psychological consequences of obesity. *Annals of Internal Medicine* 103:1062–1067, 1985.
73. Wallgren, A. Breast-milk consumption of healthy full-term infants. *Acta Pediatrica* 32:778–790, 1945.
74. Waxman, M., and A.J. Stunkard. Caloric intake and expenditure of obese boys. *Journal of Pediatrics* 96:187–193, 1980.
75. Weil, W.B. Current controversies in childhood obesity. *Journal of Pediatrics* 91:175–187, 1977.
76. Weisenburg-Delorme, C.L., and K.L. Harris. Effects of diet on lipoprotein lipase activity in the rat. *Journal of Nutrition* 105:447–451, 1975.
77. Wilkinson, P.W., J.M. Parkin, G. Pearlson, H. Strong, and P. Sykes. Energy intake and physical activity in obese children. *British Medical Journal* 1:756, 1977.
78. Zack, P.M., W.R. Harlan, P.E. Leaverton, and J. Cornoni-Huntley. A longitudinal study of body fatness in childhood and adolescence. *Journal of Pediatrics* 95:126–130, 1979.
79. Zucker, L.M., and H.N. Antoniades. Insulin and obesity in the Zucker genetically obese rat "fatty". *Endocrinology* 90:1320–1330, 1972.
80. Zucker, L.M., and T.F. Zucker. Fatty, a new mutation in the rat. *The Journal of Heredity* 52:275–278, 1961.

DISCUSSION

HORTON: My comments focus on the energy balance equation and looking at "energy in" equals "energy out" plus "storage". You've really addressed each aspect of this equation in your paper, but I think it should really be focused around factors that affect either intake, expenditure, or storage. On the "intake" side, I agree with Claude on the *adipsin* story that it is still very premature and we really don't know where it's going. On the "energy intake" side, you quoted studies from our group on absorption and pointed out that differences in absorption could be a factor in energy intake. Those data were reported several years ago by our group. The percent of calories absorbed did not change, and I think that the impression you gave was that there could be major differences in calories absorbed on different diets. We measured stool fat and energy content, and it was before and after long periods of overfeeding. It was a fairly constant 5% of calories. Expressed as percentage of caloric intake, there were no differences among our groups. In our early studies of overfeeding, it was quite clear that overfeeding a high fat diet resulted in a much more efficient gain in weight than overfeeding a mixed diet. I think several other people have shown that fat is metabolically more efficiently digested, absorbed, and stored as fat than carbohydrate. Certainly from our early data in humans, it was quite clear that fat was much more efficient in terms of producing obesity.

On the energy expenditure side of the equation, you referred to Roberts' very nice paper using the double-labelled water method in infants and the fact that, measured at three months, energy expenditure was lower in those infants that gained more weight during the first year of life. It presumed to represent differences in physical activity, but that actually was not clearly measured. I think there are many unresolved issues on the energy expenditure side regarding differences in resting metabolic rate, thermic effect of food, or the thermic effect of exercise, which are the three major components that go into 24-hour energy expenditure. Moreover, the very good studies coming from the Phoenix group have clearly shown that there is familial clustering of resting metabolic rate data as well as 24-hour energy expenditure, suggesting genetic influences. This low resting metabolic rate clearly has predictive value for weight gain over the subsequent two or three years.

Exercise is the most variable component of energy expenditure, and one can influence energy expenditure more by changing levels of physical activity than by changing the other components. Changes in resting metabolic rate with overfeeding and underfeeding are probably limited to the range of about 10 to 15% max. While there are some studies suggesting that there may be a slightly lower thermic effect of food in obese individuals, changes in the thermic effect of food are relatively minor differences, i.e., 1% or so. Although it can be calculated that over a long period of time, e.g., over a year, even a 1% difference in the thermic effect of food can result in very substantial gain in weight, one should be able to overcome those differences in efficiency by increasing physical activity. So it really gets down to the questions of whether or not one can alter physical activity levels to cause a major impact on weight gain. We have trained Zucker rats for prolonged periods of time and Judy Stern has done the same. You cannot prevent obesity from developing in the Zucker rat. So I don't think the Zucker rat is a good model for the human situation unless it's a model for the very selected genetic form of obesity. We desperately need studies on the effects of physical training on 24-hour energy expenditure and body composition in children. The double-labelled water method is being used in this area and should give us more data. Another area that I think is very important is the interaction between exercise and the thermic effect of food.

OSCAI: I appreciate the comments. First of all, the Zucker rat results have been poor in terms of trying to prevent obesity. The reason for bringing the Zucker rat into the paper is that it is the most extensively used model for early onset obesity, and lipoprotein lipase has been so extensively studied in the obese Zucker rat. It's the feeling of many that lipoprotein lipase, being the gatekeeper for fat entering the fat cell, may be the mechanism or play a role in the deposition of carcass fat. It's been my opinion that the measurements of lipoprotein lipase in adipose tissue have not been entirely correct; that was the reason for pointing it out.

GISOLFI: Larry, you indicated that high sugar intake increases percent fat. Are we talking about sucrose or carbohydrates in general? Also, with regard to exercise, we often tell people who are exercising to ingest a high carbohydrate diet; yet, you're saying that a high sugar diet leads to obesity. How do we reconcile these two concepts?

OSCAI: It seems that sugar alone is an obesity-promoting agent. It doesn't seem to be the complex carbohydrates in general. For example, when we use cornstarch in place of sugar, the animals do not become severely obese as they do with sugar. I don't know the reason why. It may be that sugar is rapidly split and forms the very low density lipoprotein in the liver that is then handled by lipoprotein lipase in adipose tissue much the same way that the chylomicron is handled in adipose tissue by LPL.

For a number of years, people have suspected that sugar is an obesity-promoting agent. As I pointed out, the studies have been short term in nature so that only small increases in fat cell size or in fat pad size were observed. So this was the reasoning behind putting rats on a sugar-rich diet and conducting the study until body weight stabilized or until obesity fully manifested itself. When we did that, we found that they indeed were severely obese. When we used cornstarch in place of sucrose, we didn't see this. Obesity occurs without the animals overeating. They take in the same number of calories as the animals eating Purina Chow or the animals eating the cornstarch diet. One of the reasons why we didn't mention information on the cornstarch diet is the animals tend to spill their food, thus making it difficult to quantitate caloric intake. This is not true for Purina Chow, the sugar diet, or the fat-rich diet.

GISOLFI: Does it make a difference when you exercise animals and put them on the high sugar diet?

OSCAI: We haven't done this yet. The next step, I think, is to show the effect of exercise and try to understand how sugar works to make the animal fat.

BALDWIN: In popular magazines you read about the "metabolic set-factor" or the "metabolic thermostat." Is this part of the genetic component? What are your thoughts on this topic as it relates to the general problem of obesity in youth as well as in adulthood?

OSCAI: It's been long known that there is a set-factor or set-point for body weight. What's difficult for me to reconcile is if you feed an animal a diet of Purina Chow, the animal's body weight will stabilize around 650 grams; but, if you put that animal on a fat-rich diet, body weight stabilizes at a much higher level. If you put the animal on a sugar-rich diet, body weight stabilizes at a much higher level—up to 1,700 grams. I don't know how the set theory fits into this.

BLAIR: Larry, when you are feeding high-fat and high-sugar diets, is the effect the same in the four-litter rats as in the 22-litter rats?

OSCAI: Yes, but the data presented was on rats raised in litters of four. In our initial studies, we also saw obesity in litters of 22 pups, but we focused on the small litters because the obesity was more exaggerated.

DAVIS: Larry, just a quick comment on the high sucrose diets. Have you looked at the insulin levels in those animals? My guess is that sucrose stimulates insulin, and insulin would be the major factor leading to the obesity in those rats. Secondly, exercise would reduce obesity in those animals much more so than it would in any of the other treatments you used.

OSCAI: That's right. These animals have never been characterized metabolically. I think it's an important thing to do, and I think that since exercise has such a profound effect on insulin sensitivity, this would be a very important area.

HALABY: In the classical study done by Mickelsen, medium chain triglycerides did not result in fat deposition as compared to long chain triglycerides.

OSCAI: We used the combination of lard and corn oil, so we use mixtures of fat. Mickelsen used an exaggerated amount of fat in those experiments, 85% of the calories came from Crisco. It was 60% Crisco by weight. But the point is, no matter what type of fat you feed, the animal is going to get fat.

TIPTON: I'd like to follow up on Ed Horton's point. I think you need to address the importance of the elevation in metabolism after exercise to energy balance. This has been studied for a long time, but most recently I think that the thorough study by Hermansen needs to be cited.

HORTON: I just wanted to add a comment about the sucrose overfeeding. It's very interesting that you've done the long-term studies with sucrose overfeeding and have commented that shorter term studies have not necessarily shown it. We've done studies with rats just on a chow diet with free access to sucrose for periods of six to eight weeks. In that short period of time, the animals have not increased total caloric intake significantly. They like sucrose. They eat sucrose. They cut back on their chow consumption, but total weight gain, total body fat content, and, interestingly, insulin levels are not significantly different in the animals, at least in a short-term exposure to sucrose. What happens over the longer term is less clear. In the studies that have been done with the so-called "cafeteria diets" of different composition (whether they're high carbohydrate, or high fat, or what have you), several people have reported quite a bit of individual variation in diet. I'm thinking of one study in which quite a variation in weight gain was found on a high carbohydrate "cafeteria-type diet," and weight gain was correlated with the development of insulin resistance and the development of abnormal glucose tolerance. Looking at insulin levels and insulin resistance is very important.

I'm glad that Chuck got up and made another plea for the energy balance equation, because all of these things really depend on the storage component, which really has to do with how diet affects energy expenditure and the various components of resting metabolic rate, thermic effect of the food itself, and the role of exercise. It's so difficult, when you review the literature, to find controls for all three elements. You usually see either emphasis on diet alone or emphasis on exercise alone without good measurements of the balance between energy intake and expenditure. It's still a very confusing field. The data in animals have been much more extensive than in humans, but the human data are beginning to emerge now that we have better techniques. I think that the double-labelled water method is going to give us a lot of long-term total energy expenditure data. These data should be coming out now fairly soon. It's particularly nice because you can use this methodology in children.

BROOKS: My own interest, Larry, and perhaps that of yourself and Steve Blair, is in the epidemiology of the human population. What's the prevalence of obesity in active children? Can we address that? What is the current status of the literature on that?

BLAIR: It's just about nonexistent. If you look at the least fit or the least active quartile or quintile, that's the group where the prevalence of obesity will be much higher. To my knowledge, there are just no prospective studies where activity levels in childhood have been assessed and children have been followed for the incidence of obesity.

DRINKWATER: I have a comment related to the emphasis on obesity. I would make a plea that when we talk about obesity, we talk about reaching an appropriate weight or an appropriate body composition and not necessarily concentrate on losing body fat. The prevalence of eating disorders in this country among young women is becoming an epidemic and, by over emphasizing obesity, we may be adding fuel to the fire. Is there any way of getting into this chapter the whole concept, which I think Russ and the people who have worked with fitness testing are trying to adapt, that there is a level of obesity that has adverse health consequence and a level of skinniness that also has adverse health consequences?

SUTTON: I'd like to address my question to Claude, and I wonder if he might enlarge upon the point he made about the differences in morbidity and mortality of the abdominally obese as opposed to the peripherally obese. To what extent is there a spectrum between these two different types of obesity? Are they clearly very distinct populations among us? Perhaps you could tell us why you think the abdominally obese are at more risk for developing hypertension than the peripherally obese.

BOUCHARD: No, but, the mortality differences are obvious. The abdominally obese have, depending on the study, from about eight to 15 times more cases of diabetes than the peripherally obese. That's a very high relative risk difference. In the case of differences in cholesterol, triglyceride, or reduced HDL, the risks again are several times higher in the abdominally obese than in the peripherally obese. The risks are a little bit lower for high blood pressure, but nevertheless, the trend is there. The mechanism is not quite clear. There's a good paper written by Lou Lansberg on how the data fit together to account for the differences we see in blood pressure; but it seems that the insulin effect on sympathetic nervous system activity dominates the mechanistic description of the relationship.

SUTTON: Are they completely discrete groups, or is there a merger going from one to the other?

BOUCHARD: No! They are not completely discrete groups. You have people with what we call an android type of obesity and those with a gynoid type of obesity, but of course you have differences between these two extremes. But no matter how you define them, you find these trends anyway. Comparing for example the quintiles—the quartile, the tertiles, it doesn't matter. You find the same trend.

PATE: My question also pertains to abdominal obesity. I'm curious as to whether we know the extent to which abdominal obesity or measures thereof track from childhood into adulthood. And secondly, if we have any idea why the abdominally obese might be more responsive to exercise training than peripherally obese.

BOUCHARD: I know of no data. When we talk about abdominally obese, I would like to keep the focus on visceral fat, and of course there are no tracking data for that compartment. If we measure it with total abdominal fat, we can use skinfolds or circumference data, and again it tracks much better at the extremes around the mean. The mechanism for the higher response of the abdominally obese to exercise is unknown to us, but it might be associated with the reduction of fat cell size associated with weight loss, which translates into a decrease in lipolysis and therefore mobilization of fat from that area. It might affect preferentially, perhaps, the visceral or the omental adipocytes more than the superficial or the subcutaneous adipocytes. But I know of no data that have looked into that carefully.

SHEPHARD: I think from the public health point of view the issue of the prevalence of obesity is one of the major foci that there should be in this section of the book, and I really sense that we haven't reached a consensus on that in our discussion. I certainly would not be very happy with the suggestion that 25% fat in boys and 30% fat in girls are figures that we should be considering as an indicator of how many in a population were obese. I wonder whether, as an alternative approach to this, one might consider looking at the distribution of body fat at different ages. In our study, we found that in young children 6 and 7 years old, there was a relatively normal distribution of the skin-fold thicknesses and the estimates of the percentages of body fat, but by the time they were 10 and 12 years old, there was a section of the population who were skewed to the right.

7

Cardiovascular Responses and Adaptations to Exercise in Childhood

DAVID S. BRADEN, M.D.

WILLIAM B. STRONG, M.D.

293

INTRODUCTION

The purpose of this chapter is to describe the cardiovascular responses to dynamic and isometric exercise in children, and the methods by which these responses may be evaluated. These responses will be discussed as they relate to the normal child and also to the child with cardiovascular disease. The cardiovascular responses to athletic training will also be reviewed.

I. TYPES OF EXERCISE TESTS

A. Dynamic exercise tests have been divided into maximal and submaximal. A maximal exercise test is one in which the test is continued until the individual's oxygen uptake ($\dot{V}O_2$) no longer increases with an increase in workload. This is presumed to be the individual's maximum aerobic power and is usually expressed as the $\dot{V}O_2$ max. A submaximal test consists of exercising an individual to a predetermined level that is less than maximal. In general, this end-point in the pediatric population is a heart rate of 170 beats per min. Adults generally use 85% of the predicted maximum heart rate (i.e., 220 minus subject's age in years). Dynamic exercise testing is performed utilizing either continuous or intermittent protocols. These protocols are usually graded in nature, i.e., the intensity of exercise is increased throughout the test. Dynamic testing is performed utilizing either cycle or treadmill ergometers.

B. Isometric tests. These tests are performed at submaximal intensity because of the child's inability to sustain a maximal isometric contraction for an interval long enough to make stable hemodynamic measurements. Patients are requested to perform a maximum voluntary contraction (MVC) using a hand grip dynamometer. The child is then instructed to maintain the isometric contraction in the range of 30 to 50% of the MVC for a predetermined amount of time, usually three to five min. Heart rate, blood pressure, and electrocardiographic measurements are usually made during this time.

II. CARDIOVASCULAR RESPONSES TO EXERCISE IN CHILDREN

A. Maximum Oxygen Consumption

Table 7-1 lists the results of maximum oxygen consumption ($\dot{V}O_2$ max) tests for children obtained from numerous authors. This table, like many others in this paper, cannot be presented in a uniform manner because of the methods by which the data were presented. Therefore, in Table 7-1, the measure of $\dot{V}O_2$ is $ml \cdot kg^{-1} \cdot min^{-1}$ or liters/min, a non-indexed value. Additionally, the data of Bar-Or (1983) and Godfrey (1974) are presented graphically and are not readily comparable to the presentations of the other authors.

    1. Measure of Aerobic Power. The $\dot{V}O_2$ is a measure of the amount of O_2 taken up at the lungs, and is proportional to the amount of work performed. It increases up to tenfold in children at maximal effort. $\dot{V}O_2max$ is defined as the rate of $\dot{V}O_2$ at the highest workload that a subject can perform and is a commonly used expression of maximal aerobic power. $\dot{V}O_2max$ increases with age from about 1 L/min in a 6-year-old to about 3 L/min in a 15-year-old. Its peak value is approximately 3.8 L/min in persons 20 years of age and steadily declines thereafter (Godfrey, 1974).

    2. Effect of Sex, Weight, Ethnic Background, Type of Exercise on Maximal Oxygen Consumption. At any age girls have a lower $\dot{V}O_2$ max than boys, with a difference seen as early as age 5 years (Bar-Or, 1983). This is demonstrated in Figure 7-1.

    $\dot{V}O_2$ is strongly related to lean body mass, and this may partially explain the sex-related difference. This difference disappears when $\dot{V}O_2max$ is indexed by weight in kg (Washington et al., 1988). Figure 7-2 illustrates that $\dot{V}O_2max$ increases little in boys and actually decreases in girls with increasing age when indexed by weight (Bar-Or, 1983). The difference in $\dot{V}O_2max$ between the sexes is actually a controversial point (Shephard, 1982; Rutenfranz et al., 1981).

    The greater the muscle mass used, the greater the $\dot{V}O_2$. This explains the higher values for $\dot{V}O_2max$ observed on the treadmill compared with cycle ergometry.

    The magnitude of the increase in $\dot{V}O_2$ observed in children from rest to maximum is somewhat less than in adults. A reasonably conditioned adult is able to increase his $\dot{V}O_2$ 10- to 15-fold during exercise, compared with only a 10-fold increase in children. Training also affects the $\dot{V}O_2$ with highly trained athletes being able to achieve a 20-fold increase.

B. Cardiac Output Response to Exercise

    Cardiac output (CO) increases in an almost linear manner concomitant with increasing $\dot{V}O_2$. There is a three- to four-fold increase in CO from rest to maximal exercise. Table 7-2 lists values for cardiac index derived from five studies of healthy children performed in either the supine or sitting positions using a cycle ergometer.

    An increase of CO occurs in the pre-exercise period, at the beginning of exercise, and in transition to each higher level of exercise.

TABLE 7-1. $\dot{V}O_2max$ as Determined by Various Authors.

Author/Year	Age(Yrs)	Ethnic	Sex	Value	Instrument	Protocol
Anderson et al. 1987 (8)	16–19	SC	M	51.7	Cycle	Continuous
			F	40.0		
Åstrand 1952 (10)	10–11	SC		56.1	Treadmill	
	12–13			56.5		
Cooper et al. 1984 (19)	6–11	USA	F	38±7	Cycle (electronically braked)	Ramp
	6–13		M	42±6		
	12–17		F	34±4		
	14–17		M	50±8		
Cumming et al. 1978 (22)	7	C		40.2±0.4	Treadmill	Bruce; third minute of stage 3 (submaximal)
				36.5±5.3		
				35.2±3.2		
				37.7±3.5		
Cunningham et al. 1984 (23)	9–10	C	M	48.8–51.3	Cycle	Graded; interrupted
Eriksson et al. 1973 (33)	11–13	SC	M	1.74 L/min	Supine in Cath Lab	Continuous
Eriksson et al. 1971 (32)	13–14	SC	M	2.51±0.11 L/min	Cycle	Continuous
Hermansen & Oseid 1971 (38)	10–12	SC	M	54.3–58.1	Treadmill	Maximal
				48.1–52.1	Cycle (mechanically braked)	Submaximal
Ikai 1971 (39)	10–11	J	M	54.4	Treadmill	Continuous
Krahenbuhl et al. 1978 (43)	6–9	USA		45.2	Treadmill	Continuous progressive

TABLE 7-1. (continued)

Reference	Age	Country	Sex	Value	Equipment	Protocol
Kramer & Lurie 1964 (44)	10–15	USA	M	45.8–48.8	Cycle	Continuous, single stage
Paterson et al. 1982 (58)	10–14	USA	M	57.9±1.2	Cycle	Intermittent
Reybrouck et al. 1982 (62)	5–18	B	M	44.0–56.6	Treadmill	Continuous; graded
			F	40.0–43.7		
Rutenfranz et al. 1981 (67)	8–15	SC	M	51.4–61.4	Cycle	Continuous; graded
			F	43.6–53.6		
	12–17	G	M	47.1–57.4		
			F	33.4–47.9		
Shephard et al. 1969 (72)	11	C		48.3	Treadmill	Continuous, progressive
	12–13			45.8		
Skinner et al. 1971 (74)	6–15	USA	M	50.0–51.6	Treadmill	Continuous, progressive
			F	43.0–45.7		
			M	53.0		
			F	44.8		
Washington et al. 1988 (84)	7–12	W	M	46–47	Cycle (electronically braked)	Continuous progressive
			F	41–43		

*All values in ml·kg^{-1}·min^{-1} unless otherwise stated
SC = Scandinavia
USA = United States of America
C = Canada
W = White (USA)
B = Belgium
G = West Germany
J = Japan

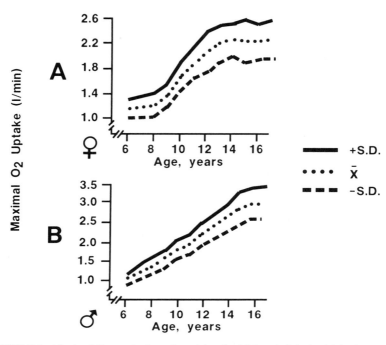

FIGURE 7-1. *Maximal O₂ uptake in male and female children in L/min. Males have greater values from about age 8 onward. (Reproduced with permission from Bar-Or, 1983).*

Steady state CO is usually achieved within 2 min of each new workload. In children, the level of CO is somewhat lower at each metabolic level than that observed in adults. CO increases by approximately 20 ml/min for every cm increase in height for children working at the same $\dot{V}O_2$ (Godfrey, 1974). Upright exercise yields significantly higher values for maximum CO than does supine exercise (Table 7-2), and treadmill ergometry causes a higher maximal CO than does cycle ergometry.

C. Heart Rate Response to Maximal Exercise

Cardiac output is determined by heart rate (HR) and by stroke volume (SV). Tables 7-3a-c list values for maximal HR (HR max) utilizing treadmill, cycle, and supine protocols.

At maximum effort, HR increases two- to threefold from the resting state (Table 7-2). It is markedly sensitive to an increase or decrease in conditioning and serves as a valuable gauge in determining fitness and compliance to exercise programs. Figure 7-3 illustrates HR max by age, sex, and race using a cycle ergometer.

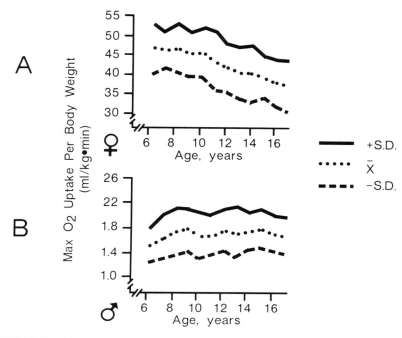

FIGURE 7-2. *Maximal O₂ uptake in male and female children when indexed by weight in kg. Maximal O₂ uptake decreases with increasing age in girls when indexed by body weight. (Reproduced with permission from Bar-Or, 1983).*

Treadmill exercise causes slightly higher HR max values than does cycle ergometry.

Children have a higher maximal HR than adults, which ranges from 195 to 215 b/min. After maturity, it decreases with age at a rate of 0.7 to 0.8 b/min per year of age (Bar-Or, 1983). This value is independent of sex, level of conditioning, climate, or other environmental conditions.

Women have faster heart rates than men at any given workload. Traditionally, this has been considered secondary to the lower Hgb values as well as smaller lean body mass values of women at any given weight. However, this same difference in HR is found in 6-year-olds who have equal hemoglobin concentrations (Godfrey et al., 1971). Other possible reasons for this difference include the lower SV in females and sex-related differences in autonomic cardiac regulation. Qualitative differences in regulatory mechanisms have been reflected in the fact that younger boys have a more rapid decrease in HR on cessation of exercise. Higher HRs have also been found in obese children, in hot and humid climates, and in times of emo-

TABLE 7-2. *Cardiac Index by Cycle Ergometry.*

Author/Year	Age(Yrs)	Ethnic	Sex	Value ($L \cdot min^{-1} \cdot m^{-2}$) REST	MAX	Instrument	Protocol
Cumming, 1977 (21)	5–6	C	M	3.92+0.20	10.1±1.75	*Supine* Cycle in Cath Lab	Intermittent, graded
			F	4.0±0.74	8.6±1.81		
Eriksson et al. 1973 (33)	11–13	SC	M	3.9	12.5	*Seated* Cycle in Cath Lab	Continuous
Eriksson et al. 1971 (32)	13–14	SC	M	5.25±0.50	17.41±0.88	Cycle	Continuous
Lock et al. 1978 (48)	5–16	USA	M	4.41±0.15	8.0±0.27	*Supine* Cycle in Cath Lab	Fixed Work Load (Probably submaximal)

C = Canadian
SC = Scandinavian
USA = United States of America

TABLE 7-3a. *Maximum Heart Rate by Treadmill Ergometry from Various Studies.*

Author/Year	Age(Yrs)	Ethnic	Sex	Value (BPM)	Protocol
Åstrand, 1952 (10)	10–11	SC		211	Treadmill
	12–13			205	
Cumming et al. 1978 (22)	4–18	C	M/F	193–206	Bruce
Hermansen & Oseid, 1971 (38)	10–12	SC	M	207–206	
Krahenbuhl et al. 1978 (43)	6–9	USA	M	200	Continuous, progressive
			F	202	
Riopel et al. 1979 (63)	4–21	B	M	179–186	Balke/Ware with alterations by Austin
			F	181–194	
		W	M	183–192	
			F	187–191	
Shephard et al. 1969 (72)	11–13	C	M/F	193	Continuous, progressive
Skinner et al. 1971 (74)	6–15	USA	M	198–201	Continuous, progressive
			F	203–204	
			M	199	
			F	203	
Smit et al. (75)	16	W(SA)	M	191–194	*STEPS*, continuous
			F	197	
		B(SA)	M	201	

USA = United States of America
C = Canadian
SC = Scandinavian
B = Black (USA)
W = White (USA)
B(SA) = Black—South African
W(SA) = White—South African

TABLE 7-3b. *Maxmum Heart Rate by Cycle Ergometry from Various Studies.*

Author/Year	Age(Yrs)	Ethnic	Sex	Value (BPM)	Protocol
Alpert et al. 1981 (3)	6–15	B	M	188–194	Continuous, graded
			F	185–195	(mechanically braked)
		W	M	191–194	
			F	191–195	
Eriksson et al. 1971 (32)	13–14	SC	M	197–204	Continuous
Goldberg et al. 1966 (36)	6–16	USA	M	185–203	Continuous
			F	185–201	
James et al. 1980 (41)	5–33 (Ave 14.3)	95% W 5% B	M/F	187–199	James; continuous, progressive
Kramer & Lurie, 1964 (44)	10–15	USA	M	187–201	Continuous, single-staged
Mocellin et al. 1971 (55)	13–14	WG	M	195	Continuous, progressive (trained)
Strong et al. 1978 (80)	7–14	B	M	186–194	Continuous; modification of Bruce/Hornsby and Cummings (mechanically braked)
			F	184–197	
Washington et al. 1988 (84)	7–12	W	M	191–193	James (electronically braked)
			F	196	

USA = United States of America
SC = Scandinavian
WG = West German
B = Black (USA)
W = White (USA)

TABLE 7-3c. *Maximum Heart Rate by Supine Cycle Ergometry.*

Author/Year	Age(Yrs)	Ethnic	Sex	Value (BPM)	Protocol
Cumming, 1977 (21)	5–16	C	M F	170 174	Intermittent, graded
Lock et al. 1978 (48)	5–16	USA	M/F	142	Fixed workload (probably submaximal)

C = Canadian
USA = United States of America

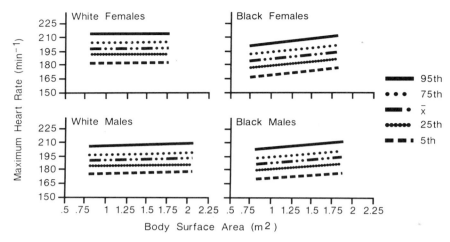

FIGURE 7-3. *Relationship of maximum HR to age, race and sex utilizing cycle ergometry. (Reproduced with permission from Alpert et al., 1982).*

tional stress. In a study of a biracial population of children at the Medical College of Georgia, no racial difference between HR values were obtained in healthy white children and black children (Alpert et al., 1982). This is also illustrated in Figure 7-3. In the supine position, there is an increase in venous return to the heart, which leads to an increased SV at rest and a concomitant decrease in resting, submaximal, and maximal heart rates.

D. Stroke Volume Response to Exercise

SV substantially rises when progressing from rest to one-third of maximum power with little further increase thereafter. Further increases in CO are more dependent on increasing HR rather than SV. Factors that affect the SV are the venous return to the heart (pre-load), distensibility of the ventricles, and force of contraction of the ventricle in relation to the pressure in the aorta (afterload). Catecholamines have been found to play a role by improving the force-generating potential of muscle fibers in addition to increasing HR (Åstrand & Rodahl, 1986). Table 7-4 lists values for SV index from five studies performed in either the supine or seated positions using cycle ergometry.

E. Effect of Exercise on Arteriovenous Oxygen Difference

Oxygen delivery is dependent upon CO and hemoglobin concentration. At rest, the normal oxygen saturation of arterial blood

TABLE 7-4. *Stroke Volume Index by Cycle Ergometry.*

Author/Year	Age(Yrs)	Ethnic	Sex	Value (mL · beat^{-1} · m^{-2}) REST	Value (mL · beat^{-1} · m^{-2}) MAX	Instrument	Protocol
Cumming, 1977 (21)	5–16	C	M	51.9±5.9	55.7±12.7	*Supine* Cycle in Cath Lab	Intermittent graded
			F	44.5±6.3	46.3±3.1		
Eriksson et al. 1973 (33)	11–13	SC	M	49.4	66.9	*Seated* Cycle in Cath Lab	Continuous
Eriksson et al. 1971 (32)	13–14	SC	M	61.8±6.2	86.8±3.9	Cycle	Continuous
Lock et al. 1978 (48)	5–16	USA	M/F	52.7±2.0	57.3±2.3	*Supine* Cycle in Cath Lab	Fixed Work load (probably submaximal)

C = Canadian
SC = Scandinavian
USA = United States of America

is approximately 97%, and mixed venous oxygen saturation is approximately 70%. During exercise there is an increase in muscle blood flow, which occurs secondary to sustained local vasodilatation. The exercising muscle mass may receive as much as 80% to 85% of the CO during maximal exercise compared with 15% at rest. The result of this is a marked decrease in the mixed venous oxygen saturation to the range of 30%. This leads to almost a threefold increase in the arteriovenous oxygen difference (A-$\dot{V}O_2$ diff) with maximal exercise (Table 7-5).

In children, A-$\dot{V}O_2$ difference is somewhat higher than that found in adults (Bar-Or, 1983). As the child approaches maximal exercise, there can be no further increase in peripheral oxygen extraction. This may be a potential handicap if heat stress is combined with maximal exercise. Under such conditions, the circulatory system may not be able to fully meet the increased metabolic needs of the patient and the maximal effort cannot be sustained.

Thus, the normal cardiac response to exercise involves the integrated effects of the myocardium to increased HR, sympathetic stimulation and the operation of the Frank-Starling mechanism. During maximal levels of exercise, the ventricular myocardium requires all three of these influences to sustain a level of activity sufficient to satisfy the augmented oxygen requirements of exercising skeletal muscles.

F. Effect of Exercise on Blood Pressure and Vascular Resistance

1. Systemic Responses. At maximal effort, CO increases three- to fourfold. CO is directly proportional to blood pressure (BP). Therefore, if mean arterial pressure (MAP) increased fourfold (i.e., MAP of 80 mm HG to 320 mm Hg), an excessive increase in myocardial energy demand ($M\dot{V}O_2$) would be required. This increased $M\dot{V}O_2$ would be most difficult to meet even with an increased HR. Therefore, the body compensates by decreasing systemic vascular resistance to decrease the work required of the heart.

The response of BP to exercise is determined by the type of exercise, i.e., dynamic versus static exercise. Dynamic exercise leads to an increased contractile force of the myocardium with a concomitant increase in interventricular systolic pressure (wall stress). This results in an increased SBP. DBP changes to a minimal degree because vasodilatation reduces peripheral resistance; MAP rises. The increase in CO is greater than the increase in MAP, and this results in a decreased systemic vascular resistance (SVR).

Isometric exercise elevates both SBP and DBP. When voluntary contraction of a muscle is maintained at 50% of its maximal value,

TABLE 7-5. *Arteriovenous Difference Utilizing Cycle Ergometry.*

| Author/Year | Age(Yrs) | Ethnic | Sex | Value (mL/100 mL) | | Instrument | Protocol |
				REST	MAX		
Eriksson et al. 1973 (33)	11–13	SC	M	4.6	14.2	*Supine* Cycle in Cath Lab	Continuous
Eriksson et al. 1971 (32)	13–14	SC	M	6.99±0.6	14.51±0.4	Cycle	Continuous
Lock et al. 1978 (48)	5–16	USA	M/F	3.63±0.08	8.54±0.36	*Supine* Cycle in Cath Lab	Fixed Work load (probably submaximal)

SC = Scandinavian
USA = United States of America

TABLE 7-6. *Maximum Blood Pressure Responses to Exercise Utilizing Cycle Ergometry.*

Author/Year	Age(Yrs)	Ethnic	Sex	BSA(m²)	Value		Instrument	Protocol
					MAX	△BP*		
Eriksson et al. 1973 (33)	11–13	SC	M		SBP 160	45	*Supine cycle*	Continuous
					DBP 71	5		
					MAP 105	20		
Eriksson et al. 1971 (32)	13–14	SC	M		MAP 129.3	25	Cycle	Continuous
	5–33	95% W			SBP 119–130	25–28		
James et al. 1980 (41)	(AVE 14.3)	5% B	M/F	<1	DBP 70–73	9	Cycle	James
					SBP 145–148	37–40		
			M/F	1–1.19	DBP 71–77	(−1)+8		
					SBP 142–240	37–76		
			M	>1.2	DBP 70–73	(−9)–10		
					SBP 160–181	40–62		
			F	>1.2	DBP 84–88	5–10		
Strong et al. 1978 (79)	7–14	B	M		SBP 139–167	55 ± 17	Cycle	Continuous
			F		SBP 140–167	47 ± 6		
Washington et al. 1988 (84)	7–12	W	M	<1	SBP 122	19	Cycle	James
					DBP 77	11		
				1–1.19	SBP 130	28		
					DBP 83	16		
				>1.2	SBP 139	35		
					DBP 81	13		
			F	<1	SBP 126	24		
					DBP 77	14		
				1–1.19	SBP 131	34		
					DBP 79	11		
				>1.2	SDP 142	38		
					DBP 80	11		

SC = Scandinavian
W = White (USA)
B = Black (USA)
* △ BP = increase in BP from rest to maximal exercise

SBP rises to near maximum levels within 1 min. In adults, this increase in SBP is unrelated to the absolute force, but rather is related to the intensity of the contraction of the respective muscle group relative to the maximum voluntary contraction of that muscle group. Therefore, a hand grip (relatively small muscle mass) at 50% maximum intensity will bring about a similar BP increase as the contraction of both quadriceps (relatively large muscle mass) at 50% of their maximal voluntary contraction. Data on children are limited to the hand grip dynamometer. Researchers at the Medical College of Georgia found no correlation between the change in BP with isometric exercise and the maximal change of BP with dynamic exercise, suggesting that different mechanisms were responsible for isometric and dynamic responses (Strong et al., 1978). Table 7-6 lists BP responses to maximal exercise as determined by various authors.

There is an increase in both systolic and diastolic BP responses to exercise with increasing age and increasing body size (Figure 7-4). Because males have a higher maximum SV than females, they have traditionally been thought to have a higher SBP response than females. In a study of 170 healthy black boys and girls at the Medical College of Georgia, this difference was not observed (Alpert et al.,

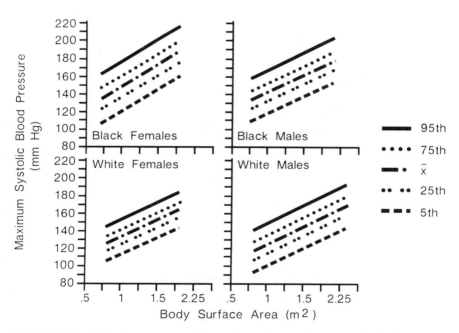

FIGURE 7-4. *Effect of race, sex, and body size on the maximum stystolic blood pressure (mmHg). (Reproduced with permission from Alpert et al., 1982).*

1981). Utilizing a treadmill protocol, Riopel et al. (1979) studied 288 healthy children and found few racial differences with respect to SBP responses to exercise. Utilizing cycle ergometry, Alpert et al. (1981) observed that black males had a higher exercise blood pressure than white males, both by age and surface area, suggesting a difference in the BP response to dynamic exercise within the black population. However, the black youths tended to have a greater aerobic power (Figure 7-5).

    2. Pulmonary Responses. There is only a minimal increase of mean pulmonary artery pressure, even with a four-fold increase in CO. A markedly reduced pulmonary vascular resistance occurs during exercise.

G. Electrocardiographic Responses to Exercise

    1. Myocardial Oxygen Supply and Demand. Exercise electrocardiography is useful as a measure of myocardial oxygen supply and demand. Myocardial oxygen consumption ($M\dot{V}O_2$) is determined by contractility, pre-load, afterload, HR, and, of course, by work performed. $M\dot{V}O_2$ is proportional to myocardial tension de-

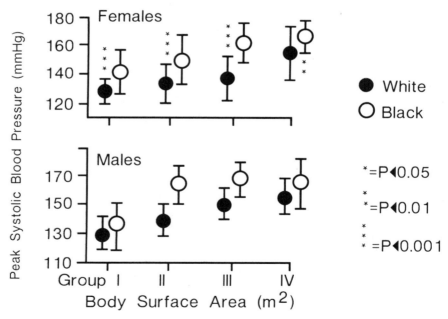

FIGURE 7-5. *Effect on sex on peak systolic blood pressure. (Reproduced with permission from Alpert et al., 1981).*

velopment and hence the Law of Laplace (T = P × R) where T is tension, P is pressure, and R is radius.

The pathologic nature of ST segment depression during exercise can be substantiated by evaluating the oxygen supply/demand ratio of the left ventricle. This can be accomplished in children by utilizing aortic and left ventricular pressure curves obtained at the time of cardiac catheterization of patients with aortic stenosis (Kveselis et al., 1985). It has also been substantiated by radionuclide assessment of ejection fraction responses and wall motion abnormalities in children with sickle cell anemia (Covitz et al., 1983). However, investigators differ in their definition of what constitutes an ischemic ST segment response. Figure 7-6 illustrates the PR isoelectric method of measuring ST segment depression and J point.

Figure 7-6 illustrates the method used at the Medical College of Georgia in which the baseline (P-R isoelectric line) is superimposed on the PR segment of each QRS-T complex for identifying J point depression. A depression in the J point greater than 1 mm accompanied by a depression in the ST segment below the isoelectric line for 40 to 60 msec after the J point is strongly suggestive of inequality of myocardial oxygen demand. In the author's experience, positive responses have been observed in only 1 to 2% of the healthy subjects studied (Thapar et al., 1978).

P–R Isoelectric
Method of Measuring the "J" Point

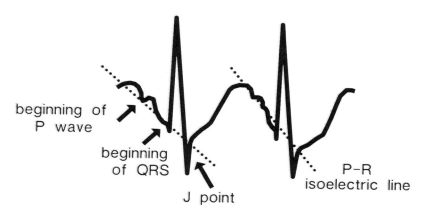

FIGURE 7-6. *The Pr isoelectric method of measuring the "J" point during exercise. A line is drawn from the beginning of the P wave to the beginning of the QRS. (Reproduced with permission from Thapar et al., 1978).*

Ischemic responses are often seen in patients with severe aortic stenosis or severe pulmonic stenosis; in patients who have undergone either the Mustard or Fontan procedure, coronary artery fistulae; patients with an aberrant left coronary artery from the anterior (right) sinus of valsalva, coronary aneurysms secondary to Kawasaki disease, aortic or mitral insufficiency; and in patients with a single ventricle. Similar changes are seen in patients with mitral valve prolapse, hyperventilation syndrome, vasoregulatory abnormalities, left ventricular hypertrophy, bundle branch block, paced rhythm, administration of drugs (i.e., Digoxin), and in those patients with non-specific ST-T wave changes at rest. The significance of the ECG change in these situations is not understood, but may represent a repolarization process influenced by the autonomic nervous system.

2. **Cardiac Rhythm Responses to Exercise.** Exercise testing is also useful in the provocation, characterization, and therapeutic evaluation of cardiac dysrhythmias. Exercise may induce or promote rhythm disturbances by changing autonomic tone or by enhancing sympathetic discharge, thereby increasing myocardial excitability. Some normal children may therefore have extrasystoles during submaximal exercise, maximal exercise, or recovery. Children with "benign premature ventricular contractions" (PVCs), and otherwise normal hearts and a negative cardiovascular history, respond to exercise with a decrease or abolition of the uniform PVCs observed at rest. Ventricular ectopy, induced or exacerbated by exercise, is more suggestive of an underlying cardiac abnormality. Exercise testing is also useful in the pre- and post-operative evaluation of children with congenital heart disease and reveals characteristic abnormalities that will be outlined later in this chapter.

H. Ventilatory (Anaerobic) Threshold: A Measure of Performance

Figure 7-7 shows the relationship between HR, $\dot{V}O_2$ max, serum lactate concentration, and $\dot{V}CO_2$. This graph is shown to illustrate the concept of the ventilatory threshold (VT), which is being used frequently in clinical exercise testing.

The VT occurs at the "point" during progressively graded exercise when the minute ventilation ($\dot{V}_E$) and the $\dot{V}CO_2$ curves separate from the linear rise of the $\dot{V}O_2$. Some investigators believe that the VT occurs at the point illustrated on the graph at which there is an accumulation of lactate in the blood. There is a great deal of controversy concerning the significance and etiology of this observation, but many would believe that it is merely a manifestation of lactate accumulation secondary to the inability of various tissues

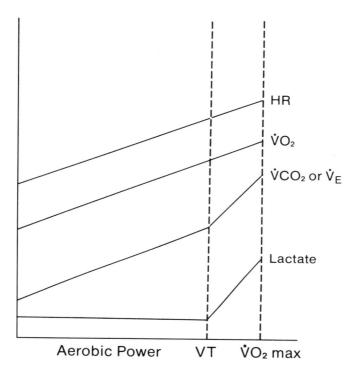

FIGURE 7-7. *The relationship between HR, $\dot{V}O_2max$ and the ventilatory threshold.*

(kidney, liver, heart, skeletal muscle) to clear it as rapidly as it is produced. Table 7-7 lists lactate levels at maximal exercise determined by various authors.

Figure 7-8 illustrates the increase in the maximum blood lactate that occurs with increasing age (Åstrand, 1952; Davies et al., 1972). The marked increase in blood lactate and the marked increase in $\dot{V}_E$ and $\dot{V}CO_2$ may not occur at the same point. Therefore, it has been difficult to identify a consistent point at which the VT occurs. In spite of the inconsistencies, some exercise physiologists consider the VT to be a good measure of one's exercise "efficiency". It is often expressed as a percentage of either $\dot{V}O_2max$, exercise time, and/or HR max. Expressed as a percentage of HRmax, it increases with training. Table 7-8 lists values for VT as determined by various authors.

Wolfe et al. (1986) assessed the VT in 10 prepubertal female cross-country runners as a possible predictor of athletic performance. VT was determined by the breaking point of the ventilatory equivalent for oxygen from the ventilatory equivalent for carbon dioxide. $\dot{V}O_2$

TABLE 7-7. *Maximum Lactate Values.*

Author/Year	Age(Yrs)	Ethnic	Sex	Value (mMol/L) REST	Value (mMol/L) MAX	Instrument	Protocol
Åstrand, 1952 (10)	10–11	SC			9.2	Treadmill	
	12–13				8.7		
Eriksson et al. 1973 (33)	11–13	SC	M	1.2	5.6	*Supine* Cycle in Cath Lab	Continuous
Eriksson et al. 1971 (32)	13–14	SC	M	0.89±0.12	8.16±0.72	Cycle	Continuous
Saltin-Thoren, 1968 (68)	Ave. 12.8	SC	M		7.3	Treadmill Cycle	
					8.4		
Shephard et al. 1969 (72)	11	C	M/F		8.1	Treadmill	Continuous, progressive
					7.7		

SC = Scandinavian
C = Canadian

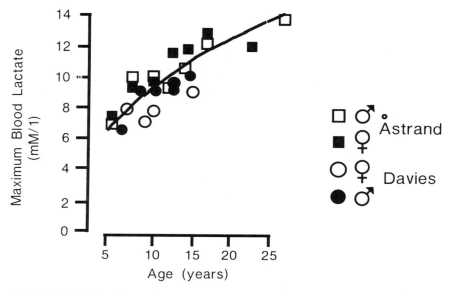

FIGURE 7-8. *Effect of increasing age on the maximum blood lactate from work by Åstrand (1952) and Davies (1972). The maximum blood lactate increases with increasing age. (Reproduced with permission from Åstrand, 1952; Davies et al., 1972).*

max predicted performance rank at a statistically significant level. VT, expressed as a conventional percentage of VO_2 max, was less significant as a predictor of performance rank. The best predicator was the VT expressed as a percentage of either endurance time or HRmax.

III. CARDIOVASCULAR ADAPTATIONS TO EXERCISE IN CHILDREN

A. Effect of Training on Cardiovascular Measurements

With training, there is an increase in total blood volume and total Hgb. This increased blood volume increases venous return and, thus, increases SV. However, there is no increase in absolute Hgb concentration, and some athletes actually have "sports anemia". Trained pubertal children, similar to adults, have an increased SV at rest and with all exercise levels. This has not been demonstrated in prepubertal children. It is felt that the increased SV of pubertal children is secondary to the higher blood volume and improved venous return and/or improved myocardial contractility. Trained athletes have lower resting heart rates, lower heart rates at all exercise levels, and a faster rate of post-exertional recovery than non-athletes. Resting and submaximal heart rates are the most sensitive re-

TABLE 7-8. *Values for Anaerobic Threshold from Three Investigators.*

Author/Year	Age(Yrs)	Ethnic	Sex	$\dot{V}O_2$ at AT $mL \cdot kg^{-1} \cdot min^{-1}$	% $\dot{V}O_2$ Max $mL \cdot kg^{-1} \cdot min^{-1}$	Instrument	Protocol
Cooper et al. 1984 (19)	6–11	USA	F	23 ± 4	61 ± 7	Cycle (electronically braked)	Ramp
	6–13		M	26 ± 5	58 ± 8		
	12–17		F	19 ± 3	64 ± 6		
	14–17		M	27 ± 6	55 ± 10		
Reybrouck et al. (61)	5–18	B	M	26.5–34.8	50.5–74.4	Treadmill	Continuous; graded
			F	24.3–29.4	53.8–69.2		
Washington et al. 1988 (84)	7–12	W	M	33–35	71–75	Cycle (electronically braked)	James
			F	30	68–72		
*Wolfe et al. 1986 (85)	10–13	USA	F	29.3–49.5	62–85	Treadmill	Bruce

*10 highly conditioned cross-country runners
USA = United States of America
W = White (USA)
B = Belgium

sponses to conditioning and often precede any change in maximum aerobic power. The slower HR is accompanied by a decrease in myocardial work and myocardial $\dot{V}O_2$. This sensitivity of the HR response is the basis of fitness tests in which $\dot{V}O_2$ max is indirectly assessed from the submaximal HR. These changes in HR are opposed by changes in SV in the opposite direction, thus producing little change in CO at a given metabolic level. Maximum CO in children increases with training in proportion to the increase in $\dot{V}O_2$ max.

Children are also trainable. Table 7-9 represents data compiled by Dr. Peter Snell, outlining the increases in $\dot{V}O_2$max secondary to training as observed by several authors.

B. Cardiovascular Responses in Young Athletes

1. Measures of Performance. With an ever-increasing number of children participating in competitive athletics, it is important to briefly consider cardiovascular adaptations to training seen in competitive childhood athletes (Table 7-10).

2. Echocardiographic Characteristics. Endurance training in children produces an increase in myocardial mass (Table 7-11). Allen et al. (1977) demonstrated normal chamber dimensions but increased ventricular free wall and septal thickness in championship childhood swimmers. This is in contrast to the values found in adults in which dynamic training such as running or swimming results in a larger left ventricular cavity with normal wall thickness, and in which isometric training results in cardiac hypertrophy. Cohen et al. (1987) studied wrestlers who underwent combined isometric and dynamic training. The results observed were more compatible with those found in adults and revealed increased ventricular cavity size compared to normal subjects. However, these children also exhibited increased ventricular free wall and septal thickness. Because the subjects participated in both resistance or strength and dynamic training, it could not be ascertained with certainty which particular aspect of training contributed to which specific morphologic change. The increase in left ventricular diameter and concomitant increase in wall thickness were felt to be compensatory mechanisms for the normalization of myocardial wall stress.

IV. ALTERED CARDIOVASCULAR RESPONSES IN DISEASE STATES

A. Cardiovascular Responses to Exercise in Children with Sickle Cell Anemia

Certain pathologic states produce alterations in the cardiovascular system and thus alterations in the cardiovascular responses to

TABLE 7-9. Responses of $\dot{V}O_2$ max to Training of Chidren. (Reproduced with permission from Snell, 1988).

	Brown et al. (15)	Ekblom (30)	Lussier & Buskirk (49)	Eriksson & Koch (33)	Vaccaro & Clarke (83)	Massicotte & MacNab (50)	Rotstein et al. (65)
Number	12	6	16	9	15	9	28
Sex	F	M	M,F	M	M,F	M	M
Age (y)	8–13	11	8–12	11–13	9–11	11–13	10–12
Weeks	6,12	24	12	16	28	6	9
Time/Session		45	45	60		12	45
Days/Week	4–5		4	3	4	3	3
% Increase in $\dot{V}O_2$ max	18,26	10	7	16	10	11	8

TABLE 7-10. *HR max and $\dot{V}O_2$ max Values in Childhood Athletes.*

Author/Year	Age	Ethnic	Sex	Activity	Duration	HR max (BPM)	$\dot{V}O_2$ Max*
Cunningham et al. 1976 (24)	10	C	M	Hockey	4.4 yrs	197 + 8	56.6 + 7.7
Daniels et al. 1978 (25)	10–18	USA	M	Middle-distance running	2–5 yrs	—	59.0–61.2
Docherty et al. 1987 (27)	11–13	C	M	Omni-kinetic equipment & stationary cycling	4 wks	195–199	46.2–47.0 PRE 54.7–55.1 POST
Vaccaro & Clarke, 1978 (83)	9–11	USA	M/F	Swimming	7 months	198	47.27 PRE 55.38 POST

C = Canadian
USA = United States of Americaa
*mL · kg^{-1} · min^{-1}

TABLE 7-11. *Echocardiographic Characteristics in Young Athletes.*

Author/Year	Age	Sex	Activity	LV Chamber Dimensions	LV Wall Thicknesses
Allen et al 1977 (2)	5–17 (Ave 10.8)	M/F	Swimming	NL	↑
Cohen et al 1987 (18)	15–19	M	Wrestling	↑	↑
Pearson et al 1986 (59)	19–38	M	Weightlifters	↑	↑

↑ = increased compared to controls
NL = not sigificantly different from controls
All studies done in United States of America

exercise. Extensive work has been done at the Medical College of Georgia regarding cardiovascular manifestations and cardiovascular responses to exercise in patients with sickle cell anemia. There is a sustained increase in CO when Hgb concentration is less than 8 g/dL—a typical figure encountered in sickle cell anemia. This results in an elevation of SV with minimal elevation of resting HR. Because of this anemia present, oxygen-carrying capacity of the blood is reduced. There is also a concomitant rightward shift of the oxyhemoglobin dissociation curve secondary to an increase of 2,3-DPG. This serves to decrease the binding of oxygen to Hgb and increases oxygen delivery at the tissue level (Rodman et al., 1959).

Exercise testing has become quite helpful in demonstrating cardiovascular abnormalities in patients with sickle cell disease. Alpert et al. (1981) showed that these pediatric sickle cell patients do indeed have an increased resting HR, which is in contrast to children with other forms of anemia and to adult sickle cell patients. Fifteen percent of the patients studied had ischemic responses to exercise with a lower HRmax response. Another 34% had equivocally ischemic responses without a decrease in HRmax. These investigators further demonstrated that patients with sickle cell anemia had decreased BP responses to maximum voluntary effort and a marked reduction of maximum work capacity compared to controls. Those patients with evidence of definite ischemia had the lowest maximal power achieved and also the lowest hemoglobin values. The male ischemic group had a lower BP response to exercise than did the female ischemic group. The explanation for the ischemic response, the decreased BP rise, and the reduced working capacity is probably the result of a limitation of oxygen transport to the myocardium. The already tenuous oxygen supply is stressed beyond the patient's ability to compensate during exercise.

Covitz et al. (1983), utilizing radionuclide angiography, demonstrated a reduction in HR, CO, and power at maximal exercise when compared with controls. These reductions were related to the degree of anemia. Left ventricular end-diastolic volume fell during exercise and was most marked in patients with ischemic exercise electrocardiograms. Four of the 22 patients who demonstrated electrocardiographic signs of ischemia also had evidence of an abnormal ejection fraction. By utilizing digitized M-mode echocardiography, Balfour et al. (1988) demonstrated abnormalities of diastolic function (impaired left ventricular filling) in patients with sickle cell anemia compared with normal subjects. Those patients who had abnormal ejection fractions during radionuclide studies had significantly more impaired diastolic function and did less exercise than those with normal ejection fractions.

B. Exercise Responses in Hypertensive Individuals

The BP response to exercise of hypertensive individuals generally parallels that of normal individuals, although at a higher level. Some individuals with mild hypertension at rest will have a normal BP response to exercise, while some with a high normal BP at rest will have a BP response to exercise that exceeds the 95th percentile. Exercise testing in the hypertensive individual may help identify those with an exaggerated BP response, ST-T wave changes, or dysrhythmias that may warrant restriction of certain physical activities such as isometric exercise (e.g., powerlifting). Exercise testing has been proposed as a helpful selective screening test for detecting prehypertensive youths. Although current data are controversial, some investigators have found a limited, but positive predictive value for future hypertension in the BP response to exercise.

Recent work at the Medical College of Georgia (Arensman et al., 1988) utilizing Doppler derived cardiac outputs and SVR, suggests that white and black pre-adolescents have similar BP responses to exercise. However, blacks have lower CO and greater SVR both at rest and in response to maximal exercise. This greater vascular resistance might help explain the greater incidence of hypertension in the black population.

C. Cardiovascular Response in Children with Congenital Heart Disease

Abnormal cardiovascular responses to exercise are also encountered in children with congenital heart defects. It is beyond the scope of this chapter to review all the abnormal cardiovascular responses to exercise observed in children with congenital heart disease. For an excellent report on the assessment of the athlete with congenital heart disease, the reader is referred to the monograph "Cardiovascular Abnormalities in the Athlete: Recommendations Regarding Eligibility for Competition". (*Journal of the American College of Cardiology* 6:1189, 1985). Tables 7-12 and 7-13 outline adaptations to exercise seen with specific congenital heart lesions (Christiansen & Strong, 1988).

A less than normal increase in SBP with exercise is often seen in aortic stenosis, in Ebstein's anomaly of the tricuspid valve, and in those patients who have undergone a Fontan procedure for tricuspid or pulmonary stenosis. A fall in SBP with exercise reflects serious impairment of the systemic ventricular output and/or an ab-

TABLE 7-12. *Exercise Characteristics in Various Acyanotic Congenital Heart Defects. (Reproduced with Permission from Christiansen and Strong, 1988).*

Lesion/ Abnormality	HR	BP	ECG (Ischemia)	Aerobic Power	Dysrhythmia
Acyanotic					
Aortic Stenosis					
Pre-op	N-↓	N-+ Inferolateral	N-↓	−	
Post-op	n	n	+ Leads	N-↓	+/−
Pulmonic Stenosis			+/− Inferior leads		
Pre-op	N	N	leads	N	−
Post-op	N		V2, V3	n	+/−
Coarctation					
Pre-op	N	↑	+/−	N-↓	−
Post-op	N	n-↑	+/−	N	−
Atrial Septal Defect					
Pre-op	N	N	N	N	−
Post-op	N	N	N	n	+/−
Ventricular Septal Defect					
Pre-op	N	N	−	N	−
Post-op	N	N	−	n	+/−
Acyanotic					
Aortic Insufficiency	n	↑	+	n	−
Mitral Insufficiency	n	n-↑	+/−	n	+/−
Mitral Valve Prolapse	N	N	+ (many false postives)	n	+

Legend: N-High Probability of Normal Response Until Disease Progresses Significantly
n-Less Likely to be Normal in Its Usual Condition
+-Present > 25% of Time
↑-Greater Than Normal Elevation
↓-Lower Than Normal
+/−-Occasional
−-Rare
RBBB-Right Bundle Branch Block
···-Insufficient Data

TABLE 7-13. *Exercise Charcteristics in Various Cyanotic Congenital Heart Defects. (Reproduced with Permission from Christiansen and Strong, 1988).*

Lesion/Abnormality	HR	BP	ECG (Ischemia)	Aerobic Power	Dysrhythmia
Cyanotic					
Tetralogy of Fallot					
Pre-op	↓	N	+	↓	..
Post-op	↓	N	RBBB	↓	+
D-Transposition of Great Arteries					
Post-op (Mustard)	↓	N	+ V1,V2	N	+
Complex Cyanotic (Single Ventricle, Tricuspid Atresia)					
Pre-op	↓	↓	+	↓	+
Post-op (Fontan)	↓	↓	+	↓	+

Legend

N - High Probability of Normal Response Until Disease Progresses Significantly
n - Less Likely to be Normal in Its Usual Condition
+ - Present > 25% of Time
↑ - Greater Than Normal Elevation
↓ - Lower Than Normal
+/− - Occasional
− - Rare
RBBB - Right Bundle Branch Block
·· - Insufficient Data

normal autonomic regulation of systemic resistance vessels. An exaggerated BP response may be due to either an increase in ventricular contractility, an exaggerated SV response, or an increase in vascular reactivity. This may be secondary to volume overload of the left ventricle as is seen in mitral regurgitation or aortic regurgitation or pressure overload of the left ventricle as noted with systemic hypertension or coarctation of the aorta.

Children with cardiac disease often have other abnormalities that affect maximal performance. These include hypoxemia, cyanosis, anemia, polycythemia, myocardial dysfunction, and ventilatory abnormalities. Figure 7-9 illustrates the theoretical situation occurring in a patient with tricuspid atresia when subjected to exercise.

At rest, this child's arterial saturation is reduced (e.g., 80%). Pulmonary blood flow is totally dependent on a Blalock-Taussig anastomosis, which limits pulmonary blood flow. Pulmonary saturation is equal to arterial saturation, and resting mixed venous O_2 saturation is diminished to 60%. With increased peripheral muscle extraction of oxygen during exercise, mixed venous O_2 saturation falls to 20%. When right atrial blood mixes with pulmonary venous blood in the left atrium, O_2 saturation of blood in the aorta and pulmonary artery falls to 50%. Thus, although the A-$\dot{V}O_2$ diff has increased, there is evidence of marked hypoxemia with exercise. This

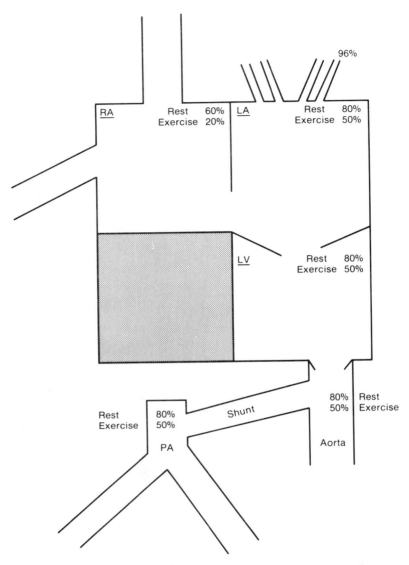

FIGURE 7-9. *Exercise in the patient with tricuspid atresia and a Blalock-Taussig shunt. For explanation, see text.*

is compromised further if systemic resistance is reduced and thus decreases the driving force into the pulmonary circuit. Hypoxemia produces acidosis, a rightward shift of the oxyhemoglobin dissociation curve, and a dilatation of systemic vessels. Pulmonary vasoconstriction may also occur, which would limit pulmonary blood flow if not for the fixed shunt. This theoretical model illustrates the increasing desaturation observed in patients with cyanotic congenital heart disease that is often associated with reduced exercise capacity. Diminished HR responses have also been observed in these patients, with hypoxemia implicated as a common etiology; however, this cannot explain the persistence of a blunted HR response to exercise in some of these children after surgical repair. Abnormal SV or ejection fraction responses to exercise have also been observed in these patients, as well as in patients with aortic stenosis and regurgitation, atrial septal defect, and mitral valve prolapse.

Children who undergo surgical correction of Ebstein's anomaly of the tricuspid valve or tetralogy of Fallot have post-operative $\dot{V}O_2max$ values closer to expected normals than those who have had a Fontan operation for a functional univentricular heart (Figure 7-10). This is probably related to chronic volume overload in those children with tricuspid atresia or single ventricle.

D. Responses to Exercise in Cardiac Transplant Patients

Studies have recently been done evaluating cardiorespiratory responses of adult cardiac transplant patients to graded exercise (Pflugfelder et al., 1987; Savin et al., 1980). These studies have pro-

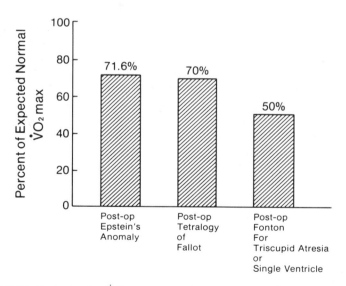

FIGURE 7-10. *Post-operative $\dot{V}O_2max$ expressed as a percentage of normal from studies at the Mayo Clinic. Children who have had surgical repair of tetralogy of Fallot or Ebstein's anomaly have post-op $\dot{V}O_2max$ closer to normal when compared to children who have undergone a Fontan operation for a functional univentricular heart. (Reproduced with permission from data from Driscoll et al., 1986; Driscoll et al., 1988; Hannon et al., 1985).*

vided evidence of a blunted HR response to exercise in these patients. Radionuclide studies indicate that this blunted HR response is associated with a plateau of SV at an earlier phase after the initiation of exercise. This combination results in a peak cardiac index approximately 25% lower than that found in normal subjects doing supine exercise. However, exercise duration among these transplant recipients did not differ significantly from values observed in normal subjects. Exercise testing has also been performed on transplant recipients utilizing graded treadmill protocols (Savin et al., 1980). These patients also exhibited blunted HR responses as well as a diminished BP response when compared with normal patients. These patients also exhibited diminished VO_2 and diminished work time compared to normals. Transplant patients also have an earlier increase in their ventilatory rate as well as higher post-exercise lactate levels, indicating an earlier onset of anaerobiosis. This was felt to be consistent with decreased oxygen delivery to exercising muscles. At this time, studies in transplant patients are limited to adults.

SUMMARY

The cardiovascular responses to exercise have been reviewed in both the normal child and in the child with evidence of cardiovascular disease. Many of these changes are similar in qualitative terms to those seen in adults, with quantitative aspects being dependent upon the size, age, and dimensions of the child. Some of the cardiovascular changes seen are also affected by sex and race. Methods by which these responses are measured have been described as well as the changes observed with training.

Exercise produces a linear increase in VO_2 with increasing exercise intensity producing a tenfold increase at maximal effort. CO, HR, and A-VO_2 increase in a parallel manner up to VO_2max. SV also increases, with the largest increase occurring at one-third of maximal effort. SBP increases parallel to the increase in CO, with the MAP increasing little, secondary to a concomitant decrease in SVR. VO_2max and VT may serve as indicators of aerobic power in children.

BIBLIOGRAPHY

1. Adams, F.H., L.M. Linde, and H. Miyoke. The physical working capacity of normal school children. *Pediatrics* 28 (suppl 1):55–64, 1961.
2. Allen, H.D., S.J. Goldberg, D.J. Sahn, N. Schu, and R. Wojcik. A quantitative echocardiographic study of champion childhood swimmers. *Circulation* 55:142–145, 1977.
3. Alpert, B.S., E.V. Dover, D.L. Booker, A.M. Martin, and W.B. Strong. Blood pressure response to dynamic exercise in healthy children—black vs. white. *The Journal of Pediatrics* 99:556–560, 1981.

4. Alpert, B.S., N.L. Flood, W.B. Strong, E.V. Dover, R.H. Durant, A.M. Martin, and D.L. Booker. Responses to ergometer exercise in a healthy biracial population of children. *The Journal of Pediatrics* 101:538–545, 1982.
5. Alpert, B.S., E.V. Dover, W.B. Strong, and W. Covitz. Longitudinal exercise hemodynamics in children with sickle cell disease. *American Journal of Disease of Children* 138:1021–1024, 1984.
6. Alpert, B.S., P.A. Gilman, W.B. Strong, M.F. Ellison, M.D. Miller, J. McFarlane, and T. Hayashidera. Hemodynamic and ECG responses to exercise in children with sickle cell anemia. *American Journal of Diseases of Children* 135:362–366, 1981.
7. Anderson, S.D. and S. Godfrery. Cardiorespiratory response to treadmill exercise in normal children. *Clinical Science* 40:433–442, 1971.
8. Anderson, L.B., P. Henckel, and B. Saltin. Maximal oxygen uptake in Danish adolescents 16–19 years of age. *European Journal of Applied Physiology* 56:74–82, 1987.
9. Arensman, F.W., M.P. Gruber, F.A. Trieber, and W.B. Strong. Differences in cardiac output, blood pressure and systemic vascular resistance responses to exercise in a biracial population of healthy males. (Abstract submitted for publication), 1988.
10. Åstrand, P-O. Experimental studies of physical working capacity in relation to sex and age, 1952.
11. Åstrand, P-O. and K. Rodahl. Body fluids, blood and circulation. *Textbook of Work Physiology: Physiological Bases of Exercise* 4:127–208, 1986.
12. Balfour, I.C., W. Covitz, F.W. Arernsman, C. Eubig, M. Garrido, and C. Jones. Left ventricular filling in sickle cell anemia. *The American Journal of Cardiology* 61:395–399, 1988.
13. Bar-Or, O. Physiologic responses to exercise of the healthy child. *Pediatric Sports Medicine for the Practitioner: From Physiologic Principles to Clinical Applications* 1:1–65, 1983.
14. Brown, C.H., J.R. Harrower, and M.F. Deeter. The effects of cross country running on preadolescent girls. *Medicine and Science in Sports* 4:1–5, 1972.
15. Christiansen, J.L. and W.B. Strong. Exercise testing. In F. Adams, and G. Emmanouilides (eds.). *Moss' Heart Disease in Infants, Children and Adolescents.* Baltimore: Williams and Wilkins (in press), 1988.
16. Cohen, C.R., H.D. Allen, J. Spain, G.R. Marx, R.W. Wolfe, and J.S. Harvey. Cardiac structure and function of elite high school wrestlers. *American Journal of Diseases of Children* 141:576–581, 1987.
17. Cooper, D.M., D. Weiler-Ravell, B.J. Whipp, and K. Wasserman. Aerobic parameters of exercise as a function of body size during growth in children. *Journal of Applied Physiology* 561:628–634, 1984.
18. Covitz, W., C. Eubig, I.C. Balfour, R. Jerath, B.S. Alpert, W.B. Strong, and R.H. Durant. Exercise-induced cardiac dysfunction in sickle cell anemia: a radionuclide study. *The American Journal of Cardiology* 51:570–575, 1983.
19. Cumming, G.R. Hemodynamics of supine bicycle exercise in "normal" children. *American Heart Journal* 93:617–622, 1977.
20. Cumming, G.R., D. Everett, and L. Hastman. Bruce treadmill test in children: normal values in a clinic population. *The American Journal of Cardiology* 41:69–75, 1978.
21. Cunningham, D.A., D.H. Paterson, C.J.R. Blimkie, and A.P. Donner. Development of cardiorespiratory function in circumpubertal boys: a longitudinal study. *Journal of Applied Physiology* 56(2):302–307, 1984.
22. Cunningham, D.A., P. Telford, and G.T. Swart. The cardiopulmonary capacities of young hockey players: age 10. *Medicine and Science in Sports* 8:23–25, 1976.
23. Daniels, J., N. Oldridge, F. Nagle, and B. White. Differences and changes in $\dot{V}O_2$ among young runners 10 to 18 years of age. *Medicine and Science in Sports* 10:200–203, 1978.
24. Davies, C.T.M., C. Barnes, and S. Godfrey. Body composition and maximal exercise performance in children. *Human Biology* 44:195–214, 1972.
25. Docherty, D., H.A. Wenger, and M.L. Collis. The effects of resistance training on aerobic and anaerobic power of young boys. *Medicine and Science in Sports and Exercise* 19:389–392, 1987.
26. Driscoll, D.J., G.K. Danielson, F.J. Puga, H.V. Schaff, C.T. Heise, and B.A. Staats. Exercise tolerance and cardiorespiratory response to exercise after the Fontan operation for tricuspid atresia or functional single ventricle. *Journal of the American College of Cardiology* 7:1087–1094, 1986.
27. Driscoll, D.J., C.D. Mottrom, and G.V. Danielson. Spectrum of exercise tolerance in 45 patients with Ebstein's anomaly and observations on exercise tolerance in 11 patients after surgical repair. *Journal of the American College of Cardiology* 11:831–836, 1988.
28. Ekblom, B. Effect of physical training in adolescent boys. *Journal of Applied Physiology* 27:350–355, 1969.
29. Eriksson, B.O. Physical training, oxygen supply and muscle metabolism in 11 to 13-year-old boys. *Acta Physiologica Scandinavica Supplementum* 384:1–48, 1972.

30. Eriksson, B.O. and G. Koch. Effect of physical training on hemodynamic response during submaximal and maximal exercise in 11 to 13-year-old-boys. *Acta Physiologica Scandinavica Supplementum* 87:27–39, 1973.
31. Godfrey, S. The response of normal children to exercise. *Exercise Testing in Children* 4:66–101, 1974.
32. Godfrey, S., C.T.M. Davies, E. Wozniak, and C.A. Bomes. Cardiorespiratory response to exercise in normal children. *Clinical Science* 40:419–431, 1971.
33. Goldberg, S.J., R. Weiss, and F.H. Adams. A comparison of the maximal endurance of normal children and patients with congenital cardiac disease. *The Journal of Pediatrics* 69:46–55, 1966.
34. Hannon, J.D., G.K. Danielson, F.J. Puga, C.T. Heise, and D.J. Driscoll. Cardiorespiratory response to exercise after repair of tetralogy of Fallot. *Texas Heart Institute Journal* 12:393–400, 1985.
35. Hermansen, L. and S. Oseid. Direct and indirect estimation of maximal oxygen uptake in pre-pubertal boys. *Acta Paediatrica Scandinavica Supplementum* 217:18–23, 1971.
36. Ikai, M. Physiology of exercise test. *Japanese Circulation Journal* 35:23–26, 1971.
37. James, F.W., C.G. Blomqvist, M.D. Freed, W.W. Miller, J.H. Moller, E.W. Nugent, D.A. Riopel, W.B. Strong, and H.V. Wessel. AHA standards of exercise testing in the pediatric age group. *Circulation* 66 (suppl A):1377–1397, 1982.
38. James, F.W., S. Kaplan, G.J. Glueck, J. Tsay, M.J.S. Knight, and C.J. Sarwar. Responses of normal children and young adults to controlled bicycle exercise. *Circulation* 61:902–912, 1980.
39. James, F.W., D.C. Schwartz, S. Kaplan, and S.P. Spilkin. Exercise electrocardiogram, blood pressure, and working capacity in young patients with valvular or discrete subvalvular aortic stenosis. *The American Journal of Cardiology* 50:769–775, 1982.
40. Krahenbuhl, G.S., R.P. Pangrazi, G.W. Petersen, L.N. Burkett, and M.J. Schneider. Field testing of cardiorespiratory fitness in primary school children. *Medicine and Science in Sports* 10:208–213, 1978.
41. Kramer, J.D. and P.R. Lurie. Maximal exercise tests in children. *American Journal of Diseases of Children* 108:283–297, 1964.
42. Kulangara, R.J. and W.B. Strong. Exercise stress testing in children. *Comprehensive Therapy* 5:51–61, 1979.
43. Kveselis, D.A., A.P. Rocchini, A. Rosenthal, D.C. Crowley, M. Dick, A.R. Snider, and C. Moorehead. Hemodynamic determinants of exercise-induced ST-segment depression in children with valvar aortic stenosis. *The American Journal of Cardiology* 55:1133–1139, 1985.
44. Lange Anderson, K., V. Seliger, J. Rutenfranz, and J. Skrobak-Kaczynski. Physical performance capacity of children in Norway; Part IV: The rate of growth in maximal aerobic power and the influence of improved physical education in children in a rural community—population parameters in a rural community. *European Journal of Applied Physiology* 35:49–58, 1976.
45. Lock, J.E., S. Einzig, and J.H. Moller. Hemodynamic responses to exercise in normal children. *The American Journal of Cardiology* 41:1278–1284, 1978.
46. Lussier, L. and E.R. Buskirk. Effects of an endurance training regimen on assessment of work capacity in prepubertal children. *Annals of the New York Academy of Sciences* 301:734–747, 1977.
47. Massicotte, D.R. and R.B.J. MacNob. Cardiorespiratory adaptations to training at specified intensities in children. *Medicine and Science in Sports* 6:242–246, 1972.
48. McNamarar, D.G., J.T. Bricker, F.M. Galioto, T.P. Graham, F.W. James, and A. Rosenthal. Cardiovascular abnormalities regarding eligibility for competition—Task Force I: Congenital heart disease. *Journal of the American College of Cardiology* 6:1200–1208, 1985.
49. Mitchell, J.H., B.J. Sproule, C.B. Chapman. Factors influencing respiration during heavy exercise. *Journal of Clinical Investigation* 37:1693–1701, 1958.
50. Musewe, N.N., J. Reisman, L.N. Benson, D. Wilkes, H. Levison, R.M. Freedom, G.A. Trusler, and G.J. Canny. Cardiopulmonary adaptation at rest and during exercise 10 years after Mustard atrial repair for transposition of the great arteries. *Circulation* 77:1055–1061, 1988.
51. Nadel, E.R. Physiological adaptations to aerobic training. *American Scientist* 73:334–343, 1985.
52. Paterson, D.H., D.A. Cunningham, M.J. Plyley, C.J.R. Blimkie, and A.P. Donner. The consistency of cardiac output measurement (CO_2 rebreathe) in children during exercise. *European Journal of Applied Physiology* 49:37–44, 1982.
53. Pearson, A.C., M. Schiff, D. Mrosek, A.J. Lobovitz, and G.A. Williams. Left ventricular diastolic function in weightlifters. *The American Journal of Cardiology* 58:1254–1259, 1986.
54. Pflugfelder, P.W., P.D. Purves, F.N. McKenzie, and W.J. Kostuk. Cardiac dynamics during supine exercise in cyclosporine-treated orthotopic heart transplant recipients: assessment by radionuclide angiography. *Journal of the American College of Cardiology* 10:336–341, 1987.

55. Reybrouck, T., M. Dumoulin, and L.G. Van der Hauwaert. Cardiorespiratory exercise testing after venous switch operation in children with complete transposition of the great arteries. *The American Journal of Cardiology* 61:861–865, 1988.
56. Reybrouck, T., M. Weymans, H. Stijns, J. Knops, and L. Van der Hauwaert. Ventilatory anaerobic threshold in healthy children—age and sex differences. *European Journal of Applied Physiology* 54:278–284, 1985.
57. Riopel, D.A., A.B. Taylor, and A.R. Hohn. Blood pressure, heart rate, pressure rate product and electrocardiographic changes in healthy children during treadmill exercise. *The American Journal of Cardiology* 44:697–704, 1979.
58. Rodman, T., H.P. Close, R. Cathcart, and M.K. Purcell. The oxyhemoglobin dissociation curve in the common hemoglobinopathies. *American Journal of Medicine* 27:558–566, 1959.
59. Rotstein, A., R. Doton, O. Bar-Or, and G. Tenenbaum. Effect of training on anaerobic threshold, maximal aerobic power and anaerobic performance of pre-adolescent boys. *International Journal of Sports Medicine* 7:281–286, 1986.
60. Rutenfranz, J., K. Lange Anderson, V. Seliger, J. Ilmarinen, F. Klimmer, H. Kylian, M. Rutenfranz, and M. Ruppel. Maximal aerobic power affected by maturation and body growth during childhood and adolescence. *European Journal of Pediatrics* 139:106–112, 1982.
61. Rutenfranz, J., K. Lange Anderson, V. Seliger, F. Klimmer, I. Berndt, and M. Ruppel. Maximum aerobic power and body composition during the puberty growth period: similarities and differences between children of two European countries. *European Journal of Pediatrics* 136:123–133, 1981.
62. Saltin, B. and C. Thoren. Unpublished results from Eriksson, B.O. (1972). Physical training, oxygen supply and muscle metabolism in 11–13 year old boys. *Acta Physiologica Scandinavica Supplementum* 384:1–48, 1968.
63. Savin, W.M., W.L. Haskell, J.S. Schroeder, and E.B. Stinson. Cardiorespiratory responses of cardiac transplant patients to graded symptom-limited exercise. *Circulation* 62:55–60, 1980.
64. Shephard, R.J. Growth of physical fitness. *Physical Activity and Growth* 5:86–106, 1982.
65. Shephard, R.J., C. Allen, O. Bar-Or, C.T.M. Davies, S. Deare, R. Hedmon, K. Ishii, M. Koneko, J.R. LaCour, P.E. di Prampero, and V. Seliger. The working capacity of Toronto school children, Part I. *Canadian Medical Association Journal* 100:560–566, 1969.
66. Shepherd, J.T. Circulatory response to exercise in health. *Circulation* 76 (Supplement 6):3–10, 1987.
67. Skinner, J.S., O. Bar-Or, V. Bergsteinova, C.W. Bell, D. Royer, and E.R. Buskirk. Comparison of continuous and intermittent tests for determining maximal oxygen intake in children. *Acta Paediatrica Scandinavica Supplementum* 217:24–28, 1971.
68. Smit, P.J. Anthropometric motor performance and physiological studies on South Africa children involved in a nutritional status survey. *Research Report* 273:1–470, 1968.
69. Smodlaka, V.N. Treadmill vs. bicycle ergometers. *The Physician and Sports Medicine* 10:75–80, 1982.
70. Sprynarova, S., J. Parizkova, and V. Bunc. Relationships between body dimensions and resting and working oxygen consumption in boys aged 11 to 18 years. *European Journal of Applied Physiology* 56:725–736, 1987.
71. Strong, W.B. Sickle cell anemia and exercise. *Current therapy in sports medicine* 1985–86:92–93, 1985.
72. Strong, W.B., M.D. Miller, M. Striplin, and M. Salehbhai. Blood pressure response to isometric and dynamic exercise in healthy black children. *American Journal of Diseases of Children* 132:587–591, 1978.
73. Strong, W.B., D. Spencer, M.D. Miller, and M. Salehbhai. The physical working capacity of healthy black children. *American Journal of Disease of Children* 132:244–248, 1978.
74. Thapar, M.K., W.B. Strong, M.D. Miller, L. Leatherbury, and M. Salehbhai. Exercise electrocardiography of healthy black children. *American Journal of Disease of Children* 132:592–595, 1978.
75. Vaccoro, P. and D.H. Clarke. Cardiorespiratory alterations in 9- to 11-year-old children following a season of competitive swimming. *Medicine and Science in Sports* 10:204–207, 1978.
76. Washington, R.L., J.C. von Gundy, C. Cohen, H.M. Sandheimer, and R.R. Wolfe. Normal aerobic and anaerobic exercise data for North American school-age children. *The Journal of Pediatrics* 112:223–233, 1988.
77. Wolfe, R.R., R. Washington, E. Daberkow, J.R. Murphy, and H.L. Brommel. Anaerobic threshold as a predictor of athletic performance in pre-pubertal female runners. *American Journal of Diseases of Children* 140:922–924, 1986.

CARDIOVASCULAR RESPONSES TO EXERCISE **329**

DISCUSSION

COYLE: Is it critical to train intensely through adolescence to maximize stroke volume and $\dot{V}O_2$max as an adult? If so, do you have any insight into the mechanisms involved? Are there adaptations of the pericardium?

STRONG: From the data gathered by Dr. Snell and Dr. Eriksson, you can get a very significant effect in youngsters. The question is, were these subjects preselected to show those kinds of changes? I don't have an answer, but others in the audience may do much better than me in answering that.

BAR-OR: I think the question may be raised regarding the prepubescent child rather than the adolescent child with regard to trainability. There are several studies that have shown either no change in $\dot{V}O_2$max or low increases in $\dot{V}O_2$max as a result of training periods lasting one week to eight to 10 weeks. More recent studies with prepubescents have shown that by using training regimens considered optimal for nonathletic adults, one can induce changes in the prepubescent.

MICHELI: Has anyone tried to correlate results of fitness in the run-walk with $\dot{V}O_2$max?

PATE: If the question is, are field tests of distance running valid estimates of $\dot{V}O_2$max, the data are clearly mixed. The issue has certainly been studied. I think the general answer that's given is that the correlations tend to be moderate, up to 0.7. There are a few in the literature that are higher than that, but there are certainly some that are lower. Clearly, there are other determinants of running performance than $\dot{V}O_2$max. One would be the economy of running. Another would be body composition.

STRONG: As part of an NIH collaborative study, we have begun to evaluate children 3 and 4 years of age. We are looking at their habitual physical activity patterns and how they correlate with treadmill tests.

BARR-OR: Regarding this relationship between field tests and lab criteria, we have done some work with children as well as with military recruits. Our conclusion was, for those subjects with high aerobic fitness, you can get a reasonable correlation, let's say around 0.8, 0.85. However, for subjects with low fitness levels we found correlations anywhere from 0.2 to 0.5. Our explanation for this is that those who are less fit probably also don't know how to pace the 12 min run. They just don't know how pace themselves, and as a result, this kind of test for them is not very useful. We even took Cooper's own data for his 12 min run and simply divided his own computation into those who were very fit and those who were not very fit. We left a grey group in the middle, and there was a major difference in the correlations. He has reported correlations of around 0.8, and these are really not true for unfit people. When you have people who are unfit, give them at least one chance to run this without taking any measurements. Tutor them on how to run. Correct their running, so to speak, and then a couple of days later, give them another run and evaluate the results.

NADEL: The ability of the heart to deliver a high output during exercise is related, at least to some extent, to the preload or to the ability to maintain a high filling pressure. This is in some way related to the absolute blood volume. Adults have a wide range of blood volume from say 50 or 55 ml/kg up to over 100 ml/kg and this tends to correlate well with the state of training. My questions are: "What is the range of blood volume in children and adolescents," and "Is it known whether they are able to expand blood volume with training?"

STRONG: I don't know of any specific data, but that does not mean that it's not available. We have determined the $\dot{V}O_2$max of approximately 700 individuals with sickle cell disease, and looking at their natural history, we have longitudinal data over about a 15-year period of time. What we have observed is a much stiffer myocardium that does not fill well. This is one of the earliest manifestations of sickle cell disease on the heart. It's on the diastolic phase of filling, not on the systolic component.

SUTTON: Bill, when one looks at the evolution of oxygen uptake against increasing work, do we know anything about the proportion of the oxygen, the increase in oxygen uptake, that is accounted for by the increase in cardiac output as opposed to the widening of the $\dot{V}O_2$ difference in children as they grow, and how does that compare with what we know about adults?

STRONG: As far as the a-$\dot{V}O_2$ difference is concerned, the four studies that were presented here show a relatively normal distribution as far as adults are concerned. However, there is some suggestion in the literature that children can extract more oxygen at a given workload than adults.

LEMON: Is there any evidence of cardiovascular problems in children running marathons?

STRONG: To my knowledge there has been no reported problem as far as the cardiovascular system is concerned in children.

BAR-OR: A scientist from Milwaukee has been accumulating cardiologic data on marathon runners, and most of them are less than 10 years of age. Based on ECG and echocardiographic analysis, he could not find any deviations in children who were training for as long as two to five years. Obviously, we need much more information.

MALINA: Bill, a question about some of your data where you compare blacks and whites and quite often you use surface area as your point of reference. Given race differences in body proportions of extremeties to trunk, are there race differences in surface area that might influence your interpretation? And second, what is the aerobic capacity or response to exercise of those with the sickle cell trait?

STRONG: As far as the black children are concerned, we have looked at them by weight, body surface area, and by height, and there do not seem to be any significant differences among those data. As far as the sickle trait patient is concerned, we looked at about 45 children with sickle cell trait and found that their maximum heart rates were somewhat less than those of our healthy black population, but they were higher than the SS children. As far as their working capacity was concerned, it was slightly less than normal and significantly more than the SS population. So they look much more normal, compared to the SS patient, who has very significant differences.

FREEDSON: Bill, you mentioned that you are doing treadmill testing in 4 year olds. What type of information do you hope to gain from that type of evaluation?

STRONG: First, that we can do it. Second, to look at their blood pressure responses to exercise and also their duration on the treadmill compared to the information gathered from their physical activity questionnaires. We want to determine the correlation between their habitual physical activity and their "aerobic" power.

FREEDSON: So you are implying some type of fitness measure from the treadmill test?

STRONG: Yes.

FREEDSON: Do you have any concern about the level of motor development that a 4 year old has reached that might limit the treadmill test ability to measure a so-called fitness parameter in this age group?

STRONG: I did before we started, and I think in going back and reviewing the literature that Gordon Cummings has certainly been able to demonstrate with 4-year-olds the ability to test them quite effectively. Obviously you can't test all of them, but the vast majority that we have tested have done quite well. It takes a technician working closely with the child to get him started, but I've been impressed by that technician's ability to work with children to get them on the treadmill and then get them going and work them up through a maximum voluntary effort.

FREEDSON: I guess my concern would be the individual variability that you would see among different 4-year-olds that might provide you with a relatively good measure for some 4-year-olds, whereas for others it would not. But I guess then you can use heart rate as an index to see whether or not you have obtained a true maximum performance.

STRONG: What we're really looking at, Patty, are longitudinal changes. Some of them we're not going to be able to get at 4 years of age. Some will start at 5 and 6 before we really feel the data are acceptable.

BOUCHARD: My comment is on the notion that there might be a period during growth in which training might have more important effects than any other time during life. I think that notion is not supported by any data, and we should probably discard it. If it was happening, it probably would imply that we increase transcription to adapt to the stress of training during growth, which would somehow give some advantage later on in the regulation of transcription at the other level, and I don't see any mechanism that could do that. Even in a young adult, when we train and then detrain and retrain again, we don't see any difference between the response to the first training and the second training. In other words, even by just a detraining phase of two to three months, you don't maintain any of the transcriptional "advantages" that could have been generated by the first training program. Thus, I don't see how we can justify the notion that there might be a period during growth in which training may produce a greater response and eventually lead to some advantage later on in life.

STRONG: You can do it with skill, for example, Claude.

BOUCHARD: That's learning. Yes.

8

Temperature Regulation During Exercise in Children and Adolescents

Oded Bar-Or, M.D., F.A.C.S.M.

I. INTRODUCTION

A. Background and Scope

There has been abundant research on the temperature regulation of exercising adults. This topic has received much attention regarding occupational, military, athletic, and public health issues.

335

Much less information is available on the thermoregulatory capability of the exercising child. One reason for such a paucity of information is that military and occupational issues are irrelevant to children in most societies. Another reason is the ethical consideration: In most studies on temperature regulation, subjects have been exposed to "hostile" environments such as extreme heat, high humidity, or cold. Other protocols induce extreme levels of hypohydration. Such experiments may entail risk to the health and well-being of children. Scientists have therefore been reluctant to conduct studies in which children are exposed to taxing environmental conditions.

In general, children's thermoregulatory responses to exercise in the heat or in the cold are similar to those of adults. There are, however, age- and maturation-related differences in these responses. This chapter is intended to review the evidence for such differences, to explain their possible mechanisms and to point out their implications to the child's physical performance and well-being. The development of temperature regulation in the newborn and in infancy has been studied extensively. For a recent review see Mellor and Cockburn (1986). The relevance of this early development to temperature regulation during exercise in later years is unknown.

B. Physical and Physiologic Principles of Temperature Regulation

This section is meant to provide the reader with some basic concepts and terms in temperature regulation. For a more systematic review see Leithead and Lind (1964), Mount (1979), and Nadel (1988). Metabolic heat, which is created primarily at the body core, must first be transferred to the periphery, from where it is dissipated to the environment. Such a transfer can be achieved either by conduction or by convection through the blood. While conduction is a passive process, the rate of which depends on some physical characteristics of adjacent tissues, the rate of convection is controlled by changes in the blood flow to the skin. The greater the skin blood flow, the higher the rate of convection from core to periphery.

Dissipation of heat from the skin is done by either conduction, convection, radiation, or evaporation, or by a combination thereof. Heat can also be dissipated from the respiratory airways. In humans who are exposed to ambient heat, this avenue is of minor importance and will not be discussed in this chapter. Heat can be gained from the environment or lost to the environment by conduction, convection, and radiation, depending on the temperature gradient between the skin and the environment. The greater the temperature gradient, the faster the heat exchange through these three avenues.

In contrast, evaporation causes only heat loss, even when air temperature exceeds skin temperature. Therefore, on hot days, when ambient temperature exceeds skin temperature, evaporation is the only avenue for heat dissipation. The evaporation of one gram of water induces cooling of 2.42 kJ (0.58 kcal). The rate of evaporation is enhanced by wind and reduced by high humidity. Most importantly for any discussion of body size and temperature regulation, the rate of heat exchange at any of the four avenues depends on the surface area of the skin.

The two physiologic processes that are activated for enhanced heat dissipation in humans are vasodilatation of skin blood vessels (enhancing heat conduction from core to periphery) and sweating (enhancing evaporation from the skin). During exercise, when large amounts of heat are to be dissipated, evaporation of sweat is the most important physiologic means for cooling the body. Passive evaporation of water from the epidermis takes place even without the production of sweat, and there is also evaporative heat loss from the bronchial mucosa. Their rates, however, are much lower than that achieved through active sweating.

Physiological processes that prevent excessive body cooling include peripheral vasoconstriction and an increase in metabolic heat production through non-shivering thermogenesis or through shivering.

II. GEOMETRIC AND PHYSIOLOGIC CHARACTERISTICS OF CHILDREN

Children have several geometric and physiologic characteristics that have a direct bearing on their ability to dissipate or preserve body heat. These are summarized in Table 8-1.

A. Surface Area-to-Mass Ratio

Based on geometric considerations, body surface area is a function of length^2 while body mass is a function of length^3. Therefore, the smaller the individual, the greater the surface area-to-mass ratio. A 6-year-old child, for example, has a ratio that is some 50% greater than in an adult. During most physical activities, metabolic heat is proportional to body mass. Heat transfer between the environment and the body, on the other hand, depends on the surface area of the body that is in touch with, or is exposed to, the environment. Thus, heat exchange per mass unit between the body and the environment is *a priori* greater, the smaller the individual (e.g., Epstein et al., 1983; Robinson, 1942). The implication is that, compared with larger individuals, children will absorb heat faster from the envi-

TABLE 8-1. *Geometric and Physiologic Characteristics of Children as Related to Their Thermoregulatory Ability.*

Variable	Compared with Adults	Implications to Thermoregulation
Surface area per unit body mass	Larger	Greater heat gain in hot climate, loss in cold climate
Metabolic heat production per unit mass during walking or running	Larger	Greater strain on the thermodissipatory systems
Sweating rate	Much lower (until puberty	Lower capacity for evaporative cooling
Cardiac output at a given metabolic level	Somewhat lower	Lower capacity for heat convection to periphery; potentially limited O_2 transport during intense exercise in the heat

Modified with permission from Bar-Or (1986).

ronment in hot climates (whenever ambient temperature exceeds skin temperature) and lose heat faster to the environment in cold climates. These differences will become particularly evident once the temperature gradients between the environment and the skin, both in the heat and in the cold, are extreme.

B.   Metabolic Heat Production

For reasons not fully understood, children's metabolic rate at any given walking or running speed is greater than that of adolescents or adults. (For a review, see Bar-Or, 1985.) An inverse, non-linear relationship has been described between the age (Åstrand, 1952; Skinner et al., 1971) and the body height (MacDougall et al., 1983) of children and adolescents and their oxygen uptake ($\dot{V}O_2$) per kg body mass at any walking/running speed. As seen in Figure 8-1, the energy expenditure while running, at a wide range of speeds, is consistently higher the younger the child and irrespective of gender. For example, at a running speed of 10 km·hr^{-1} the energy expenditure of a 6-year-old girl is some 20% higher than that of a 16-year-old girl. As all the metabolic energy is converted ultimately into heat, one can conclude that the metabolic heat production per body mass unit during walking or running is considerably greater in children than in adolescents and adults. This poses greater demands on the heat dissipatory systems of children.

C.   Sweating Pattern

When exercise is intense, or is performed in high environmental temperatures, evaporation is the main avenue for heat dissipation. When ambient temperature exceeds skin temperature, evaporation

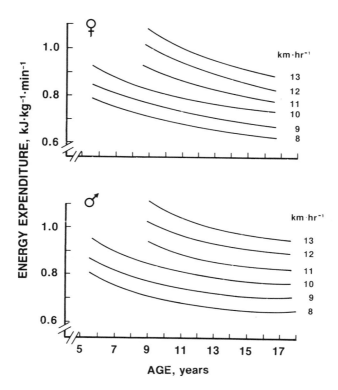

FIGURE 8-1. *Metabolic heat production in boys and girls as a function of age and running speed. Data from Åstrand (1952). Adapted with permission from Bar-Or (1983).*

of sweat is the *only means* for heat dissipation (with the addition of much smaller amounts of evaporated water from the respiratory tract and the epidermis). It is therefore apparent that a person's capacity for sweating may determine her/his ability to dissipate heat and sustain exercise in hot climates. This section will focus on the sweating pattern of children in terms of sweating rate (i.e., the volume of sweat that is produced per time unit), the population density (glands per unit area of the skin) of heat-activated sweat glands (HASG), the rate of sweat production by a single gland, the composition of sweat, and the sensitivity of the glands to thermal stimuli. A discussion of the possible changes in sweating pattern that take place during puberty will follow.

1. **Sweating Rate.** The measurement of maximal sweating rate (SR) is commonly used as an index for the capability of heat dissipation through evaporation. It should be realized, however, that, at any given combination of humidity and air temperature, there is a

ceiling to the rate of evaporation. When SR exceeds this level, the extra sweat will drip off the skin.

Table 8-2 summarizes findings related to SR in prepubescents and adults of both sexes. It is quite apparent that, when expressed per unit body surface area, SR of boys is distinctly lower than that of men. In contrast, there is little or no difference between the SR of girls and women. This pattern holds true also for SR induced by pilocarpine iontophoresis. SR of pre-pubertal boys seems similar to, or somewhat higher than, that of pre-pubertal girls. More direct comparisons are needed, however, between the gender groups to reach a definitive conclusion about such differences.

The wide range of SR, as shown in the table, reflects the various climatic and exercise conditions chosen by the authors. While not all authors report whether the elicited rates were maximal, it seems that children's SR, even under intense climatic heat and exercise stresses, seldom exceed 400 $ml \cdot m^{-2} \cdot hr^{-1}$, while that of adults can reach 800 $ml \cdot m^{-2} \cdot hr^{-1}$ under similar conditions. One might argue that the above age-related differences in SR reflect a lower level of heat acclimatization or of aerobic fitness in the children (see sections IV and V below). However, neither the reported level of acclimatization (Inbar, 1978; Wagner et al., 1972) nor that of maximal aerobic power (Davies, 1981; Drinkwater et al., 1977; Inbar, 1978) were different between the age groups.

2. Population Density of Heat-Activated Sweat Glands. A basic question is whether the lower SR potential of children reflects a smaller number of HASG per unit area or is due to a lower production of sweat by each gland. The following data are limited to the eccrine sweat glands, which are activated primarily by heat stress, as compared with the apocrine glands, which, in humans, respond mostly to emotional stimuli (Kuno, 1956; Sato, 1977). Nor will this section discuss the newly discovered apoeccrine glands (see section II.C.6.)

Figure 8-2 summarizes the relationship between the population density of HASG and body surface area in sixty 10- to 12-year-old children (Bar-Or, 1976) and nineteen 18- to 27-year-old adults (Bar-Or et al., 1968) of both sexes. All were tested during rest in a hot, dry environment (29–31° C effective temperature). HASG were counted using the starch-iodine technique (Bar-Or et al., 1968). It is quite apparent that the population density of HASG is inversely related ($r = -0.59$) to body surface area, even though there is a wide range of HASG counts at each level of surface area. This pattern is similar to that described by Kawahata (1939) for 16 Japanese, 35 days to 35 years of age. The same pattern seems to hold whether the individual rests or exercises (Bar-Or, 1980). One can conclude,

TABLE 8-2. Comparison of Sweating Rate (SR, $ml \cdot m^{-2} \cdot hr^{-1}$) Between Pre-pubescents and Adults, Females and Males.

Reference	Climatic and Exercise Conditions	Sex	Children		Adults		p
			Age	SR	Age	SR	
Kawahata (1960)	45° C, 97% RH Rest	F	9	303	21–26	297	
		M	9	455	21–27	815	.0001
Wagner et al. (1972)	49° C, 17% RH 5.6 km·hr⁻¹	M	11–14	491	25–30	579	signif.
Drinkwater et al. (1977)	35° C, 65% RH 30% VO₂max	F	12	155	20.6	180	
Inbar (1978)	43° C, 20% RH 50% VO₂max	M	8–10	310	20–33	459	.01
Araki et al. (1979)	29° C, 60% RH "heavy" exercise	M	9	320	20	870	.05
Davies (1979)	21° C, 50% RH 50% VO₂max	M, F	12.9	344	36	575	.01
Rees & Shuster (1981)	Pilocarpine iontophoresis	F	9–10	165	20–35	115	
		M	9–10	185	20–35	280	signif.

Temperatures are all dry bulb, ages in years.
RH = relative humidity.
Signif. = Differences were significant, but p value was not reported.

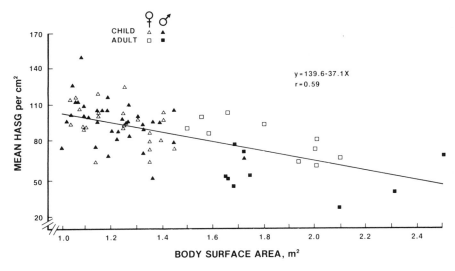

FIGURE 8-2. *Population density of heat-activated sweat glands (HASG) in relationship to body surface area. Each data point represents an arithmetic mean calculated from several sites in one subject, who was resting in a hot, dry environment. Based on data by Bar-Or (1976) and Bar-Or et al. (1968).*

therefore, that the low SR in children occurs in spite of their larger population density of active sweat glands. It might be noted that a similar pattern is evident when one counts by histological methods *all glands* and not only the heat-activated ones (Kawahata, 1939).

3. **Sweat Production by a Single Gland.** By combining a measurement of SR and a count of HASG, one can calculate the sweat production per single gland. This was first done by Tanaka (1956) and later by Kawahata (1960), who exposed Japanese 9-year-old girls and boys and 21- to 27-year-old women and men to rest in 34° C, 40% relative humidity (RH). As seen in Figure 8-3, both the SR and the sweat production per gland were much higher in the men than in the boys. Sweat production per gland in the boys was only 40% that of the men. Among the females, there was no difference in SR, but the girls' production per gland was only 70% that of the women, which reflected the greater concentration of HASG in the girls. A similar difference in sweat production per gland was found also during exercise in the heat between fifteen 8- to 10-year-old boys and sixteen 20- to 23-year-old men (Inbar, 1978). The children activated some 56% more glands per cm², but their sweat production per gland was only 43% that of the adults. Similarly, when sweating was induced by pilocarpine iontophoresis in a thermoneutral environment, 1- to 13-year-old children had an output per gland of

only some 45% of that of adults (Huebner et al., 1966). When induced by intradermal injection of 2 mg acetylcholine, sweat production per gland in newborns (seven to 10 days old) was only 32% that of young adults (Foster et al., 1969).

The reason for a low sweat production per gland is not clear. It may result from the smaller size of the secretory coil in children's glands (Landing et al., 1968; Bar-Or, 1980). But, it could also reflect differences in sudomotor innervation or in the sensitivity of the glands to acetylcholine and possibly other transmitters.

4. Sensitivity of the Sweat Glands to Thermal Stimuli. One index for the sensitivity of the sweating apparatus to thermal stimuli is the core temperature at which sweating starts. Another index is the increase in SR as a function of a given increase in core temperature above a certain threshold (e.g., 37° C). As shown in the upper portion of Figure 8-4, which is based on data by Araki et al. (1979), the threshold for sweating among 20-year-old men who exercised at 29° C, 60% RH, was a 0.2° C increase in rectal temperature. The

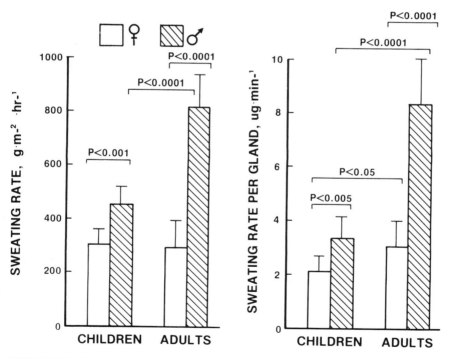

FIGURE 8-3. *Sweating rate and sweating rate per gland in 9-year-old girls (n = 7) and boys (n = 7) and in young women (n = 7) and men (n = 8) sitting at 34° C, 40% relative humidity. Based on data by Kawahata (1960).*

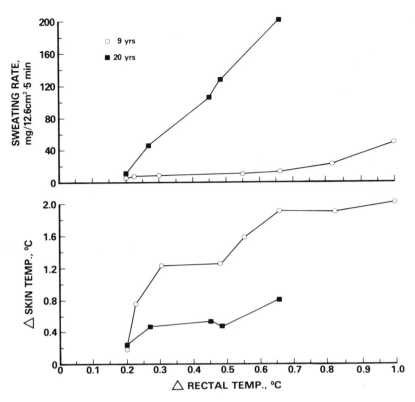

FIGURE 8-4. *Sweating rate and the increase in mean skin temperature in relationship to the increase in rectal temperature. Comparison between a 9-year-old boy and a 20-year-old man, both exercising continuously on a cycle ergometer. Based on data by Araki et al. (1979). Reproduced with permission from Bar-Or (1982).*

respective threshold for a 9-year-old boy was about 0.7° C. The above finding, according to the authors, was representative of a group of seven boys and seven adults. Unfortunately, these authors did not relate their sweating threshold to an *absolute* level of rectal temperature. A similarly higher sweating threshold was described for 11- to 14-year-old boys, compared with young men (Wagner et al., 1972). In a study by Inbar (1978), the mean SR per degree increase in rectal temperature above 37° C was 531.4 ml·hr^{-1} in 20- to 23-year-old men and only 216.2 ml·hr^{-1} in 8- to 10-year-old boys. Ideally, particularly in studies on the control of temperature regulation, one would like to measure core temperature at sites other than the rectum (e.g., esophagus). The above studies, however, have only measured rectal temperatures. Due to ethical considerations, it is unlikely that other sites will be used with children in future research.

One implication for the above findings is shown in the lower portion of Figure 8-4. It describes the corresponding increase in mean skin temperature, which is considerably greater in a 9-year-old boy than in a young man. Such a high skin temperature may have resulted from lower evaporative cooling, but it could also reflect a higher vasodilatation in the child (see section II.D.). Whatever the causes of the higher skin temperature, the resulting narrowing of temperature gradient between core and skin imposes a greater strain for convection of heat from core to periphery.

5. **Concentration of Electrolytes in the Sweat.** Both in adults and in children, the concentration of sweat sodium and chloride increases with the rise in sweating rate. This reflects the shorter time that the sweat column travels along the sweat duct, allowing less reabsorption of the electrolytes from the lumen back into the extracellular compartment. However, at any given sweat rate, children's sweat osmolality seems lower than that of adults (Ohara, 1950; Araki et al., 1979; Sato & Sato, 1987). As shown by Araki et al. (1979), the maximal chloride concentration in the sweat of pre-pubescent boys who exerted at heart rates of 160 to 170 b·min did not exceed 30–40 $mEq·L^{-1}$, as compared with 50–60 $mEq·L^{-1}$ in pubescent boys. In contrast, measurements taken in a desert outdoors (35–42° C) (Dill et al., 1967) revealed a similar sweat chloride concentration in 9- to 13-year-old boys (19.7 $mEq·L^{-1}$) and in male adolescents (21.5 $mEq·L^{-1}$). In a recent study, Sato & Sato (1987) stimulated with metacholine and epinephrine single axillary eccrine glands of adults, using an *in vitro* dissected preparation. Sodium concentration in the sweat ranged from 60 to 90 $mEq·L^{-1}$, irrespective of SR. There are no comparable *in vitro* data on children. The reason for the possibly lower electrolyte concentration in children's sweat is not clear. This pattern seems to represent a more economical way of preserving body salt and, if confirmed by other studies, it should be taken into account when planning fluid and electrolyte replenishment for child athletes.

6. **Sweating Pattern and Puberty.** The considerable differences in sweating pattern between children and adults suggest that some changes occur during puberty. One recently documented change is the development of the apoeccrine gland. Sato and colleagues (1987) made an axillary skin biopsy in nine 6- to 18-year-old Caucasian males. All individual sweat glands were then dissected out and photographed. In the adults, the authors identified glands that were neither eccrine nor apocrine but had some morphological characteristics of both. They therefore termed them "apoeccrine." Figure 8-5 summarizes the above experiment and indicates that, in males, these glands first appear during puberty. Some morphological changes,

however, were found in some eccrine glands of the pre-pubescents, suggesting that they may be precursors for the apoeccrine glands. While no such age-related analysis is available on females, the authors did find apoeccrine glands in adult females. Research is now needed to find out the relevance of these glands to temperature regulation.

Based on experiments with elderly people, Kawahata (1960) suggested that "testosterone is sudorific." This was also stated by other Japanese authors (Tanaka, 1956, as reported by Araki et al., 1979). If true for other age groups, this effect can explain, at least in part, the gender-related differences in the sweating pattern of adults and the slight gender-related difference in the sweating of children (Figure 8-3). The possible effect of testosterone might also explain why the sweating pattern changes markedly during puberty. However, experimental proof for the sudorific effect of testosterone is lacking. In a study with 20- to 35-year-old healthy females, Rees & Shuster (1981) found no increase in SR (induced by pilocarpine iontophoresis at rest) following a seven-day topical ap-

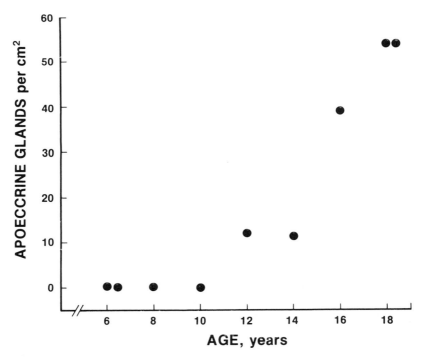

FIGURE 8-5. *Population density of axillary apoeccrine sweat glands in 6- to 18-year-old males. Data by Sato et al. (1987).*

plication of testosterone propionate ointment. Nor did intradermally injected testosterone ester induce any increase in SR. In another experiment, 20- to 35-year-old males were treated for a week with topically applied flutamide or with oral intake at 100 mg cyproterone acetate (both are anti-androgen compounds). Neither treatment effected a decrease in SR. Subsequent observations by these authors suggest that male adults with eunuchoidism of pre-pubertal origin have lower SR than healthy ones. Rees & Shuster (1981) suggested, therefore, that the SR is determined "by androgen-induced gene expression during puberty and not by androgen modulation in adult life." One can conclude, therefore, that possible relevance of testosterone and other puberty-related endocrine changes to the sweating pattern in puberty is still unclear. Studies are needed to establish the relationships between endocrine variables and sweating before, during, and after puberty.

D. Cardiac Output and Skin Blood Flow

Convection of heat from body core to the periphery is markedly dependent upon the blood flow to the skin, which, in turn, depends on cardiac output and on the fraction of cardiac output that is diverted to the periphery. For a recent review of the cardiovascular responses in adults to exercise in the heat, see Brengelmann (1983). Only few observations are available on such responses in children. In a thermoneutral environment, children's cardiac output at any given metabolic level is somewhat lower than in adults (e.g., Bar-Or et al., 1971; Eriksson, 1971). In only one study (Drinkwater et al., 1977; Drinkwater & Horvath, 1979) was children's cardiac output measured during exercise in the heat. Five 12-year-old girls and five young women, matched for $\dot{V}O_2$max, walked in thermoneutral (28° C, 45% RH), warm (35° C, 65% RH) and hot (48° C, 10% RH) environments, at about 30% of $\dot{V}O_2$max. The girls' cardiac output was consistently lower than that of the women, particularly in the hot climate. This pattern was even more marked for the stroke index, while heart rate (HR) was consistently higher in the girls. Post-exertional forearm blood flow increased somewhat more in the girls than in the women. The authors attributed the lower tolerance time of the girls (see section III.C.) to their greater cardiovascular strain, manifested by a higher "percent HR reserve" and a lower stroke volume, which suggests a lower venous return. They further suggested that the greater surface area per body mass in the girls required a higher fraction of their cardiac output to be diverted to the skin, which, in turn, may reduce the central blood volume and the blood flow to the exercising muscles (Rowell, 1977). Another age-related difference in the above study is the greater increase in plasma volume in the girls, which could be compensatory to the demands for perfusion of central organs.

In a series of experiments with resting subjects, Araki et al. (1980) measured the responses of 11-year-old boys and those of 19- to 23-year-old men exposed to heat and to cold. Compared with the adults, the children's skin temperature rose faster in the heat and fell faster in the cold. In contrast, metabolic rate during these exposures increased more in the adults. The authors, based on the above study and on a report by another Japanese group (Suzuki et al., 1971), concluded that children resort more than adults to vasodilatation in the heat and vasoconstriction in the cold. Greater vasoconstriction during rest in the cold (16–17° C, 50% RH) was also found in American 10- to 13-year-old boys, compared with older males (Wagner et al., 1974).

The above pattern may explain the greater reliance on convective and radiative heat loss among children, as described by Davies (1981) (see also Figure 8-6). A possible contradiction to the above notion can be derived from a study by Laszczynska & Sliwinska (1984), who found a greater heat loss by convection plus radiation per m^2 skin in 7-year-old boys than in 14-year-old boys, all resting at 20° C. Adults exposed to the same conditions had an even smaller heat loss. While the authors explained these differences by the thinner skinfold thickness in the younger children, it is also possible that the vasoconstrictive response of these children was less effective.

Without doubt, many gaps still exist in our understanding of the differences between children and adults in their cardiovascular response to exercise in the heat and in the cold.

III. EFFECTIVENESS OF TEMPERATURE REGULATION DURING EXERCISE

While some studies suggest that children's temperature regulation is as effective as that of adolescents and adults (Davies, 1981; Docherty et al., 1986; Gullestad, 1975; Piekarski et al., 1986), others indicate that children are less effective thermoregulators (Dill et al., 1966; Drinkwater et al., 1977; Haymes et al., 1974; Sloan & Keatinge, 1973; Sohar & Shapira, 1965; Van Beaumont, 1965; Wagner et al., 1972). A major reason for the above discrepancy is that authors have not qualified their conclusions to the specific ambient conditions that prevailed during their experiments. Based on theoretical considerations, as discussed in section II.A., if differences do exist between the thermoregulatory effectiveness of children and adults, they should become more evident the greater the temperature gradient between

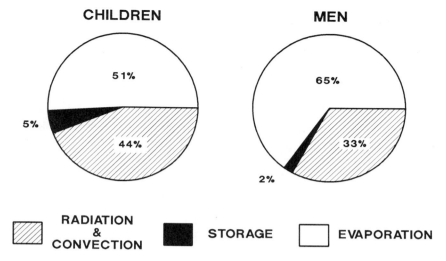

CHILDREN

51%

5%

44%

MEN

65%

33%

2%

RADIATION & CONVECTION

STORAGE

EVAPORATION

FIGURE 8-6. *Heat dissipation and storage, as a percentage of metabolic heat, in children and adults who exercised in a thermoneutral environment. Summary of findings by Davies (1979) on 13 girls (13.8 + 0.7 y) and boys (12.9 + 0.8 y) and eight adults (36.1 + 6.7 y) who ran for one hour at about 68% maximal aerobic power, at 21 degrees C, at 67% relative humidity. Modified with permission from Davies (1981).*

the environment and the skin, both in the heat and in the cold. The following discussion is therefore divided into four general ambient conditions: thermoneutral (conditions in which the need to dissipate or preserve heat is minimal), warm, extremely hot, and cool. Special attention will be given to the environment-to-skin temperature gradient in these conditions.

A.   Thermoneutral Environment

Davies (1981) compared the thermoregulatory responses of athletic pre-pubescent boys (12.9 ± 0.8 y), pubescent girls (13.8 ± 0.7 y) and men (36.1 ± 6.7 y), who exercised in an air-conditioned room (21° C, 67% RH). Subjects ran on a treadmill for 60 min at about 68% of their $\dot{V}O_2$max. Even though the children's evaporative rate was lower and their skin temperatures higher than in the adults, the increase in rectal temperature (1.2° C) and the mild heat storage were not different among the groups. As shown in Figure 8-6, the adults dissipated heat by evaporation twice as much as by convection plus radiation. In contrast, the children's "strategy" was to dissipate heat almost equally by evaporation and by radiation plus convection. A similar difference in the relative use of evaporation on the one hand and convection plus radiation on the other was found between 12-year-old girls and 20.6-year-old women who exercised at 30% $\dot{V}O_2$max in 28° C, 45% RH (Drinkwater et al., 1977). It is of anecdotal interest to note that large desert animals resort more to sweating than do smaller ones (who rely on other evaporative routes of heat loss), even within the same species (Taylor, 1977).

Gullestad (1975) studied the responses of 11-year-old boys to a 60-min exercise at 22 ± 4° C, 35–55% RH. Each child cycled on separate days at 31–39%, 45–56%, and 61–69% of his $\dot{V}O_2$max. All children reached a thermal balance at each of the exercise intensities, which suggests an adequate thermoregulatory response. The author reported somewhat lower rectal temperatures at any given exercise intensity than those found in studies among adults.

These studies indicate that, even though children use a different strategy for heat dissipation, their thermoregulatory ability during exercise in a thermoneutral environment is similar to that of adults.

B. Warm Environment

Several studies are available that compare the response of children and adults to exercise in warm climates. When the dry bulb temperature was below, or not more than 5° to 7° C above, skin temperature, the children seemed to dissipate their body heat effectively and to complete the prescribed tasks (Blanchard, 1987; Docherty et al., 1986; Drinkwater et al., 1977; Haymes et al., 1974; 1975; Inbar, 1978; Mackova et al., 1984; Piekarski et al., 1986).

Studying 8- to 10-year-old children, Blanchard (1987) found that, within the "safe" and the "caution" zones (various combinations of air temperatures and humidity levels, at which air temperature did not exceed 24.5° C and humidity was 90% RH or less), the climatic heat stress did not seem to affect the child's ability to exercise (30 min at 60% $\dot{V}O_2$max). When twenty-three 10- to 13-year-old boys walked (6 km · hr^{-1}, 0% grade) at 30° C, 80% RH, only one, because of dizziness, could not complete the 60-min task (Docherty et al., 1986). Core temperature approached a plateau after 30 min. While surface area-to-mass ratio, ectomorphy, and mesomorphy did not affect the thermoregulatory effectiveness of these boys, endomorphy was associated with somewhat less effective thermoregulation, confirming previous observations by Haymes et al. (1975). A less impressive exercise tolerance was shown by three of seven 8- to 14-year-old girls who could not complete a 3 × 20 min walk (50% $\dot{V}O_2$max) at 30° C, 50% RH (Mackie, 1982). They felt dizziness, nausea, and faintness even though their body temperatures and HRs were not excessively high. The above finding is somewhat surprising in light of the relatively light climatic and metabolic stresses. It is not clear whether the three girls who could not complete the task were less fit or less motivated than those who did complete it.

Two studies are available that compared the exercise tolerance of girls and young women in warm climates. Drinkwater et al. (1977) found no difference in the ability of 12-year-old girls and 20.6-year-old women to sustain two one-hour walks (30% $\dot{V}O_2$max) at 28° C, 45% RH. However, at 35° C, 65% RH, only 40% of the girls completed the second walk, compared with 100% completion among the women. In comparing 9- to 11-year-old girls (Haymes, 1973) with 9- to 22-year-old women (Bar-Or et al., 1969), all walking (3 × 20 min) at 4.8 km·hr^{-1} 0% grade in dry heat (effective temperatures ranging from 21.1–29.4° C, dry bulb = 23–42° C), there were no age-related differences in the ability to complete the prescribed task, in core temperature or in heat storage. Furthermore, the "prescriptive zone" at the above exercise intensity was identical in the two groups (highest effective temperature = 26.7° C).

The above studies all suggest that, when children exercise for up to one hour in warm climates (air temperature not higher than 5–7° C above skin temperature, low to moderate humidity), they thermoregulate their core temperatures as effectively as adults. No information is available on the relative tolerance of children to exercise performed at the above environmental conditions for more than one hour.

C. Very Hot Environment

Studies in which air temperatures exceeded skin temperatures by about 10° C or more (i.e., 45–47° C or more) have shown that the exercise tolerance of children was lower than that of young adults (Drinkwater et al., 1977; Haymes et al., 1974; Bar-Or et al., 1969; Wagner et al., 1972) and somewhat similar to that of middle-aged or elderly people (Drinkwater et al., 1977; Drinkwater & Horvath, 1979; Wagner et al., 1972).

One way of comparing exercise tolerance to the heat is to prescribe an exercise task at increasingly more taxing ambient conditions. Those individuals who, at a certain climatic heat stress, cannot complete the task are considered less tolerant than those who can complete it. Criteria for "incompletion" can be subjective (based on the subject's symptoms) or objective (based on physiological indices of heat strain). Drinkwater et al. (1977), in addition to studying the response of pre-pubertal girls and young women to 28° C, 45% RH, and 35° C, 65% RH, as discussed in section III.B. above, exposed them also to 48° C, 10% RH. The prescribed task was to walk twice for 50 min each at 30% $\dot{V}O_2$max. While all the women completed the first walk at 48° C, 80% (n = 4) of the girls could not complete it. The second walk was completed successfully by 60% (n = 3) of the women and by only 20% (n = 1) of the girls. As discussed in section II.D., the authors assigned the girls' lower tolerance to their less effective cardiovascular adaptation; their heart rate being consistently higher and stroke index lower than in the women. Interestingly, the only girl who did complete the task was a highly competitive distance runner.

Similarly, when nonobese 9- to 11-year-old girls (Haymes et al., 1974) and young women (Bar-Or et al., 1969) were exposed to identical protocols at several heat stress conditions, only some of the girls completed the one-hr walk at 32.2° C effective temperature (46.7–51.6° C, 13% RH), while all of the women completed it. Some of the women, but none of the girls, also completed the task at 35° C effective temperature (54.5–57.0° C, 17% RH). As shown in Figure 8-7, while the heat storage (per kg) of both groups was similar at the more mild heat stress, the girls had a distinctly higher storage than the women at 32.2° C.

Wagner et al. (1972) compared the tolerance of unacclimated prepubertal 11- to 14-year-old boys with that of post-pubertal boys (15–16 y) and young adult males. All subjects were expected to walk (5.6 km · hr^{-1}, 0% grade) at 49.0° C, 17% RH. On the average, the tolerance time of the pre-pubescents was only 50 min, compared with 67 min in the post-pubescents, and 79 min in the adults. While body temperatures—skin temperatures in particular—were highest in the pre-pubescents, evaporative heat loss per m^2 was highest in the adults and lowest in the pre-pubescents.

Ideally, any study that is designed to assess the affects of age and maturation should be longitudinal, spanning the period under scrutiny. The only longitudinal data on temperature regulation in childhood and adolescence are those by Piekarski et al. (1986). Three boys and one girl were tested periodically from ages 10.0 to 15.5 y. Dry bulb temperatures each year ranged from 25° C to 55° C, and vapor pressure was kept below 10 milibars. The exercise tasks were six 30-min walks (4.0 km · hr^{-1}, 0% grade), interspersed with 3-min rest periods. While suggesting that only some of the sessions were fully completed, the authors did not specify the environmental conditions and the ages at which the children could not complete the prescribed task. They only mentioned that, for the girl, "the progress of puberty reduced the frequency" of "vertigo, drowsiness, or collapse." As also observed in the subjects of Drinkwater et al. (1977; Drinkwater & Horvath, 1979), this girl's subjective inability to sustain the tasks was not accompanied by a particularly high heat strain, but by a "reduced stability of the peripheral circulation."

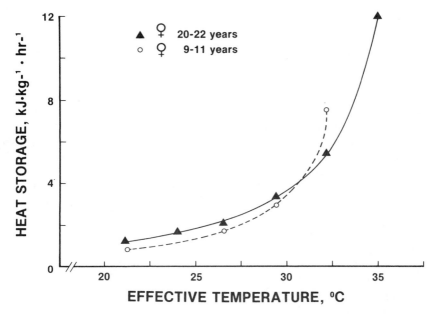

FIGURE 8-7. *Heat storage in five 9- to 11-year-old lean girls and four 20- to 22-year-old lean women. Subjects walked on a treadmill (three 20-min bouts, interspersed by 5 min rest periods) at 4.8 km · hr^{-1}, 5% grade. Based on Bar-Or et al. (1969) and Haymes et al. (1974).*

In conclusion, a child's ability to dissipate heat and sustain exercise in warm climates is not different from that of adults. When ambient heat is extreme, however, (e.g. air-to-skin gradient of 10 or more degrees C), children's exercise tolerance is lower. While the reasons for such low tolerance are not fully elucidated in the above studies, the three main culprits are probably the child's higher area-to-mass ratio, lower sweating capacity, and less effective cardiovascular adjustment to exercise in the heat (perhaps inability to maintain arterial blood pressure due to low central blood volume and cardiac output). The above conclusions are based almost exclusively on studies performed in dry heat. Information is still needed regarding exercise in humid environments. Also indicated are epidemiological studies to determine whether the lower heat tolerance of children is manifested also by a higher incidence of heat-related illness during "fun runs" and other prolonged activities in hot environments.

D. Cool Environment

In most sports, metabolic heat is sufficient to compensate for the heat loss during exercise, even when performed in a cool or cold environment. Furthermore, proper clothing can insulate the body and usually prevent excessive heat loss. Hypothermia during exercise is therefore seldom an issue. One exception is exercise in water. As the heat conductance of water is some 25 times that of air, heat loss is extremely fast in the immersed individual. Hypothermia may ensue, even if water temperature is only marginally lower than skin temperature. Because heat loss by conduction and convection depends on the surface area between the body and the environment, the larger surface-to-mass ratio of children suggests *a priori* that they will be more susceptible than adults to hypothermia when immersed in water. Indeed, as shown by Sloan & Keatinge (1973) for members of a swim club, the smaller (and leaner) the individual, the faster was the heat loss during a prolonged practice swim at 20.3° C. On the average, the 8-year-old swimmers, of either sex, had to leave the water some 18–20 min into the swim, compared with a sustained 30-min swim by their 18-year-old counterparts. When they left the water, the younger children's oral temperature dropped approximately 2–3 degrees C, compared with little or no drop in the older adolescents. It is important to note that the rate of heat loss in the cold also depends on the thickness of the subcutaneous fat layer. The thicker it is, the greater the thermal insulation that it provides (Buskirk et al., 1969; Nadel et al., 1974; Sloan & Keatinge, 1973). A lean child, therefore, will be more susceptible to heat loss than a child with thicker skinfolds. Pre-pubescent girls, as a group, are leaner than the more mature girls and women and are therefore more prone to excessive heat loss in the cold.

Few data are available on heat loss of children in cool air. Some observations were made on the resting child at 18° C (Araki et al., 1980; Matsushita & Araki, 1980; Wagner et al., 1974) and one study tested the thermoregulatory response to prolonged exercise at 10° C effective temperature (Mackova et al., 1984). Even though, compared with adults, children seem to rely more on vasoconstriction and less on thermogenesis (see section II.D.), the effectiveness of a child's temperature regulation in cool air does not seem to be different from that of adults. No information is available on exercise tolerance of children in very cold air.

In summary, in spite of their geometric and physiologic characteristics, children seem to be as effective thermoregulators as adults in ambient conditions that are neither very hot nor very cold. In very hot air and in cool water, however, their tolerance time is shorter than that of adults. Figure 8-8 is a schematic summary of the relative exercise tolerance of children and adults, as a function of the air-to-skin temperature gradient.

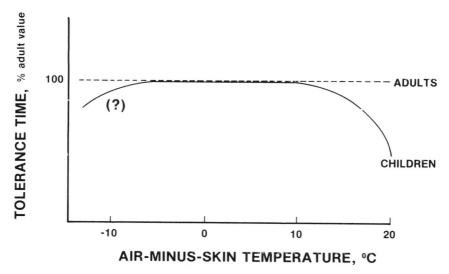

FIGURE 8-8. *A schematic comparison of Heat tolerance during exercise in children and adults as a function of the air-to-skin temperature gradient. Modified with permission from Bar-Or (1984).*

IV. ACCLIMATIZATION AND ACCLIMATION TO HEAT

Heat acclimatization encompasses the physiological and perceptual changes that take place during repeated natural exposure to hot climates. Heat acclimation is the respective process that is achieved during structured exposures in a climatic chamber. Both processes are useful as a means of improving performance and well-being following transition to a hot climate.

Two studies are available that compared the ability of children and of adults to acclimate to the heat. Wagner et al. (1972) exposed 11- to 14-year-old pre-pubescent boys, 15- to 16-year-old post-pubescent boys and 25- to 30-year-old men to exercise (5.6 km·hr⁻¹) in dry heat (47.7–49.0° C, 17% RH) on eight consecutive days. While all three groups showed a decrease in heart rate and body temperatures and an increase in sweating rate and in the sweating threshold, the changes in heart rate and body temperatures among the pre-pubescents were less than in the older groups. Subjects of all groups managed to increase their tolerance time as a result of heat acclimation. Findings by Inbar (1978) extended this pattern to boys 8 to 10 y, who acclimated similarly to young men through six 3-per-week sessions at 43° C, 21% RH, but took longer than the adults to reach their respective acclimation level. It was further shown that 8- to 10-year-old boys can also heat acclimate by sitting in a hot-dry chamber (Inbar et al., 1985). Such a phenomenon does not seem to occur in adults, who need to exercise in the heat to become acclimated. The authors suggested that, in these children, resting in the heat might have caused a sufficient heat storage during each session to induce acclimation. Another group of 8- to 10-year-old boys trained for two weeks in a thermoneutral environment (Inbar et al., 1981) and improved their thermoregulatory ability. For details, see section V.

The slower and somewhat lesser heat acclimation (and, possibly, natural acclimatization) in pre-pubertal boys has implications to their physical performance and health. Retrospective information, for example, on high school heatstroke fatalities (Barcenas et al., 1976; Fox et al., 1966) suggests that they occurred almost invariably on the first or second day of the practice season when, most likely, the victims had not yet achieved heat acclimatization.

The relatively slow change in the physiological functions of the above 8- to 10-year-old boys during heat acclimation contrasts with a faster reduction in their rating of perceived exertion (Bar-Or & Inbar, 1977). The implication is that the partially acclimated child might have less inhibition to exercise in the heat than would an adult who is at the same stage of acclimation. Potentially, such a child may be more prone to heat-related illness.

V. EFFECT OF TRAINING ON TEMPERATURE REGULATION

Several studies in adults (e.g., Gisolfi, 1973; Nadel et al., 1974a; see also a review by Taylor, 1986) have shown that physical training in a thermoneutral environment can improve heat tolerance. Inbar et al. (1981) compared the responses of 8- to 10-year-old boys to a 60-min exercise in 43° C, 21% RH, before and after a two-week cycling program (six sessions in total) in an air-conditioned room. Training was at 85% of the predetermined maximal HR for 60 min. Another age-matched group of boys performed a similar program, but in a climatic chamber at 43° C, 21% RH. This latter program was meant to acclimate them to exercise in the heat. As seen in Figure 8-9, both programs induced a reduction in rectal temperature. However, while the acclimation-induced reduction in rectal temperature became manifested only some 25 min into the session—probably reflecting improved heat dissipation—the respective reduction following training was right from the beginning of the session—probably reflecting a training effect *per se*. A similar pattern was evident

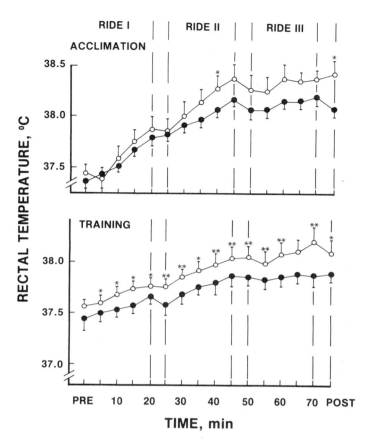

FIGURE 8-9. *Rectal temperature of 8- to 10-year-old boys during two cycling sessions in dry heat, before (○—○) and after (●—●) a two-week acclimation (upper panel) or training (lower panel) program. Modified with permission from Inbar et al. (1981).*

for HR. Neither program induced a significant increase in sweating rate. It thus seems that, in these children, aerobic training improved temperature regulation through a different mechanism than that of acclimation. In this regard it is noteworthy that, in a cross-sectional comparison (Docherty et al., 1986), $\dot{V}O_2$max accounted for only 16% of the variance of increase in rectal temperature among 10- to 13-year-old boys who exercised (6 km·hr^{-1}, 0% grade) for 60 min at 30° C, 80% RH.

A similar conclusion was reached by Matsushita & Araki (1980) and by Araki et al. (1980) who, in a series of cross-sectional and longitudinal experiments, compared the responses of untrained and trained pre-pubertal boys to resting in the heat or in the cold. While cross-sectional experiments suggested that the trained child responded to the heat and to the cold with less change (increase or decrease, respectively, in body temperatures) than did the untrained, a 40-day running program did not affect body temperatures or sweating pattern.

VI. CONCLUSIONS

There are still numerous gaps in our understanding of how and why children differ from adults in their thermoregulatory responses to exercise in the heat or cold. While some of the following conclusions are agreed upon by workers in the field, others are based on a single, yet unreplicated observation, which merits further research.

1. Compared with post-pubescents and adults, pre-pubescent children have a lower sweating rate when performing a given exercise task, a lower sweat production per single eccrine gland, a lower sensitivity of the eccrine glands to an increase in core temperature, and a lower concentration of electrolytes in the sweat. The underlying mechanisms for these differences are not clear.

2. Apoeccrine sweat glands develop in males during puberty. Their relevance to the maturation-related differences in temperature regulation is not clear. Nor is it known whether the same pattern of their emergence exists in females.

3. During exercise in thermoneutral or warm environments, children's thermoregulatory efficiency is adequate. However, compared with adults, children dissipate heat less through evaporation and more through convection plus radiation, which is achieved by greater vasodilatation.

4. In extremely hot environments (e.g., 45° C and higher), children's tolerance time and ability to dissipate heat are compromised, possibly because of their larger surface area-to-mass ratio, limited sweating capacity and lower central blood volume and cardiac output.

5. The "prescriptive zone" of pre-pubertal girls is similar to that of young women. No similar comparison is available for males.

6. Inability of children to complete an exercise task in a warm or hot environment is usually due to dizziness, faintness, and nausea, which are felt before the child has reached the objective criteria of excessive heat strain. These symptoms

might be related to an inability to maintain arterial blood pressure, due to a lower cardiac output and central blood volume.

7. When resting in a cool environment, ability of children to maintain core temperature is similar to that of adults. However, while the adults use both vasoconstriction and an increase in metabolic rate, children primarily use vasoconstriction, which results in a greater drop in skin temperature.

8. When swimming in cool water, the convective heat loss of children is greater than that of adolescents and adults, due to the large surface area-to-mass ratio of children and, particularly in females, to lower subcutaneous fat insulation.

9. Pre-pubertal boys can acclimate to exercise in the heat, but their rate of acclimation is slower than that of adults. This poses a potential health risk to children who are newly exposed to a hot/humid climate. No data are available on the heat acclimation and acclimatization of girls.

10. While theoretical considerations and experiments in the laboratory strongly suggest a greater susceptibility of children to heat- or cold-induced illness, there are no epidemiological data on the relative risk in children. Because such illness is always preventable, there is an urgent need for further research in this area, particularly in light of the increasing participation of children in sports that require prolonged exertion.

The scope of this chapter does not allow for the elaboration of other issues relevant to temperature regulation in the exercising child. These include gender-related differences in temperature regulation, temperature regulation of the child with a disease, dehydration and body fluid replenishment, effects of environmental conditions on short-term, high-intensity exercise, and the health-related risks of exercising in cold or hot climates. Information on these topics can be found in previous publications (Bar-Or, 1983; 1986; 1988; Bar-Or et al., 1980; Dotan & Bar-Or, 1980).

BIBLIOGRAPHY

1. Araki, T., Y. Toda, K. Matsushita, and A. Tsujino. Age differences in sweating during muscular exercise. *Japanese Journal of Physical Fitness and Sports Medicine* 28:239–248, 1979.
2. Araki, T., J. Tsujita, K. Matsushita, and S. Hori.. Thermoregulatory responses of prepubertal boys to heat and cold in relation to physical training. *Journal of Human Ergology* 9:69–80, 1980.
3. Åstrand, P.-O. *Experimental Studies of Physical Working Capacity in Relation to Sex and Age.* Copenhagen: Munskgaard, 1952.

4. Bar-Or, O. Distribution of heat activated sweat glands in 10- to 12-year-old Israeli girls and boys who differ in ethnic origin (in Hebrew). Research report, 1976.
5. Bar-Or, O. Climate and the exercising child—a review. *International Journal of Sports Medicine* 1:53–65, 1980.
6. Bar-Or, O. Physiologische Gesetzmassigkeiten sportlicher Aktivitat beim Kind. In H. Howald, and E. Han, (eds.). *Kinder im Leistungssport*. Basel:Birkhauser. 18–30, 1982.
7. Bar-Or, O. *Pediatric Sports Medicine for the Practitioner. From Physiologic Principles to Clinical Application*. New York:Springer Verlag, 1983.
8. Bar-Or, O. Children and physical performance in warm and cold environments. Chapter 5 in R.A. Boileau, (ed.). *Advances in Pediatric Sports Sciences, Volume I*. Champaign, Ill.: Human Kinetics. 117–129, 1984.
9. Bar-Or, O. The O_2 cost of child's movement in health and disease. In P. Russo, and G. Gass (eds.). *Exercise, Nutrition and Performance*. Sidney:Cumberland College. 97–104, 1985.
10. Bar-Or, O. The exercising child in heat and cold stress. Chapter 10 (77) In V.C. Kelley (ed.). *Practice of Pediatrics*. Philadelphia: Lippincott, 1986.
11. Bar-Or, O. The pre-pubescent female. In M. M. Shangold and G. Mirkin (eds.). *Women and Exercise: Physiology and Sports Medicine*. Philadelphia:Davis. 109–119, 1988.
12. Bar-Or, O., R. Dotan, O., Inbar, A. Rotshtein, and H. Zonder. Voluntary Hypohydration in 10- to 12-year-old boys. *Journal of Applied Physiology* 48:104–108, 1980.
13. Bar-Or, O. and O. Inbar. Relationship between perceptual and physiological changes during heat acclimatization in 8- to 10-year-old boys. In H. Lavallee and R.J. Shephard (eds.). *Frontiers of Activity and Child Health*. Quebec:Pelican. 205–214, 1977.
14. Bar-Or, O., H.M. Lundegren, and E.R Buskirk. Heat tolerance of exercising obese and lean women. *Journal of Applied Physiology* 26:403–409, 1969.
15. Bar-Or, O., H.M. Lundegren, L.L. Magnusson, and E.R. Buskirk. Distribution of heat-activated sweat glands in obese and lean men and women. *Human Biology* 40:234–248, 1968.
16. Bar-Or, O., R.J. Shephard, and C.L. Allan. Cardiac output of 10- to 13-year-old boys and girls during submaximal exercise. *Journal of Applied Physiology* 30:219–223, 1971.
17. Barcenas, C., H.P. Hoeffler, and J.T. Lie. Obesity, football, dog days and siriasis: a deadly combination. *American Heart Journal* 92:237–244, 1976.
18. Blanchard, S. Effects of ambient temperature and relative humidity on 8- and 10-year-old children involved in endurance activities working at 60% of maximal oxygen consumption. Ph.D. Dissertation, University of Maryland, 1987.
19. Brengelmann, G.L. Circulatory adjustments to exercise and heat stress. *Annual Review of Physiology* 45:191–212, 1983.
20. Buskirk, E.R., O. Bar-Or, and J. Kollias. Physiological effects of heat and cold. In N.L. Wilson (ed.). *Obesity*. Philadelphia:F.A. Davis. 119–139, 1969.
21. Davies, C.T.M. Thermoregulation during exercise in relation to sex and age. *European Journal of Applied Physiology* 42:71–79, 1979.
22. Davies, C.T.M. Thermal responses to exercise in children. *Ergonomics* 24:55–61, 1981.
23. Dill, D.B., F.G. Hall, and W. Van Beaumont. Sweat chloride concentration: sweat rate, metabolic rate, skin temperature, and age. *Journal of Applied Physiology* 21:99–106, 1966.
24. Dill, D.B., S.M. Horvath, W. Van Beaumont, G. Gehlsen, and K. Burrus. Sweat electrolytes in desert walks. *Journal of Applied Physiology* 23:746–751, 1967.
25. Docherty, D., J.D. Eckerson, and J.S. Hayward. Physique and thermoregulation in prepubertal males during exercise in a warm, humid environment. *American Journal of Physical Anthropology* 70:19–23, 1986.
26. Dotan, R. and O. Bar-Or. Climatic heat stress and performance in the Wingate anaerobic test. *European Journal of Applied Physiology* 44:237–243, 1980.
27. Drinkwater, B.L., and S.M. Horvath. Heat tolerance and aging. *Medicine and Science in Sports* 11:49–55, 1979.
28. Drinkwater, B.L., I.C. Kupprat, J.E. Denton, J.L. Crist, and S.M. Horvath. Response of prepubertal girls and college women to work in the heat. *Journal of Applied Physiology: Respiratory Environmental Exercise Physiology* 43:1046–1053, 1977.
29. Epstein, Y., Y. Shapiro, and S. Brill. Role of surface area-to-mass ratio and work efficiency in heat tolerance. *Journal of Applied Physiology: Respiratory Environmental Exercise Physiology* 54:831–836, 1983.
30. Eriksson, B.O. Cardiac output during exercise in pubertal boys. *Acta Paediatrica Scandinavica* Supplement 217:53–55, 1971.
31. Foster, K.G., E.N. Hey, and G. Katz. The response of the sweat glands of the newborn baby to thermal stimuli and to intradermal acetylcholine. *Journal of Physiology* 203:13–29, 1969.
32. Fox, E.L., D.K. Mathews, W.S. Kaufman, and R.W. Bowers. Effects of football equipment on thermal balance and energy cost during exercise. *Research Quarterly of the American Association of Health and Physical Education* 37:332–339, 1966.

33. Gisolfi, C.V. Work-heat tolerance derived from interval training. *Journal of Applied Physiology* 35:349–354, 1973.
34. Gullestad, R. Temperature regulation in children during exercise. *Acta Paediatrica Scandinavica* 64:257–263, 1975.
35. Haymes, E.M. Heat tolerance of exercising lean and heavy pre-pubertal girls. Ph.D. Dissertation. Pennsylvania State University, 1973.
36. Haymes, E.M., E.R. Buskirk, J.L. Hodgson, H.M. Lundegren, and W.C. Nicholas. Heat tolerance of exercising lean and heavy pre-pubertal girls. *Journal of Applied Physiology* 36:566–571, 1974.
37. Haymes, E.M., R.J. McCormick, and E.R. Buskirk. Heat tolerance of lean and obese pre-pubertal boys. *Journal of Applied Physiology* 39:457–461, 1975.
38. Huebner, D.E., C.C. Lobeck, and N.R. McSherry. Density and secretory activity of eccrine sweat glands. *Pediatrics* 38:613–618, 1966.
39. Inbar, O. Acclimatization to dry and hot environment in young adults and children 8- to 10-years-old. Ed.D. Dissertation. Columbia University, 1978.
40. Inbar, O., O. Bar-Or, R. Dotan, and B. Gutin. Conditioning versus exercise in the heat as methods for acclimatizing 8- to 10-year-old boys to dry heat. *Journal of Applied Physiology: Respiratory Environmental Exercise Physiology* 50:406–411, 1981.
41. Inbar, O., R. Dotan, O. Bar-Or, and B. Gutin. Passive versus active exposures to dry heat as methods of heat acclimatization in young children. In R.A. Binkhorst, H.C.G. Kemper, and W.H.M. Saris (eds.). *Children and Exercise XI.* Champaign, Ill.: Human Kinetics. 329–340, 1985.
42. Kawahata, A. Variation in the number of active human sweat glands with age (in Japanese). *Journal of the Physiological Society of Japan* 4:438–444, 1939.
43. Kawahata, A. Sex differences in sweating. In H. Yoshimura, K. Ogata, and S. Itch (eds.). *Essential Problems in Climatic Physiology.* Kyoto:Nankodo. 169–184, 1960.
44. Kuno, Y. *Human Perspiration.* Springfield, Ill:C.C. Thomas, 1956.
45. Landing, B.H., T.R. Wells, and M.L. Williamson. Studies on the growth of the eccrine sweat glands. In B.D. Cheek (ed.). *Human Growth.* Philadelphia:Lea and Febiger, 382–395, 1968.
46. Laszczynska, J. and E. Sliwinska. Thermoregulation in boys at pre-pubertal age (7–15 years). *Acta Physiologica Polonica* 35:398–402, 1984.
47. Leithead, C.S. and A.R. Lind. *Heat Stress and Heat Disorders.* Philadelphia:F.A. Davis, 1964.
48. MacDougall, J.D., P.D. Roche, O. Bar-Or, and J.R. Moroz. Maximal aerobic capacity of Canadian school children: prediction based on age-related oxygen cost of running. *International Journal of Sports Medicine* 4:194–198, 1983.
49. Mackie, J.M. Physiological responses of twin children to exercise under conditions of heat stress. M.Sc. Thesis. University of Waterloo, 1982.
50. Mackova, J., M. Sturmova, and M. Macek. Prolonged exercise in pubertal boys in warm and cold environments. In J. Ilmarinen and I. Valimaki (eds.). *Children and Sport.* Berlin:Springer Verlag. 135–141, 1984.
51. Matsushita, K. and T. Araki. The effect of physical training on thermoregulatory responses of pre-adolescent boys to heat and cold. *Japanese Journal of Physical Fitness and Sports Medicine* 29:69–74, 1980.
52. Mellor, D.J. and F. Cockburn. A comparison of energy metabolism in the newborn infant, piglet and lamb. *Quarterly Journal of Experimental Physiology* 71:361–379, 1986.
53. Mount, L.E. *Adaptation to Thermal Environment: Man and his Productive Animals.* Baltimore:University Park Press, 1979.
54. Nadel, E.R. Temperature regulation and prolonged exercise. In D.R. Lamb, and R. Murray (eds.). *Perspectives in Exercise Sciences and Sports Medicine. Volume 1: Prolonged Exercise.* Indianapolis:Benchmark Press. 125–151, 1988.
55. Nadel, E.R., I. Holmer, U. Bergh, and P.-O. Åstrand. Energy exchanges of swimming man. *Journal of Applied Physiology* 36:465–471, 1974a.
56. Nadel, E.R., K.B. Pandolf, M.F. Roberts, and J.A.J. Stolwijk. Mechanisms of thermal acclimation to exercise and heat. *Journal of Applied Physiology* 37:515–520, 1974.
57. Ohara, K. Chloride concentration in sweat: its individual, regional, seasonal, and some other variations and interrelations between them. *Japanese Journal of Physiology* 16:274–290, 1950.
58. Piekarski, C., P. Morfeld, B. Kampmann, R. Illmarinen, and H.G. Wenzel. Heat-stress reactions of the growing child. In J. Rutenfranz, R. Mocellin, and F. Klimt (eds.). *Children and Exercise XII.* Champaign, Ill.:Human Kinetics. 403–412, 1986.
59. Rees, J. and S. Shuster. Pubertal induction of sweat gland activity. *Clinical Science* 60:689–692, 1981.
60. Robinson, S. The effect of body size upon energy exchange in work. *American Journal of Physiology* 36:363–368, 1942.

61. Rowell, L.B. Competition between skin and muscle for blood flow during exercise. In E.R. Nadel (ed.), *Problems with temperature regulation during exercise*. New York: Academic Press. 49–76, 1977.
62. Sato, K. The physiology, pharmacology, and biochemistry of the eccrine sweat gland. *Physiology Biochemistry and Pharmacology* 79:51–131, 1977.
63. Sato, K., R. Leidal, and F. Sato. Morphology and development of an apoeccrine sweat gland in human axillae. *American Journal of Physiology* 21:R166-R180, 1987.
64. Sato, K. and F. Sato. Sweat secretion by human axillary apoeccrine sweat gland in vitro. *American Journal of Physiology* 21:R181–R187, 1987.
65. Skinner, J.S., O. Bar-Or, V. Bergsteinova, C.W. Bell, D. Royer, and E.R. Buskirk. Comparison of continuous and intermittent tests of determining maximal oxygen intake in children. *Acta Paediatrica Scandinavica* Supplement 217:24–38, 1971.
66. Sloan, R.E.G. and W.R. Keatinge. Cooling rates of young people swimming in water. *Journal of Applied Physiology* 35:371–375, 1973.
67. Sohar, E. and Y. Shapira. The physiological reactions of women and children marching during heat (abstract). *Proceedings of the Israel Physiology and Pharmacology Society* 1:50, 1965.
68. Suzuki, M., K. Kasahara, Y. Oba, and H. Funakawa. Effect of environmental temperature upon children (in Japanese). Gakko Hoken Gakkai, the 18th meeting, 1971.
69. Tanaka, M. Studies on the important biological factors influencing the ability to perspire. Part I. Effect of age on ability to perspire (in Japanese). *Journal of the Physiological Society of Japan* 18:390–394, 1956.
70. Taylor, C.R. Exercise and environmental heat loads: different mechanisms for solving different problems? In D. Robertshaw (ed.). *International Review of Physiology. Environmental Physiology II, Vol. 15*. Baltimore:University Park Press. 119–146, 1977.
71. Taylor, N.A.S. Eccrine sweat glands: adaptation to physical training and heat acclimation. *Sports Medicine* 3:387–397, 1986.
72. Van Beaumont, W. Thermoregulation in desert heat in respect to age (abstract). *Physiologist* 8:294, 1965.
73. Wagner, J.A., S. Robinson, and P. Marino. Age and temperature regulation of humans in neutral and cold environments. *Journal of Applied Physiology* 37:562–565, 1974.
74. Wagner, J.A., S. Robinson, S.P. Tzankoff, and R.P. Marino. Heat tolerance and acclimatization to work in the heat in relation to age. *Journal of Applied Physiology* 33:616–622, 1972.

DISCUSSION

BAR-OR: Regarding the fitness of people in the various studies that we performed, indeed not in all cases have I mentioned the level of fitness of the individuals, but I don't think that the differences that we found are because of fitness rather than because of some difference in maturation. Barbara Drinkwater's subjects were all healthy, active, but nonathletic individuals. In our studies at Wingate, we matched our subjects by aerobic fitness and by percentage of body fat. During the exposures, we were sure that the activities were equated as much as possible as a percentage of maximal aerobic power. Training, and the state of acclimatization, can indeed throw data in any direction. I'm not sure, Carl, why our children in the Inbar, 1981, study managed to acclimate sitting in a hot chamber for two weeks. Every second day they sat for about an hour and a half without exercising, and at the end of the two weeks we found that they acclimated about the same level as did those who trained in the climatic chamber. One possibility is that maybe there is some sort of optimal stimulus for heat acclimatization. We hypothesized in that study that maybe sitting in the chamber by itself was a sufficient stimulus for these children to get enough heat storage and become acclimatized. I'm not completely happy with this explanation, but I can't think of a better one. We have some heat balance data, by the way, that showed comparable levels of heat storage in the resting and exercising groups.

BALDWIN: Some years ago in the literature of sweat gland physiology, there was the concept of sweat gland fatigue, and also there were observations that sweat glands were dependent upon glycogen. In view of the sigmoidal relationship that you show with development in terms of sweat gland capacity and function, have any studies been done to see if there are developmental changes in glycogen content in sweat glands, especially in regard to sweating capacity in girls vs. adult women? Could any of this be related to the biochemistry of what is taking place within the sweat gland?

BAR-OR: Well, as you may guess, there is no such information; at least I don't know of any such development-related information. It is interesting, however, that the rate of glycolysis in children during exercise is lower than that of adolescents and adults. This is in muscle. Maybe something similar takes place in sweat glands.

ROGOL: I'm wondering about a practical aspect. Are there differences between adults and children in response to things like aspirin and caffeine?

BAR-OR: I'm really not aware of any research in this area.

BLIMKIE: I think we know that a lot of the normalization that you are using here is with surface area. And yet the proportions of lean to fat tissue vary quite substantially throughout growth and development in the child. Certainly there is a sex difference in terms of the proportion of muscle to fat that occurs during adolescence, too. I think that would be a very interesting aspect to consider in the paper. The other comment that I have, Oded, is that you have made some reference to the possible role of testosterone in regulating some of these mechanisms. I wonder if testosterone is just an indirect aspect to consider.

BAR-OR: Regarding body composition, females have *an increase* in body fat, if anything, before puberty and during puberty all the way to younger adulthood. There are several reasons why obesity will present a handicap to the individual. So you might ask, why don't women have a greater handicap than girls when it comes to exercising in the heat? And I don't think any data show that is so. There is a small difference in adiposity between a 10- to 12-year-old boy and a 20-year-old adult. So again, I don't think this would be the major reason for the maturation-related differences. Regarding testosterone, I'm not sure. We need much more work to even approach that question.

HORTON: I have a question about thermal regulation in cold environments in children. Up where I live we do a lot of cross country skiing, and I've seen several cases of hypothermia develop in youngsters, mainly teenagers, who are participating in long distance ski racing when the temperatures are down around 0 degrees F or −20 degrees C, particularly if it's windy. Are there data on respiratory heat loss under these conditions? I don't know the detail in this area, but I certainly have been told that a major source of heat loss in cross-country ski racing or distance running or whatever, with cold, dry environments, is respiratory heat loss. I wonder if the differences in children and adults would be a significant factor?

BAR-OR: As Ethan has also alluded to, one important point to consider here is body surface area. Obviously children's relative area is greater; therefore, they lose more heat. There is one study, the only study in the literature, looking at cooling rate vs. age in young swimmers. The older the child, the lower the cooling rate. Sloan and Keatinge found that it wasn't just the surface area that explained the greater heat loss, but rather a combined index, which was the reciprocal of fat thickness times the surface area-to-mass ratio that explained most of the variance of the rate of fall in body temperature. One thing that we would like to do in the future, and Joe Blimkie is a prime mover in that potential study, is to look at the combination of exercise and exposure to the cold in obese children as some sort of enhancement of weight loss and maybe even a way of treating them to initiate a quick weight loss and thus increase their motivation. One could make a case that just the respiratory heat loss by itself during exposure to the cold could induce enough calorie loss, without any biochemical changes such as enhanced lipolysis.

NADEL: The respiratory water loss, as a function of the pulmonary ventilation, can be as high as approximately 2 g/min during maximal pulmonary ventilation.

DISHMAN: How much variation in heat tolerance can be due to behavioral or perceptual differences among subjects? Perhaps your work with perceived exertion may have touched on this previously.

BAR-OR: There is really a large number of criteria for heat tolerance. In industry, for example, one is interested in the "prescriptive zone" at which the worker can sustain work for several hours. For a soldier "tolerance" may mean an entirely different concept. Another way is to evaluate what environmental conditions or a combination of environmental and metabolic heat stresses the adult can perform at and the child cannot, or vice versa. There are objective criteria when a session should be stopped, based on rectal temperature, heart rate, and blood pressure. According to the work by Wenzel from Germany and our own experience, sometimes you really cannot explain why a subject suddenly feels that he or she cannot carry on. They complain of dizziness, weakness, nausea, and sometimes apprehension develops following some apathy. So I'm not sure that we do have a foolproof criterion or a set of criteria for heat tolerance in children and adults.

Regarding perception, we have made a set of observations on perception of the heat strain and thirst at rest and during exercise. We have recently completed a study on children with cystic fibrosis. We assumed *a priori* that they would dehydrate because they don't know how much they should drink (due to the hypo-osmolality in their body fluids). And we found indeed that these children drank half as much as the healthy children when exercising in a hot chamber and dehydrated twice as much. We also took several perceptual measurements including thermal comfort, dryness of the mouth, feeling of thirst, etc.. We are still analyzing these data. As to the perception of acclimation, it seems that by several repeated exposures to the heat, children's rate of perceived exertion goes down faster than the drop in their physiological strain. So there is kind of a false sense of security in the child. So from a health point of view, that may be a problem. Physiological strain does not drop as fast, and yet their perceptual strain drops faster than that of the adults.

SUTTON: Do we have any information as to whether children do suffer more problems related to exercise in the heat? Do they develop more heat stroke? Also, I wonder if you could comment on the possible mechanisms that might be involved in shorter races. In fun runs, and more and more children are engaging in these, several investigators have reported heat stroke in adults. And, clearly, gross dehydration or even significant dehydration could not be one of the most important causal factors. Some of the work by Hales has suggested a dramatic rise in the rate of heat production and a change in blood flow to the vital organs compared to the skin. Effectively there is a shutdown of skin blood flow preventing heat loss.

BAR-OR: You mean with dehydration?

SUTTON: Without dehydration. That was the point. In these situations where the races are short, this occurs in the absence of dehydration. Do we have any information at all on children under such conditions? And the final clinical point is in relation to what happens to very young people, I mean infants; when they get hot, they have the problem of thermal convulsions. Do we know what age group this concerns and what actually happens? Is there some change in the brain function that allows the susceptibility to those sorts of thermal problems resulting from the same sort of thermal insult as the child grows older?

BAR-OR: Well, you've talked about quite a number of things, John, and as you know very well, until you and I do an epidemiologically sound study, there will be no such evidence that children do or do not suffer more in the heat than adults. I know really nothing about any observation regarding the short-term fun run. I really can't even comment on that.

SUTTON: When very young kids get hot, they often convulse, and I don't know what happens when they get older. Do they become resistant to that same thermal stress?

BAR-OR: I'm not sure about febrile convulsions. As you know, some of them remain epileptic in later years. So maybe there is a predisposition to seizures which has nothing to do with thermal loading.

SUTTON: Have there been any reports on young kids having heat stroke in these fun runs?

BAR-OR: Not really. What we have are some reports of high-school age children, but then again, not in fun runs. I can think of one study on dehydration on a wrestler who ended up with a pulmonary embolism. Another set of data by Ed Fox reviewed casualties among high-school football players. When I reanalyzed his data, there were two apparent phenomena: these children died either on the first or second day of practice, which was probably when they were unacclimatized. And secondly, that they were quite obese.

DRINKWATER: If we want to match men and women in terms of cardiovascular fitness, we don't match them on milliliters per kilogram body weight because we know there are certain biological differences, and we generally assume that women will be of comparable fitness if they have about 10 percent lower $\dot{V}O_2max$. I think that I've been hearing, with the cardiovascular data, that indeed these relatively high $\dot{V}O_2max$ values in children don't represent a high cardiovascular fitness, or at least not a comparable one. So that's one thing, I think, we have to look at. The other thing is that we also worked our subjects at the same relative workload. And that may be why we didn't see a marked difference in sweating response. When you were showing your data with the males having the higher sweating rate, were they working at the same relative workload?

BAR-OR: Absolutely. Forty-five to 50% of $\dot{V}O_2max$.

DRINKWATER: Okay, then the men were actually producing more metabolic heat.

BAR-OR: In absolute terms?

DRINKWATER: In absolute terms.

BAR-OR: Not per unit mass.

DRINKWATER: Are you sure about that?

BAR-OR: Oh, yes.

DRINKWATER: Okay, because I think a lot of the data confuses the response to relative versus the response to absolute workload. We must be very careful about that.

BAR-OR: But they are all working on the treadmill, i.e., weight-bearing exercise. The data on the metabolic heat production in the heat balance equation show that it was practically identical in the two groups, maybe just a little higher in the children, per kilogram body weight.

DRINKWATER: I think a number of groups have come out with opinion statements or position stands suggesting that youngsters not participate in long-term endurance events, not only on the basis of potential orthopedic problems, but on the basis of the apparent problems with thermal regulation. When we looked at one young woman who was a marathon runner, we saw that her response was far superior to anybody, including the older women. I've been trying to convince Oded he should get a group of young children, male or female, who actually have for months or even years participated in endurance activities that raise core temperature, and see if their response isn't slightly different from children that have not had that experience.

BAR-OR: If I may just make a quick comment about your last sentence. We don't have such data, obviously, but one thing that we did do in Israel, just before I left for Canada, was to look at the heat activated sweat glands in children of different ethnic origins, including North Africans, Asians, Europeans, and others. We also subdivided them according to where they lived the first two years of their lives. The Japanese have stated that it depends on where you live the first two years of your life that may determine to some extent your sweating rate. However, we could not find the slightest hint of a difference among these groups regarding the number of heat activated sweat glands per surface area. But I agree that this is an area to explore further.

9

Nutrition for Muscular Development of Young Athletes

PETER W.R. LEMON, Ph.D.

INTRODUCTION

In the past several decades it has become increasingly clear that nutritional habits play a significant role in athletic performance. Indeed, the disciplines of athletic nutrition and exercise physiology have become very closely integrated. In recent years, basic and applied scientists in both areas have become much more knowledgeable in each other's disciplines. As a result, there is now a sizeable number of individuals trained in both fields of study. This has produced a considerable amount of new information and substantial revision of traditional nutritional recommendations for athletes. Undoubtedly, this advancement in nutrition has contributed to the continued assault on the record books by current athletes.

Unfortunately, the vast majority of the experimental evidence on athletic nutrition has been obtained on male athletes aged 20 to 35 y. Much less information is available on the older male athlete and/or on female athletes of any age; however, some data have been accumulating in recent years (Drinkwater, 1986; Puhl & Brown, 1986; Sutton & Brock, 1987). For adolescent athletes (10 to 18 y), even less is known. This is a group that merits future study because adolescents are not simply young adults. They are unique, not only physiologically, but psychologically and sociologically as well.

Obviously, it would be impossible to review all of the important nutritional concerns of adolescent athletes in one chapter. Instead, this chapter focuses on the known or estimated requirements for selected nutrients (FAO/WHO/UNU, 1985; U.S. Food & Nutrition Board, 1980) that, based on the limited data available, may be important for muscle development in adolescents. Further, it discusses the possible role of active exercise training on these requirements. Because there is a dearth of available data on adolescent athletes, many of the studies cited involve young adults (20 to 35 y). Carbohydrate and water have considerable significance relative to athletic performance, but these topics have been extensively reviewed elsewhere (Costill, 1988; Gisolfi, 1986; Sherman & Lamb, 1988; Williams, 1985) and will not be discussed here.

I. GROWTH DURING ADOLESCENCE

Both males and females experience a rapid increase in growth during puberty. During this period, individuals may gain 20% of their final adult height. Growth rate during puberty is similar to that in the second year of life (Tanner, 1978). This rapid growth continues for about 1-2 y. Typically, girls experience an earlier and shorter spurt than boys. Prior to this growth spurt, the body composition of males and females is similar; however, during adolescence, the typical adult sex differences become established (Figures 5-1, 5-2, this volume). In general, nutritional requirements are substantially increased during this period of rapid growth (Table 9-1). Of the nutrients affected, those of most importance relative to muscle devel-

TABLE 9–1. *Estimated Daily Increments in Body Content of Selected Nutrients During Adolescence (modified from Forbes, 1981)*

Nutrient	Mean for Period 10–20 years of age mg/d		Peak Growth Spurt Spurt mg/d	
	Males	*Females*	*Males*	*Females*
Calcium	210	110	400	240
Iron	0.57	0.23	1.1	0.9
Magnesium	4.4	2.3	8.4	5.0
Protein	2000	1000	3800	2200
Zinc	0.27	0.18	0.50	0.31

opment and exercise performance are probably energy, protein, and some minerals (calcium and magnesium), or trace elements (iron, zinc, and chromium).

II. SELECTED NUTRITIONAL REQUIREMENTS DURING ADOLESCENCE

A. Energy

Due to the variable timing of the adolescent growth spurt, both between the sexes and among individuals of the same sex, height and weight at any given age can be widely divergent. For this reason, energy requirements during adolescence are usually expressed per unit height or weight rather than age. It seems logical to express energy requirements per kg body weight because the most important single factor influencing energy requirements is the basal metabolic rate, which itself is largely determined by body weight (FAO/WHO/UNU, 1985). Estimates of energy requirements (Table 9-2) have been determined for a large number of subjects (FAO/WHO/UNU,

TABLE 9–2. *Daily Dietary Energy Requirement for Adolescents (FAO/WHO/UNU, 1985)*

Age (y)	Median Weight (kg)	Daily BMR* per kg (kJ)	(kcal)	Daily Energy Requirement per kg (kJ)	(kcal)
		Males			
10–12	34.5	152.7	36.5	266.7	63.8
12–14	44.0	135.9	32.5	227.3	54.5
14–16	55.5	123.4	29.5	200.0	47.7
16–18	64.0	115.0	27.5	185.9	44.5
		Females			
10–12	36.0	138.0	33.0	227.8	54.2
12–14	46.5	119.2	28.5	189.2	45.2
14–16	52.0	110.8	26.5	173.1	41.3
16–18	54.0	106.6	25.5	166.7	39.8

*basal metabolic rate

1985). These are based on measures of basal metabolic rate, growth, and additional activities (exercise). As such, they represent reasonable values for groups (Table 9-3) but, of course, could be inaccurate for a given individual. For example, as discussed later, an individual involved in a high intensity and/or a long duration regular exercise training program would have higher energy requirements.

B. Protein

For reasons similar to those mentioned above, protein requirements should be expressed relative to weight rather than age. Recommendations for an adequate or safe level of protein intake (Table 9-4) have been made based on estimates of maintenance (major component) and growth requirements, as well as an adjustment to account for individual variation (two standard deviations above the mean). Boys and girls are presented separately in these charts because the onset and duration of the adolescent growth spurt can vary between the sexes. Although these intakes may be marginal for some adolescents at the peak of the growth spurt (Table 9-1), this fact is probably of minor importance because it appears that most American adolescents consume diets that contain excess protein content (Table 9-3). However, the subjects on which the recommendations are based were involved in substantially less exercise than would be completed by adolescents in active exercise training. Therefore, these recommendations may not apply to the adolescent athlete (especially one who is trying to develop additional muscle

TABLE 9–3. *Percent of American Adolescents (n = 836–1671) Whose Diet Contains Excess (>100% Recommended Dietary Allowance) or Marginal (<60% Recommended Dietary Allowance) Intake of Selected Nutrients. Data based on three-day averages. (From Crocetti & Guthrie, 1982).*

Nutrient		Age			
		11–15 y		16–18 y	
		Excess	Marginal	Excess	Marginal
			%		
Calcium	M*	35.5	20.0	41.0	20.3
	F#	16.8	36.4	12.2	50.0
Iron	M	21.7	18.6	35.3	11.6
	F	5.9	43.4	6.0	50.8
Magnesium	M	19.2	24.4	18.9	28.0
	F	15.0	25.4	12.7	37.2
Energy	M	22.6	13.2	34.4	11.4
	F	24.4	12.9	24.1	16.2
Protein	M	98.1	—	95.3	0.1
	F	92.3	0.2	87.6	1.5

*Male
#Female

TABLE 9-4. *Safe or Recommended Level of Daily Dietary Protein Intake (FAO/WHO/UNU, 1985)*

Age (y)	Maintenance ($mg \cdot kg^{-1} \cdot d^{-1}$)	Growth ($mg \cdot kg^{-1} \cdot d^{-1}$)	Total ($mg \cdot kg^{-1} \cdot d^{-1}$)	Total +2 SD ($mg \cdot kg^{-1} \cdot d^{-1}$)	Safe Protein Intake ($mg \cdot kg^{-1} \cdot d^{-1}$)
		Males			
10–11	688	106	794	994	0.99
11–12	681	106	787	981	0.98
12–13	675	131	806	1006	1.00
13–14	669	106	775	969	0.97
14–15	662	106	768	963	0.96
15–16	656	81	737	919	0.92
16–17	650	69	719	900	0.90
17–18	644	44	688	856	0.86
		Females			
10–11	688	119	807	1006	1.00
11–12	681	106	787	981	0.98
12–13	675	94	769	962	0.96
13–14	669	81	750	938	0.94
14–15	662	56	718	900	0.90
15–16	656	44	700	875	0.87
16–17	650	12	662	825	0.83
17–18	644	0	644	644	0.80

mass). Other factors known to affect protein requirements include protein quality and digestibility, energy intake, and nutritional status (FAO/WHO/UNU, 1985; U.S. Food & Nutrition Board, 1980). Foods high in protein include fish, meat, poultry, eggs, dairy products, and some vegetables (legumes).

C. Minerals

In general, mineral needs increase with the adolescent growth spurt. Calcium and magnesium are especially critical during this time period because of their role in the development of muscle and skeletal mass (Mahan & Rees, 1984). Due to a greater maximal growth rate and the resulting larger absolute body size, the adolescent male has higher mineral requirements than the female.

1. Calcium. A 70 kg body contains about 1,200 g of calcium. The requirement for calcium is based on skeletal growth and retention of deposited calcium to maintain body density (99% of calcium is located in the skeleton [U.S. Food & Nutrition Board, 1980]). Adequate intake is important during adolescence because at least 45% of skeletal mass is laid down during this period (Garn and Wagner, 1969). Calcium also plays a vital role in controlling the excitability of peripheral nerves and muscle, and it is necessary for blood coagulation and muscle contractility. Unfortunately, data indicate that 20% of American adolescent males and up to 50% of adolescent females consume diets that are marginal relative to calcium content (Table 9-3).

During the growth spurt, accumulation of calcium may be as much as 400 and 240 mg·d^{-1} in adolescent males and females, respectively (Mahan & Rees, 1984). The current calcium recommended dietary allowance (RDA) for adolescents is 1200 mg·d^{-1} for both sexes (U.S. Food & Nutrition Board, 1980). Intake must be high because absorption of calcium is usually only about 20–30% (Wilkinson, 1976), but it can vary widely. Calcium absorption depends on the nature of the diet, and many factors are involved (Weiser, 1984). In general, absorption tends to decrease when protein intake is high (Allen et al., 1979) or when the calcium/phosphorus ratio in the diet is low (Zemel & Linkswiler, 1981). Although this latter effect is considered minor at the levels of calcium and phosphorus consumed by most North Americans, it may be important for adolescents who typically consume diets low in calcium (dairy products) and high in phosphorus (carbonated beverages, processed meats, and refrigerated bakery products). Because low dietary calcium contributes to the development of osteoporosis (Recker, 1987), the adequacy of dietary calcium should be of added concern to the female adolescent.

The best dietary sources of calcium are milk and milk products, but significant calcium can also be obtained from green leafy vegetables and seafood (especially clams, oysters, and sardines).

2. Magnesium. A 70 kg body contains about 20–28 g of magnesium. Most magnesium is found in intracellular compartments (27% in muscle) and in bone (60–65%) (Shils, 1988), but only about 50% is exchangeable (Cohen, 1984). It is an important factor in many enzymatic reactions of energy metabolism, is involved in extraction of oxygen by cells, and helps maintain membrane potentials in both muscle and nerve (Caldwell, 1968). Determining magnesium requirements is difficult because of the complex interaction of factors that affect magnesium absorption and/or excretion (Wacker & Parisi, 1968). Actual rates of absorption can vary from about 24–85% of intake. The RDA for magnesium is higher for adult men (350 mg·d^{-1}) than for adult women (300 mg·d^{-1}) (U.S. Food & Nutrition Board, 1980).

Magnesium allowances are slightly increased for the adolescent male (400 mg·d^{-1}) during years 15–18 (presumably due to the accelerated growth at this time) but are not increased for adolescent females (U.S. Food & Nutrition Board, 1980). It is unclear why there is an increase for the adolescent male but not for the adolescent female. Approximately 25% of American adolescent males and as many as 37% of adolescent females consume diets that are marginal in magnesium content (Table 9-3). Good sources of dietary magnesium include nuts, cereal grains, dark green vegetables, and seafood.

D. Trace Elements

As with minerals, trace element requirements are generally increased during the adolescent growth spurt, especially in the male, who has a greater growth rate and resulting absolute size. Of particular interest are iron (blood volume), zinc (muscle and skeletal mass), and chromium (carbohydrate and fat metabolism).

1. **Iron.** Iron is needed primarily for oxygen transport and is found in hemoglobin (70%), myoglobin (5%), and in bone marrow, liver, and spleen (25%) (Haymes, 1987). When iron intake is insufficient, previously stored iron is depleted before hemoglobin is affected. Thus, anemia does not occur until the later stages of iron deficiency (U.S. Food & Nutrition Board, 1980). During adolescence, iron requirements increase for both sexes due to the increased tissue mass and blood volume and, in the female, because of increased iron losses during menstruation. Despite the menstrual losses, absolute iron needs are greater in adolescent males because of their greater growth rate.

Iron requirements in adolescents can vary two- to fourfold in girls and boys, respectively, by virtue of the timing of the growth spurt (Hepner, 1976). Despite this fact, the RDA for both sexes during adolescence is reported as 18 mg·d^{-1} (U.S. Food & Nutrition Board, 1980). Although this intake is likely to be inadequate during the peak growth spurt, it is generally assumed that 18 mg·d^{-1} will provide sufficient stores of iron to meet overall requirements during adolescence. However, this belief may need to be reexamined because absolute iron stores are very small, even in the adult (perhaps 1 g in men and 300 mg in women [Cook et al., 1976]. Furthermore, iron intake of 18 mg·d^{-1} is very difficult to obtain, for females or for any individual with a small mass because such individuals have relatively small energy intakes (Mahan & Rees, 1984). A final reason for reexamination of the RDA for iron is that iron deficiency is the most prevalent nutritional problem in North America (Haymes, 1987). About 15% of American adolescent males and close to 50% of adolescent females consume diets that are marginal in iron content (Table 9-3). The proportion of dietary iron that is absorbed from the gut is quite low (5–10%) and is highest when dietary iron is derived from animal protein, when the amount of dietary iron is small, or when iron is consumed with vitamin C (Clydesdale, 1983; Sjolin, 1981). The best dietary source of iron is liver; however, shellfish, kidney, heart, lean meat, poultry, and fish are also good.

2. **Zinc.** A 70 kg body contains about 1.4–2.3 g of zinc (Czajka-Narins, 1984). Zinc plays an important role in nucleic acid metabolism and, therefore, is found in almost all body tissues. Moreover, it is a cofactor for enzymes of the metabolic pathways for carbohydrates, fats, and proteins (Underwood, 1977). Zinc is stored in bone, but these stores are not readily available. As a result, zinc deficiency can occur very quickly (U.S. Food & Nutrition Board, 1980). For each kg of lean mass about 28 mg of zinc are required (Widdowson & Dickerson, 1964), and, therefore, zinc intake should increase substantially during the growth spurt of adolescence.

The RDA for zinc is 15 mg·d^{-1} for both adolescent males and females (U.S. Food & Nutrition Board, 1980). Many Americans consume less than 50% of this amount (Smith et al., 1983). The percentage of dietary zinc absorbed is about 40% (Smith et al., 1983) but, as with iron, can vary greatly according to source and quantity of zinc intake. High intakes of iron, phytate, and/or fiber lead to decreases in zinc absorption (Mahan & Rees, 1984). In addition, high zinc intakes decrease copper absorption (Klevay et al., 1979) and reduce high density lipoprotein cholesterol in serum (Hopper et al., 1980). Because a low concentration of high density lipoprotein cholesterol in blood serum is often associated with accelerated atherosclerosis, this adverse effect of zinc may be especially significant. Good dietary sources of zinc include chicken or turkey (dark meat), oysters, beef, and liver.

3. **Chromium.** The total body content of chromium is quite low (probably less than 6 mg [Li & Vallee, 1973]). It is found in many tissues, with the highest concentrations in skin, fat, adrenal glands, brain, and muscle. As with zinc, chromium is required for normal carbohydrate and fat metabolism. Chromium potentiates the effects of insulin by increasing glucose and amino acid uptake, and it decreases blood fat concentrations. The concentration of chromium in tissues decreases with age (Czajka-Narins, 1984), and this may play a role in the development of maturity-onset diabetes and atherosclerosis (Anderson, 1981).

The RDA for chromium is 50–200 µg·d^{-1} (U.S. Food & Nutrition Board, 1980). It has been estimated that the dietary intake of up to 90% of Americans may be below this level (Anderson & Kozlovsky, 1985). Further, high intakes of simple sugars increase urinary chromium losses (Kozlovsky et al., 1986).

Chromium is found in mushrooms, oysters, black pepper, brewer's yeast, wine, beer, and in potatoes and apples with skins, but it is important to note that considerable losses of chromium can occur in these foods when they are processed (Borel & Anderson, 1984).

III. SELECTED NUTRITIONAL REQUIREMENTS FOR ADOLESCENTS IN ACTIVE EXERCISE TRAINING

A. Energy

Daily energy requirements can be increased substantially during regular exercise training. Based on the duration and intensity of training bouts utilized by athletes, daily energy requirements could increase by perhaps 35–85% as a result of exercise training (Table 9-5). Strength training is generally considered to require less total energy than endurance training; however, studies on both adolescents and young adults indicate that strength training requires an absolute energy expenditure similar to that of endurance training (Alexandrov & Shishina, 1978; Celejowa & Homa, 1970; Dragan et al., 1985; Laritcheva et al., 1978). These data are consistent with the fact that body builders consume vast amounts of food (unpublished observations) and suggest that actual energy requirements in these individuals are higher than generally believed. Such high energy requirements may in part be caused by an increased basal metabolic rate required by the large lean body mass of strength athletes.

An energy deficit, whether caused by decreased intake or increased expenditure, leads to negative nitrogen balance (Goranzon and Forsum, 1985) and subsequent losses in lean body mass. Therefore, to preserve muscle mass, it is necessary to at least match any increased energy expenditure with additional dietary intake. Maintaining muscle mass is especially critical for athletes because a reduced muscle mass negatively affects exercise performance as strength is lost. Furthermore a loss of muscle mass may lower total energy need as a result of decreasing basal metabolic rate (Cunningham, 1980); this could increase body fat content unless energy intake is reduced. Unfortunately, if energy intake decreases, the chances of incurring a nutritional deficiency are greatly increased, especially for adolescent athletes, because of their accelerated growth requirements. The result could be permanent negative effects on

TABLE 9–5. *Average Daily Energy Expenditure for Males (modified from American College of Sports Medicine, 1971)*

Group	Daily Energy Expenditure		
	$(kJ \cdot kg^{-1})$	$(kcal \cdot kg^{-1})$	Relative to Non-athletes
Non-athletes	205	49	100
Cross-country skiers	377	90	184
Marathon runners	364	87	178
Weightlifters	318	76	155
Shotput, discus throwers	285	68	139

growth. Therefore, during adolescence, it seems prudent to carefully match energy intake with expenditure in order to minimize losses of lean body mass. Moreover, it may even be wise to attempt to increase basal metabolic rate to prevent decreases in energy requirements. This is best accomplished by increasing muscle mass. To maximize muscle mass, surplus energy intake must occur in combination with heavy resistance exercise training.

These potentially adverse effects of energy deficits may be particularly relevant to adolescent athletes who diet on a cyclic basis, e.g., dancers, gymnasts, runners, and wrestlers, in an attempt to maintain an arbitrary body weight for their activity. Numerous negative metabolic and performance effects of this cyclical behavior have been reported. Some of these include loss of lean body mass, dehydration, reduced muscle glycogen content, lowered blood volume, greater electrolyte losses, impaired temperature regulation, tachycardia, decreased muscular strength and/or endurance, and disturbed reproductive function (American College of Sports Medicine, 1976; Cumming et al., 1985; Drinkwater et al., 1984; Hackney et al., 1987; Houston et al., 1981, Tipton, 1982; Wheeler et al., 1984).

Whether any of these adverse effects of cyclical dieting significantly alter growth rates and/or cause any irreversible damage to adolescent athletes is largely unknown; however, some data indicate that there may be reason for concern. First, excessive preoccupation with body weight and diet may lead to serious eating disorders such as anorexia nervosa or bulimia (Peterson, 1982; Smith, 1980). Second, loss of bone mineral in young women due to training and/or diet (Brooks et al., 1984; Drinkwater et al., 1984) may increase their susceptibility to stress fractures and might even result in a greater incidence of osteoporosis in later life. These issues are extremely critical. Unfortunately, definitive answers are not likely to be available until the appropriate longitudinal studies are completed.

Because carbohydrate is such an important exercise fuel (Costill, 1988; Sherman & Lamb, 1988; Tesch et al., 1986), and because glycogen stores in the body are limited (Bergstrom et al., 1967), most of the increased energy intake associated with exercise training should presumably be in the form of carbohydrate. However, it appears that protein intake should also increase (see following section). Generally, it is recommended that athletes (especially endurance athletes) increase their carbohydrate intake from that of the typical North American diet (45–55% of total energy intake) to 60–70% (Costill, 1988; Costill & Miller, 1980). This should provide enough carbohydrate for any athlete, but it is important to realize that it may not if total energy intake is inadequate. For this reason, it might be wise to express carbohydrate intake relative to body weight to be sure that carbohydrate intake is sufficient (perhaps 7–8 g $kg^{-1} \cdot d^{-1}$) to maximize glycogen resynthesis following training bouts (Blom et al., 1987; Costill et al., 1981). It is even possible to obtain sufficient carbohydrate at less than 60–70% of total calories if energy intake is high (Costill, 1986).

A large quantity of carbohydrate can contribute excessive bulk to the diet and be very difficult for young athletes to consume, especially if most of the carbohydrate is in the form of starch. Eating four to six meals per day will reduce the impact of the bulk, but it may be necessary to add simple carbohydrate snacks and/or liquid carbohydrate supplements to maintain energy balance.

As emphasized earlier, maintaining adequate energy intake is of added importance to adolescent athletes because of the already elevated energy requirements associated with their rapid growth. Body weight changes can be monitored to assess energy balance, and, if consistent changes occur in either direction, body composition analysis should be employed to determine if the changes are in fat or lean body mass. Although in sedentary individuals high carbohydrate intakes are associated with elevated blood triglyceride concentrations (Nestle & Barter, 1973), this is not the case with more active individuals, probably because the carbohydrate is used to restore liver and muscle glycogen rather than to synthesize fat (Costill et al. 1979).

B. Protein

Based on the results of uncontrolled, trial and error, self-experimentation, many athletes (especially strength athletes) routinely consume protein far in excess of nutritional recommendations. Although this practice is generally considered of little value by most nutritionists, it might be wise to reexamine this issue because several types of studies completed during the past 10–15 y suggest that both endurance and strength training increase protein needs (Lemon, 1987). For example, Gontzea et al. (1974), utilizing the classic nitrogen balance technique to determine dietary protein needs, observed that nitrogen balance became negative when untrained subjects (21–29 y) began an endurance exercise program while consuming 125% of the RDA for protein. This negative nitrogen balance, if continued, would lead to a decreased muscle mass and presumably to impaired athletic performance. In contrast, when the experiment was repeated at 188% of the RDA for protein, nitrogen balance remained positive, indicating that this protein intake was sufficient to maintain muscle mass (Figure 9-1). These data indicate an increased protein need during strength training.

However, based primarily on data from studies of lower intensity exercise it has been suggested that this increased protein need is transient, lasting only a few weeks at the beginning of a training program (Butterfield, 1987). If so, one would not expect to observe a negative nitrogen balance in experienced endurance athletes. However, in a study similar to that of Gontzea et al. (1974), we obtained essentially the same results as Gontzea's group for endurance athletes (24–29 y) who had been training regularly (94 ± 21 km·wk^{-1}) for more than 5 y (Friedman and Lemon, in press). These results suggest that protein needs are elevated chronically if one engages in regular strenuous endurance exercise.

Perhaps protein needs are increased in both beginners and experienced endurance athletes, but for entirely different reasons. For the beginner, additional protein may be necessary to minimize the decrease in blood proteins (sports anemia) that typically occurs at the initiation of endurance training. In an extensive review of 25 y of their work, Yoshimura et al. (1980) reported that this anemia could be prevented when protein intake was 250% of the RDA, but not when protein intake was 162–168% of the RDA. Using isotopic techniques, Yoshimura's group concluded that, as part of the normal adaptive response (2–3 wk) to strenuous endurance training, blood proteins are utilized to increase myoglobin concentration in muscle. They speculated that additional dietary protein was beneficial because it not only minimized the destruction of red blood cells, but

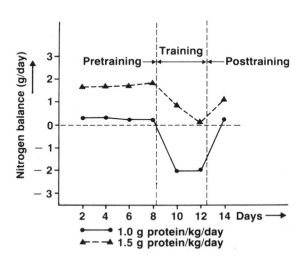

FIGURE 9-1. *Effect of initiation of endurance training on nitrogen balance in individuals consuming 125% and 188% of the recommended dietary allowance for protein. (From Gontzea et al., 1974)*

also promoted their regeneration (Figure 9-2). Further, due to differing changes in the blood lipid profile (and its associated effects on the red cell), animal protein appears to be more protective of red cells than vegetable protein (Yamada et al., 1987).

For the experienced endurance athlete, this anemic response presumably plays no role in protein requirements because, as mentioned above, it occurs only during the first few wks of a training program. However, several factors known to affect amino acid oxidation during exercise can differ substantially between the exercise programs of beginners and experienced endurance athletes. These include exercise intensity (Figure 9-3) (Felig & Wahren, 1971; Henderson et al., 1985; Kasperek & Snider, 1987), exercise duration (Figure 9-4) (Dohm et al., 1982, Haralambie & Berg, 1976), endurance training (Figure 9-3) (Dohm et al., 1977; Henderson et al., 1985), carbohydrate availability (Figure 9-5) (Lemon & Mullin, 1980), and perhaps even the exercise environment (Figure 9-6) (Dolny & Lemon, 1988; Lamont et al., 1987). In some combination, these factors could result in a greater protein need for the experienced endurance athletes due to a greater absolute amino acid oxidation. Moreover, additional dietary protein may assist in the repair of muscle fibers that are damaged as a result of endurance exercise (Amstrong et al., 1983; Byrnes et al., 1985; Kuipers et al., 1983).

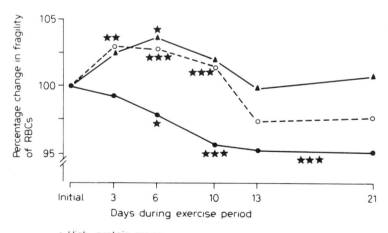

- High-protein group
- Standard-protein group
- Low-protein group

FIGURE 9-2. *Percent change in red blood cell fragility during 21 of cycle exercise training at 8 Met intensity. The stars indicate significance from control (P < .05, .01, and, .001). (From Yoshimura et al., 1980)*

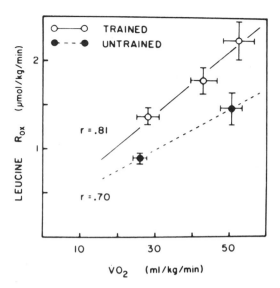

FIGURE 9-3. *Effect of exercise intensity and endurance training on in vivo oxidation of leucine at rest and during exercise. (From Henderson et al., 1985)*

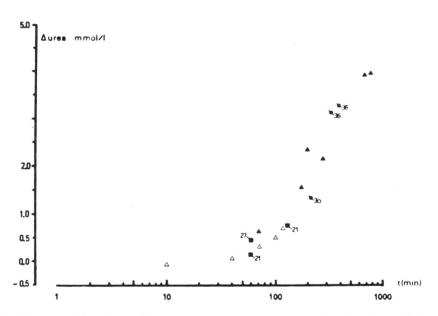

FIGURE 9-4. *Effect of exercise duration on serum urea concentration. Numbers indicate data from different studies. (From Haralambie & Berg, 1976)*

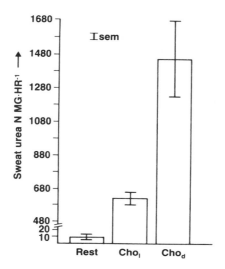

FIGURE 9-5. *Effect of initial carbohydrate stores [carbohydrate loaded (CHO₁) vs. carbohydrate depleted (CHOₐ)] on sweat urea excretion during 60 min of cycle exercise at 61% VO₂max. (From Lemon & Mullin, 1980)*

Sports anemia appears to be specific to endurance exercise because Hickson et al. (1985; 1988) did not observe it in subjects (18–26 y) who completed a four-week weight lifting program. The reasons for this exercise-specific effect are unknown, but possibly are

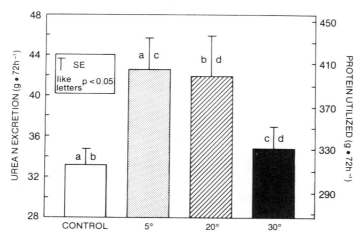

FIGURE 9-6. *Effect of ambient temperature on urea excretion in urine and sweat and on calculated protein utilized as a result of 90 min of cycle exercise at 65% VO₂max. Like letters indicate significant differences between temperature conditions. (From Dolny & Lemon, 1988)*

related to the differing training stimuli in these two types of exercise, i.e., weight training would not be expected to stimulate an increase in myoglobin synthesis and, therefore, should not affect blood proteins to the same extent as endurance training. However, there are other data available that suggest additional dietary protein will benefit athletes involved in strength training. For example, Torun et al. (1977), utilizing the potassium[40] technique to assess total body potassium (an estimate of total cell mass), found a decreased cell mass after six weeks of strength training with subjects (18–21 y) who consumed 100% of the RDA for protein and adequate total energy. When protein intake was increased to 200% of the RDA and the program repeated, cell mass actually increased.

Celejowa & Homa (1970) observed a negative nitrogen balance in five of 10 weightlifters (20–35 y) consuming 250% of the protein RDA. Only one of the five athletes who were in negative nitrogen balance was in negative energy balance, so it appears that protein need was elevated in at least 40% of these lifters. A relatively large intersubject variability in nitrogen balance was also observed in this study. This may have been due to large differences in exercise intensity among individuals because this study was conducted during a period of general training. Further, this variability illustrates the difficulty of using this technique in exercise studies.

Utilizing a double blind, crossover design, Dragan et al. (1985) obtained impressive gains over several months in both muscle strength (5%) and size (6%) when elite Romanian weightlifters increased their protein intake from 225% to 438% of the RDA.

Based on nitrogen balance measures, Tarnopolsky et al. (1988) reported that the protein intake for zero nitrogen balance was greater in both bodybuilders (24 ± 1 y, mean ± SE) and endurance athletes (22 ± 1 y) than for sedentary subjects (22 ± 1 y) (Figure 9-7). From these data, they estimated the recommended or safe protein intake to be 112% and 162% of the current protein RDA for bodybuilders and endurance runners, respectively. In this study, energy intake averaged at least 178% of requirement, so it is unlikely that protein needs of these athletes were elevated due to insufficient dietary energy.

At the present time, the underlying mechanism responsible for the potentially beneficial effects of additional dietary protein on muscle strength and size are unclear. However, two of the studies discussed above may offer some insight into this problem. Based on the nitrogen balance technique, Tarnopolsky et al. (1988) found that the bodybuilders' protein requirement was elevated relative to sedentary controls. However, the increase in protein intake was very modest relative to what typical strength athletes routinely consume

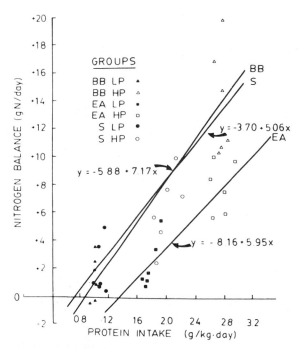

FIGURE 9-7. *Predicted protein intake for zero nitrogen balance determined from extrapolation of regression equation for bodybuilders (BB), endurance athlete (EA), and sedentary subjects (S) on low protein (LP) and high protein (HP) diets. (From Tarnopolsky et al., 1988)*

or to the intakes that produced substantial gains in strength and size in the study of Dragan et al. (1985). Perhaps what this means is that strength athletes can maintain positive nitrogen balance with a protein intake equal to or slightly above the current RDA, but maximal gains in muscle strength and size are not realized unless greater protein intake occurs. Therefore, it may be that the optimal stimulus for muscle fiber hypertrophy induced by resistance exercise requires not just a positive, but rather a highly positive, nitrogen balance. If so, this could help explain the controversy that exists between nutritional scientists, whose opinion regarding protein need is based primarily on nitrogen balance experiments, and strength athletes, whose opinion is based exclusively on gains in muscle strength and size.

Taken together, these recent data appear to contradict the traditional belief that protein needs of athletes are similar to those of sedentary individuals. Many nutrient needs are increased with exercise, so the finding that greater protein intake during training may be beneficial for athletes should not be too surprising. Further, it is

NUTRITION FOR MUSCULAR DEVELOPMENT **385**

already acknowledged that muscle development requires additional protein (U.S. Food & Nutrition Board, 1980), but the dietary allowances are designed for relatively inactive individuals, not for athletes (FAO/WHO/UNU, 1985; U.S. Food & Nutrition Board, 1980). This seems to be an important limitation of the recommended allowances.

If increased dietary protein is advantageous, it is important to document whether there are any negative side effects in healthy individuals with high intakes. Although it is frequently stated that such diets can lead to liver or kidney disease, there is actually little evidence for this, except in cases of preexisting abnormalities in kidney function.

Clearly, more study is necessary before it will be possible to make definitive recommendations regarding protein requirements or optimal protein intakes for specific athletic groups. However, the data that suggest a need by athletes for more protein are especially interesting for the adolescent athlete because her/his nutritional reserve is very low as a result of growth and/or poor dietary habits. As a general rule, it appears that protein intake should be sufficient for the adolescent athlete if it represents 12–15% of total dietary energy. Assuming an adequate total energy intake, this should provide on a daily basis about 1.2–2.0 g of protein per kg body weight (120–250% of the RDA, depending on age).

Nevertheless, at least two situations exist where this protein intake recommendation may be inadequate. Both circumstances involve high carbohydrate diets. First, if an adolescent athlete consumes a diet high in complex carbohydrates, the total energy intake may be insufficient due to excess food bulk. This could cause a need for protein in excess of 12–15% of total calories because of the effect of negative energy balance on protein requirements. Second, if dietary carbohydrate increases much above 70% of total energy intake, assuming some of the remainder is fat, protein intake may be marginal. Both of these scenarios could reduce gains in muscle mass and might even result in muscle atrophy.

Finally, the Dragan et al. (1985) data showing increased strength and size with 438% of protein RDA are intriguing, and more study is needed to determine if prolonged maintenance of a highly positive nitrogen balance will optimize muscle growth in strength athletes who are training intensely.

C. Minerals

1. Calcium. The current recommended dietary allowances do not discuss the effect of exercise on calcium requirements (U.S. Food & Nutrition Board, 1980). However, calcium is lost in the sweat of individuals who exercise, and the magnitude may be significant. In college age subjects, Costill & Miller (1980) reported that the calcium concentration in sweat decreased nearly linearly from about 4.5 to 2.0 mM at sweat rates of 0.2 to $1.1 \cdot h^{-1}$ (Figure 9-8). This means that during a 1 h training bout, 80 mg (2.0 mmols) of calcium could easily be lost. Assuming a daily intake of 1200 mg calcium and 25% absorption of that calcium, this loss represents about 27% of absorbed calcium. Although it appears that sweat rates may be reduced in young children (Table 8-2, this volume), this difference in sweating disappears at puberty, perhaps due to the appearance of apoecrrine glands (Figure 8-5, this volume). Therefore, it is likely that large calcium losses in sweat occur in adolescents as well as in adults. In view of the important role of calcium in bone growth (Garn & Wager, 1969), muscle contraction (Cohen, 1975), muscle fatigue (Green, 1987), and osteoporosis (Recker, 1987) these exercise-induced calcium losses may be important. Adolescent athletes in general, and females in particular, are likely to be high risk groups for inadequacy of calcium reserves because of low calcium and/or high phosphorus intake and hormonal effects on calcium mobilization (Cumming et al., 1985; Drinkwater et al., 1984).

2. **Magnesium.** As with calcium, there is no recognized increased magnesium allowance for exercising individuals (U.S. Food & Nutrition Board, 1980). Magnesium concentration in sweat is about 2 mM, regardless of sweat rate (Figure 9-8) (Costill & Miller, 1980). Therefore, during 1 h of exercise, 49 mg of magnesium (2.0 mmols) could easily be excreted in sweat. Assuming a daily intake of 350

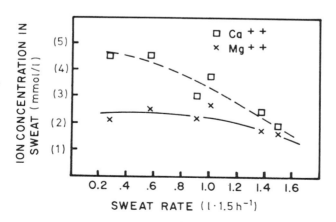

FIGURE 9-8. *Changes in sweat calcium and magnesium concentrations at varied rates of sweating. (From Costill & Miller, 1980)*

mg magnesium and 54% magnesium absorption, this loss represents about 23% of magnesium absorbed. These losses could explain the decreased serum magnesium concentrations that have been observed following exercise (Figure 9-9) (Rose et al., 1970; Stendig-Lindberg et al., 1987).

Because magnesium is critical in both energy metabolism and muscle contraction, one would expect large magnesium losses to negatively affect exercise performance. Some data exist that support this possibility. Von Stocke et al. (1979) reported that trained subjects who had low serum magnesium concentrations performed better on a discontinuous bicycle ergometer test following magnesium supplementation. Further, in magnesium depleted rats, both muscle mitochondrial oxygen consumption (Brautbar et al., 1985) and endurance exercise capacity are reduced (Keen et al., 1987). In the latter study, associated hematologic changes (increased packed cell volume, decreased red cell number, decreased hemoglobin concentration) were prevented with magnesium supplementation. Future experiments are needed to assess the significance of these results relative to adolescent athletes and to determine whether magnesium supplementation is advisable.

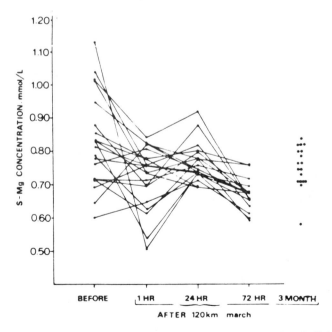

FIGURE 9-9. *Effect of a 120 km hike on serum magnesium concentration. Individual subject responses are plotted. (From Stendig-Lindberg et al., 1987)*

D. Trace Elements

1. **Iron.** As with both minerals discussed above, the recommended dietary allowance for iron is not increased for athletes (U.S. Food & Nutrition Board, 1980). Yet, several studies (Clement & Sawchuk, 1984; Dufaux et al., 1981; Ehn et al., 1979; Plowman & McSwegin, 1981) have reported an incidence of iron deficiency (anemia, reduced bone marrow iron, low serum ferritin, decreased transferrin saturation) in trained subjects that is approximately twice that observed in the normal population. Further, iron supplementation (100 mg $\cdot$ d^{-1}) has been shown to improve exercise performance in anemic athletes (Haymes, 1987). In rats fed iron-poor diets, restoration of depressed hemoglobin concentration by iron supplementation is sufficient to restore $\dot{V}O_2$max to near control values, but improvements in endurance performance are not observed until after muscle mitochondrial iron deficiences are reversed (Figure 9-10) (Davies et al., 1982; Davies et al., 1984).

Possible causes of iron depletion include low dietary iron intake (Table 9-3), and/or elevated urinary, fecal, and sweat excretion of iron (Haymes, 1987). Because iron is critical for increased muscle growth and red blood cell production, the potential for exercise-induced iron depletion needs to be closely monitored in adolescent athletes.

2. **Zinc.** As with iron, the officially recommended dietary allowance for zinc is not greater for athletes (U.S. Food & Nutrition Board, 1980). Yet, accumulating evidence suggests that chronic exercise may in fact elevate zinc needs. Endurance training can lead to hypozincemia (Dressendorfer & Sockolov, 1980; Haralambie, 1981). Further, zinc supplementation can reduce muscle fatigue in rats (Richardson & Drake, 1979) and increase muscular strength and endurance in women (Krotkiewski et al., 1982). The underlying reason for the apparently increased requirement for zinc in exercising persons is unclear, but probably involves the interaction of low dietary zinc intake and increased losses of zinc in sweat (Keen & Hackman, 1986) and urine (Anderson et al., 1986a). Zinc intake is closely related to energy intake, and the typical U.S. diet contains about 1 mg zinc $\cdot$ 1000 kJ^{-1} (Anderson et al., 1986a). Therefore, a sedentary individual would need to consume about 15,000 kJ $\cdot$ d^{-1} to meet the recommended dietary allowance (15 mg $\cdot$ d^{-1}). Frequently, intake of zinc is less than this (Keen & Hackman, 1986), and one would expect smaller individuals, especially women, to be at highest risk. Although increased energy intake during exercise training could help alleviate this shortage of zinc, the increased zinc excretion with such exercise may further confound the problem. This would be espe-

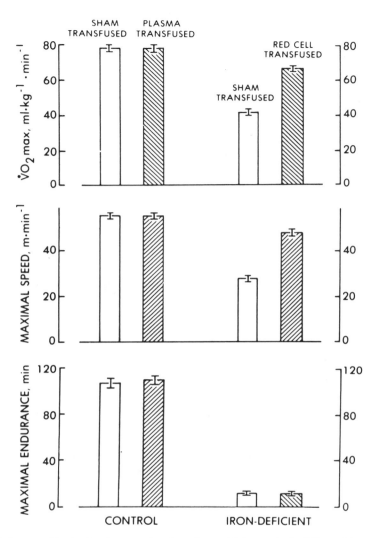

FIGURE 9-10. *Maximal endurance time (running at 20.1 m · min^{-1}, 15% grade), maximal speed of V̇O$_2$max test, and V̇O$_2$max of transfused (red cell, plasma, and sham) iron deficient and control rats. (From Davies et al., 1984)*

cially true in individuals who were using both diet and exercise to reduce body weight.

Little is known regarding the effects of exercise on zinc requirements in adolescents. However, this information could be important because it is known that zinc needs increase substantially with growth, because the zinc reserve is so small that deficiency can occur quickly, and because inadequate zinc intakes produce devastating results, i.e., growth retardation, delayed sexual maturation, infertility, decreased wound healing, impaired immunity, and altered taste acuity (Prasad, 1966; Underwood, 1977).

    3. Chromium. As with the other trace elements discussed, there is no officially increased recommended dietary chromium allowance for athletes (U.S. Food & Nutrition Board, 1980). However, in subjects aged 23–46 y, exercise (running 10 km) has been shown to increase 24 h urinary chromium loss by at least 200% (Anderson et al., 1982; Anderson et al., 1986a). Sweat losses may add to this, but are presently unknown. Exercise training effects are unclear. Non-exercise day urinary chromium losses are reduced in trained adult runners relative to their sedentary counterparts (Anderson et al., 1986b). However, it is unknown whether this is due to depletion of body chromium or whether it represents a training adaptation to minimize chromium losses.

    As with zinc, chromium intakes are generally low because chromium content in the typical U.S. diet is low (about $3.6 \ \mu g \cdot 1000 \ kJ^{-1}$ [Anderson et al., 1986a]). Hopefully, the increased energy intake usually observed in people undergoing exercise training (unless one is dieting) is sufficient to counter the added losses induced by exercise. This seems especially critical because even in healthy adults chromium supplementation $(200 \ \mu g \cdot d^{-1})$ improves glucose tolerance and increases high density lipoprotein cholesterol (Riales & Albrink, 1981). Whether inadequate dietary chromium intake accelerates diabetes and/or atherosclerosis needs to be determined.

SUMMARY

    In general, the effects of exercise training on nutritional requirements of adolescents are not well-known. This dearth of information is of considerable significance because the potential for malnourishment is high in growing adolescents who have preexisting elevated requirements for nutrients. In addition, the varied time of onset and duration of the adolescent growth spurt further complicates the situation. Evidence indicates that chronic rigorous exercise training may increase the requirements for some nutrients (energy, protein, and iron) and, although the data are more speculative, may increase the needs for calcium, chromium, magnesium, and zinc as well. Hopefully, definitive experimental data will be available in the near future that will enable us to provide sound recommendations for nutrition that, when combined with active exercise training, will allow optimal muscular development in adolescents.

ACKNOWLEDGEMENTS

Sincere appreciation is expressed to Dr. R. Michael Jenkins for his helpful suggestions during the preparation of this manuscript, to reactors Dr. David R. Lamb and Dr. J. Mark Davis for their critical reviews, and to Ms. Christine M. Myers for her expert secretarial assistance.

BIBLIOGRAPHY

1. Alexandrov, I.I. and N.N. Shishina. Study of energy metabolism and nutritional status of young athletes. In: J. Parizkova, and V.A. Rogozkin, (eds.). *Nutrition, Physical Fitness, and Health.* Baltimore: University Park Press. 124–130, 1978.
2. Allen, L.H., E.A. Oddoye, and S. Margen. Protein-induced hypercalciuria: a longer term study. *American Journal of Clinical Nutrition* 32:741–749, 1979.
3. American College of Sports Medicine. *Encyclopedia of Sports Sciences and Medicine.* New York: MacMillan. 1128–1129, 1971.
4. American College of Sport Medicine. Position stand on weight loss in wrestlers. *Medicine and Science in Sports* 8(2):xi–xiii, 1976.
5. Anderson, R.A. Nutritional role of chromium. *Science Total Environment* 17:13–29, 1981.
6. Anderson, R.A., M.M. Polansky, N.A. Bryden, E.E. Roginski, K.Y. Patterson, and D.C. Reamer. Effect of exercise (running) on serum glucose, insulin, glucagon, and chromium excretion. *Diabetes* 31:212–216, 1982.
7. Anderson, R.A. and A.S. Kozlovsky. Chromium intake, absorption and excretion of subjects consuming self-selected diets. *American Journal of Clinical Nutrition* 41:1177–1183, 1985.
8. Anderson, R.A., M.M. Polansky, N.A. Bryden, and H.N. Guttman. Strenuous exercise may increase dietary needs for chromium and zinc. In: F.I. Katch, (ed.). *Sport, Health, and Nutrition.* Champaign, IL.: Human Kinetics. 83–99, 1986a.
9. Anderson, R.A., N.A. Bryden, M.M. Polansky, and P.A. Deuster. Controlled exercise effects on chromium excretion of trained and untrained runners consuming a constant diet (Abstract). *Federation Proceedings* 45:971, 1986b.
10. Armstrong, R.B., R.W. Ogilvie, and J.A. Schwane. Eccentric exercise-induced injury to rat skeletal muscle. *Journal of Applied Physiology* 54:80–93, 1983.
11. Bergstrom, J., L. Hermansen, E. Hultman, and B. Saltin. Diet, muscle glycogen and physical performance. *Acta Physiologica Scandinavica* 71:140–150, 1967.
12. Blom, P.C.S., A.T. Hostmark, O. Vaage, K.R. Kardel, and S. Maehlum. Effect of different post-exercise sugar diets on the rate of muscle glycogen synthesis. *Medicine and Science in Sports and Exercise* 19:491–496, 1987.
13. Borel, J.S. and R.A. Anderson. Chromium. In: E. Frieden, (ed.). *Biochemistry of the Essential Ultratrace Elements.* New York: Plenum. 175–199, 1984.
14. Brautbar, N., K. Anderson, A. Tran, and S.G. Massry. Impaired skeletal muscle cellular bioenergetics in magnesium depletion (Abstract). *Federation Proceedings* 44:1280, 1985.
15. Brooks, S.M., C.F. Sanborn, B.H. Albrecht, and W.W. Wagner. Diet in athletic amenorrhea. *Lancet* i:559–560, 1984.
16. Butterfield, G.E. Whole-body protein utilization in humans. *Medicine and Science in Sports and Exercise* 19 (No. 5 Supplement):S157–S165, 1987.
17. Byrnes, W.C., P.M. Clarkson, J.S. White, S.S. Hsieth, P.N. Frykman, and R.J. Maughen. Delayed onset muscle soreness following repeated bouts of downhill running. *Journal of Applied Physiology* 59:710–715, 1985.
18. Caldwell, P.C. Factors governing movement and distribution of inorganic ions in nerve and muscle. *Physiological Reviews* 48:1–64, 1968.
19. Campbell, W.W. and R.A. Anderson. Effects of aerobic exercise and training on the trace minerals chromium, zinc and copper. *Sports Medicine* 4:9–18, 1987.
20. Celejowa, I. and M. Homa. Food intake, nitrogen and energy balance in Polish weightlifters, during a training camp. *Nutrition and Metabolism* 12:259–274, 1970.
21. Clement, D.B. and L.L. Sawchuk. Iron status and sports performance. *Sports Medicine* 1:65–74, 1984.
22. Clydesdale, F.M. Physiochemical determinants of iron bioavailability. *Food Technology* 37:133–138, 144, 1983.
23. Cohen, C. The protein switch of muscle contraction. *Scientific American* 233(11):36–45, 1975.
24. Cohen, R.D. Body fluids. In E.J.M. Campbell, C.J. Dickinson, J.D.H. Slater, C.R.W. Edwards, and K. Sikora (eds.). *Clinical Physiology.* Oxford: Blackwell Scientific Publications. 1–40, 1984.
25. Cook, J.D., C.A. Finch, and N.J. Smith. Evaluation of the iron status of a population. *Blood* 48:449–455, 1976.

26. Costill, D.L., W.J. Fink, J.L. Ivy, L.H. Getchell, and M. Witzmann. Lipid metabolism in skeletal muscle of endurance-trained males and females. *Diabetes* 28:818–822, 1979.
27. Costill, D.L. and J.M. Miller. Nutrition for endurance sport: carbohydrate and fluid balance. *International Journal of Sports Medicine* 1:1–14, 1980.
28. Costill, D.L., W.M. Sherman, W.J. Fink, C. Maresh, M. Witten, and J.M. Miller. The role of dietary carbohydrates in muscle glycogen resynthesis after strenuous running. *American Journal of Clinical Nutrition* 34:1831–1836, 1981.
29. Costill, D.L. *Inside Running.* Indianapolis: Benchmark Press. 58–84, 1986.
30. Costill, D.L. Carbohydrates for exercise: dietary demands for optimal performance. *International Journal of Sports Medicine* 9:1–18, 1988.
31. Crocetti, A.F. and H.A. Guthrie. *Eating Behavior and Associated Nutrient Quality of Diets.* Washington: U.S.D.A. Report 53-22U4-9-192. Chapter 5. 4–15, 1982.
32. Cumming, D.C., M.M. Vickovic, S.R. Wall, and M.R. Fluker. Defects in pulsatile LH release in normally menstruating runners. *Journal of Clinical Endocrinology* 57:671–673, 1985.
33. Cunningham, J.J. A reanalysis of factors influencing basal metabolic rate. *American Journal of Clinical Nutrition* 33:2372–2374, 1980.
34. Czajka-Narins, D.M. Minerals. In: M.V. Krause and L.K. Mahan (eds.). *Food, Nutrition, and Diet Therapy.* Philadelphia: Saunders. 144–180, 1984.
35. Davies, K.J.A., J.J. Maguire, G.A. Brooks, P.R. Dallman, and L. Packer. Muscle mitochondral bioenergetics, oxygen supply, and work capacity during dietary iron depletion and repletion. *American Journal of Physiology* 242:E418–E427, 1982.
36. Davies, K.J.A., C.M. Donovan, G.J. Refino, G.A. Brooks, L. Packer, and P.R. Dallman. Distinguishing effects of anemia and muscle iron deficiency on exercise bioenergetics in the rat. *American Journal of Physiology* 246:E535–E543, 1984.
37. Dohm, G.L., A.L. Hecker, W.E. Brown, G.J. Kalin, F.R. Puente, E.W. Askew, and G.R. Beechere. Adaptation of protein metabolism to endurance training. Increased amino acid oxidation in response to training. *Biochemical Journal* 164:705–708, 1977.
38. Dohm, G.L., R.T. Williams, G.J. Kasperek, and A.M. van Rig. Increased excretion of urea and N^t-methylhistidine by rats and humans after a bout of exercise. *Journal of Applied Physiology* 52:27–33, 1982.
39. Dolny, D.G. and P.W.R. Lemon. Effect of ambient temperature on protein breakdown during prolonged exercise. *Journal of Applied Physiology* 64:550–555, 1988.
40. Dragan, G.I., A. Vasiliu, and E. Georgescu. Effect of increased supply of protein on elite weight-lifters. In: T.E. Galesloot & B.J. Tinbergen, (eds.). *Milk Proteins.* Wageningen, Netherlands: Pudoc. 99–103, 1985.
41. Dressendorfer, R.H. and R. Sockolvov. Hypozincemia in runners. *Physician and Sportmedicine* 8(4):97–100, 1980.
42. Drinkwater, B.L., K. Nilson, C.H. Chesnut, W.J. Bremner, S. Shainholtz, and M.B. Southwoth. Bone mineral content of amenorrheic and eumenorrheic athletes. *New England Journal of Medicine* 311:277–281, 1984.
43. Drinkwater, B.L. (ed.). *Female Endurance Athletes.* Champaign, IL: Human Kinetics, 1986.
44. Dufaux, B., A. Hoederath, Streitberger, W. Hollman, and G. Assman. Serum ferritin, transferrin, haptoglobin, and iron in middle- and long-distance runners, elite rowers, and professional racing cyclists. *International Journal of Sports Medicine* 2:43–46, 1981.
45. Ehn, L., B. Carlmark, and S. Hoglund. Iron status in athletes involved in intense physical activity. *Medicine and Science in Sports and Exercise* 12:61–64, 1979.
46. Food and Agricultural Organization, World Health Organization, and United Nations University. *Energy and Protein Requirements.* Geneva: World Health Organization Technical Report Series 724, 1985.
47. Felig, P. and J. Wahren. Amino acid metabolism in exercising men. *Journal of Clinical Investigation* 50:2703–2714, 1971.
48. Forbes, G.B. Nutritional requirements in adolescence. In: R.M. Suskind, (ed.). *Textbook of Pediatric Nutrition.* New York:Raven Pres. 381–391, 1981.
49. Friedman, J.E. and P.W.R. Lemon. Effect of chronic endurance exercise on retention of dietary protein. *International Journal of Sports Medicine,* in press.
50. Garn, S.M. and B. Wagner. The adolescent growth of skeletal mass and its implication to mineral requirements. In: F.P. Heald, (ed.). *Adolescent Nutrition and Growth.* New York:Appleton-Century-Crofts. 139–161, 1969.
51. Gisolfi, C. Impact of limited fluid intake on performance. In: *Predicting Decrements in Military Performance due to Inadequate Nutrition.* Washington: National Academy Press. 17–28, 1986.
52. Gontzea, I., P. Sutzescu, and S. Dumitrache. The influence of muscular activity on the nitrogen balance and on the need of man for protein. *Nutrition Reports International* 10:35–43, 1975.
53. Goranzon, H. and E. Forsum. Effect of reduced energy intake versus increased physical

activity on the outcome of nitrogen balance experiments in man. *American Journal of Clinical Nutrition* 41:919–928, 1985.

54. Green, H.J. Neuromuscular aspects of fatigue. *Canadian Journal of Sport Sciences* 12(Supplement 1):7S–19S, 1987.

55. Hackney, A.C., W.E. Sinning, and B.C. Bruot. Hypothalmic-pituitary-testicular function of endurance trained and untrained males (Abstract). *Medicine and Science in Sports and Exercise* 19:S9, 1987.

56. Hagg, S.A., E.L. Morse, and S.A. Adibi. Effect of exercise on rates of oxidation, turnover, and plasma clearance of leucine in human subjects. *American Journal of Physiology* 242:E407–E410, 1982.

57. Haralambie, G. Serum zinc in athletes in training. *International Journal of Sportsmedicine* 2:135–138, 1981.

58. Haralambie, G. and A. Berg. Serum urea and amino nitrogen changes with exercise duration. *European Journal of Applied Physiology* 36:39–48, 1976.

59. Haymes, E.M. Nutritional concerns: need for iron. *Medicine and Science in Sports and Exercise* 19(No. 5 Supplement):S197–S199, 1987.

60. Henderson, S.A., A.L. Black, and G.A. Brooks. Leucine turnover and oxidation in trained rats during exercise. *American Journal of Physiology* 249:E137–E144, 1985.

61. Hepner, R. Adolescent nutrient requirements and recommended dietary allowances—general discussion. In: J.I. McKigney & H.N. Munro (eds.). *Nutrient Requirements in Adolescence*. Cambridge:MIT Press. 171–178, 1976.

62. Hickson, Jr., J.F. and K. Hinkelmann. Exercise and protein intake effects on urinary 3-methylhistidine excretion. *American Journal of Clinical Nutrition* 41:246–253, 1985.

63. Hickson, Jr., J.F. and I. Wolinsky. Protein intake level and introductory weight training exercise on selected blood measurements in untrained men. *Nutrition Reports International* 37:575–582, 1988.

64. Hooper, P.L., L. Visconti, P.J. Garry, and G.E. Johnson. Zinc lowers high-density lipoprotein-cholesterol levels. *Journal of the American Medical Association* 244:1960–1961, 1980.

65. Houston, M.E., D.A. Marrin, H.J. Green, and J.A. Thomson. The effect of rapid weight loss on physiological functions in wrestlers. *Physician and Sportsmedicine* 9(11):73–78, 1981.

66. Kasperek, G.J. and R.D. Snider. Effect of exercise intensity and starvation on activation of branched-chain keto acid dehydrogenase by exercise. *American Journal of Physiology* 252:E33–E37, 1987.

67. Keen, C.L. and R.M. Hackman. Trace elements in athletic performance. In: F.I. Katch, (ed.). *Sport, Health, & Nutrition*. Champaign, IL.: Human Kinetics. 51–65, 1986.

68. Keen, C.L., P. Lowney, M.E. Gershwin, L.S. Hurley, and J.S. Stern. Dietary magnesium intake influences exercise capacity and hematologic parameters in rats. *Metabolism* 36:788–793, 1987.

69. Klevay, L.M., S.J. Reck, and D.F. Barcome. Evidence of dietary copper & zinc deficiencies. *Journal of the American Medical Association* 241:1916–1918, 1979.

70. Kozlovsky, A.S., P.B. Moser, S. Reiser, and R.A. Anderson. Effects of diets high in simple sugars on urinary chromium losses. *Metabolism* 35:515–518, 1986.

71. Krotkiewski, M., M. Gudmundsson, P. Backstrom, and K. Mandroukas. Zinc and muscle strength. *Acta Physiologica Scandinavia* 116:309–311, 1982.

72. Kuipers, H., J. Drukker, P.M. Frederik, P. Geurten, and G.V. Kranenburg. Muscle degeneration after exercise in rats. *International Journal of Sports Medicine* 4:45–51, 1983.

73. Lamont, L.S., P.W.R. Lemon, and B.C. Bruot. Menstrual cycle and exercise effects on protein metabolism. *Medicine and Science in Sports and Exercise.* 19:106–110, 1987.

74. Laritcheva, K.A., N.I. Yalovaya, V.I. Shubin, and P.V. Smirnov. Study of energy expenditure and protein needs of top weight lifters. In: J. Parizkova and V.A. Rogozkin, (eds.). *Nutrition, Physical Fitness, and Health*. Baltimore:University Park Press. 155–163, 1978.

75. Lemon, P.W.R. Protein and exercise: update 1987. *Medicine and Science in Sport and Exercise* 19(5, Supplement):S179–S190, 1987.

76. Lemon, P.W.R. and J.P. Mullin. Effect of initial muscle glycogen levels on protein catabolism during exercise. *Journal of Applied Physiology* 48:624–629, 1980.

77. Lemon, P.W.R., N.J. Benevenga, J.P. Mullin, and F.J. Nagle. Effect of daily exercise and food intake on leucine oxidation. *Biochemical Medicine* 33:67–76, 1985.

78. Li, T-K. and B.L. Vallee. The biochemical and nutritional role of trace elements. In: R.S. Goodhart and M.E. Shils, (eds.). *Modern Nutrition in Health and Disease*. Philadelphia:Lea & Febiger. 372–399, 1973.

79. Mahan, L.K. and J.M. Rees. *Nutrition in Adolescence*. St. Louis:Times Mirror/Mosby, 1984.

80. Nestle, P.J. and P.J. Barter. Triglyceride clearance during diets rich in carbohydrate and fats. *American Journal of Clinical Nutrition* 26:241–245, 1973.

81. Peterson, M.S. Nutritional concerns for the dancer. *Physician and Sportsmedicine* 10(3):137–143, 1982.

82. Plowman, S.A. and P.C. McSweigin. The effects of iron supplementation on female cross-country runners. *Journal of Sports Medicine* 21:407–416, 1981.
83. Prasad, A.S. Metabolism of zinc and its deficiency in human subjects. In: A.S. Prasad, (ed.). *Zinc Metabolism*. Springfield, IL:Thomas. 250–301, 1976.
84. Puhl, J.L. and C.H. Brown, (eds.). *The menstrual cycle and physical activity*. Champaign, IL.:Human Kinetics, 1986.
85. Recker, R.R. Calcium nutrition and bone mass. In: H.K. Genant, (ed.). *Osteoporosis Update 1987*. San Francisco: University of California Printing Services. 249–251, 1987.
86. Riales, R. and M.J. Albrink. Effect of chromium chloride supplementation on glucose tolerance and serum lipids including high density lipoprotein of adult men. *American Journal of Clinical Nutrition* 34:2670–2678, 1981.
87. Richardson, J.H. and P.O. Drake. The effects of zinc on fatigue on striated muscle. *Journal of Sports Medicine* 19:133–134, 1979.
88. Rose, L.I., D.R. Carroll, S.L. Lowe, E.W. Peterson, and K.H. Cooper. Serum electrolyte changes after marathon running. *Journal of Applied Physiology* 29:449–451, 1970.
89. Sherman, W.M. and D.R. Lamb. Nutrition and prolonged exercise. In: D.R. Lamb and R. Murray, (eds.). *Perspectives in Exercise Science and Sports Medicine Vol. I. Prolonged Exercise*. Indianapolis: Benchmark Press. 213–280, 1988.
90. Shils, M.E. Magnesium. In: M.E. Shils and V.R. Young, (eds.). *Modern Nutrition in Health and Disease*. Philadelphia:Lea & Febiger. 159–192, 1988.
91. Sjolin, S. Anemia in adolescence. *Nutrition Reviews* 39:96–98, 1981.
92. Smith, N.J. Excessive weight loss and food aversion in athletes simulating anorexia nervosa. *Pediatrics* 66:139–142, 1980.
93. Smith, Jr., J.C., E.R. Morris, and R. Ellis. Zinc requirements, bioavailabilities and recommended dietary allowances. In: A.S. Prasad, A.O. Cavar, G.J. Brewer, and P.J. Aggett, (eds.). *Zinc Deficiency in Human Subjects*. New York:Liss. 147–168, 1983.
94. Stendig-Lindberg, G., Y. Shapiro, Y. Epstein, E. Galun, E. Schonberger, E. Graff, and W.E.C. Wacker. Changes in serum magnesium concentration after strenuous exercise. *Journal of the American College of Nutrition* 6:35–40, 1987.
95. Sutton, J.R. and R.M. Brock, (eds.). *Sports Medicine for the Mature Athlete*. Indianapolis: Benchmark Press, 1987.
96. Tanner, J.M. *Foetus into Man*. Cambridge:Harvard University Press. 6–23, 1978.
97. Tarnopolsky, M.A., J.D. MacDougall, and S.A. Atkinson. Influence of protein intake and training status on nitrogen balance and lean mass. *Journal of Applied Physiology* 64:187–193, 1988.
98. Tesch, P.A., E.B. Colliander, and P. Kaiser. Muscle metabolism during intense, heavy resistance exercise. *European Journal of Applied Physiology* 55:362–366, 1986.
99. Tipton, C.M. Consequences of rapid weight loss. In: W.L. Haskell, J. Scala, and J. Whittam, (eds.). *Nutrition and Athletic Performance*. Palo Alto:Bull Publishing. 176–197, 1982.
100. Torun, B., N.S. Scrimshaw, and V.R. Young. Effect of isometric exercises on body potassium and dietary protein requirements of young men. *American Journal of Clinical Nutrition* 30:1983–1993, 1977.
101. Underwood, E.J. *Trace Elements in Human and Animal Nutrition*. New York:Academic Press. 196–242, 1977.
102. U.S. Food & Nutrition Board. *Recommended Dietary Allowances*. Washington:National Academy Press, 1980.
103. Von Stocke, K., K.W. Kron, G. Schardt, H.H. Ertel, and R. Schiller. Der einflub orater magnesiumzufuhr auf die leist ungsfahigkeit des menschlichen organismus unter standardisierter ergometrischer bel astung. *Deutsche Zeitschrift Fur Sportmedizin* 1:22–27, 1979.
104. Wacker, W.E.C. and A.F. Parisi. Magnesium metabolism. *New England Journal of Medicine* 278:658–663, 1968.
105. Weiser, M.M. Calcium. In: N.W. Solomons and I.H. Rosenburg, (eds.). *Absorption and Malabsorption of Mineral Nutrients*. New York:A.R. Liss. 15–68, 1984.
106. Wheeler, G.D., S. Wall, A.N. Belcastro, and D.C. Cumming. Reduced serum testosterone and prolactin levels in male distance runners. *Journal of the American Medical Association* 252:514–516, 1984.
107. Widdowson, E.M. and J.W.T. Dickerson. Chemical composition of the body. In: C.L. Comar and F. Bronner, (eds.). *Mineral Metabolism: An Advanced Treatise, Volume 2, Part A, The Elements*. New York:Academic Press. 2–247, 1964.
108. Wilkinson, R. Absorption of calcium, phosphorus and magnesium. In: B.E.C. Nordin, (ed.). *Calcium, Phosphate and Magnesium Metabolism*. New York:Livingstone. 36–112, 1976.
109. Williams, M.H. *Nutritional Aspects of Human Physical and Athletic Performance*. Springfield: C.C. Thomas. 219–271, 1985.
110. Yamada, T., M. Tohori, T. Ashida, N. Kajiwara, and H. Yoshimura. Comparison of effects of vegetable protein diet and animal protein diet on the initiation of anemia during vig-

orous physical training (sports anemia) in dogs and rats. *Journal of Nutritional Science and Vitaminology* 33:129–149, 1987.
111. Yoshimura, H., T. Inoue, T. Yamada, and K. Shivaki. Anemia during hard physical training (sports anemia) and its causal mechanism with special reference to protein nutrition. *World Review of Nutrition and Dietetics* 35:1–86, 1980.
112. Zemel, M.B. and H.M. Linkswiler. Calcium metabolism in the young adult male as affected by level and form of phosphorus intake and level of calcium intake. *Journal of Nutrition* 111:315–324, 1981.

DISCUSSION

CLARKSON: We are seeing dancers younger and younger, sometimes as young as 8 and 9 years old, that are adopting fad diets. One of the similarities between dancers and wrestlers is they diet for short periods of time. Usually, adolescent dancers, especially dancers who are in preprofessional companies, have maybe two or three performances a year. The month before each performance, they severely restrict diet. Thus, three times per year these dancers will undergo three to four weeks of very large restrictions in caloric intake, and then will return to normal diets. What do you think are the consequences of these short bouts of acute caloric restriction?

LEMON: I would suspect that a short-term energy restriction would have less effect than a more chronic diet because of "catch up" phenomena. However, I'm not aware of any systematic study on humans which answers this question. This is an area that requires further work.

BLAIR: I know Kelly Brownell's group has data on wrestlers which suggest that the weight cycling seems to permanently drive down the basal metabolic rate (BMR). He has measured high school wrestlers in summer when they are not competing but are at the wrestling camp at the University of Iowa, all eating the same diet, sleeping in the same dormitory, etc. They have classified these young men into those who have to severely restrict calories to make weight and those who don't. The dieters have BMRs that are much, much lower. Brownell's hypothesis is that weight cycling is harmful in the long term, and his data on lab animals support that contention.

LEMON: That's interesting because BMR, of course, is very closely related to lean body mass, and if these wrestlers are decreasing their BMR, I wonder what is happening to their lean body mass.

HORTON: Kelly's data on animals suggest that if you put an animal on a low calorie diet, feed it again, let it regain the weight, and then put it on a low calorie diet a second time, the animal doesn't lose weight at the same rate as the first time. Brownell's group is postulating that this is associated with some permanent carryover effect on resting metabolic rate or on other factors that affect the fat homeostasis. They are trying to look at that in relationship to cyclic dieting in the human situation, but I don't think they've tied it in with physical activity yet.

BLAIR: Kelly's hypothesis is that very vigorous activity may cause some of the same adaptations as caloric restriction, but I don't think he really has much data on that. Obviously these wrestlers are getting a lot of activity as well as manipulating the diet. But Ed Horton is quite right: Most of the data are on caloric restriction. There are now some very limited epidemiologic data that really show increased mortality risk in populations of men who cycled their weights up and down. There is little data on physical activity in those populations, but presumably when middle-aged men are gaining and losing weight, they are probably doing it on the basis of dietary manipulation. And it seems to be harmful.

LEMON: Gail Butterfield has some data indicating very low energy intakes in female athletes who are maintaining body weight. She believes there is some sort of activity adapatation that makes this possible. Perhaps this is due to changes in lean mass and BMR.

DAVIS: Without exercise, much of the weight loss during dieting is actually lean tissue. But if you exercise while dieting, there is some evidence that suggests you can prevent most of that loss of lean body mass and lose mostly fat.

CLARKSON: One of the most noticeable differences between ballet dancers and the general public is very thin upper arms in the dancers; this probably indicates a very small muscle mass in the body areas that aren't being used for the activity.

LEMON: I am not surprised. A similar phenomenon is apparent in long distance runners, and we know that animals exercising on an energy deficient diet can experience atrophy in inactive muscles at the same time that hypertrophy is occurring in active muscles.

BLIMKIE: Peter, you implied that at very high sweat rates children might lose about 25 percent of their daily intake of magnesium and calcium. Now those data obviously weren't collected on children, and, given the reduced sweat rate in children, I'm wondering if you just might be overplaying that potential nutrient loss or overemphasizing that particular issue for the adolescent group.

LEMON: Based on the data of Sato et al. reviewed by Oded Bar-Or earlier today you may be correct for children under approximately 12 years of age. However, as you know, these types of measures (nutrient losses) are not well-documented in adults or children. For those who have at least reached puberty, I suspect the nutrient losses would be similar to adults. Finally, I would like to clarify one point. The loss is not 25 percent of the daily intake but 25 percent of what is absorbed, which of course is considerably less than their actual intake. One reason that RDA is so high is because one absorbs a lot less than what is consumed.

BLIMKIE: Pete, you discussed a study of weightlifters who were taking in double the recommended intake of protein but yet were still in negative nitrogen balance. The Tarnapolsky study used body builders, and this Polish group was weightlifters; you might want to comment about whether or not there is anything different in the types of training in those two groups that would influence the nutrient intake.

LEMON: The training is significantly different for body builders and weightlifters. Generally, weightlifters employ heavier weights and fewer repetitions than body builders. In the Tarnapolsky et al. study, I'm not sure exactly what the training involved, but in the Polish study, the athletes were not peaking for competition. It was regular training, and there was quite a bit of variability in terms of the actual exercise among the individuals. That might have accounted, at least in part, for the large between-subject variability, some subjects being in negative nitrogen balance, and some positive. The type of training for the two studies was, I suspect, quite a bit different.

BALDWIN: We have found that if you put rats into a caloric deficit down to about 25 to 30 percent of their normal daily caloric intake, this has a significant impact on the type of isomyosin that is expressed in the heart; it shifts to an isoform that has a low ATPase, and it looks as though it's a mechanism to conserve energy. However, if the calorie-restricted animal consumes primarily carbohydrates, this down-regulation of isomyosin can be changed or repressed. This raises an interesting question in terms of nutrition, caloric deficits, and how the body's muscles or cardiovascular system will attempt to adjust things to maintain a positive energy balance. We can apply this to the dancer, possibly, or to the wrestler, and I think more research should look to biochemical mechanisms that are involved in the nutritional and metabolic interactions.

We have only made observations to date on the heart, but we are beginning to examine the skeletal muscles as well. One of the things that is known is that there appears to be a signal to gene expression in muscle that involves thyroid hormones and a carbohydrate signal. We think that the T3 receptors in the muscle cell may be able to be modified in their T3 sensitivity by carbohydrate. If this has any applicability to humans, caloric restriction may change the whole thyroid axis of the individual.

SUTTON: With severe caloric restriction, the potential for hepatic glycogen depletion is quite real, and, therefore, individuals would be predisposed to develop frank hypoglycemia during exercise, perhaps even relatively short periods of exercise. Although I don't know if that has been frequently documented, it certainly has been seen in people who have undergone short athletic events in which they have actually developed frank hypoglycemia with blood glucose between 20 and 30 milligrams per 100 milliliters. So I don't see why it may not also be likely to occur with wrestling or ballet for that matter.

HORTON: Frank hypoglycemia has not been seen in ballerinas. It certainly can occur in people with anorexia nervosa if they are really starved for a long period of time. Because there is a high incidence of anorexia in ballerinas, I'm sure hypoglycemia would occur.

SUTTON: It has certainly been documented in fun runs.

HORTON: Pete, that's a very dramatic urinary loss of chromium you have described with acute exercise, but I don't know of any study that has shown chromium deficiency in highly trained athletes. Are you aware of any data on chromium deficiency as a complication of people who train at a high level?

LEMON: No, certainly not any deficiency symptoms. What has been seen with training is a reduction in chromium content or concentration in the blood, and that may be a beginning of deficiency that results in a reduced loss of chromium in the urine. Whether that's a conservation mechanism or a loss of stores in the body showing up as a decreased urinary chromium excretion, I'm not sure. Chromium, as you may know, is a very difficult substance to measure. As a result, few studies on chromium have been completed.

MORGAN: Several years ago, we did a study with wrestlers who lost 5% of their weight during five days. We monitored anxiety daily, and their anxiety increased significantly at the outset, as we had hypothesized. But much to our surprise, as the semistarvation and dehydration continued, the wrestlers had a significant decrease in anxiety. Now once they have that decrease in anxiety, they go back to their baseline level. Thus, the psychometric effect of periodic weight cycling like this seems to be one of a transitory nature. So there are effects that take place during the rapid weight loss, but they don't seem to persist.

If you manipulate carbohydrate levels, you can alter mood states, and to the extent that mood state impacts on performance, you would expect performance effects to occur. The question I have is whether or not there has been any attention paid to dietary protein/fat ratios. The carbohydrate diet has a monoamine effect, in particular tryptophan, at a central level, but the effect only occurs when the diet is carbohydrate-rich and protein-poor or protein-free. So the key isn't the carbohydrate at all with respect to the mood state alterations that occur; it has to do with the ratio of fat to protein in the remainder of the diet. Has any of these studies of carbohydrate manipulation that you have referred to described how the ratio of fat to protein was handled?

LEMON: Very few. In general, the carbohydrate intake in the high concentration situation is 60–70% carbohydrate. The remainder is made up of fat and protein, but the mixture varies in different studies.

10

Exercise and Fitness in Childhood: Implications for a Lifetime of Health

STEVEN N. BLAIR, P.E.D.

DEBRA G. CLARK

KIRK J. CURETON, PH.D.

KENNETH E. POWELL, M.D.

INTRODUCTION

Most scientists and laypersons accept the notion that regular exercise is a good health habit. This view is supported by numerous recent studies, but detailed knowledge about many aspects of the issue is still lacking. The appropriate and necessary amount of exercise for health, especially in children and youth, is not well-documented. A conceptual model illustrating several potentially important relationships between childhood exercise and lifetime health status is presented in Figure 10-1.

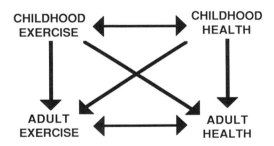

FIGURE 10-1. *Conceptual model of how childhood exercise habits may affect health throughout life. Arrows indicate possible relationships.*

The association between childhood exercise and childhood health is bi-directional. Serious health problems in childhood may well affect exercise participation. Several other chapters in this volume present evidence on the impact of exercise on the treatment and management of certain diseases in children and youth. However, exercise is unlikely to have a significant impact on prevention of the major causes of morbidity and mortality in the adolescent population in the United States. Blum (1987) notes that 77% of adolescent deaths in the United States are caused by accidents, suicide, and homicide. There is little reason to believe that sedentary living habits could increase the risk of death due to these causes; in fact, exercise is probably a causal factor in some of the accidental deaths. Regular exercise is also unlikely to reduce the impact of the major morbidities of adolescence: unwanted pregnancy, substance abuse, physical/sexual abuse, and concern over stress and nervousness (Blum, 1987).

Furthermore, childhood exercise habits are probably not associated with adult health status. Paffenbarger et al. (1986) found no benefit in college sports participation on mortality later in life. Athletic participation in youth is not associated with coronary risk factor status in middle age in Cooper Clinic patients (Brill et al., 1988). Thus, adult exercise has a much greater beneficial effect on adult health status than does childhood exercise. However, the possible association of childhood exercise to adult exercise habits is an issue that deserves study. It seems reasonable to assume that children who are quite physically active might be more likely to maintain their habits into adulthood; if this is true, childhood exercise might have a strong indirect impact on adult health. Unfortunately, there is little evidence to support this hypothesis. Three recent papers examined this issue and reported equivocal results (Dishman, 1988;

Powell & Dysinger, 1987; Brill et al., 1988). More research is needed on this important topic.

There is considerable research on adult exercise and adult health, and we review this evidence later in this chapter. We use the adult studies to estimate how much exercise may be appropriate for children. This approach is imperfect, but we do not have (and probably never will have) exercise and health data on a sizable cohort of children followed into middle age and beyond. Thus, it is necessary to determine how much exercise is required for health maintenance in adults and to then extrapolate backwards to estimate appropriate exercise levels for children and youth.

The primary focus of this paper is on appropriate exercise for children and youth, but very little data exist directly related to the issue (Simons-Morton et al., 1987). There is a considerable amount of data on physical fitness in young people, but few studies have assessed exercise behavior. This is partly due to the difficulty in assessment of exercise habits, especially in children and youth. Fitness testing is well established in the schools and is administratively simpler and is less time consuming than exercise behavior assessment. Therefore, we will discuss appropriate exercise for children and youth, but will also relate the findings to physical fitness.

It is widely believed that children and youth in the United States are sedentary and physically unfit. Frequent press releases with the message that our children and youth are unfit reinforce this belief. Physical educators and other professionals have endorsed the concept of a crisis in the physical fitness in young people (AAHPERD, 1988). A sample of recent comments is illustrative: "Children in the United States are under-exercised" (Reiff et al., 1986); "some 29,000,000 adolescents are in poor physical condition" (Former HEW Secretary J. Califano, quoted in Reiff et al., 1986); "regional studies and clinical evidence strongly indicate the seriously low levels of fitness in many school-aged populations" (Hayes, 1984); and "there is still a low level of performance in important components of physical fitness by millions of our youth" (Reiff et al., 1986).

An alternative perspective, and one that we believe is more likely to be correct, is that children in the United States are naturally physically active and physically fit. Casual observation suggests that children and youth are by far the most physically active segment of the United States population, as anyone who ever tried to keep up with a young child can confirm (Simons-Morton et al., 1987). Aerobic power measurements show that children and youth have considerably higher scores than adults. (Tuxworth, 1988).

How did the concept of unfit children and youth arise? Many believe it resulted from studies by Kraus and Hirshland (1954) in which children in the United States were much more likely to fail a physical fitness test than European children. Widespread concern over these results led President Eisenhower to create the President's Council on Youth Fitness (the name was later changed to the President's Council on Physical Fitness and Sports—PCPFS). The test administered by Kraus and associates was scored pass or fail for each item; and if one item was failed, the student failed the test. A majority of failures for children and youth in the United States was on a flexibility item. Thus, our children were labeled unfit because many could not touch their toes. Surprisingly, the major national physical fitness test batteries used by the PCPFS and the American Alliance for Health, Physical Education, Recreation, and Dance (AAHPERD) for the next 25 years did not include a flexibility item.

Another problem has been lack of a clear definition of physical fitness. The most widely used tests of physical fitness from 1950 to 1979 primarily measured motor fitness or, as some have termed it, athletic fitness (Pate, 1983a; Blair et al., 1983). Leg power (50-yd dash, standing long jump, shuttle run, etc.) was the primary performance characteristic assessed by these tests. The first AAHPERD test also included a softball throw for distance. The definition of physical fitness began to change from a motor fitness orientation to more of a health-related perspective in the late 70s (Pate, 1983a; Blair et al., 1983; Committee on Sports Medicine, 1987). Thus, early decisions about the fitness of children and youth were actually based on results from tests of motor fitness and not on health or capacity for activities of daily living.

Few questioned the conclusion from the mid-1950s that U.S. children were unfit, although there is little evidence that careful evaluation of test results was done. Most seemed willing to accept the unfit label simply because of poorer test results than for the European children. The question of how much fitness might be enough was not addressed; hence, the conclusion was based only on a competitive basis. The issue was not really whether our children were fit, but that they might be less fit than the children of other countries. A cynical perspective holds that those with a vested interest (physical educators, PCPFS, etc.) benefit from increased concern about physical fitness. Therefore, they are interested in maintaining a "crisis" state of concern about lack of fitness.

AAHPERD and PCPFS (jointly or separately) conducted physical fitness surveys on representative samples of schoolchildren in 1958, 1965, 1975, and 1985. The AAHPERD Youth Fitness Test was used in the first three surveys, whereas PCPFS developed its own battery for 1985 (although many of the same items from previous surveys were used). The national scores showed significant improvement from 1958 to 1965. Professionals were enthusiastic about these improvements and believed the physical fitness of the nation's children and youth was improving. A more realistic interpretation is that school children were learning how to take the test, due to repeated exposure from 1958 to 1965. True improvement on the test items was unlikely because the test battery at that time primarily measured leg power (standing long jump, 50-yd dash, shuttle run, and 600-yd run). Power is mainly determined by genetic factors, so marked improvement in test scores on power items is not likely to result from physical training.

Performance on the physical fitness test has essentially been unchanged in the 1965, 1975, and 1985 surveys. This has been interpreted by professionals as further evidence for a youth fitness crisis (Hayes, 1984; Reiff et al., 1986). There has been an outcry about the declining status of physical education in the schools (Hayes, 1984; AAHPERD, 1988). If physical education affects students' physical fitness scores, and if there has been progressively less emphasis on physical education across the nation, national physical fitness norms should have declined over the past 20 years.

In summary, there has been widespread concern over the past 30 years about apparently low physical fitness in children and youth in the United States. This concern has been based on comparison to scores of European children and on an emotional reaction. There have been few systematic efforts to define and establish acceptable or appropriate evaluation standards for exercise and physical fitness. In this paper we attempt to describe and justify acceptable standards for physical fitness and exercise. Our orientation is primarily toward health, although performance of everyday tasks is also considered. Physical fitness tests have historically placed considerable emphasis on fitness components such as speed and power, which are related to success in sports. We will not include speed and power items in this discussion.

I. HEALTH BENEFITS OF PHYSICAL ACTIVITY

Sedentary living habits are clearly associated with an increased risk of chronic disease (Paffenbarger et al., 1986; Leon et al., 1987; Powell et al., 1987). The major impact of physical activity on health is probably an activity-induced decreased risk of cardiovascular disease. Since cardiovascular disease and other chronic diseases are quite rare in children, the studies reviewed here are in adults.

A. Physical Activity and Mortality

Paffenbarger et al. (1986) followed 16,936 Harvard alumni for 12 to 16 y. Physical activity habits were assessed at baseline by questionnaire. The Harvard Study found that 2,000 kcal/week expended in physical activity was associated with a decreased risk of disease and an increased longevity. Table 10-1 shows age-adjusted death rates and relative risks for various levels of physical activity. Energy expenditure is also presented as $kJ \cdot kg^{-1} \cdot d^{-1}$. This measure was calculated from the kilocalorie values by assuming an average weight of 75 kg for the participants. The recalculated measure of energy expenditure is to facilitate comparison to other studies and to apply to children. The $kJ \cdot kg^{-1} \cdot d^{-1}$ score is a relative expression of energy expenditure that allows for comparison between groups with discrepant body mass, such as adults and children. A notable result in Table 10-1 is the major reduction in death rates associated with modest activity. Death rates for men in the second activity category (5.2 $kJ \cdot kg^{-1} \cdot d^{-1}$) were 20.2/10,000 (93.7–73.5) man-years (22%) lower than for the least active group, so health benefits may occur at relatively low levels of physical activity. It is clear from Paffenbarger et al. that all-cause death rates are significantly lower at energy expenditure levels of 12–13 $kJ \cdot kg^{-1} \cdot d^{-1}$.

British civil servants (n = 17,944) who engaged in vigorous exercise had coronary heart disease (CHD) death rates that were approximately 40% as high as for their peers who reported no vigorous exercise (Morris et al., 1980). Vigorous exercise was defined as an energy expenditure of 31.5 $kJ \cdot min^{-1}$ in vigorous sports or heavy work. Energy expenditure at this rate for 30 min per day (a conservative estimate of the habits of the civil servants) results in a total expenditure of 11.8 $kJ \cdot kg^{-1} \cdot d^{-1}$, a value also associated with a considerably reduced risk of all-cause mortality in the Harvard alumni study.

Leon et al. (1987) reported higher all-cause, CHD, and sudden death rates in sedentary men compared with active men in the Multiple Risk Factor Intervention Trial (MRFIT). Men in this study were

TABLE 10-1. *Age-Adjusted All-Cause Death Rates by Energy Expenditure in 16,936 Harvard Alumni (from Paffenbarger et al., 1986).*

Physical Activity Index		Age-adjusted Death	
kcal · week^{-1}	$kJ \cdot kg^{-1} \cdot d^{-1}$ (mid-point)	Rates per 10,000 Man-years	Relative Risk of Death
<500	<3.6	93.7	1.00
500–999	5.2	73.5	0.78
1,000–1,499	8.8	68.2	0.73
1,500–1,999	12.3	59.3	0.63
2,000–2,499	15.8	57.7	0.62
2,500–2,999	19.3	48.5	0.52
3,000–3,499	22.9	42.7	0.46
≥3,500	≥24.7	58.4	0.62

all in the upper 15% (most in the upper 10%) of risk for CHD, based on serum cholesterol, cigarettes smoked, and diastolic blood pressure. The 12,138 men were followed for seven years for mortality. Physical activity was assessed by an extensive interview (Taylor et al., 1978). Energy expenditure in leisure-time physical activity was calculated from the interview data. Mean energy expenditure in $kJ \cdot kg^{-1} \cdot d^{-1}$ for tertiles was 3.6, 11.0, and 31.3 respectively. These categories correspond closely to the low, medium, and high groups in the Harvard alumni study (Table 10-1). Death rates by energy expenditure tertile in MRFIT men are shown in Table 10-2. Death rates in tertile two are significantly lower than tertile one for all analyses. There is no apparent further benefit associated with the higher levels of activity in tertile three.

In all three studies reviewed above, with different populations and different methods of assessing physical activity, it is remarkable that an energy expenditure of approximately 11 or 12 $kJ \cdot kg^{-1} \cdot d^{-1}$ is consistently associated with lower risk of all-cause and CHD mortality. Is this amount of eneregy expenditure an appropriate standard for health? In the following paragraphs additional perspectives on this issue are presented.

B. Energy Intake and Coronary Heart Disease

Under most conditions, energy expenditure and energy intake in humans are in relative balance. Thus, an alternative way of studying physical activity and health is to examine energy intake. People with higher intake are more physically active (Blair, Jacobs & Powell, 1985). CHD and diet were examined in three prospective studies in 16,349 men ages 45–64 y (Gordon et al., 1981). Baseline 24-h dietary recalls were obtained on men in the Framingham Study, the Honolulu Heart Study, and the Puerto Rico Heart Health Program. Incidence of CHD was ascertained for up to 6 y of follow-up. The main finding was an increased risk of CHD in men with lower energy intake. Results are shown in Table 10-3. The differences in $kJ \cdot kg^{-1} \cdot d^{-1}$ between men who developed CHD compared with those

TABLE 10-2. *Age-Adjusted Death Rates by Energy Expenditure Tertiles in 12,138 MRFIT Men (from Leon et al., 1987)*

Mean Energy Expenditure $(kJ \cdot kg^{-1} \cdot d^{-1})$	Coronary Heart Disease Death Rate per 1,000	Sudden Death Death Rate per 1,000	All-causes Death Rate per 1,000
3.6	24.6	15.6	47.7
11.0	15.4	9.8	33.7
31.3	15.8	10.1	39.5

TABLE 10-3. *Age-Adjusted Mean Energy Intakes in CHD Cases and Controls in Three Prospective Studies (from Gordon et al., 1981)*

	Framingham	Honolulu	Puerto Rico
Controls	143[a]	155	151
CHD Cases	130	143	139
Difference	13	12	12

[a]Values are energy intake in $kJ \cdot kg^{-1} \cdot d^{-1}$

who did not (12–13 $kJ \cdot kg^{-1} \cdot d^{-1}$) are comparable to the values for energy expenditure differences between active and sedentary groups in the studies reviewed in the previous section.

C. Other Studies of Energy Expenditure and Health

In this section we review some additional studies on the level of energy expenditure associated with health. These studies provide additional perspective on how reasonable the 12–13 $kJ \cdot kg^{-1} \cdot d^{-1}$ energy expenditure standard is in terms of health.

Health surveys in four California cities were done as part of community intervention studies (Sallis et al., 1985; Blair, Haskell et al., 1985). The measure of physical activity developed for these surveys include a 7 d physical activity recall that yielded an estimate of total daily energy expenditure. Other exercise questions were designed to identify habitually active individuals. These latter questions asked about regular physical activity during the past three months. People who reported walking, jogging, or running at least 10 miles per week (or the equivalent amount of swimming, cycling, racquet sports, or other strenuous sports) were classified as vigorous exercisers. Representative community samples were drawn, and 1,077 men and 1,206 women completed the survey. Men classified as vigorous exercisers (from another series of questions, vigorous exercise = 10 miles/week of running or its equivalent in other vigorous sports) expended 11.8 $kJ \cdot kg^{-1} \cdot d^{-1}$ more energy than their sedentary peers. The corresponding difference for active and sedentary women was 18.1 $kJ \cdot kg^{-1} \cdot d^{-1}$ (Blair, Haskell, et al., 1985).

A sample of 81 sedentary, middle-aged men was recruited, and the men were randomly assigned to exercise and control groups for a study on exercise and lipoproteins (Wood et al., 1983). After one year of training, the exercisers had generally favorable changes in their lipoprotein profiles. Physical activity was assessed by the same seven-day recall interview as for the community study described above. The exercisers increased average energy expenditure by 11.8 $kJ \cdot kg^{-1} \cdot d^{-1}$ (Blair, Haskell et al., 1985).

Fifty-six sedentary young men (21–37 y) with mild hypertension (diastolic blood pressure: 90–104 mm Hg) were randomly assigned to exercise and control groups (Duncan et al., 1985). After 16 weeks of walk, jog, and run training, diastolic blood pressures declined 7.1 mm Hg in exercisers and increased 2.1 mm Hg in controls. By the end of the study, exercisers were expending approximately 12 $kJ \cdot kg^{-1} \cdot d^{-1}$ in supervised exercise.

Several studies on energy flux and health have been reviewed in this section. The papers include studies on physical activity and mortality, exercise training and CHD risk factors, energy intake and CHD, and community health surveys. The congruence of results is striking and strengthens the inference that increased energy expenditure is associated with health and health-related changes, and that 11–13 $kJ \cdot kg^{-1} \cdot d^{-1}$ is a reasonable standard, although Paffenbarger et al. (1986) (see Table 10-1) suggest that an even lower energy expenditure may have benefit. The energy expenditure of 11–13 $kJ \cdot kg^{-1} \cdot d^{-1}$ is consistent with the recommendations from a thorough review of physical activity and health by Haskell, Montoye, and Orenstein (1985). They conclude that 11.2–22.4 $kJ \cdot kg^{-1} \cdot d^{-1}$ expended in physical activity is associated with diverse health benefits. To reiterate, the data reviewed here are from studies in adults, but, until better data are forthcoming, the standards proposed here are reasonable to consider for children.

II. PHYSICAL FITNESS STANDARDS

Physical fitness tests have been administered to a large number of children and youth over the past 30 y. Reiff et al. (1986) estimated that the AAHPERD Youth Fitness Test was given to 65 million students from 1958 to 1975. Interpretation of individual test results typically has been by comparison to normative data. This approach has led to statements such as "55 percent of all girls tested could not hold their chin over a raised bar for more than 10 s" and "approximately 50 percent of girls ages 6–17 and 30 percent of boys ages 6–12 could not run a mile in less than 10 min" (President's Council on Physical Fitness and Sports, 1987). It is difficult to evaluate such statements. A primary question that can be raised is, How many seconds are appropriate for girls to hold their chins above a raised bar, and how fast should children of different ages run a mile? It seems reasonable to establish acceptable standards for fitness tests so teachers, students, and parents can make a more meaningful evaluation of test performance.

One of the first attempts to establish physical fitness test standards in the United States was for the South Carolina Physical Fitness Test (Pate, 1983b). This test includes a distance run, sit-ups, sit and reach, and skinfold measurements. Acceptable standards for each sex by various ages for children, youth, and adults are given in Table 10-4. These standards were established by expert opinion and are intended to represent fitness standards that are consistent with good health. Standards for adults were developed also.

The Governor's Commission on Physical Fitness in Texas created a Youth Fitness Task Force to develop a health fitness program. After extensive discussion and a pilot test of the program with approximately 20,000 students, the Fit Youth Today (FYT) program was released in 1986 (American Health and Fitness Foundation, 1988; Squires & Smith, 1986). This program was the first to include additional material on health and lifestyle factors and a specific conditioning protocol that is designed to prepare students for the fitness test. The FYT is a health-oriented test with specific items of: a 20-min steady jog, sit-ups, sit and reach, and skinfold measurements. FYT is probably the first fitness test to include no normative scales and present only acceptable fitness standards for each test item by grade level for boys and girls. Standards were established by expert consensus and are achievable by a high percentage of students. Examples of standards for students in grades 7–12 are: 20-min steady jog = 2.4 miles for boys and 2.2 miles for girls; sit-ups in 2 min = 40 for both boys and girls.

The first test in widespread use in the United States of America that uses a standards approach was developed by the Institute for Aerobics Research (IAR) (Meredith, 1987; Weber et al., 1986). FITNESSGRAM is a computer scored physical fitness test that has a health-related fitness focus. FITNESSGRAM has been in use since 1982, and was completely revised for the 1987–88 school year. The revised test utilizes age- and sex-specific acceptable health fitness standards to interpret test items. FITNESSGRAM standards are shown in Table 10-5 for girls and Table 10-6 for boys. These standards were established by an expert panel. There is very little empirical evidence on which to establish standards for the sit and reach, sit-ups, and upper body strength items. There is some evidence relating these fitness components to health and routine function, but there are inadequate data on which to create a standard. For these musculoskeletal fitness items, clinical opinion was the primary method for setting standards. More definitive methods are needed. There are more data available to establish standards for aerobic power and body composition. The methods of establishing standards for these items follow.

A. Standards for Aerobic Power (One-Mile Run)

Aerobic power is associated with several measures of health and clinical status in adults. Cross-sectional epidemiologic studies show

Table 10-4. Criterion Referenced Fitness Standards for the South Carolina Physical Fitness Test (Pate, 1983b)

Students

Age Groups (Years) Physical Fitness Components	9 — M F[a]	10 — M F	11 — M	11 — F	12 — M	12 — F	13 — M	13 — F	14 — M	14 — F	15 — M	15 — F	16 — M	16 — F
Mile run (s)	600	585	550	575	510	570	480	540	480	540	480	540	480	540
9 min run (yards)	1580	1620	1730	1650	1860	1670	1980	1760	1980	1760	1980	1760	1980	1760
Sit-ups (1 min)	25	28	32	30	34	30	35	30	38	32	40	33	40	34
Sit and Reach (cm)[b]	23	23	23		23		23		23		23		23	
Skinfolds (mm)[c]	25	25	28		29		30		34		34		34	

Adults

Age Groups (Years) Physical Fitness Components	20–29 — M	20–29 — F[a]	30–39 — M	30–39 — F	40–49 — M	40–49 — F	50–59 — M	50–59 — F
Mile run (s)	480	540	510	570	540	600	570	630
9 min run (yards)	1980	1760	1960	1670	1760	1580	1670	1500
Sit-ups (1 min)	49	34	36	30	33	27	30	24
Sit and Reach (cm)[b]	23				23			
Skinfolds (mm)[c]	34				34			

[a] M = males, F = females
[b] 23 cm is at the toes
[c] sum of triceps and abdominal skinfolds

TABLE 10-5. *Health-Referenced Standards for Girls, FITNESSGRAM*

| Age (Years) | One Mile Run/Walk[a] (min:s) | Body Composition | | Sit and Reach (in)[b] | Sit-ups (in 1 min) | Pull-ups | Flexed Arm Hang (s) |
		Percent Fat[a]	Body Mass Index[a]				
5	17:00	32%	20	10:0	20	1	5
6	16:00	32%	20	10.0	20	1	5
7	15:00	32%	20	10.0	20	1	5
8	14:00	32%	20	10.0	25	1	8
9	13:00	32%	20	10.0	25	1	8
10	12:00	32%	21	10.0	30	1	8
11	12:00	32%	21	10.0	30	1	8
12	12:00	32%	22	10.0	30	1	8
13	11:30	32%	23	10.0	30	1	12
14	10:30	32%	24	10.0	35	1	12
15	10:30	32%	24	10.0	35	1	12
16	10:30	32%	24	10.0	35	1	12
16+	10:30	32%	25	10.0	35	1	12

[a]Lower scores indicate better performance
[b]10 inches is at the toes

TABLE 10-6. *Health-Referenced Standards for Boys, FITNESSGRAM*

| Age (Years) | One Mile Run/Walk[a] (min:s) | Body Composition | | Sit and Reach (in)[b] | Sit-ups (in 1 min) | Pull-ups | Flexed Arm Hang (s) |
		Percent Fat[a]	Body Mass Index[a]				
5	16:00	25%	20	10:0	20	1	5
6	15:00	25%	20	10.0	20	1	5
7	14:00	25%	20	10.0	20	1	5
8	13:00	25%	20	10.0	25	1	10
9	12:00	25%	20	10.0	25	1	10
10	11:00	25%	21	10.0	30	1	10
11	11:00	25%	21	10.0	30	1	10
12	10:00	25%	22	10.0	35	1	10
13	9:30	25%	23	10.0	35	2	10
14	8:30	25%	24	10.0	40	3	15
15	8:30	25%	24	10.0	40	5	25
16	8:30	25%	25	10.0	40	5	25
16+	8:30	25%	26	10.0	40	5	25

[a]Lower scores indicate better performance
[b]10 inches is at the toes

a more favorable coronary heart disease risk factor profile in more fit men (Cooper et al., 1976) and women (Gibbons et al., 1983). There is a 50% increased risk of physician-diagnosed hypertension in low fit men and women (Blair et al., 1984). Aerobic power is inversely associated with myocardial infarction (Peters et al., 1983), and all-cause mortality in women (Clark et al., 1988) and men (Kohl & Blair, 1988). Randomized clinical trials of exercise training sufficient to improve aerobic power show improved lipoprotein profiles (Wood et al., 1983) and lower blood pressures (Duncan et al., 1985) in the exercise group. It is difficult to select a precise health standard for aerobic power because there are different endpoints, populations, and assessment methods in the various studies. Twenty years ago Cooper recommended a $\dot{V}O_2$max of 42 mL $\cdot$ kg^{-1} $\cdot$ min^{-1} for young men and 35 mL $\cdot$ kg^{-1} $\cdot$ min^{-1} for young women as a health standard. Research reviewed above confirms that these standards are associated with better health and clinical status. Some of the studies suggest that lower levels of aerobic power are beneficial, but a conservative view is that these standards are reasonable and perhaps can be lowered when additional studies are completed.

Aerobic power standards for FITNESSGRAM are based on the assumption that 42 mL $\cdot$ kg^{-1} $\cdot$ min^{-1} for young men and 35 mL $\cdot$ kg^{-1} $\cdot$ min^{-1} for young women are reasonable $\dot{V}O_2$max standards. These $\dot{V}O_2$max standards are approximately one standard deviation below the mean for college age students. The process of converting these standards to distance-run times for boys and girls of different ages is described in the following paragraphs. A more complete description of the methods is available (Cureton, in review).

The same criterion for aerobic power (42 mL $\cdot$ kg^{-1} $\cdot$ min^{-1}) was used for boys of all ages, because mean values for aerobic power expressed relative to body weight stay essentially constant during childhood and adolescence (Krahenbuhl et al., 1985). The criterion values for girls were adjusted, however, to take into account the effect of the increase in sex-specific essential fat on aerobic power that occurs in girls following puberty. The adjusted criterion values are shown in Table 10-7. The criterion value was increased by one

TABLE 10-7. *FITNESSGRAM Criterion Values for Aerobic Power*

Age (Years)	$\dot{V}O_2$max (mL $\cdot$ kg^{-1} $\cdot$ min^{-1})	
	Boys	Girls
5	42	40
6	42	40
7	42	40
8	42	40
9	42	40
10	42	39
11	42	38
12	42	37
13	42	36
14	42	35
15	42	35
16	42	35
17	42	35

$mL \cdot kg^{-1} \cdot min^{-1}$ for each one year decrease in age from 14 to 9 y, the time during which most of the change in the body fatness occurs in young girls (Lohman, 1986). The 5 $mL \cdot kg^{-1} \cdot min^{-1}$ higher value for $\dot{V}O_2$max for the younger girls reflects the effect of 10% less body fatness (Cureton et al., 1978). A criterion of 40 $mL \cdot kg^{-1} \cdot min^{-1}$ was used for girls 5–9 y.

The mile run times estimated to correspond to the criterion values for aerobic power were calculated based on the oxygen requirement of running at different speeds in children and on the assumed percentage of aerobic power utilized during a mile run. An example of the calculation for 9- and 15-year-old boys is shown in Table 10–8.

First, the criterion $\dot{V}O_2$max was multiplied by the average percentage of $\dot{V}O_2$max assumed to be maintained during the run. The product is an estimate of the average $\dot{V}O_2$ ($mL \cdot kg^{-1} \cdot min^{-1}$) that could be maintained during the run, if the individual had a $\dot{V}O_2$max equal to the criterion. The assumed values for % $\dot{V}O_2$max utilized were based on data for adults with age-related adjustments to take into account hypothesized developmental changes. It was assumed that the average $\dot{V}O_2$ during the run would correspond to 100% of $\dot{V}O_2$max in boys and girls 14 to 17 y, 90–98% in children 10 to 13 y, and 80–85% in children 5 to 9 y. Data on adults suggests that during steady-state running, a $\dot{V}O_2$ equal to 80–100% $\dot{V}O_2$max can be maintained for an event that lasts from 5 to 18 min (Astrand & Rodahl, 1970, p. 292; Londeree, 1986). The percentage increases with endurance training. Higher percentages were used for older than younger children because 1) the average duration of the run is less for older children, and the % $\dot{V}O_2$max that can be maintained increases as the duration of a maximal effort decreases, and 2) younger children were assumed to be less willing to tolerate discomfort and exert themselves. These assumptions probably are inaccurate; however, no data are available on the % $\dot{V}O_2$max utilized by children and adolescents of different ages during a mile run. This information is needed and is the weak link in the estimations.

TABLE 10-8. *Derivation of FITNESSGRAM Criterion-Referenced Mile Run Standards for 9- and 15-Year-Old Boys*

Variable	Age 9 Years	Age 15 Years
Criterion $\dot{V}O_2$max ($mL \cdot kg^{-1} \cdot min^{-1}$)	42	42
% $\dot{V}O_2$max Utilized	85	100
Average Run $\dot{V}O_2$ ($mL \cdot kg^{-1} \cdot min^{-1}$)	36	42
Average Run Speed ($km \cdot h^{-1}$)	8.0	10.8
Mile Run Time (min)	12.1	8.7
Mile Run Criterion Standard (min:s)	12:00	8:30

The second step in calculating mile run time criterion scores was to estimate the average run speed needed to elicit the average run $\dot{V}O_2$ calculated above by using Astrand's (1952) graphical data on the oxygen uptake during running at various speeds for children of different ages. The oxygen uptake during running at a given submaximal speed decreased progressively with age from 5 to 16 y. Therefore, the speed needed to elicit a given submaximal $\dot{V}O_2$ increases with age. Then, this speed was converted to a mile run time. The criterion-referenced mile run standards were based on these calculated times. The standards adopted for some ages differed from the calculated time to avoid changes in time of more than 1 min for adjacent ages. This "smoothing" was to avoid the standard becoming dramatically higher after the child has a birthday. The calculated times and standards adopted are shown in Table 10-9.

We view the standards as tentative and expect they will change with new research or improved logic underlying the calculations. Until improvements are made, however, we believe that these are reasonable standards for aerobic power in children and youth. These standards are consistent with fitness levels that are associated with health in adults, and allow for special physiological and growth characteristics of children and youth. These standards do not represent high levels of distance running achievement. Indeed, the proportion of students meeting or exceeding the standards is high, as shown later in this chapter.

B. Standards for Body Composition

Obesity is well-established as a risk factor for several chronic diseases in adults (Bjorntorp, 1987). Overweight children also ben-

TABLE 10-9. *FITNESSGRAM Mile Run Health-Fitness Standards*

Age (Years)	Boys		Girls	
	Calculated Time (min)	Standard (min:s)	Calculated Time (min)	Standard (min:s)
5	16.1	16:00	17.6	17:00
6	16.1	15:00	17.6	16:00
7	12.1	14:00	12.9	15:00
8	12.1	13:00	12.9	14:00
9	12.1	12:00	12.9	13:00
10	11.0	11:00	11.5	12:00
11	11.0	11:00	11.8	12:00
12	10.0	10:00	11.8	12:00
13	9.7	9:30	11.6	11:30
14	8.7	8:30	10.4	10:30
15	8.7	8:30	10.4	10:30
16	8.7	8:30	10.3	10:30
17	8.7	8:30	10.3	10:30

efit from achieving more normal body composition (Ward & Bar-Or, 1986). Establishment of a health standard for body composition in children and youth is difficult. FITNESSGRAM standards for girls and boys are shown in Tables 10-5 and 10-6. The standards were selected to identify children and youth with more than 25% fat for boys and 32 percent fat for girls. These values are conservative and may not represent the ideal, but reflect the % fat levels that correspond in adults to an increase in mortality (Bray, 1987). Some children who meet the acceptable standards might become obese later in life and could benefit from some weight loss. We believe that programs should be established to identify children who do not meet the body composition standard; these children should be monitored for possible follow-up and intervention.

Percent body fat can be estimated from skinfold measurements at the triceps and lateral calf (Lohman et al., 1988). Charts and standards have been established for children 6 to 17 y of age to help professionals assess and evaluate body fatness (Lohman, 1988). For teachers who elect not to do skinfold measurements, body composition can be estimated by the body mass index (BMI) (weight (kg)/height (m^2)). However, because the BMI values correlate with various measures of frame size and lean body mass almost as well as they correlate with body fatness (Dietz, 1987), we do not recommend BMI as optimal, especially for adolescents.

C.   How Fit are United States Children and Youth?

In this section we report analyses on the application of the FITNESSGRAM standards (Tables 10-5 and 10-6) to a population of 37,454 children and youth who were tested during the 1987–88 school year. The number and percent of children who met the standards are shown in Tables 10-10 and 10-11. In general, the percent meeting the standards is higher in younger children than in older children. Boys are somewhat more successful in meeting the standards than girls, especially in the older ages. To our knowledge, this is the first time that specific health fitness standards have been applied to test results from a relatively large sample of U.S. children and youth. These analyses suggest that most U.S. children and youth have acceptable physical fitness, assuming that the standards have some validity. The students are least successful in meeting the standard for upper body strength.

The FITNESSGRAM population is an opportunistic sample of students from the U.S. population. They are students in schools who elected to participate in FITNESSGRAM and who decided to use the Institute for Aerobics Research service bureau method of producing FITNESSGRAMS (Weber et al., 1986). The majority of

TABLE 10-10. *Girls Achieving Fitness Standards, FITNESSGRAM Project, 1987–88*

Age (Years)	Number in Group	One-Mile Run	Body Composition	Sit-and-Reach	Sit-Ups	Upper Body Strength
6	1,088	84[a][b]	96	93	63	49
7	1,381	86[b]	92	93	80	57
8	1,379	76[b]	90	91	72	44
9	1,517	72[b]	83	88	76	45
10	2,018	63[b]	83	84	64	46
11	2,050	68	77	85	67	46
12	2,272	73	83	90	72	45
13	1,665	64	80	89	73	30
14	1,799	49	83	89	53	25
15	1,549	49	81	91	53	27
16	852	51	79	83	62	32
17	596	51	77	89	62	32
6–17	18,179	63	84	89	67	40

[a]Values are percent of total in the age group meeting the standard
[b]Many of the younger girls did not take the one-mile run; missing values for this category range from 40–80% of the total.

TABLE 10-11. *Boys Achieving Fitness Standards, FITNESSGRAM Project, 1987–88.*

Age (Years)	Number in Group	One-Mile Run	Body Composition	Sit-and-Reach	Sit-Ups	Upper Body Strength
6	1,031	76[a][b]	96	98	64	53
7	1,394	76[b]	93	98	77	60
8	1,516	77[b]	90	98	73	54
9	1,561	77[b]	86	96	82	57
10	1,997	70	81	98	76	57
11	2,191	73	75	96	77	56
12	2,416	70	78	96	67	64
13	1,809	67	79	97	78	60
14	1,927	59	83	94	70	59
15	1,543	62	82	94	74	50
16	1,022	74	81	90	77	60
17	856	71	80	93	79	71
6–17	19,275	69	83	96	74	58

[a]Values are percent of total in the age group meeting the standard
[b]Many of the younger boys did not take the one-mile run; missing values for this category range from 30–85% of the total.

schools in FITNESSGRAM produce their own reports on microcomputers. Thus, the data presented here are from a sample of the total FITNESSGRAM population. Questions about the representativeness of this sample are appropriate. To address this issue, we compared the percent of students in FITNESSGRAM who qualified for the *I'm Fit* award (i.e., met the standards on at least four of the five test items) with the percent of students in the National Children and Youth Fitness Study I (NCYFS I) (Ross et al., 1985) who met the same standards. For boys, 54.5% of FITNESSGRAM students qualified for the award, compared with 63% of the NCYFS I boys. The percent of girls who qualified was 45.4% in FITNESSGRAM and 42.8% in NCYFS I. The FITNESSGRAM girls did slightly better and the boys somewhat poorer, compared with the NCYFS I group. Since NCYFS I was done in a representative sample of U.S. children and youth, the FITNESSGRAM group appears to be reasonably representative of the U.S. population and is not a highly select and extraordinarly fit group of students.

III. HOW ACTIVE ARE U.S. CHILDREN AND YOUTH?

The review of studies on physical activity and health in this chapter suggests that energy expenditure of $11-13$ kJ $\cdot$ kg^{-1} $\cdot$ d^{-1} in physical activity is associated with reduced risk of mortality in adults. If this level of energy expenditure is an appropriate health standard for adults, it may also be appropriate for children and youth. This conclusion requires certain assumptions that may or may not be true, but until better evidence or a more convincing rationale is available, the $11-13$ kJ $\cdot$ kg^{-1} $\cdot$ d^{-1} standard can be used.

To determine the proportion of U.S. children and youth meeting this standard, data from the NCYFS I (students 10–18 y old) were analyzed. In addition to physical fitness assessments, the students were interviewed about their physical activity habits (Ross et al., 1985). The students were asked about the frequency and duration of their participation in 86 different physical activities. Energy expenditure values for each activity were multiplied by the hours spent in the activity per day to obtain an estimate of energy expenditure in that activity in kJ $\cdot$ kg^{-1} $\cdot$ d^{-1}. These energy expenditure estimates were totaled across each child's 10 most frequent physical activities. Students were categorized as active if their energy expenditure score was ≥ 12.6 kJ $\cdot$ kg^{-1} $\cdot$ d^{-1}. There were 956 girls with complete activity data in the sample, and 843 (88%) were classified as active. Out of 1,307 boys, 1,222 (94%) were active. The proportions of students meeting the 12.6 kJ $\cdot$ kg^{-1} $\cdot$ d^{-1} standard and a higher standard of 16.8 kJ $\cdot$ kg^{-1} $\cdot$ d^{-1} are shown in Table 10-12. The percentage of boys meeting the physical activity standards is slightly greater than for girls, but the passing rates are quite high in all age and sex groups. More than 75% of these students exercise at a rate that is 33% higher (16.8 kJ $\cdot$ kg^{-1} $\cdot$ d^{-1}) than the health standard as developed from the studies on physical activity and health (12.6 kJ $\cdot$ kg^{-1} $\cdot$ d^{-1}).

A. Energy Expenditure and Mile Run Performance.

We examined the association between energy expenditure estimates and students' performance on the one-mile run. Mean times for the run for sedentary and active boys and girls in various groups

TABLE 10-12. *Proportion of Girls and Boys Meeting Selected Leisure-Time Energy Expenditure Standards by Age Groups, NCYFS I.*

Age Group (Years)	Girls			Boys		
	Number	% Meeting 12.6 KKD[a]	% Meeting 16.8 KKD	Number	% Meeting 12.6 KKD	% Meeting 16.8 KKD
10–12	235	86	77	343	94	86
13–15	444	90	83	544	95	87
16+	277	87	79	420	90	82

[a]KKD = $kJ \cdot kg^{-1} \cdot d^{-1}$

are shown in Table 10-13. There is little difference between sedentary and active students in the 10–12 y age group and for the oldest girls. The 13–15 y old girls and the two oldest age groups for boys show apparent differences between the activity groups on mile run times. It may be that the youngest children are incapable of providing accurate reports of their physical activity patterns, thus leading to invalid activity classifications. Lack of motivation to exert themselves or inability to pace themselves during the run would lead to unreliable (and also invalid) data for the younger children. These possible misclassifications make interpretation of the data in Table 10-13 uncertain. The data for the teenagers, however, does suggest a pattern, with three of the four groups showing relatively impressive (≥ 45 seconds) lower mile run times in the more active students. The congruence between the activity and fitness data in the older age groups provides some modest expectation of validity for the two measures.

TABLE 10-13. *Mile run performance (in minutes) in sedentary and active boys and girls by age groups, NCYFS I.*

Age Group (Years)	Girls			Boys		
	Number	Mean	SD	Number	Mean	SD
10–12						
Sedentary[a]	34	11.13	2.27	19	9.12	1.26
Active[b]	201	11.65	2.26	324	9.45	2.22
13–15						
Sedentary	43	11.61	2.11	25	9.17	3.05
Active	401	10.73	2.22	519	8.21	1.88
16+						
Sedentary	36	10.79	1.80	41	8.43	1.79
Active	241	10.81	2.00	379	7.68	1.93

[a]$< 12.6 \ kJ \cdot kg^{-1} \cdot d^{-1}$
[b]$\geq 12.6 \ kJ \cdot kg^{-1} \cdot d^{-1}$

SUMMARY

Regular physical activity seems to improve health and reduce the risk of cardiovascular disease and all-cause mortality in adults. A review of existing studies suggests that physical activity resulting in energy expenditure of at least 12.6 kJ·kg^{-1}·d^{-1} is a reasonable health standard for adults. Using this criterion, the overwhelming majority of children and youth in the United States are physically active. Children are, by far, the most physically active and fit group in the United States. Most children and youth meet physical fitness standards established by an expert panel for the FITNESSGRAM project. A majority of students who meet the physical activity standard of 12.6 kJ·kg^{-1}·d^{-1} also meet the fitness standard for the one-mile run in FITNESSGRAM.

These summary points suggest that the "youth fitness crisis" may be exaggerated. There are, however, some children who are sendentary and physically unfit. Comprehensive physical fitness education programs need to be widely available to identify sedentary and unfit students for special intervention efforts (Simons-Morton et al., 1987). The educational program is also important for all children to teach exercise and fitness concepts and to encourage the maintenance of lifelong physical activity.

ACKNOWLEDGEMENTS

We thank Harold W. Kohl for statistical advice, Drs. Tim Lohman and Patty Freedson for comments on an earlier draft, Dr. Marilu Meredith for the FITNESSGRAM data, and Kathryn A. Henry for typing the manuscript.

FITNESSGRAM is funded by a grant from the Campbell Soup Company.

BIBLIOGRAPHY

1. American Alliance for Health, Physical Education, Recreation and Dance. Congress passes P.E. resolution. *Journal of Physical Education, Recreation and Dance* 59:12, 1988.
2. American Health and Fitness Foundation. Fit Youth Today: An innovative program of health fitness for school age youth. *Texas Association for Health, Physical Education, Recreation, and Dance Journal* 56:41–50, 1988.
3. Åstrand, P.O. *Experimental Studies of Physical Working Capacity in Relation to Sex and Age.* Copenhagen:Ejnar Munksgaard, 1952.
4. Åstrand, P.O. and K. Rodahl. *Textbook of Work Physiology.* New York: McGraw-Hill, 1970.
5. Bjorntorp, P. Classification of obese patients and complications related to the distribution of surplus fat. *The American Journal of Clinical Nutrition* 45:1120–1125, 1987.
6. Blair, S.N., H.B. Falls, and R.R. Pate. A new physical fitness test. *The Physician and Sportsmedicine* 11:87–95, 1983.
7. Blair, S.N., N.N. Goodyear, L.W. Gibbons, and K.H. Cooper. Physical fitness and the incidence of hypertension in healthy, normontensive men and women. *Journal of the American Medical Association* 252:487–490, 1984.
8. Blair, S.N., W.L. Haskell, P. Ho, R.S. Paffenbarger, K.M. Vranizan, J.W. Farquhar, and

P.D. Wood. Assessment of habitual physical activity by seven-day recall in a community survey and controlled experiments. *American Journal of Epidemiology* 122:794–804, 1985.

9. Blair, S.N., D.R. Jacobs, Jr., and K.E. Powell. Relationships between exercise or physical activity and other health behaviors. *Public Health Reports* 100:172–180, 1985.

10. Blum, R. Contemporary threats to adolescent health in the United States. *Journal of the American Medical Association* 257:3390–3395, 1987.

11. Bray, G.A. Overweight is risking fate. *New York Academy of Science* 499:4–28, 1987.

12. Brill, P.A., H.E. Burkhalter, H.W. Kohl, N.N. Goodyear, and S.N. Blair, (in press). The impact of previous athleticism on exercise habits, physical fitness, and coronary heart disease risk factors in middle-aged men. *Research Quarterly for Exercise and Sport*.

13. Clark, D.G., H.W. Kohl, and S.N. Blair. Physical fitness and all-cause mortality in healthy women. *Medicine and Science in Sports and Exercise* 20:S7. (abstract), 1988.

14. Committee on Sports Medicine & Committee on School Health. Physical fitness and the schools. *Pediatrics* 80:449–450, 1987.

15. Cooper, K.H., M.L. Pollock, R.P. Martin, S.R. White, A.C. Linnerud, and A. Jackson. Physical fitness levels vs. selected coronary risk factors: a cross-sectional study. *Journal of the American Medical Association* 236:166–169, 1976.

16. Cureton, K.J. FITNESSGRAM criterion-referenced standards for the mile run test. In review.

17. Cureton, K.J., P.B. Sparling, B.W. Evans, S.M. Johnson, U.D. Kong, and J.W. Purvis. Effect of experimental alterations in excess weight on aerobic capacity and distance running performance. *Medicine and Science in Sports* 10:194–199, 1978.

18. Dietz, W.H. Childhood obesity. *New York Academy of Science* 499:47–54, 1987.

19. Dishman, R.K. Supervised and free-living physical activity: no differences in former athletes and non-athletes. *American Journal of Preventive Medicine* 4:153–160, 1988.

20. Duncan, J.J., J.E. Farr, S.J. Upton, R.D. Hagan, M.E. Oglesby, and S.N. Blair. The effects of aerobic exercise on plasma catecholamines and blood pressure in patients with mild essential hypertension. *Journal of the American Medical Association* 254:2609–2613, 1985.

21. Gibbons, L.W., S.N. Blair, K.H. Cooper, and M. Smith. Association between coronary heart disease risk factors and physical fitness in healthy adult women. *Circulation* 67:977–983, 1983.

22. Gordon, T., A. Kagan, M. Garcia-Palmieri, W.B. Kannel, W.J. Zukel, J. Tillotson, P. Sorlie, and M. Hjortland. Diet and its relation to coronary heart disease and death in three populations. *Circulation* 63:500–515, 1981.

23. Haskell, W.L., H.J. Montoye, and D. Orenstein. Physical activity and exercise to achieve health-related physical fitness components. *Public Health Reports* 100:202–212, 1985.

24. Hayes, A. Youth physical fitness hearings. *Journal of Physical Education, Recreation, and Dance* 55(9):29–32, 40, 1984.

25. Kohl, H.W. and S. N. Blair. Physical fitness and mortality from any cause in adult men with chronic disease. *Medicine and Science in Sports and Exercise* 20:S7 (abstract), 1988.

26. Krahenbuhl, G.S., J.S. Skinner, and W.M. Kohrt. Developmental aspects of maximal aerobic power in children. *Exercise and Sport Science Reviews* 13:503–538, 1985.

27. Kraus, H. and R.P. Hirshland. Minimum muscular fitness tests in school children. *Research Quarterly* 25:178–187, 1954.

28. Leon, A.S., J. Connett, D.R. Jacobs, and R. Rauramaa. Leisure-time physical activity levels and risk of coronary heart disease and death. The multiple risk factor intervention trial. *Journal of the American Medical Association* 258:2388–2395, 1987.

29. Lohman, T.G. Applicability of body composition techniques and constants for children and youth. *Exercise and Sports Sciences Reviews* 14:325–357, 1986.

30. Lohman, T.G. The use of skinfolds to estimate body fatness in children and youth. *Journal of Physical Education, Recreation, and Dance* 58:98–102, 1987.

31. Lohman, T.G., S.B. Going, M.H. Slaughter, and R.A. Boileau. Concept of chemical development in children and youth. Implications for estimating obesity in childhood. *Human Biology*, In press, 1989.

32. Londeree, B. The use of laboratory tests with long distance runners. *Sports Medicine* 3:201–213, 1986.

33. Meredith, M.D. FITNESSGRAM User's Manual. Dallas, Texas: Institute for Aerobics Research, 1987.

34. Morris, J.N., R. Pollard, M.G. Everitt, S.P.W. Chave, and A.M. Semmence. Vigorous exercise in leisure-time: Protection against coronary heart disease. *Lancet* 2:1207–1210, 1980.

35. Paffenbarger, R.S., Jr., R.T. Hyde, A.L. Wing, and C. Hsieh. Physical activity, all-cause mortality, and longevity of college alumni. *New England Journal of Medicine* 314:605–613, 1986.

36. Pate, R.R. A new definition of youth fitness. *The Physician and Sportsmedicine* 11:77–83, 1983a.

37. Pate, R.R. *South Carolina Physical Fitness Test Manual. Test Procedures and Norms.* Columbia, South Carolina: South Carolina Association for Health, Physical Education Recreation and Dance, 1983b.
38. Peters, R.K., L.D. Cady, Jr., D.P. Bischoff, L. Bernstein, and M.C. Pike. Physical fitness and subsequent myocardial infarction in healthy workers. *Journal of the American Medical Association* 249:3052–3056,1983.
39. Powell, K.E. and W. Dysinger. Childhood participation in organized school sports and physical education as precursors of adult physical activity. *American Journal of Preventive Medicine* 3:276–281, 1987.
40. Powell, K.E., P.D. Thompson, C.J. Caspersen, and J.S. Kendrick. Physical activity and the incidence of coronary heart disease. *Annual Review of Public Health* 8:253, 281–287, 1987.
41. President's Council on Physical Fitness and Sports *The Presidential Physical Fitness Award Program Instructor's Guide.* Washington, D.C.: President's Council on Physical Fitness and Sports, 1987.
42. Reiff, G.G., W.R. Dixon, D. Jacoby, G.X. Ye, C.G. Spain, and P.A. Hunsicker. The President's Council on Physical Fitness and Sports 1985. *National School Population Fitness Survey.* Ann Arbor: University of Michigan, 1986.
43. Ross, J.G., Dotson, C.O., and Gilbert, G.G. Are kids getting appropriate activity? *Journal of Physical Education, Recreation and Dance* 56:82–85, 1985.
44. Sallis, J.F., W.L. Haskell, P.D. Wood, S.P. Fortman, T. Rogers, S.N. Blair, and R.S. Paffenbarger, Jr. Physical activity assessment methodology in the Five City Project. *American Journal of Epidemiology* 121:91–106, 1985.
45. Simons-Morton, B.G., N.M. O'Hara, D.G. Simons-Morton, and G.S. Parcel. Children and fitness: a public health perspective. *Research Quarterly for Exercise and Sport* 58:295–302, 1987.
46. Squires, W.G., and E. Smith. *Fit Youth Today Program Manual.* Austin, Texas: American Health and Fitness Foundation, 1986.
47. Taylor, H.L., D.R. Jacobs, Jr., B. Schucker, J. Knudsen, A.S. Leon, and G. DeBacker. A questionnaire for the assessment of leisure time physical activities. *Journal of Chronic Diseases* 31:741–755, 1978.
48. Tuxworth, W. The fitness and physical activity of adolescents. *Medical Journal of Australia* 148 (Special supplement):S13–S21, 1988.
49. Ward, D.S. and O. Bar-Or. Role of the physician and physical education teacher in the treatment of obesity at school. *Pediatrician* 13:44–51, 1986.
50. Weber, D.G., H.W. Kohl, M.D. Meredith, and S.N. Blair. An automated system for assessing physical fitness in school children. In: *Health Statistics Make a Difference.* Department of Health and Human Services Publication No. (PHS) 86-1214. Hyattsville, MD.: National Center for Health Statistics, 145–148, 1986.
51. Wood, P.D., W.L. Haskell, S.N. Blair, P.T. Williams, R.M. Krauss, F. T. Lindgren, J.J. Albers, P.H. Ho, and J.W. Farquhar. Increased exercise level and plama lipoprotein concentration: a one-year, randomized, controlled study in sedentary, middle-aged men. *Metabolism* 32:31–39, 1983.

DISCUSSION

BLAIR: We need to carefully look at the way most fitness tests are given in the public schools. I think that teachers do not follow the recommendations we write in the manuals, i.e., they should teach a fitness unit first, they should train the children over a period of six or eight weeks (which is what we recommended in Fit Youth Today and in FITNESSGRAM), and, furthermore, they should teach them how to run.

How valid are these tests? Well, they are less valid if the children don't know how to run and pace themselves. I think a lot of those kids who don't meet the standard don't need to be trained anymore; they just need to be taught how to run and how to pace themselves.

When we look at standards for aerobic power in men and women in our data, the standards really seem to me to be quite low, i.e., 10 times the resting metabolic rate, i.e., 10 METS in men, 9 METS in women. That's not an enormous amount of fitness; it's a level that virtually all adults without chronic disease can achieve. I suspect that we can ultimately find a similar standard for children. I think that the standard that we finally settle on should be low enough that almost everyone can reach it.

ORENSTEIN: You discount the influence of childhood sports, at least on adult activity. You drew your data from folks who go to the Cooper Clinic, and I think you showed that 80 some percent, both of the previous athletes and previous non-athletes, did adopt the exercise program that was recommended. Since there wasn't any difference between those groups, you suggested, therefore, maybe having been an athlete doesn't seem to help. But isn't that a very selective group of folks who choose to come to the Cooper Clinic, knowing that it stands for exercise?

BLAIR: Every grant reviewer, every editor, every paper reviewer, has asked that question, so I'm ready for you. The Cooper Clinic population, on the first visit to the Clinic, is, in terms of lipids, not different from the LRC prevalence study. In terms of skinfolds and body mass index, they are not different from the LRC prevalence study. A crude measure of exercise, i.e., answering whether one is sedentary or not, for men and women is not different from the National Health Interview Survey. The $\dot{V}O_2$max values estimated from our treadmill tests are virtually identical to the only population-based fitness data we have in North America, i.e., the data from the Fitness Canada Survey for both sexes in the various age groups. However, they are clearly different in terms of social-economic strata. But on coronary heart disease risk factors, on exercise level, and on fitness level, they really don't seem to be different from other populations of North Americans. They may still be different on their health awareness and their willingness to take advice and change habits; I don't have any data on that, so they may well be considerably different there from Mr. and Mrs. Average, but maybe not from Mr. and Mrs. Average College Graduate.

ORENSTEIN: But even specifically about their attitudes toward exercise; why did they go to Cooper instead of going to Mayo?

BLAIR: I don't have data on attitudes about exercise. Many of them are sent there by their businesses for executive physicals, so that subgroup is probably a less selected group than the subgroup of persons who fly on their own accord from Pittsburgh or Des Moines to Dallas to get on Dr. Cooper's treadmill rather on someone's treadmill in Pittsburgh or Des Moines. They have to be different in some of those ways. But I don't see why there would be a bias interjected in the sense that the former athletes or the former non-athletes might have differences in their willingness to take physicians' advice.

HENKE: Would it not be helpful for physicians who cannot or will not administer fitness tests to have some type of questionnaire to help them evaluate children's fitness?

BLAIR: One of the Surgeon General's recommendations for health objectives for 1990 was that America's physicians should take a careful exercise history. I don't think it speaks specifically to children or adults; it's just a general recommendation. Yes, I think pediatricians and family physicians should be asking all their patients about how much exercise they get.

The exercise history questionnaires for children are really not very well developed. In the absence of that, I think as a starting point we should be recommending to pediatricians that they at least talk to the parents about whether or not the child is active or is watching six hours of television a day. Although I've made the point that most American children are active and fit, there certainly is a subset of unfit children. As the body composition data are showing, the American kids are getting fatter, and that doesn't auger well for exercise. Exercise questionnaires need to be developed, but pediatricians could start immediately in their normal history-taking procedure, by asking the parents and the adolescents themselves about their exercise habits and by recommending exercise to them. We don't have to get very technical for kids or adults in talking about an exercise prescription. I think there is a lot of good to be gained on a public health basis if physicians would just take an exercise history and make general recommendations to become more active.

MALINA: Alec Roche's data suggest that the body mass index (BMI) has no relevance for the fatness, absolute or relative, of boys. I'm just wondering why they persist in putting BMI in fitness surveys. Some of our anthropometric measures on youngsters classified as obese by the BMI show these children to be physically quite different from those classified as obese by skinfolds. This is especially true for muscularity, skeletal framework size, and also for skeletal maturity status. So depending on what criteria you use, you might be identifying different types of overweight, but not necessarily obese, youngsters.

BLAIR: The reason the BMI is used by me and others in data sets like this is that there has been a resistance on the part of physical education teachers to take skinfold measures. I think this reluctance has been fanned by the controversy between various groups about what is the appropriate kind of fitness testing. Many physical educators seem to be worried about lawsuits if they start measuring skinfolds. I think teachers who are college graduates are fully capable of being trained to take skinfolds. The reason we allow the use of BMI is so that we have *something* if the teacher won't take the skinfolds. Now you're suggesting that the BMI may be worse than nothing, but I'd like to have Tim Lohman comment on that.

LOHMAN: My hope is that as we look back a few years from now, hopefully sooner rather than later, body mass index will become extinct both in the research community and in practice. BMI should be replaced by a fat mass index, a bone mass index, and a muscle mass index. We're developing methods for those. What we have with body mass index is a composite, of course, of bone, muscle and fat. It's particularly troublesome in children because of the differential growth of muscle, bone, and fat through late childhood and adolescence. BMI is equally as well correlated with frame size in many samples of children as it is with body composition and body fatness. For some kids, BMI is picking up muscle, and for other kids, it's picking up fat. But in a practical sense, if you look at the correlation between body fatness in all 6–8 year olds with body mass index, it's moderate—0.6 in the National Health Survey. Thus, it is only moderately correlated with fatness, but also with frame size. In puberty, adolescence, and in adults, the correlations drop, so BMI becomes a worse predicator. There is some value in it as a predictor for body composition, especially in young children. But I think BMI is giving the wrong message, educationally, to teach kids about weight per height as a measure of fatness, when BMI means so much more. There are so many confounding factors related to ethnicity, athletic participation, and body type. BMI is not completely meaningless. It is picking out some kids who are definitely obese. But the use of BMI should be very temporary, as I see it.

BLAIR: As Russ Pate has been telling us for years, it's probably instructive to take that pinch of skin and fat. It helps communicate more to the child, to the teacher, and to the parent, that we are talking about fat.

BOUCHARD: I take the opposite view, as a matter of fact. So I think it's time to say it. I hope the body mass index is around and more popular than it is now, because this is the most direct and reliable measurement that we have. There is no standard error of estimate around the BMI. What you measure is what you get. Now the interpretation of that is the difficult part. In my judgment, the interpretation is made much easier if you use the skinfold data. We decide with the BMI whether a child is too heavy or not, and then, using the skinfold, we determine whether that heaviness is fat or not. A BMI has no standard error of estimate, and the skinfold has a very low standard error of estimate. The problem is when we take the BMI or the skinfolds and try to translate that into fat. Then we are playing with witchcraft. We are transforming these measures into things that they are not. It is there that we start to make errors in classification and introduce a larger error component. So I think the BMI should be around, but it has to be used properly.

DISHMAN: I endorse philosophically the educational dividend of the material that you've been addressing. But I think we want to be a little more conservative in our estimates of how much impact the information coming from fitness testing is really going to have on behavior change. We would hope that there would be more impact than has been demonstrated in adults. But the information that I'm aware of in adults shows that if there is any effect, it will be a short-term effect. Evidence to support the idea that health risk appraisals or fitness testing evaluations will cause subsequent increases in activity is virtually nonexistent as far as I know. It may be that the education needs to be expanded beyond just the fitness testing to include considerations about the factors that we believe that are more direct determinants of participation. Certainly the fitness testing can be an important part of a bigger package, but I don't think anyone would want to suggest that all we need to do is assess fitness, and then expect to make a big change in children's behavior.

BLAIR: I wholeheartedly agree. When I refer to fitness testing or fitness education, I am just recognizing the fact that fitness testing is so deeply ingrained in the system that we're not going to be doing away with it overnight. I just want to reduce the importance of testing so it becomes the least important part of the program. This is what we tried to do in the Fit Youth Today manual, and we are doing the same in the coming year in FITNESSGRAM. We've already done it with the FITNESSGRAM awards, i.e., the emphasis is much more on behavior. The important aspect is participation, i.e., going through a training program and participating in various sports and games. I think we can do a much better job of teaching the cognitive aspect of fitness in our schools than we are at the moment. I don't want to suggest that the fitness testing is a central focus, except that at the present time it is our main entree into the schools.

SCANLON: I think what you are really talking about is a long-term goal of continued participation at someone's personal optimal level. And that is truly a motivational issue. A key variable is understanding the sources of enjoyment for exercise at various stages of the lifespan. I believe that they change as we age. We know in youth sport that enjoyment is the major reason kids give for participating; lack of enjoyment is the major reason they give for ceasing participation. I'm sure that the same kind of principle would apply to the exercise domain. I think we need to capture what is intrinsically and inherently motivating in that activity domain. What is it about exercise that turns everybody on in this room? I would venture to say it's not a participation award. There is something else, and if we could take advantage of what those elements are, what those sources of enjoyment are, then I think we could have a very good chance of keeping people active.

Related to that, I would like to throw out the possibility of changing the fitness goals from a criterion-referenced standard approach to a personal improvement approach. Change the orientation to a success orientation with a personal improvement goal so that kids are improving at their own level. Perhaps the ultimate goal would be to reach some general standard, but maybe not. Maybe you don't even tell them what that standard is. They are just constantly improving and are rewarded for that. Hopefully, the intrinsic reward of the activity will start being appreciated, and they will continue the activity.

What we don't want to do with a failure to achieve some standard is to undermine the motivation for activity that might come out inherently from participation in the activity. Also, we don't want to undermine the intrinsic reward of activity with extrinsic rewards. We know that extrinsic rewards, e.g., award buttons and all that, can have positive effects to initially get people into an activity. But those extrinsic rewards should be minimized as soon as possible to get children motivated by the activity itself.

BLAIR: I don't disagree, Tara, with many of the things you say; but we've had more than 30 years of fitness education in the United States with a major focus on fitness testing and giving awards. The predominant award over that entire period of time is achievable by less than 2–3% of the kids. It would be an enormous leap forward to go from that norm-referenced approach, which has been done for generations of teachers and kids, to get the physical education profession to now say, "It's not that more is better; its how much fitness is enough?" As I've tried to say over and over, I think to deemphasize any performance award is wise, and that's what many of the groups are trying to do. We should emphasize participation and enjoyment, i.e., participation in activities for the inherent joy and for improvement in fitness and health.

FREEDSON: I want to point out one thing that I think all of us intuitively know but hasn't been mentioned as an important issue with regard to maximizing participation by children in sport. The involvement of other family members to help promote the habit of regular physical activity is very important.

DRINKWATER: I was wondering, Steve, if dividing your Cooper Clinic males into athletes and non-athletes is the best way of looking at the effect of exercise during youth. It seems to me that a lot of male athletes who have been on teams may have been active but may not have enjoyed it to the same extent as a youngster who was active because the family was active, because they went camping, or because they went out and played on intramural teams. There may have been a residue of dislike of some of the activity in the "athletic" males.

BLAIR: It's a very crude approach, and you'll notice my numbers were very small.

DRINKWATER: You keep saying it's crude, and epidemiologists are burdened with that. But I still think it's worth considering that being an athlete as a child does not always mean that the child enjoyed the activity.

BLAIR: We have recently made some changes in the medical history in the Clinic and some other surveys we've done to try to get a better handle on the lifetime exercise history of the patients who come there. But I have to confess that at this moment we are not doing a very good job of assessing some of these psychological variables. We don't have much psychological expertise at the Institute.

SUTTON: What appears to me will happen if fitness education goes in the direction in which you suggest is that we will go from what was originally a criterion that only 3 percent of all children could achieve to one which virtually everyone can achieve. Why have standards at all if you're just going to keep lowering the ceiling?

BLAIR: Well, it's not lowering it. This is the first time a criterion-referenced standard has ever been presented. The earlier standard was not presented as a criterion-referenced fitness standard, but simply as a standard for an award. This is now an attempt to define how much fitness is appropriate for children. It may well come down, but it could also go up. When I said less emphasis on standards and more emphasis on behavior, I didn't necessarily mean to push the standard down more, although that may well happen as we learn more about it. I think as health professionals, it behooves us to tell parents, children, and clinicians how much fitness is enough, just as we have established standards for blood pressure, cholesterol, and other variables. I don't think we want to throw the idea of a criterion-referenced standard away.

SUTTON: But by doing this you're still implying that you actually know that such-and-such a level of fitness is associated with some sort of specific health benefit.

BLAIR: We're with fitness now where we were with cholesterol

20 years ago. It's just at an earlier point in the process. You all know what we've gone through in the last two decades trying to achieve a consensus on cholesterol levels. That has now been done in the last two or three years. I hope in 20 years from now we can be more positive about an appropriate standard for fitness.

MORGAN: There are some problems with trying to create a Walden Three in the fitness area, where everyone would be above-average, happy, and successful. I think there are many reasons why that may not work.

I'm curious about your reaction to Rod Dishman's chapter, in which he says that we have no evidence that physical education has any effect on much of anything, including physical activity in adulthood as well as psychological effects. It seems to me that before we become consumed and fixated on the issue of testing and how we go about testing, we should be concerned with whether or not the intervention has any effect.

BLAIR: When I presented my testimony to the Institute of Medicine panel that is working on the year 2000 objectives for the Surgeon General, I told them I didn't think it was useful to have a physical education objective as we have now, which suggests that physical education is needed for a certain number of minutes per week for each child. Precisely because of the evidence that physical education as it has been practiced has so little impact on some of the variables we are talking about, I don't think physical education currently makes any difference on physical fitness levels. However, as a public health approach, the schools are a vehicle through which education on this topic can be delivered. Also, I hope we're trying to speak to physicians and other clinicians as well as to those in the school program.

MORGAN: Is there any evidence that physical education programs aren't actually responsible for de-activating many active, foraging, young children? In other words, somewhere along the line, active kids learn how to become inactive. Do you have any thoughts as to how that occurs?

BLAIR: Well, physical education has a lot of help. Television, parents who restrain their kids, etc.

MICHELI: I want to share one of my patient's insights. This youngster was an injured athlete, and he said, "Doc, in my school you're either a jock, a brain, or a druggie. I'm not a brain, and I'm not a jock anymore, so guess what I will be soon?" So I think there are certain benefits of sports and exercise for children as alternatives to other lifestyles. I think that one of the ways that we can foster exercise is through fitness evaluation, and we should pursue it. But let's not lose sight of the fact that these kids are living in a very complex world now. There are parents who don't want them out in the streets exercising, for instance, because of concerns about their physical safety; they're afraid they will be snatched. There are many adverse social changes going on, including the drug problem, and I still believe that athletics is one of the ways children can get away from these other noxious activities.

11

Blood Pressure in Children

Ronald M. Lauer, M.D.

Trudy L. Burns, Ph.D.

Larry T. Mahoney, M.D.

Charles M. Tipton, Ph.D.

INTRODUCTION

Essential hypertension affects approximately 20% of the adult American population and accounts for a large portion of morbidity and mortality due to its relationship to stroke, renal disease, and

431

coronary heart disease. Many longitudinal studies carried out in adults have shown a risk for premature coronary artery disease that is directly related to the level of both systolic and diastolic blood pressure (Kannel et al., 1970, 1972). Carefully controlled large population studies in adults have shown reduction in morbidity and mortality with pharmacologic lowering of elevated diastolic blood pressure (Veterans Administration, 1967; Hypertension Detection and Follow-Up Program, 1979; Management Committee of the Australian Therapeutic Trial, 1982). Despite the important predictive value of elevated systolic blood pressure for future cardiovascular disease, the pharmacologic management of isolated systolic hypertension has not been proven to be a useful practice in young subjects. Thus, blood pressure levels that are accepted as defining hypertension in adults have been established from observation of morbidity and mortality in longitudinal studies beginning with middle-aged adults, and from observation of the beneficial effects of pharmacologic lowering of diastolic blood pressure. The definition of high blood pressure in children is based on arbitrary levels from the normal distributions observed in healthy childhood populations (Report of the Second Task Force on Blood Pressure Control in Children, 1987).

The epidemic of hypertension affecting so many adults has brought investigators to consider whether essential hypertension begins in childhood. Suggestive evidence for its origin early in life results from observations that:

1. Peer rank order of blood pressure is maintained during childhood (Levine et al., 1978; Schachter et al., 1979; Jesse et al., 1976; Beaglehole et al., 1977; Clarke et al., 1978; Rosner et al., 1977; Kuller et al., 1980; Hait et al., 1982; Zinner et al., 1971) so that those with high blood pressure are likely to become adults with high blood pressure.
2. There is familial aggregation of blood pressure (Klein et al., 1977; Holland & Beresford, 1977; Higgins et al., 1977; Platt, 1967) so parents with high blood pressure are likely to have children with high blood pressure.

I. TRACKING OF BLOOD PRESSURE IN CHILDREN

The persistence of rank order of blood pressure has been referred to as tracking. In many cross-sectional studies of children, a continuous rise of blood pressure has been observed from infancy through adolescence, and at any given age there is a wide distribution of blood pressure. If blood pressure levels were to maintain rank order from early childhood into adult life, then those with initially high pressures would likely be destined to be adults with hypertension. Thus, there would be a very good chance that children with pressure in the upper part of the distribution would be associated with increased morbidity and mortality in adult life.

Many longitudinal studies in children have shown that there is a degree of peer rank order consistency of blood pressure level. The results of some of these studies are summarized in Table 11-1. Although all of the studies indicate that there is indeed tracking of blood pressure, there is considerable lability of blood pressure rank over time. For an individual child, the prediction of future hypertension from early measurements of blood pressure is certainly not as precise as is the prediction of future height and weight from early measurements (Clarke et al., 1978).

TABLE 11–1. *Similarity Between Initial and Follow-up Blood Pressure Levels in Selected Studies*

Reference	Age at Initial Examination	Length of Follow-up	Correlation Coefficient	
			Systolic	Diastolic
deSwiet et al. (6)	4–6	4–6 weeks	0.20***	
Levine et al. (7)	2 days	12 months	0.10	0.14
	1 month	11 months	0.12	0.02
	3 months	9 months	0.01	0.03
	6 months	6 months	0.38	0.34
			(0.14–0.58)~	(.09–0.55)~
Schachter et al. (8)	3 days	6 months	0.10	0.10
	6 months	9 months	0.29***	0.45***
Zinner et al. (9)	2–14 years	8 years	0.315+***	0.155+*
Jesse et al. (10)	2–5 years	1 year	0.55#	
	15–17 years	1 year	0.75#	
Beaglehole et al. (11)	5–14 years			
	boys	1.5–3.7 years	0.31***	0.12
	girls	1.5–3.7 years	0.24**	0.07
Clarke et al. (12)	5–18 years	6 years	0.30***	0.18***
Rosner et al. (13)	5–9 years	15 years	0.24#	0.30#
	10–14 years	15 years	0.25#	0.45#
	15–19 years	15 years	0.51#	0.32#
Kuller et al. (14)	High school students			
	boys	17 years	0.44***	0.19**
	girls	17 years	0.39***	0.19**
Hait et al. (15)	6–11 years	3–4 years	0.25–0.65**	0.09–0.60**

*p<.05
**p<.01
***p<.001
~95 percent confidence limits
+Regression coefficients of follow-up blood pressures on initial blood pressure
#p value not given
(After Szklo M: Epidemiologic patterns of blood pressure in children. *Epidemiologic Reviews* 1:143–169, 1979.

II. FAMILY STUDIES OF BLOOD PRESSURE

There was a great deal of controversy in the 1950s and 1960s regarding the possible genetic mechanism involved in the determination of elevated blood pressure. Platt (1967) maintained that essential hypertension was inherited as a discrete entity due to segregation at a single autosomal focus. Pickering (1967), on the other hand, maintained that there was no discrete point of the distribution that separates normotensive from hypertensive individuals. According to the Pickering formulation, the diagnosis of essential hypertension merely selects individuals from the tail of a single continuous distribution that results from the accumulated effects of many genes modulated by various environmental factors. Although this issue has not been fully resolved, no study of blood pressure has found evidence for a major genetic locus determining the normotensive and hypertensive states.

Population studies show blood pressure to be a unimodally distributed quantitative trait that aggregates in families. Most investigators assume that the observed variability in blood pressure is multifactorial in origin, with a genetic contribution that is due to the effects of segregation at a large number of loci, each with a small effect, and numerous environmental contributions. The major focus in most family studies of blood pressure is on measurement of similarities between genetically related individuals. This information can be used to determine how much of the observed familial aggregation can be attributed to shared genes and/or shared environments.

Two main approaches have been taken to obtain information regarding the contributions of both genetic and environmental factors to blood pressure determination. One is to compare blood pressure levels among relatives living in different environments; the second is to compare blood pressure levels among relatives sharing a common environment. The family units utilized range from twins, to pairs of relatives, to nuclear families and large pedigrees. Genetic and environmental components of blood pressure variability are estimated by comparing and contrasting the blood pressure covariances or correlations that exist between members within a family unit.

A. Twin Studies

The observation that the within-pair variance for monozygotic (MZ) twins is less than that for dizygotic (DZ) twins, meaning that blood pressure levels in MZ twins are more similar than levels in DZ twins, provides one indication of a genetic component involved in the determination of blood pressure. Since MZ twins have identical genotypes and are the same age and sex, their phenotypic differences must be due to environmental influences. The similarity between MZ twins gives an idea of the degree to which blood pressure is genetically determined and to what degree its variability might be modified by environmental influences. Dizygotic twins, on the other hand, differ genetically, as do full siblings, but they still share certain environmental experiences not shared by non-twin siblings, making them similar to MZ twins in that regard. Assuming that the proportion of variability observed in blood pressure due to environmental influences is the same for both monozygotic and dizygotic twins, the variability due to genetic factors can be estimated by comparing intraclass correlation coefficients for the two types of twins.

Feinleib and co-workers (1980) found in 248 pairs of adult male MZ twins, a correlation coefficient for systolic blood pressure of 0.55 and for diastolic blood pressure of 0.58. For 264 DZ twin pairs, the correlations were 0.25 and 0.27 for systolic and diastolic blood pressure, respectively. From these data, the fraction of phenotypic variance due to genetic variability in a population was estimated to be 0.82 for systolic and 0.64 for diastolic blood pressure (Borhani et al., 1976).

Using 7-year-old MZ and DZ twins from the Collaborative Perinatal Project, Havlik and associates (1979) found evidence for a genetic influence on blood pressure variability with heritability estimates of 0.23 for systolic and 0.53 for diastolic blood pressure. These findings indicate that variability in diastolic pressure due to genetic differences can be detected reasonably early in life.

One purpose of genetic studies is to obtain results that can be applied to the general population. Twin studies are sometimes criticized because there may be differences in the trait under study between twins and non-twins that make inferences to the general population invalid. There is also evidence that the genetic component of variability is overestimated when twin data are used (Morton et al., 1980; Ward, 1979).

B. Adoptive Studies

A further indication of a genetic component in the determination of blood pressure comes from adoptive studies showing significant parent-natural child correlation and negligible parent-adoptee correlation. If all possible types of transmission, except genetic, are eliminated through the severing of social and environmental relationships between adoptees and their relatives, studying these individuals and their adoptive families can provide information necessary to reject the hypothesis of a purely environmental etiology in favor of one that includes a genetic component.

Two different designs are used for adoptive studies. The first, which is seldom used because of the difficulty in obtaining the required data, compares the blood pressure of the adoptee with that of both the natural parents and the adoptive parents. The second design focuses on the adoptee and the adoptive home, comparing parent-natural child and natural sibling-natural sibling similarities with parent-adoptee and adoptee-adoptee similarities. This approach was used in the Montreal Adoption Survey, which included families with only adopted, only natural, or both natural and adopted children (Biron, 1977).

The data from this survey were used to estimate the genetic and environmental effects on blood pressure determination (Annest et al., 1979). The degree of similarity between household members and evidence for familial aggregation of blood pressure can be seen in Tables 11-2a and 11-2b. These data (Table 11-2a) indicate a much stronger similarity between the blood pressures of parents and their natural children and between natural siblings than between parents and their adoptive children and between adoptive siblings. Shared home experiences, such as diet, stress, or other environmental factors, however, do have a major role in determining the familial resemblance of blood pressure since the degree of familial aggregation of blood pressure is increased in pairs with a longer period of cohabitation (Table 11-2b).

The fraction of blood pressure variability attributed to genetic differences between unrelated individuals was estimated from this study to be 0.34 for systolic and 0.30 for diastolic blood pressure. Variability among households of effects shared by members within a household were estimated to account for 0.11 of systolic blood pressure variability in both parents and children, while for diastolic

TABLE 11-2a. *Estimates of Blood Pressure Correlations Between Household Members*

Relationships	n*	Systolic BP	Diastolic BP
Father-adoptee	442	.0889	.1343**
Mother-adoptee	442	.0779	.0991
Natural child-adoptee	119	.1863	.2689***
Adoptee-adoptee	154	.1643	.2856***
Spouses	521	.1465***	.1752***
Father-natural child	198	.2368***	.2052**
Mother-natural child	198	.2713***	.2604***
Natural child-natural child	94	.3822***	.5253***

*Number of sets of relatives.
**Significant at the 0.01 level of probability.
***Significant at the 0.001 level of probability.

TABLE 11-2b. *Cohabitation Effects On Correlation Between Non-biologically Related Members of the Household.*

		Subsamples				
		Cohab-1#			Cohab-2#	
Relationship	n*	Systolic BP	Diastolic BP	n*	Systolic BP	Diastolic BP
Father-adoptee	184	.0855	.1319	258	.1346	.1286
Mother-adoptee	184	−.0276	−.1074	258	.1492	.2762
Natural child-adoptee	53	−.0672	.0885	66	.4130***	.5750***
Adoptee-adoptee	91	.1530	.2573	63	.1775	.3280**
Spouses	184	.2053**	.1794	258	.1621	.0787
Unweighted average		.0698	.1099		.2073	.2773

*Number of sets of relatives.
**Significant at the 0.01 level of probability.
***Significant at the 0.001 level of probability.
#Cohab-1, cohabitation of family members <4 years; Cohab-2, cohabitation >4 years.
(Adapted from Annest, JL et al., [28])

blood pressure the fractions were 0.20 and 0.31 for parents and children, respectively.

As with twin studies, adoptive studies may not be representative of the general population. Therefore, inferences obtained from these studies and estimates of genetic, and especially common environmental, effects may not be completely applicable to the entire population.

C. Familial Aggregation of Blood Pressure

A number of studies have shown that familial aggregation of blood pressure exists. Studies by several investigators have shown that blood pressure correlations exist among siblings and also between parents and their offspring after 1 y (Table 11-3). Levine and colleagues (1980) have shown, however, that under 1 month of age, familial correlations of blood pressure are not significant. The early familial aggregation is suggestive of involvement of shared genes or shared environmental factors in determination of blood pressure levels.

Evidence for significant genetic and common environmental contributions to the determination of interindividual variation of both systolic and diastolic blood pressure has been found in studies of populations with very different cultural backgrounds (Morton et al., 1980; Ward, 1979; Moll et al., 1983). The fraction of systolic blood pressure variability that was attributed to genetic variability in these studies was from 0.24 to 0.34, while the fraction attributable to com-

TABLE 11-3. *Correlation of Blood Pressure Between Parent-Child and Between Sibling-Sibling.*

			Correlation*			
			Systolic BP		Diastolic BP	
Reference	Age of Children (yrs)	No. of families	Parent/ Child	Sib/ Sib	Parent/ Child	Sib/ Sib
Zinner (1971)	2-14	176	.16	.34	.17	.32
Klein (1977)	1-14	43	—	.27	—	.21
Holland (1977)	1-20	455	.20	.29	—	—
Higgins (1977)	1-18	—	.14	.17	—	.12

*All correlations p < 0.05.

mon environment variability was from 0.11 to 0.20. Estimates of the genetic and environmental contributions to diastolic blood pressure was similar.

III. FACTORS RELATED TO BLOOD PRESSURE LEVELS

A. Obesity and Blood Pressure

When the body mass index was used as expressed in quintiles for 272 sixth-grade students, Farinaro et al. (1987) found both systolic and diastolic blood pressures progressively increased from the lowest to the highest quintile.

There is a relationship between body weight and blood pressure, and body weight also aggregates in families (Annest et al., 1983). Multivariate models show that a large portion of the observed familial aggregation of systolic blood pressure can be explained by the familial aggregation of weight (Hanis et al., 1983). The sample for this latter study of blood pressure and weight coaggregation consisted of 998 individuals from Muscatine, Iowa, who were genetically related as full siblings and as first cousins. Forty-six percent of the full-sibling correlation for systolic blood pressure was found to be attributable to shared genes, with 36% due to genes directly affecting blood pressure and the remaining 10% due to genes directly affecting weight and only secondarily affecting systolic blood pressure. These analyses indicate that the genetic composition of the observed variability in blood pressure is greatly influenced by the distribution of body weight and genetic influences.

B. Race and Blood Pressure

Another factor that relates to elevated blood pressure in children is race. Using a reference value of 130/85 mmHg as being abnormal, Berenson et al. (1980) examined 4,238 children, of which

33% were black, from the ages of 2.5 to 14.0 yrs. The numbers with elevated pressure per thousand were 3.6 and 3.9 for white boys and girls, respectively, and 12.7 and 8.1 for black boys and girls. When black children are compared with white, the blacks exhibit an increased pressor response (Falkner et al., 1987), and blacks exhibit a greater hypertensive response on a high-salt diet when given a norepinephrine challenge (Dimsdale et al., 1987).

C. Salt Sensitivity and Hypertension

In populations, there is epidemiologic evidence linking high salt intake to hypertension. Populations of subjects who consume large amounts of sodium chloride in their diets have an unusually high incidence of hypertension and its resulting complications (Dahl & Love, 1954). There are also populations with extremely low salt intake, low blood pressure levels, and few complications resulting from hypertension (Page et al., 1974).

Two strains of rats have been bred to investigate the relationship between salt intake and hypertension: one that develops hypertension when given a high-salt diet, and another that does not develop hypertension when given a similar diet (Dahl, 1962). These mammalian models indicate that there are genetic factors related to the responsiveness of blood pressure to dietary salt. Among humans, not all individuals with hypertension are salt-sensitive. Approximately 60% of patients with essential hypertension are salt-sensitive in that blood pressure rises in response to salt loading. The remaining 40% of adults with essential hypertension are salt-resistant and show no change of blood pressure when salt-loaded. In addition, most normotensive subjects do not have a significant rise in blood pressure in response to salt (Kawasaki et al., 1978; Fujita et al., 1980).

The mechanism of salt sensitivity is incompletely understood. Salt-sensitive hypertensive individuals retain greater amounts of sodium and have greater weight gain than salt-resistant hypertensive individuals. Salt-resistant hypertensive individuals have an exaggerated natriuresis after five to six days of salt loading (Kawasaki et al., 1978). There is evidence in salt-sensitive individuals that salt loading results in sympathetic nervous system stimulation, causing an exacerbation of hypertension (Campese et al., 1982).

Other mechanisms have been postulated to link sodium, the sympathetic nervous system, and the pathogenesis of hypertension. These include alterations in synthesis, storage, and turnover of biogenic amines in central and peripheral neurons (de Champlain, 1968), baroreflex sensitivity (Berecek et al., 1983), vascular reactivity to alpha-adrenergic agonists and central and peripheral sympathetic stimulation (Berecek et al., 1983), sensitivity to pre- and post-synaptic mechanisms that govern the release and re-uptake of biogenic amines (Lokhandwala & Eikenburg, 1983), renal sodium handling (Bianchi et al., 1979), and membrane sodium transport (Canessa et al., 1980).

Increased activation of the sympathetic nervous system and an exaggerated pressor response to mental stress have been described in normotensive adolescent female offspring of hypertensive parents in comparison to age-matched offspring of normotensive parents (Falkner, 1981). Pressor responses were enhanced in the progeny of hypertensive individuals when a high-salt diet was consumed, suggesting that the increased sympathetic nervous system activity present in hypertensive kindred is accompanied by an enhanced pressor response to salt loading. Competitive mental tasks are accompanied by significant reduction in urine volume and sodium excretion in normotensive adolescent male offspring of hypertensive parents and in young hypertensive males (Light et al., 1983). Thus, retention of sodium during stress may be familial and may reflect predisposition to development of hypertension.

D. Markers For Hypertension

Even though there is probably a major genetic influence on the development of hypertension, no specific genetically coded biochemical abnormality has been described. If a preclinical marker for essential hypertension could be found, it might allow the early detection of subjects prior to their development of elevated blood pressure. Perhaps then treatment of susceptible individuals might reduce the late complications of hypertension. Recent findings of differences in cation movement across red blood cell membranes between patients with essential hypertension and normotensive individuals have led to speculation that these differences may serve as markers for essential hypertension in asymptomatic individuals.

1. Red Blood Cell Sodium-Potassium Co-Transport. The relationship between the sodium-potassium co-transport pathway and hypertension was studied by Garay and colleagues (1980). They measured net sodium and potassium rates of exchange in sodium-loaded, potassium-depleted red blood cells in three groups of individuals: those with essential hypertension, those with secondary hypertension, and those with normal blood pressure and no family history of hypertension. The ratio of sodium efflux to potassium influx was reduced in patients with essential hypertension when compared with patients with secondary hypertension or normotensive individuals. A low ratio was also found in 54% of normotensive offspring with one hypertensive parent. These findings suggest that the abnormal ratio is not simply a function of increased blood pressure since individuals with secondary hypertension exhibited a normal ratio. Another study (Duhm et al., 1982) showed little difference of the ratio in essential hypertensive subjects.

2. **Sodium-Lithium Countertransport.** Current attention in the search for a possible marker for essential hypertension is focused on the sodium-lithium countertransport (SLC) pathway. The in vitro activity of this pathway is measured by the maximal rate of flux of intracellular lithium for extracellular sodium. The mean SLC flux in red blood cells of essential hypertensive subjects, as defined by diastolic blood pressure consistently above 90 mmHg, was found to be more than twice that of normotensive individuals with neither a personal nor a family history of hypertension (Canessa et al., 1980). There was almost no overlap of SLC flux values for the individuals in this study, suggesting that this value might provide a useful diagnostic test for essential hypertension. First-degree relatives of patients with essential hypertension also had a significantly higher mean SLC flux than relatives of normotensive individuals, although the number of subjects was small. The mean blood pressures, although higher in relatives of hypertensives, were not significantly different. A study by Woods and coworkers (1982) compared a group of normotensive teenage boys whose parents were hypertensive with a group of teenage boys with normotensive parents, and found significantly increased SLC flux values in the former.

The relationship between genetic variability in SLC flux and variability in blood pressure in the general population has been estimated (Boerwinkle, 1984). From a random sample of 238 blood bank donors, only 8% of the variability in SLC flux values among individuals could be attributed to differences in age, sex, and body weight. There was a bimodal distribution of values for this random sample of individuals, with 74% of the SLC flux values in the lower mode.

Blood samples from 249 individuals in 52 randomly ascertained nuclear families were analyzed to determine whether the bimodality observed in the random sample of independent individuals could be attributed to segregation at a major genetic locus. The best-fitting genetic model was a recessive mixed model (Morton & MacLean, 1974), with 52.6% of the variability in SLC flux due to segregation at a major locus and an additional 13.7% due to polygenic differences. Therefore, 66.3% of the variability in SLC flux was due to genetic variability.

To investigate the correlation between SLC flux and blood pressure, a random sample of 55 patients with essential hypertension was selected. Significant correlations of 0.22 for systolic and 0.23 for diastolic blood pressure were found. These data, when combined with earlier results, showed that 4% of the variability in systolic blood pressure can be accounted for by SLC flux, and 53% of the variability in SLC flux can be accounted for by segregation at a single locus. Therefore, approximately 2% of the variability in systolic blood pressure of the random sample of blood donors can be attributed to segregation at a single genetic locus.

Two studies of SLC flux in families (Williams et al., 1983; Dadone et al., 1984) showed mean SLC flux values significantly higher in hypertensive subjects than normotensive individuals, whether male or female. Considerable overlap of individual values occurred, and no significant correlation with systolic blood pressure was found. In addition, there were very few youths with high values, even though most had either parents or grandparents with hypertension. Pedigree analysis of 10 large kindreds prone to hypertension and investigated by SLC studies favored a polygenic model of inheritance rather than one with a major genetic locus (Dadone et al., 1984). The proportion of the variability in SLC flux due to polygenic differences among individuals was estimated to be 71%, similar to the 66.3% due to genetic variability found (Boerwinkle, 1984).

There has been speculation about a possible causal mechanism for elevated blood pressure in relationship to abnormal sodium transport (Canessa et al., 1980). One hypothesis is that the increased intracellular concentration of sodium leads to a change in the sodium-calcium exchange mechanism, which results in increased intracellular calcium and tension in vascular smooth muscle. The increased intracellular sodium in essential hypertensive individuals may be caused by genetically determined changes in transport sites.

The finding of increased SLC flux in individuals with essential hypertension, although initially promising, is now questioned. The overlap in SLC flux values in some studies, and the uncertainty regarding the mode of inheritance, suggests that this measurement may not be a uniform marker for hypertension.

3. Other Considerations. There is an extensive literature emerging (Berglund & Anderson, 1981; Sims, 1982; Christlieb et al., 1985; Lucas et al., 1985; Manicardi et al., 1986) that associates conditions of hyperinsulinemia with the elevation of resting blood pressures in nonobese and obese individuals, especially the latter. Moreover, several epidemiological surveys link hyperinsulinemia and elevated blood pressures with coronary heart disease (Pyorola et al., 1985; Burke et al., 1986; Cambien et al., 1987). In addition to its importance in the glucose tolerance test, insulin has the capability of altering sodium reabsorption by the kidneys (DeFronzo, 1976; DeFronzo, 1981) and of eliciting sympathetic nervous system responses (Liang et al., 1982). Collectively, these physiological effects suggest that the tracking of plasma insulin concentrations would be useful in the evaluations of individuals with a propensity for borderline hypertension.

IV. PHYSICAL ACTIVITY AND BLOOD PRESSURE

A. Adult Fitness and Hypertension

The relationship between physical activity and blood pressure in adults has been studied. Although there are some studies that fail to show a relationship of exercise to blood pressure (Pickering, 1987), there is both experimental and epidemiological evidence showing an inverse relationship between physical activity and blood pressure. Studies suggest that regular exercise may retard the development of hypertension. Paffenbarger et al. (1983) followed 15,000 Harvard alumni for six to 10 years and found that men who did not exercise regularly were at 35% greater risk of being diagnosed as hypertensive than those who did exercise. In another study, Blair and co-workers (1984) assessed physical fitness by treadmill testing in 4,820 men and 1,219 women, all of whom were normotensive. After a follow-up of an average of four years, and after adjusting for age, sex, obesity, and baseline blood pressure, it was found that subjects with initial low fitness levels were 52% more likely to become hypertensive.

B. Children's Fitness and Blood Pressure

The relationship of physical activity during childhood and the development of hypertension and its complications in adult life have not been established. However, some investigations on the relationship of physical activity and blood pressure in childhood have been carried out. Panico et al. (1987) studied 1,341 school children aged 7 to 14 y (n = 598 girls, 743 boys). Using a modified Harvard step-test and measuring recovery pulse rates and correcting these for resting pulse rates, they found better recovery rates in both sexes for those with lower systolic blood pressures. In boys, this was independent of age, body mass index, height, and resting pulse rate, while in girls, this same association did not meet statistical significance.

In a similar study of 2,061 children, Hofman et al. (1987) also noted higher systolic and diastolic blood pressures in children with poor physical fitness. In addition, they noted that children who demonstrated a decrease in physical fitness over a one-year period showed the largest rise in blood pressure. They suggested that a change in blood pressure in childhood may be related to changes in physical fitness.

Fraser and colleagues (1983) studied the relationship between physical fitness and blood pressure in 228 school children using a modified Balke treadmill protocol. Systolic and diastolic blood pressures were lower in children with above-average fitness than in children with below-average fitness. Adjusting for skinfold thickness, lean arm mass, height, and age, the relationship between fitness and systolic blood pressure was statistically significant for preadolescent boys and adolescents of both genders. The relationship was not clearly seen for diastolic blood pressure. The significant correlates of fitness were obesity in preadolescents, age in adolescent boys, and height in adolescent girls.

In a small study (n = 37) of the relationship of aerobic capacity and coronary risk factors in 10th-grade males (Fripp et al., 1985), it was found that those with $\dot{V}O_2$max less than 41 mL·kg^{-1}·min^{-1} had significantly greater body mass index than those with $\dot{V}O_2$max greater than 50 mL·kg^{-1}·min^{-1}. However, no differences between systolic blood pressure, diastolic blood pressure, resting heart rates, maximal heart rates, total cholesterol, LDL-cholesterol, or HDL-cholesterol were found.

In adults, systolic blood pressure response to exercise is predictive of subsequent hypertension (Criqui et al., 1983; Wilson & Meyer, 1981). Strong (1979) has suggested that the response of a child's blood pressure to exercise stress might detect prehypertensive youths. Using stepwise regression analysis, Fixler (1985) did not find a significant contribution by blood pressure or heart rate measured during isometric or dynamic exercise to the model's prediction of future systolic or diastolic blood pressure in adolescents with significant hypertension. The best predictor of subsequent blood pressure measured two years later was initial resting blood pressure. Mahoney and colleagues (1988) also found that the best predictor of future blood pressure measured three to four years later was initial resting blood pressure. However, maximal exercise systolic blood pressure significantly added to the regression model's prediction of future systolic blood pressure.

Briedigkeit (1981) followed two groups of children of 115 subjects each, one with normal blood pressures and the other with high blood pressures, for five years. The average initial age of these subjects was 11 years. These investigators reported that children with an increased systolic pressure at rest who had an abnormally high systolic pressure at exertion had greater risk of developing hypertension in five years than children with normal resting blood pressures.

Nudel et al. (1980) studied adolescents with labile (n = 8) and sustained (n = 10) hypertension and compared them to a normal control group (n = 10). They also found no difference in their exercise capacities and no difficulties with maximal exercise testing with respect to EKG ST changes. The maximal systolic pressures of those with labile hypertension were not different from the controls; however, those with sustained hypertension were significantly higher during exercise than in controls. In some with sustained hypertension, pressures exceeded 230 mmHg systolic, which is the level that the American Academy of Pediatrics had suggested may be dangerous and should result in restriction of the subject from maximal exertion during recreation or work.

Responses to dynamic and isometric exercise were evaluated in 264 children whose blood pressures were in the lowest, middle, or highest quintiles of the blood pressure distribution (Schieken, 1983). During isometric exercise, systolic blood pressure in the high quintile group remained significantly higher compared with the low quintile group. Body size-adjusted group systolic and diastolic blood pressure level differences remained during dynamic exercise. Therefore, children with high normal blood pressure maintain a higher blood pressure during both isometric and dynamic exercise.

Klein and colleagues (1984) evaluated responses to a treadmill exercise protocol in adolescents with significant hypertension (systolic and/or diastolic blood pressures greater than the 95th percentile; n = 8), borderline hypertension (at least one blood pressure value above and one value below the 90th percentile; n = 17); and normal blood pressure (n = 21). Patients with significant hypertension demonstrated a greater tachycardic response to exercise that was associated with significantly higher peak exercise epinephrine levels. The greatest increase in systolic blood pressure was observed in the borderline hypertension group, and they also had significantly greater peak exercise norepinephrine levels compared with normotensive controls. These data suggest that the altered hemodynamic response to exercise in hypertensive adolescents may be mediated in part by altered sympathetic nervous system activity. They speculate that patients with borderline hypertension, who achieved the highest blood pressure levels, have hyperkinetic circulations related to higher cardiac outputs. The dampened response in patients with significant hypertension may be functioning at rest with elevated peripheral resistance and are limited in their ability to further change resistance and flow. The increased cardiac output during exercise must be achieved by a greater heart rate response.

Twenty-five children, average age 15.6 y, whose systolic or diastolic blood pressures were persistently above the 95th percentile for age and sex (Hagberg et al., 1984), underwent a vigorous training program of running, swimming, or cycling for a period of six months. In these subjects there was a significant drop in both systolic and diastolic pressure after the training program, and their pressures increased after a period of detraining. In five of these subjects, the effects of weight training were evaluated after endurance training. They showed a maintenance of lower systolic and diastolic blood pressure and a return to the hypertensive state after detraining. These observations suggest that not only will endurance training lower blood pressure in children, but weight training will maintain lower pressures.

Rocchini and co-workers (1987) studied obese adolescents (n = 50) who were assigned to three groups: control, dietary intervention plus behavior modification, and behavior plus exercise modifications. Exercise consisted of aerobic activities at 50% $\dot{V}O_2$ maximum. After 20 weeks, the two intervention groups exhibited significant reduction in resting blood pressure, fat percentages, and plasma insulin concentrations. The exercise group had the greatest fat loss and lowest insulin concentrations during a glucose tolerance test.

C. Left Ventricular Mass

Several studies have examined the relationship of left ventricular wall mass (LVM) to blood pressure in children. Schieken et al. (1981) have noted that children in the upper quintile of the blood pressure distribution for age, as a group, have greater LVM than children in the middle or lower quintiles, and this difference persists after adjustment of LVM for age, gender, and body size. The latter observation suggests that blood pressure in childhood affects LVM independent of body size, even though children from the upper quintile had the greatest measures of body size and ponderosity. Culpepper and colleagues (1983) have shown the LVM and the ratio of wall thickness to ventricular diameter are greater in children with borderline hypertension compared with controls. Increased LVM and asymmetric left ventricular hypertrophy in normotensive and borderline hypertensive offsprings of hypertensive patients compared with the offsprings of normotensive parents have also been found (Nielsen & Oxhoj, 1983).

In adult patients with hypertension, LVM related poorly to blood pressure at rest; however, higher correlations were found with exercise systolic blood pressure and the change in systolic blood pressure from rest to exercise (Ren et al., 1985).

Although Mahoney and colleagues (1988) found no correlation of adjusted resting systolic blood pressure with adjusted LVM in children, they did detect significant correlations with maximal exercise systolic blood pressure and the change in systolic blood pressure from rest to exercise with LVM. These authors used stepwise linear regression to identify significant predictors of future level of systolic blood pressure and LVM subsequently measured one to four years later. The subsequent systolic blood pressure was best predicted from the initial systolic blood pressure; however, maximal exercise systolic blood pressure and initial LVM added to the prediction. The final LVM was best predicted from initial LVM, and maximal exercise diastolic blood pressure added significantly to the prediction. The initial level of systolic blood pressure did not significantly relate to the final level of LVM in childhood.

Increased left ventricular mass (Levy et al., 1988) is a potent cardiovascular risk factor that appears to be related to the level of blood pressure and to a family history of heart disease. It is also known that repeated exercise results in increased left ventricular mass (DeMaria et al., 1978). Echocardiographic measures of LVM may provide an integrated view of elevations of blood pressures that occur throughout a long period of time. LVM and exercise blood pressure responses in childhood may thus be important predictors of subsequent hypertension and its complications in later years. A major unanswered question remains: Will repeated exercise training in childhood result in excessive LVM, particularly in those who are hypertension-prone, and thus increase their risk in later life?

IV. CLINICAL IMPLICATIONS

Epidemiologic studies have shown that hypertension in adults is predictive of future coronary artery disease, stroke, and renal disease. Furthermore, lowering blood pressure in adults decreases morbidity and mortality, particularly that resulting from stroke. Similar studies to verify the benefit of lowering blood pressure, however, have not been performed in children except for those with severe hypertension. Thus the strategy for management of blood pressure elevation in childhood must be inferred from less direct evidence.

Many children with elevated blood pressure for their age are obese and have no other cause for their blood pressure elevation (Lauer, Clarke et al., 1984). Since obesity acquired during childhood tends to continue into adult life, and the relationship of hypertension to obesity is well-established in adults, obese children appear to be at high risk for the development of hypertension (Johnson et al., 1975). Thus the prevention of childhood obesity also is an important health practice.

Routine continuing health care of children should include determination of blood pressure. From this measurement, hypertension from an identifiable cause may be discovered, and children tracking toward adult hypertension may be identified. To aid in the interpretation of blood pressure values obtained in children, standards have been developed for reference and are shown in Figures 11-1 through 11-6 (Report of the Task Force on Blood Pressure Con-

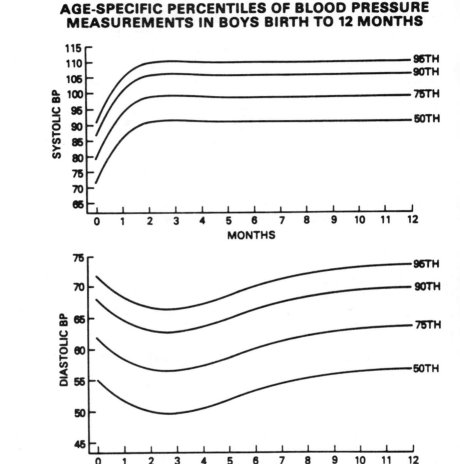

AGE-SPECIFIC PERCENTILES OF BLOOD PRESSURE MEASUREMENTS IN BOYS BIRTH TO 12 MONTHS

90TH PERCENTILE												
SYSTOLIC BP	87	101	106	106	106	105	105	105	105	105	105	105	105
DIASTOLIC BP	68	65	63	63	63	65	66	67	68	68	69	69	69
HEIGHT CM	51	59	63	66	68	70	72	73	74	76	77	78	80
WEIGHT KG	4	4	5	5	6	7	8	9	9	10	10	11	11
YEARS	0	1	2	3	4	5	6	7	8	9	10	11	12

FIGURE 11-1. *Age-specific percentiles of BP measurements in boys-birth to 12 months of age; Korotkoff phase IV (K4) used for diastolic BP.*

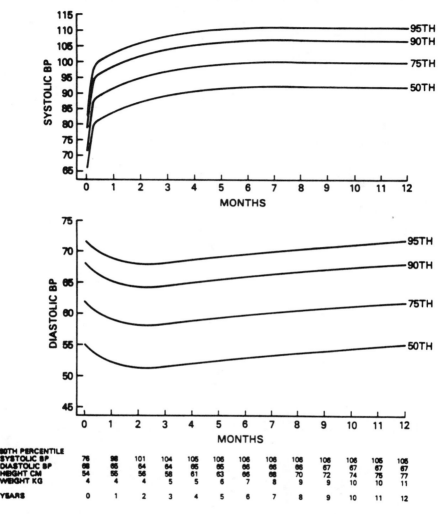

AGE-SPECIFIC PERCENTILES OF BLOOD PRESSURE MEASUREMENTS IN GIRLS BIRTH TO 12 MONTHS

90TH PERCENTILE												
SYSTOLIC BP	76	98	101	104	105	106	106	106	106	106	106	105	105
DIASTOLIC BP	68	65	64	64	65	65	66	66	66	67	67	67
HEIGHT CM	54	55	56	58	61	63	66	68	70	72	74	75	77
WEIGHT KG	4	4	4	5	5	6	7	8	9	9	10	10	11
YEARS	0	1	2	3	4	5	6	7	8	9	10	11	12

FIGURE 11-2. *Age-specific percentiles of BP measurements in girls-birth to 12 months of age; Korotkoff phase IV (K4) used for diastolic BP.*

trol in Children, 1987). In the clinical setting, height as well as weight should be used in assessing the medical significance of blood pressures that are judged to be high using such age-sex-specific standards. If a child is tall and proportionally heavy for age, a blood pressure level that is high for age is to be expected, and this is nor-

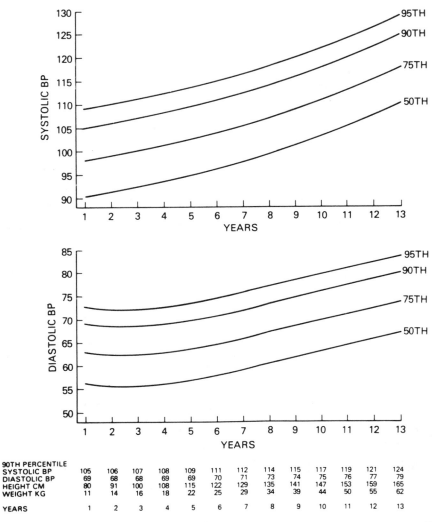

AGE-SPECIFIC PERCENTILES OF BLOOD PRESSURE MEASUREMENTS IN BOYS AGES 1 YEAR TO 13 YEARS

90TH PERCENTILE													
SYSTOLIC BP	105	106	107	108	109	111	112	114	115	117	119	121	124
DIASTOLIC BP	69	68	68	69	69	70	71	73	74	75	76	77	79
HEIGHT CM	80	91	100	108	115	122	129	135	141	147	153	159	165
WEIGHT KG	11	14	16	18	22	25	29	34	39	44	50	55	62
YEARS	1	2	3	4	5	6	7	8	9	10	11	12	13

FIGURE 11-3. *Age-specific percentiles of BP measurements in boys-1 to 13 y; Korotkoff phase IV (K4) used for diastolic BP.*

mal. For children who are tall and lean, high pressures for age are also normal. High blood pressure is also commonly observed in children with excessive weight for height, and this appears to be the result of obesity. Blood pressure levels in children also relate directly to the degree of sexual maturation as assessed by Tanner In-

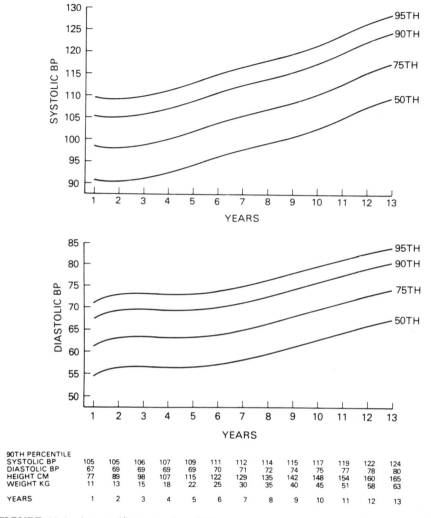

AGE-SPECIFIC PERCENTILES OF BLOOD PRESSURE MEASUREMENTS IN GIRLS AGES 1 YEAR TO 13 YEARS

90TH PERCENTILE													
SYSTOLIC BP	105	105	106	107	109	111	112	114	115	117	119	122	124
DIASTOLIC BP	67	69	69	69	69	70	71	72	74	75	77	78	80
HEIGHT CM	77	89	98	107	115	122	129	135	142	148	154	160	165
WEIGHT KG	11	13	15	18	22	25	30	35	40	45	51	58	63
YEARS	1	2	3	4	5	6	7	8	9	10	11	12	13

FIGURE 11-4. *Age-specific percentiles of BP measurements in girls-1 to 13 y; Korotkoff phase IV (K4) used for diastolic BP.*

dices (Lauer, Anderson et al., 1984). Thus, children who have accelerated sexual maturation may be expected to have a higher blood pressure than their height-matched peers.

Environmental influences can be considered in counseling. The

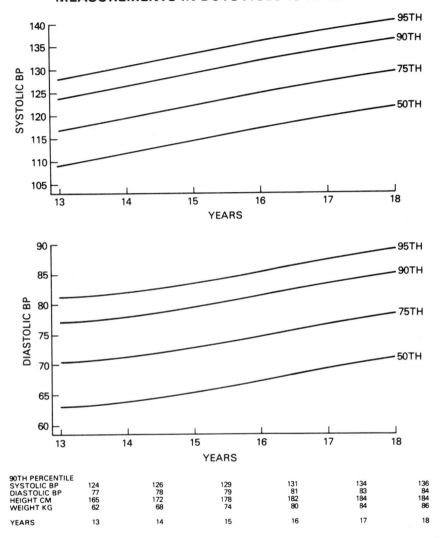

AGE-SPECIFIC PERCENTILES OF BLOOD PRESSURE MEASUREMENTS IN BOYS AGES 13 TO 18 YEARS

90TH PERCENTILE						
SYSTOLIC BP	124	126	129	131	134	136
DIASTOLIC BP	77	78	79	81	83	84
HEIGHT CM	165	172	178	182	184	184
WEIGHT KG	62	68	74	80	84	86
YEARS	13	14	15	16	17	18

FIGURE 11-5. *Age-specific percentiles of BP measurements in boys-13 to 18 y; Korotkoff phase V (K5) used for diastolic BP.*

high correlation of blood pressure among relatives and the knowledge that tracking of blood pressure occurs should be useful in counseling parents and children with high blood pressure. This knowledge should influence parents to alter the family lifestyle re-

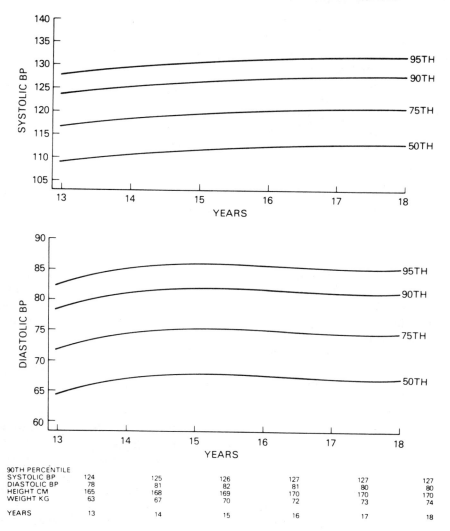

AGE-SPECIFIC PERCENTILES OF BLOOD PRESSURE MEASUREMENTS IN GIRLS AGES 13 TO 18 YEARS

90TH PERCENTILE						
SYSTOLIC BP	124	125	126	127	127	127
DIASTOLIC BP	78	81	82	81	80	80
HEIGHT CM	165	168	169	170	170	170
WEIGHT KG	63	67	70	72	73	74
YEARS	13	14	15	16	17	18

FIGURE 11-6. *Age-specific percentiles of BP measurements in girls-13 to 18 y; Korotkoff phase V (K5) used for diastolic BP.*

lated to salt intake and, for those who are obese, their caloric intake and exercise levels.

A conference of experts has recommended that adolescents with hypertension should be allowed to take part in competitive athletics as long as their diastolic pressures are less than 115 mmHg and no target organ involvement exists (Frolich et al., 1985). Target organ involvement includes cardiac, renal, and eye abnormalities. Cardiac involvement is present if:

1. There is clinical, radiographic, or electrocardiographic evidence of left ventricular abnormalities.
2. Left ventricular hypertrophy is suspected clinically and by electrocardiographic criteria or by echocardiographic criteria (that is, left ventricular wall thickening or cavity dimensions that clearly exceed the upper limit of what would be considered normal for the patient's age and body size.)

Renal involvement is present if:

1. There are elevated levels of blood urea nitrogen or creatinine confirmed by a decreased creatinine clearance.
2. There is proteinuria.

Eye involvement exists if retinal hemorrhage or exudates are present.

Most patients with mild to moderate hypertension whose blood pressure is controlled by therapy, or who have no target organ involvement, may participate in sports with high to moderate dynamic (isotonic) and low static (isometric) demand. Selected patients may participate in sports with high static demands after careful evaluation and discussion with the patient and his or her family. Those with pressures not controlled by therapy (pressure at rest greater than 140/90 mmHg) may participate in low intensity sports.

The data, which indicate that training results in a lowering of high blood pressure in childhood, suggest that children whose pressures are in the upper part of the distribution for their age should be encouraged to take part in exercise training (Hagberg et al., 1984).

In a study of South Australian children described by Maynard et al. (1987), children undergoing daily exercise decreased their skinfold thickness and diastolic pressures and increased their PWC-170 (males only). From this, these authors concluded that school-based physical health programs may have useful effects upon cardiovascular disease risk factors.

To be meaningful, exercise advocated must be prescribed with regard to specificity, intensity, duration, and mode. Studies in animals (Tipton, 1984) and humans (Kenney, 1984; Kiyonaga et al., 1985; Nomura et al., 1985; Roman et al., 1981) indicate that moderate exercise (40% to 65% $\dot{V}O_2$ maximum) of a progressive nature of more than 30 min per session three to five times per week should be prescribed to lower blood pressure. When higher intensities are prescribed, there is a risk in animals of increasing blood pressure (Tipton, 1984). The pressor responses of isometric exercise to maximal weight-lifting are sufficiently profound that prudence should prevail in the advocacy of these exercises for hypertensive-prone young people.

SUMMARY

Studies in adults clearly indicate that hypertension is an important risk factor for the development of stroke, coronary heart disease, and renal disease. The definition of hypertension in youth has not been defined by the longitudinal study of a population for a sufficient time to know the predictive value of blood pressure levels at a young age for these diseases. However, blood pressures in the young track; elevated pressures are associated with obesity in childhood; blood pressure levels aggregate in families; and dynamic exercise has been shown to have important health benefits not only in the prevention and treatment of obesity, but also on elevated blood pressure in children.

BIBLIOGRAPHY

1. Annest, J.L., C.F. Sing, P. Biron, and J.G. Mongeau. Familial aggregation of blood pressure and weight in adoptive families. II. Estimation of the relative contributions of genetic and common environmental factors to blood pressure correlations between family members. *American Journal of Epidemiology* 110:492–503, 1979.
2. Annest, J.L., C.F. Sing, P. Biron, and J.G. Mongeau. Familial aggregation of blood pressure and weight in adoptive families. III. Analysis of the role of shared genes and shared household environment in explaining family resemblance for height, weight and selected weight/height indices. *American Journal of Epidemiology* 117:492–506, 1983.
3. Beaglehole, R., C.E. Salmond, and E.F. Eyles. A longitudinal study of blood pressure in Polynesian children. *American Journal of Epidemiology* 105:87–89, 1977.
4. Berecek, K.H., S.R. Winternitz, J.M. Wyss, and S. Oparil. Exaggerated responsiveness to central sympathetic and alpha adrenergic stimulation in spontaneously hypertensive rats receiving high sodium intake. *Clinical Research* 31:487A (Abstract), 1983.
5. Berenson, G., C.A. McMahan, and A.W. Voors. Cardiovascular respectors in children: the early natural history of atherosclerosis, an essential hypertension. Berenson, G.S. (ed.), 1980.
6. Berglund, F., and O. Anderson. Body composition, metabolic and hormonal characteristics in unselected male hypertensives. *Journal of Obesity* 5:143–150. (Supplement I), 1981.
7. Bianchi, G., D. Cusi, M. Gatti, G. Lupi, P. Ferrari, C. Barlassina, G.B. Picotti, G. Bracchi, G. Colombo, D. Gori, O. Velis, and D. Mazzei. A renal abnormality as a possible cause of essential hypertension. *Lancet* 1:173–177, 1979.
8. Biron, P., J.G. Mongeau, and D. Bertrand. Familial aggregation of blood pressure in adopted and natural children. In O. Paul (ed.). *Epidemiology and Control of Hypertension*. New York: Grune & Stratton, 1977.
9. Blair, S.N., N.N. Goodyear, L.W. Gibbons, K.H. Cooper. Physical fitness and the incidence of hypertension in healthy normotensive men and women. *Journal of the American Medical Association* 252:487–490, 1984.
10. Boerwinkle, E., S.T. Turner, and C.F. Sing. The role of the genetics of sodium-lithium countertransport in the determination of blood pressure variability in the population at large. In G. Brewer (ed.). *The Red Cell: Sixth Ann Arbor Conference*. New York: Alan R. Liss, Inc., 1984.
11. Borhani, N.O., M. Feinleib, R.J. Garrison, J.C. Christian, and R.H. Rosenman. Genetic variance in blood pressure. *Acta Geneticae Medicae et Gemellologiae* 25:137–144, 1976.

12. Briedigkeit, W. et al. Untersuchungen zur Blutkruckent-wicklung bei Jungendlichen. *Deutsche Gesundhwesen* 26:1087–1090, 1981.
13. Burke, G.L., L.S. Webber, S.R. Srinivasan, B. Radhakrishnamurthy, and G.S. Berenson. Fasting plasma glucose and insulin levels and their relationship to cardiovascular risk factors in children: Bogalusa Heart Study. *Metabolism* 35:441–446, 1986.
14. Cambien, F., J.M. Warnet, E. Eschwege, A. Jacqueson, J.L. Richard, and G. Rosselin. Body mass, blood pressure, glucose and lipids. Does plasma insulin explain the relationships? *Arteriosclerosis* 7:197–202, 1987.
15. Campese, V.M., M.S. Romoff, D. Levitan, Y. Saglikes, R.M. Friedler, and S.G. Massry. Abnormal relationship between sodium intake and sympathetic nervous system activity in salt-sensitive patients with essential hypertension. *Kidney International* 21:371–378, 1982.
16. Canessa, M., N. Adragna, H.S. Solomon, T.M. Connolly, and D.C. Tosteson. Increased sodium-lithium countertransport in red cells of patients with essential hypertension. *New England Journal of Medicine* 302:772–776, 1980.
17. Christlieb, A.R., A.S. Krolewski, J.H. Warram, and J.S. Soeldner. Is insulin the link between hypertension and obesity? *Hypertension* 7:54–57, 1985. (Supplement II).
18. Clarke, W.R., H.G. Schrott, P.E. Leaverton, W.E. Connor, and R.M. Lauer. Tracking of blood lipids and blood pressure in childhood: The Muscatine Study. *Circulation* 58:626–634, 1978.
19. Criqui, M.H., W.L. Haskell, G. Heiss, H.A. Tyroler, P. Green, and C.J. Rubenstein. Predictors of systolic blood pressure response: The Lipid Research Clinics Program Prevalence Study. *Circulation* 68:225–233, 1983.
20. Culpepper, W.S., P.C. Sodt, F.H. Messerli, D.G. Ruschhaupt, and R.A. Arcilla. Cardiac status in juvenile borderline hypertension. *Annals of Internal Medicine* 98:1–7, 1983.
21. Dadone, M.M., S.J. Hasstedt, S.C. Hunt, J.B. Smith, K.O. Ash, and R.R. Williams. Genetic analysis of sodium-lithium countertransport in 10 hypertension-prone kindreds. *American Journal of Medical Genetics* 17:565–577, 1984.
22. Dahl, L.K., and R.A. Love. Evidence for a relationship between sodium (chloride) intake and human essential hypertension. *Archives of Internal Medicine* 94:525–531,1954.
23. Dahl, L.K., M. Heine, and L. Tassinari. Effects of chronic salt ingestion: Evidence that genetic factors play an important role in the susceptibility to experimental hypertension. *Journal of Experimental Medicine* 115:1173–1190, 1962.
24. de Champlain, J., L. Krakoff, and J. Axelrod. Relationship between sodium intake and norepinephrine storage during development of experimental hypertension. *Circulation Research* 23:479–491, 1968.
25. DeFronzo, R.A. The effect of insulin on renal sodium metabolism. *Diabetologia* 21:165–171, 1981.
26. DeFronzo, R.A., M. Goldberg, and Z. Agus. The effects of glucose and insulin on renal electrolyte transport. *Journal of Clinical Investigation* 58:83–90, 1976.
27. DeMaria, A.N., A. Neumann, G. Lee, W. Fowler, and D.T. Mason. Alterations in ventricular mass and performance induced by exercise training in man evaluated by echocardiography. *Circulation* 57:237–244, 1978.
28. deSwiet, M., P. Fayers, and E.A. Shinebourne. Blood pressure survey in a population of newborn infants. *British Medical Journal* 2:1–1, 1976.
29. Dimsdale, J.E., R.M. Graham, M.G. Ziegler, R.M. Zusman, and C.C. Berry. Age, race, diagnosis and sodium effects on the pressor response to infused hypertension. *Hypertension* 10:564–569, 1987.
30. Duhm, J., B.O. Gobel, R. Lorenz, and P.C. Weber. Sodium-lithium exchange and sodium-potassium cotransport in human erythrocytes. Part 2: A simple uptake test applied to normotensive and essential hypertensive individuals. *Hypertension* 4:477–482, 1982.
31. Falkner, B., Is there a black hypertension? *Hypertension* 10:551–554, 1987.
32. Falkner, B., G. Onesti, and E. Angelakos. Effect of salt loading on the cardiovascular response to stress in adolescents. *Hypertension* 3:195–199, 1981. (Supplement II).
33. Farinaro, E., E. Celentano, L.A. Ferrara, F. Jossa, V. Krogh, P. Strazzullo, and D. Giumetti. Detection of risk factors for atherosclerosis in children: Studies in Naples. In B. Hetzel and G.S. Berenson (eds.). *Cardiovascular Risk Factors in Childhood: Epidemiology and Prevention.* Amsterdam: Elsevier Science Publishers, 1987.
34. Feinleib, M., R.J. Garrison, and R.J. Havlik. Environmental and genetic factors affecting the distribution of blood pressure in children. In R.M. Lauer, and R.B. Shekelle (eds.). *Childhood Prevention of Atherosclerosis and Hypertension.* New York: Raven Press, 1980.
35. Fixler, D. E., W.P. Laird, and K. Dana. Usefulness of exercise stress testing for prediction of blood pressure trends. *Pediatrics* 75:1071–1075, 1985.
36. Fraser, G.E., R.L. Phillips, and R. Harris. Physical fitness and blood pressure in school children. *Circulation* 67:405–412, 1983.
37. Fripp, R.R., J.L. Hodgson, P.O. Kwiterovich, J.C. Werner, H.G. Schuler, and V. Whit-

man. Aerobic capacity, obesity, and atherosclerotic risk factors in male adolescents. *Pediatrics* 75:813–818, 1985.

38. Frolich, E.D., D.T. Lowenthal, H.S. Miller, T. Pickering, and W.B. Strong. Cardiovascular abnormalities in the athlete: Recommendations regarding eligibility for competition. Task Force IV: Systemic arterial hypertension. *Journal of the American College of Cardiology* 6:1218–1221, 1985.

39. Fujita, T., W.L. Henry, F.C. Bartter, C.R. Lake, and C.S. Delea. Factors influencing blood pressure in salt-sensitive patients with essential hypertension. *Kidney International* 21:371–378, 1980.

40. Garay, R.P., J.L. Elghozi, G. Dagher, and P. Meyere. Laboratory distinction between essential and secondary hypertension by measurement of erythrocyte cation fluxes. *New England Journal of Medicine* 302:769–771, 1980.

41. Hagberg, J.M., A.A. Ehsani, D. Goldring, A. Hernandez, D.R. Sinacore, and J.O. Holloszy. The effect of weight training on blood pressure and hemodynamics in hypertensive adolescents. *Journal of Pediatrics* 104:147–151, 1984.

42. Hagberg, J.M., D. Goldring, A.A. Ehsani, G.W. Heath, A. Hernandez, K. Schechtman, and J.O. Holloszy. Effect of exercise training on blood pressure and hemodynamic features of hypertensive adolescents. *American Journal of Cardiology* 52:763–768, 1983.

43. Hait, H.I., S. Lemeshow, and K.D. Rosenman. A longitudinal study of blood pressure in a national survey of children. *American Journal of Public Health* 72:1285–1287, 1982.

44. Hanis, C.L., C.F. Sing, W.R. Clarke, and R.M. Lauer. Multivariate models for human genetic analysis: Aggregation, coaggregation and tracking of systolic blood pressure and weight. *American Journal of Human Genetics* 35:1196–1210, 1983.

45. Havlik, R.J., R.J. Garrison, S.H. Katz, R.C. Ellison, M. Feinleib, and N.C. Myriantho-poulous. Detection of genetic variance in blood pressure of seven-year-old twins. *American Journal of Epidemiology* 109:512–516, 1979.

46. Higgins, M., P. Cole, S. Garn. Familial resemblance in blood pressure. *CVD Epidemiology Newsletter* 22-24 (January), 1977.

47. Hofman, A., H.J. Walter, P.A. Connelly, and R.D. Vaughan. Blood pressure and physical fitness in children. *Hypertension* 9:188–191, 1987.

48. Holland, W.W., and S.A.A. Beresford. Factors influencing blood pressure in children. In O. Paul (ed.). *Epidemiology and Control of Hypertension*. New York: Grune & Stratton, 1977.

49. Hypertension Detection and Follow-Up Program Cooperative Group. Five-year findings of hypertension detection and follow-up program. I. Reduction in mortality of persons with high blood pressures, including mild hypertension. *Journal of the American Medical Association* 242:2562–2571, 1979.

50. Jesse, M.J., J.A. Hokanson, B. Klein, R. Levine, and J. Gourley. Blood pressures in childhood: Initial versus one-year follow-up. *Circulation* 53–54 (Supplement), II-23. (Abstract), 1976.

51. Johnson, A.L., J.C. Cornoni, J.C. Cassels, H.A. Tyroler, S. Heyden, and C.G. Hames. Influence of race, sex and weight on blood pressure behavior in young adults. *American Journal of Cardiology* 35:523–530, 1975.

52. Kannel, W.B., W.P. Castelli, P.M. McNamara, P.A. McKee, and M. Feinleib. Role of blood pressure in the development of congestive heart failure: The Framingham Study. *New England Journal of Medicine* 287:781–787, 1972.

53. Kannel, W.B., P.A. Wolf, J. Verter, and P.M. McNamara. Epidemiologic assessment of the role of blood pressure in stroke: The Framingham Study. *Journal of the American Medical Association* 214:301–310, 1970.

54. Kawasaki, T., C.S. Delea, F.C. Bartter, and H. Smith. The effect of high-sodium and low-sodium intakes on blood pressure and other related variables in human subjects with idiopathic hypertension. *American Journal of Medicine* 64:193–198, 1978.

55. Kenney, W.L., and E.J. Zambraski. Physical activity in human hypertension-A mechanisms approach. *Sports Medicine* 1:459–473, 1984.

56. Kiyonaga, A., K. Arakawa, H. Tanaka, and M. Shindo. Blood pressure and hormonal responses to aerobic exercise. *Hypertension* 7:125–131, 1985.

57. Klein, A.A., W.W. McCrory, M.A. Engle, R. Rosenthal, and K.H. Ehlers. Sympathetic nervous system and exercise tolerance response in normotensive and hypertensive adolescents. *Journal of the American College of Cardiology* 3:381–386, 1984.

58. Klein, B.E., C.H. Hennekens, M.J. Jesse, J.E. Gourley, and S. Blumenthal. Longitudinal studies of blood pressure in offspring of hypertensive mothers. In O. Paul (ed.). *Epidemiology and Control of Hypertension*. New York: Grune & Stratton, 1977.

59. Kuller, L.H., M. Crook, M.J. Almes, K. Detre, G. Reese, and G. Rutan. Dormont High School (Pittsburgh, PA) blood pressure study. *Hypertension* 2:109–116. (Supplement I), 1980.

60. Lauer, R.M., A.R. Anderson, R. Beaglehole, and T.L. Burns. Factors related to tracking of blood pressure in children. *Hypertension* 6:307–314, 1984.

61. Lauer, R.M., W.R. Clarke, and R. Beaglehole. Level, trend and variability of blood pressure during childhood: The Muscatine Study. *Circulation* 69:242–249, 1984.
62. Levine, R.S., C.H. Hennekens, R.C. Duncan, E.G. Robertson, J.E. Gourley, J.C. Cassady, and H. Gelband. Blood pressure in infant twins: Birth to 6 months of age. *Hypertension* 2:29–33. (Supplement I), 1980.
63. Levine, R.S., C.H. Hennekens, B. Klein, and M.J. Jesse. Tracking correlations of blood pressure levels in infancy. *Pediatrics* 61:121–125, 1978.
64. Levy, D., R.J. Garrison, W.B. Kannel, D.D. Savage, P. Wol, and W.P. Castelli. Left ventricular mass predicts incidence of cardiovascular disease. Abstracts of the 28th Annual Conference on Cardiovascular Epidemiology, Council on Epidemiology, American Heart Association Abstract #91, 1988.
65. Liang, C.S., J.U. Doherty, R. Faillace, K. Maekawa, S. Arnold, H. Gavras, and W. Hood. Insulin infusions in conscious dogs. *Journal of Clinical Investigation* 69:1321–1336, 1982.
66. Light, L.C., J.P. Koepke, P.A. Obrist, P.W. Willis,IV. Psychologic stress induces sodium and fluid retention in man at high risk for hypertension. *Science* 22:429–431, 1983.
67. Lokhandwala, M.F., and D.C. Eikenburg. Presynaptic receptors and alterations in norepinephrine release in spontaneously hypertensive rats. *Life Sciences* 33:1527–1542, 1983.
68. Lucas, C.P., J.A. Estigarribia, L.L. Darga, and G.M. Reaven. Insulin and blood pressure in obesity. *Hypertension*:702–706, 1985.
69. Mahoney, L.T., R.M. Schieken, W.R. Clarke, and R.M. Lauer. Left ventricular mass and exercise responses predict future blood pressure: The Muscatine Study. *Hypertension* 12:206–213, 1988.
70. Management Committee of the Australian Therapeutic Trial in Mild Hypertension. Untreated mild hypertension: A report by the management committee of the Australian Therapeutic Trial in Mild Hypertension. *Lancet* 1:185–191, 1982.
71. Manicardi, V., L. Camellini, G. Bellodi, C. Coscelli, and E. Ferrannini. Evidence for an association of high blood pressure and hyperinsulinemia in obese man. *Journal of Clinical Endocrinology and Metabolism* 62:1302–1304, 1986.
72. Maynard, E., W.E. Coonan, A. Worsley, T. Dwyer, and P.A. Baghurst. The development of the lifestyle education program in Australia. In B. Hetzel and G.S. Berenson (eds.). *Cardiovascular Risk Factors in Childhood: Epidemiology and Prevention.* Amsterdam: Elsevier Science Publishers, 1987.
73. Moll, P.P., E. Harburg, T.L. Burns, M.A. Schork, and F. Ozgoren. Heredity, stress and blood pressure, a family set approach: The Detroit Project revisited. *Journal of Chronic Diseases* 36:317–328, 1983.
74. Morton, N.E., and C.J. MacLean. Analysis of family resemblance. III. Complex segregation of quantitative traits. *American Journal of Human Genetics* 26:489–503, 1974.
75. Morton, N.E., C.L. Gulbrandsen, D.C. Rao, G.G. Rhoads, and A. Kagan. Determinants of blood pressure in Japanese-American families. *Human Genetics* 53:261–266, 1980.
76. Nielsen, J.R., and H. Oxhoj. Echocardiographic variables in the progeny of hypertensive and normotensive parents. *Acta Medica Scandinavica* 693:61–64. (Supplement), 1983.
77. Nomura, G., E. Kumagai, K. Midorikawa, T. Kitano, and H. Tashiro. Physical training in essential hypertension: Alone and in combination with dietary salt restriction. *Journal of Cardiac Rehabilitation* 5:308–312, 1985.
78. Nudel, D.B., N. Gootman, S.C. Brunson, A. Stenzler, I.R. Shenker, and B.G. Gauthier. Exercise performance of hypertensive adolescents. *Pediatrics* 65:1073–1078, 1980.
79. Paffenbarger, R.S., A.L. Wing, R.T. Hyde, and D.L. Jung. Physical activity and incidence of hypertension in college alumni. *American Journal of Epidemiology* 117:245–257, 1983.
80. Page, L.B., A. Damon, and R.C. Moellering, Jr. Antecedents of cardiovascular disease in six Solomon Islands societies. *Circulation* 49:1132–1146, 1974.
81. Panico, S., E. Celentano, V. Krogh, F. Jossa, E. Farinaro, M. Trevisan, and M. Mancini. Physical activity and its relationship to blood pressure in school children. *Journal of Chronic Diseases* 40:925–930, 1987.
82. Pickering, G. The inheritance of arterial pressure. In J. Stamler, R. Stamler, and T.N. Pullman (eds.). *The Epidemiology of Hypertension.* New York: Grune & Stratton, 1967.
83. Pickering, T.G. Exercise and hypertension. *Cardiology Clinics* 5:311–318, 1987.
84. Platt, R. The influence of heredity. In J. Stamler, R. Stamler, and T.N. Pullman (eds.). *The Epidemiology of Hypertension.* New York: Grune & Stratton, 1967.
85. Pyorala, L., E. Savolainen, S. Kaukola, and J. Haapakoski. Plasma insulin as a coronary heart disease risk factor: Relationship to other risk factors and predictive value during 9 1/2 year follow-up of the Helsinki Policeman Study Population. *Acta Medica Scandinavica* 701:38–52. (Supplement), 1985.
86. Ren, J., A. Hakki, M.N. Kotler, and A.S. Iskandrian. Exercise systolic blood pressure: A powerful determinant of increased left ventricular mass in patients with hypertension. *Journal of the American College of Cardiology* 5:1224–1231, 1985.

87. Report of the Second Task Force Report on Blood Pressure Control in Children—1987. *Pediatrics* 79:1–25, 1987.
88. Rocchini, A.P., V. Katch, A. Schork, and R.P. Kelch. Insulin and blood pressure during weight loss in obese adolescents. *Hypertension* 10:267–273, 1987.
89. Roman, O., A.L. Camuzzi, E. Villalon, and C. Klenner. Physical training program in arterial hypertension: A long-term prospective follow-up. *Cardiology* 67:230–243, 1981.
90. Rosner, B., C.H. Hennekens, E.H. Kass, and W.E. Miall. Age-specific correlation analysis of longitudinal blood pressure data. *American Journal of Epidemiology* 106:306–313, 1977.
91. Schachter, J., L.H. Kuller, J.M. Perkins, and M.E. Radin. Infant blood pressure and heart rate. *American Journal of Epidemiology* 110:205–218, 1979.
92. Schieken, R.M., W.R. Clarke, and R.M. Lauer. Left ventricular hypertrophy in children with blood pressures in the upper part of the distribution: The Muscatine Study. *Hypertension* 3:669–675, 1981.
93. Schieken, R.M., W.R. Clarke, and R.M. Lauer. The cardiovascular responses to exercise in children across the blood pressure distribution: The Muscatine Study. *Hypertension* 5:71–78, 1983.
94. Sims, E.A.H. Mechanisms of hypertension in the overweight. *Hypertension* 4:43–49. (Supplement III), 1982.
95. Strong, W. Hypertension and sports. *Pediatrics* 64:693–694, 1979.
96. Tipton, C.M. Exercise training and hypertension *Exercise and Sport Science Reviews* 10:245–306, 1984.
97. Veterans Administration Cooperative Study Group on Antihypertensive Agents. Effects of treatment on morbidity in hypertension. *Journal of the American Medical Association* 202:1028–1034, 1967.
98. Ward, R.H., R.G. Chin, and I.A.M. Prior. Genetic epidemiology of blood pressure in a migrating isolate: Prospectus. In C.F. Sing, and M. Skolnick (eds.). *Genetic Analysis of Common Diseases: Applications to Predictive Factors in Coronary Disease.* New York:Alan R. Liss, Inc, 1979.
99. Williams, R.R., S.C. Hunt, H. Kuida, J.B. Smith, and K.O. Ash. Sodium-lithium countertransport in erythrocytes of hypertension prone families in Utah. *American Journal of Epidemiology* 118:338–344, 1983.
100. Wilson, N.V., and B.M. Meyer. Early prediction of hypertension using exercise blood pressure. *Preventive Medicine* 10:62–68, 1981.
101. Woods, J.W., R.J. Falk, A.W. Pittman, P.J. Klemmer, B.S. Watson, and K. Namboodiri. Increased red-cell sodium-lithium countertransport in normotensive sons of hypertensive parents. *New England Journal of Medicine* 306:593–595, 1982.
102. Zinner, S.H., P.S. Levy, and E.H. Kass. Familial aggregation of blood pressure in childhood. *New England Journal of Medicine* 284:401–404, 1971.
103. Zinner, S.H., H.S. Margolius, B. Rosner, and E.H. Kass. Stability of blood pressure rank and urinary kallikrein concentration in childhood: An eight-year follow-up. *Circulation* 58:908–915, 1978.

DISCUSSION

GONYEA: I wanted to comment on Tip's suggestion that there is something bizarre about doing static exercise and seeing an elevated blood pressure. Every time you lift something you get a pressor response. Not to study it or not to have some indications of its long-term consequences in children is to ignore the fact that it's part of what children have to adapt to. Certainly there's no longitudinal evidence that these bizarre blood pressures are not within normal physiological tolerances of what the human body is capable of withstanding. We should acknowledge it happens and get on with studying it, especially in young children. The little longitudinal evidence in humans that both Joe and Digby presented indicate that there is no increase in resting blood pressure with a long-term static exercise regimen. In fact, there may be a reduced blood pressure.

I think it's something that we definitely need to know more about. You know, we're in the 1980s before we're even saying, "look at these bizarre high blood pressure levels you can achieve with lifting." But we've been lifting every day of our lives everytime we grab hold of a bag of groceries.

LAUER: Is there anything known about the morbidity and mortality of people who have been wrestlers or weightlifters over a long period of time?

GONYEA: You get a casual report that some of them die, but we do not have any systematic long-term studies that indicate the morbidity.

LAUER: Is there a central registry of people who take part in those kinds of competitive athletics?

GONYEA: In Eastern Europe and in Russia.

BLIMKIE: This is somewhat a follow-up to Bill's comments. I realize that the focus of the presentation and the reaction to it is basically in terms of blood pressure response, but Weltman and Reen looked at issues besides blood pressure and found that resistance training tended to have a favorable effect on lipid profile. There really weren't dramatic, significant changes, but there may be other benefits achieved from resistance exercise besides the possible detrimental effects to blood pressure. In our training study of 20 weeks with children, we found no change in left ventricular mass using M-mode echocardiography.

TIPTON: First, I didn't say you shouldn't study the problem, rather, it should not be studied in hypertensive or hypotensive prone individuals. Second, if you have an individual known to have a condition that could lead to hypertension, then you would be prudent to avoid isometric exercise with that population. Third, Bill, I'm not convinced that your cat blood pressure data has been systematically presented to show either an increase or a decrease. You may have that data, but if you have published it, I haven't seen it. My recollection is that when your cat made an isometric contraction, mean blood pressure increased about 25 millimeters of mercury, as it does with our hypertensive rat hanging to perform an isometric maneuver. Now let me go one step further. We tried to produce strokes by isometric exercise, with stroke prone hypertensive animals on a high salt diet. These animals have blood pressures of 225 to 250 mmHg. We found no statistical evidence that isometric exercise would produce or accentuate a stroke. On a related matter, not all populations are responsive to endurance exercise, specifically if you have Dahl salt sensitive rats. These rats will not have lower resting blood pressure with exercise training at 40-65% VO_2 max. If you have Goldblatt or stroke-prone hypertensive rats, you cannot show a training effect. Consequently, we have speculated that renal hypertensive children will not benefit from an exercise training program as far as their resting blood pressure is concerned. Therefore, we should look to other ways to manage that condition.

SUTTON: A brief clarification about the people that develop strokes when they weightlift. The original study that was conducted, MacDougal first author, showed that the mean blood pressure during a double leg press rose to something like 350 mmHg systolic and the highest one of these had one close to 500 mmHg. What surprised us was not so much the magnitude of this response, but the possibility that this was happening regularly in people weightlifting. To back up what Bill was saying, all we were doing was describing the natural phenomenon. However, in the course of doing that study, we now have collected data on more than seven individuals who have had various types of cerebrovascular accidents, including a 16-year-old girl who had a subarachnoid hemorrhage during weightlifting, one of the Canadian Olympic weightlifters who died of a stroke during weightlifting, and another athlete who had a cerebellar lesion when he tried to lift three-quarters of a ton. So you know, these things do actually occur. I'm particularly intrigued at the possibility of predicting people who may develop sustained hypertension later on by the use of an exercise test. In the adult population, it's not uncommon to find people who are normotensive at rest and who, during an exercise test, irrespective of the criteria used, are frankly hypertensive. First, do we have any information on children? Do we actually have any long-term information on whether people with those responses do indeed develop sustained resting hypertension?

LAUER: There is some data that relates to exercise testing and blood pressure in children. It's of two kinds. One indicates that the children who are in the upper part of the distribution versus those who are in the middle or lowest part of the distribution maintain different blood pressure during exercise. In other words, the higher group gets higher and the middle group gets not quite so high, and the lowest group remains least. Thus, blood pressure maintains rank order during exercise. The second type of evidence is that those who get the greatest response of blood pressure elevations with exercise develop greater left ventricular wall mass in future years. So those who have sharp elevation of blood pressure with exertion seem to have that integrated into their myocardium as they get older. Whether this places them at greater risk for heart attack or stroke is unknown.

DISHMAN: I might direct this more to Dr. Tipton. My question is this: How plausible is it that one of the other confounding factors of training adaptations that might be added to the list of salt-sensitivity and adiposity is the host of stress-related characteristics that people carry around with them? I mention that because we have two unpublished investigations showing that resting blood pressures in the populations studied seem to have some covariation with anger in people and the way in which they tend to express their anger. What we've seen is some correlation between those anger measurements and the rise in systolic blood pressure during an acute bout of graded exercise. In one training study, we observed a correlation between those measures and the degree of adaptation. All we have controlled for is age and fitness, and I'm curious about what other things we might need to control for and if that makes any sense in the total picture? That's something that's not discussed or studied very much, and I'm curious for our own data and future studies.

TIPTON: That's a good question. I do know that if you examine blood pressure by races, black populations that are "matched" will elicit an exaggerated response to a mental test by about 1-15 mmHg. So I think your point is well-taken and a factor that has to be considered. Lastly, I think it needs to be recognized that some people are hyper-responders to any type of a stress.

VAILAS: I'd like someone to comment on the idea of stress. When one intervenes with exercise for an individual from a low socioeconomic background who probably has a poor nutritional history and/or may have a situation with a lot of parental pressure or peer pressure, what would exercise do to blood pressure? We know that a rat strain was developed by stressing animals over a series of generations to produce a hypertensive colony.

LAUER: There is some human data that bears a little bit on that in children. Bonita Falkner has provided mental stress (some by doing arithmetic, some by television games) to the progeny of hypertensive parents and to the progeny of normotensive parents. The children are normotensive at the time of the mental stress. Those who are the progeny of hypertensive parents have a significantly greater response to mental challenge than do the children of normotensive parents. It's clear that everybody who is put in a stressful situation does not respond in the same way with respect to their blood pressure. There may be ways for us to select children who are hyper-responding to their environment. But the technology for that in the human population is not very well standardized, and we're just getting the first glimpses of it now. With respect to the question that has to do with anger in and anger out and its relationship as a coronary risk factor and its mechanism through Type A behavior, its relationship to blood pressure in my view is not clear.

JAMES: I just want to make two comments. One is relative to isometric exercise. It may be dose-dependent. We did some work with Ron Wiley at Oxford University who has taken college students and given them a therapeutic dose of isometric exercise, 30 MVC handgrip intermittently over an eight-week period of time. We have demonstrated a significant drop in systolic and diastolic blood pressure in normotensive students. We are now trying to determine if there are changes that occur in this population and also in hypertensive populations. The second point is that in a significant number of borderline hypertensive children in which we have measured cardiac output during a stress test, a significant number of those kids have normalized their peak exercise blood pressure with normal cardiac output.

12

Exercise-Induced Asthma

Robert F. Lemanske, Jr., M.D.

Kathe G. Henke, Ph.D.

INTRODUCTION

Childhood asthma affects 6.7% of youths within the United States with an increased prevalence noted in blacks vs. whites (9.4% vs. 6.2%), boys vs. girls, (7.8% vs. 5.5%) and in children who live in urban vs. rural areas (7.1% vs. 5.7%) (Gergen et al., 1988). For unknown reasons, the overall prevalence of asthma is increasing. In children, asthma is a leading cause of morbidity (Gergen et al., 1988). Indeed, asthma and wheezing combined were the 10th most frequent reason for visits (approximately 2.2 million) to pediatricians from 1980 to 1981; asthmatic children have an increased number of school absences due to illness (Mitchell & Dawson, 1973; Peckham & Butler, 1978); and asthma has a disruptive influence on the functioning of both patient and family, which can result in increased divorce rates (Gergen et al., 1988). Of even greater concern is that, despite improved therapy for asthma, the rate of hospitalizations for asthma (Halfon & Newacheck, 1986) and the number of deaths attributed to asthma (Markham et al., 1986) are also increasing.

Statistics pertaining to the epidemiology of asthma have been influenced by the lack of a universally acceptable definition. In a recent report, a leading pulmonologist wrote, "We all know what (asthma) is, but who would trust anybody else's definition?" (Gross, 1980). According to the American Thoracic Society, asthma is a disease characterized by an increased responsiveness of the tracheobronchial tree to a variety of stimuli, resulting in widespread narrowing of the airways that changes in severity either spontaneously or as a result of therapy (American Thoracic Society, 1962). To the pediatric or adolescent patient, asthma means wheezing, shortness of breath, and/or cough that may restrict activities, affect school attendance, or result in chronic medication usage, emergency room visits, or hospitalization. To the clinician treating asthmatic patients, the most distinguishing and gratifying feature is the ability to reverse or attenuate the symptoms with appropriate medical therapy. To the scientist, asthma is characterized by airway reactivity; to the pathologist, by tissue inflammation. Thus, asthma means many different things to different people.

In addition to being characterized by reversible airway obstruction and airway hyperreactivity (or airway "twitchiness"), one of the distinguishing features of asthma is the ability to "trigger" asthma attacks with recognized stimuli (Table 12-1). Triggering factors in children include viral upper respiratory tract infections (Minor et al., 1974); exposure to allergens (Warner & Price, 1978); exposure to irritants such as cigarette smoke (Schenker et al., 1983) and wood-burning stoves (Honicky et al., 1985); cold air exposure; sinus infections in some (Rachelefsky et al., 1984; Friedman et al., 1984) but not all patients (Zimmerman et al., 1987); and the subject of this review, exercise (Sheppard, 1987).

Thus, exercise-induced asthma (EIA), by definition, is an attack of asthma that is provoked by exercise. Some individuals will only experience asthmatic symptoms related to exercise, while in others, asthmatic symptoms may occur on a daily basis and become exacerbated during exercise. In comparison to chronic asthma, EIA is usually self-limited and rarely results in hospitalization or death; however, its importance relates to the fact that it may significantly alter a child's participation in physical activities ranging from riding a tricycle to competing in sports.

I. CHARACTERISTICS OF EXERCISE-INDUCED ASTHMA (EIA)

A. Immediate Response

The incidence of EIA in patients with asthma has historically varied from 50% to 80% depending on the type and duration of exercise stimulus and the pulmonary function measurements used to assess changes in airway caliber. Presently, however, EIA is considered to be a universal feature of the asthmatic state, provided the exercise challenge is sufficiently stressful and conducted under optimal conditions of temperature and humidity (McFadden, 1987a). Although EIA is most commonly a problem in the asthmatic patient, it has also been reported in patients with allergic rhinitis (Pierson et al., 1972) and in children who have a past history of croup

---

TABLE 12-1. *Factors important in "triggering" asthma attacks in children and adolescents.*

Viral upper respiratory infections
Allergens (cat and dog dander, mites, pollens, molds)
Irritants (smoke, strong perfumes, pollution)
Cold, dry air
Sinus infections
Emotions (laughing and crying)
Exercise

(Loughlin & Taussig, 1979), cystic fibrosis (Silverman et al., 1978; Counahan & Mearns, 1975), or bronchopulmonary dysplasia (a chronic lung condition that follows neonatal respiratory distress) (Badger et al., 1987).

Clinically, the symptom pattern of EIA includes cough, wheezing, or shortness of breath, most commonly *following* exercise. Both clinical and laboratory observations indicate that short (4 to 10 min), intense periods of exercise are the most likely to trigger asthmatic symptoms. The precise relationships between the length and intensity of exercise in terms of their propensity to induce EIA have not been definitely established. Factors such as concomitant allergen exposure (running outdoors during pollen season), climatic conditions (temperature and humidity), and baseline airway reactivity are also important variables that will influence the response to exercise.

Laboratory evaluation of EIA has utilized a 4 to 10 min period of exercise at a level of intensity to increase the patient's heart rate to 80% of maximum. Using this exercise stimulus, the clinical pattern of EIA is very characteristic (Figure 12-1). During exercise, bronchodilation occurs; it is known that bronchodilation will continue for at least 12 min if exercise is continued (Stirling et al., 1983) and that the degree of bronchodilation is influenced by the physical fitness of the patient (Haas et al., 1985). The mechanisms respon-

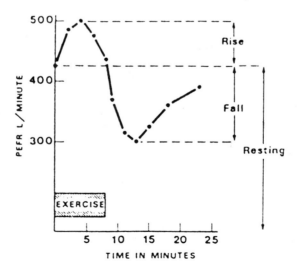

FIGURE 12-1. *Changes in PEFR and recorded during and after 8 min of treadmill running in an asthmatic patient (Reprinted with permission from: Anderson S, Seale JP, Ferris L, Schoeffel R, Lindsay DA: An evaluation to exercise-induced asthma.* J. Allergy Clin Immunol 1979; 64:612–24.)

sible for the bronchodilation are not established. The role of endogenous catecholamines (epinephrine) is questionable. In a study of normal subjects by Warren et al. (1984), beta blockade had no effect on the bronchodilation normally seen with exercise. Bronchodilation was demonstrated by measures of resistance using the panting technique. Inhibition of vagal effects caused maximal bronchodilation before exercise, and no further change was seen during exercise. Since atropine caused a similar drop in resistance as was seen with exercise, withdrawal of vagal tone may contribute to bronchial smooth muscle relaxation. Further, because beta blockade caused a significant increase in resistance *after* exercise in these normal subjects, blunted rises in catecholamines may contribute to the post-exercise bronchoconstriction.

If, after 4 to 10 min of intense exercise, the patient stops exercising, airway obstruction will begin to occur and reach its peak 1 to 10 min later. Symptoms usually disappear within 10 to 30 min. In a few asthmatic patients, exercise-related bronchospasm gets progressively worse for 30 to 60 min before it improves. In adults, symptoms often start later and last longer than they do in children (Anderson et al., 1975). Some individuals report that they are able to continue to exercise despite experiencing asthma symptoms 5 to 10 min after starting their particular activity, so-called "running through" their asthma. Although the most intense EIA is produced by continuous exercise of sufficient intensity for 6 to 8 min, exercise-provoked symptoms can occur following exercise durations ranging from 8 to 30 min (Morton et al., 1983). Any form of interrupted exercise or less severe exercise, as for example in many team sports, is much less likely to produce EIA (Godfrey, 1984).

B. Late Response

In addition to the immediate airway obstructive response that occurs following exercise of sufficient length and intensity, late asthmatic reactions have also been reported (Lee et al., 1983; Bierman et al., 1984; Horn et al., 1984; Boner et al., 1985; Foresi et al., 1986; Boulet et al., 1987). Following resolution of the immediate response, a second episode of airway obstruction can develop, which begins 2 to 4 h following challenge, peaks between 4 to 8 h, and resolves within 12 to 24 h (Figure 12-2). This late asthmatic response occurs without the patient being exposed to a second exercise stimulus. Late asthmatic responses also occur following allergen challenge, and the pathogenesis of these reactions appears to involve mast cell mediator release with the subsequent ingress of inflammatory cells (Lemanske & Kaliner, 1988). The inflammatory cells (including neutrophils, eosinophils, and lymphocytes) are thought to induce the late response through the generation of airway inflammation, mucus secretion, edema, and possibly bronchospasm. Serum levels of neutrophil chemotactic factor, a putative mast cell mediator, have been noted to rise in parallel with changes in airway function in patients who developed dual airway obstructive responses to exercise (Lee et al., 1983). These findings have been interpreted to imply that pulmonary mast cell mediator release also plays a role in the pathogenesis of EIA. However, recent work indicates that dual reactions that have been described following exercise may be related to previously unappreciated diurnal variations in pulmonary function (Rubinstein et al., 1987; McFadden, 1987b). Exercise-induced late asthmatic reactions appear to be more common in children than adults (Lee et al., 1983); in adults, the incidence of these responses has been estimated to be about 30% (Boulet et al., 1987). In individuals who develop dual reactions following exercise, there is a correlation

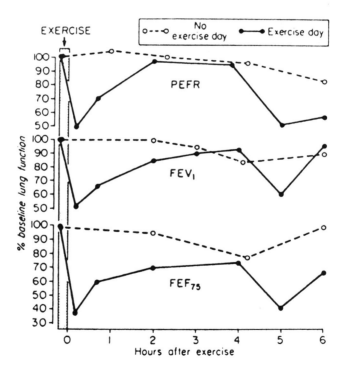

FIGURE 12-2. *Serial pulmonary function tests in a subject who complained of nocturnal asthma on days when she exercised. Following challenge, she experienced an immediate reaction, recovered spontaneously, then developed a late reaction. (Reprinted with permission from: Bierman CW: A comparison of late reactions to antigen and exercise. J Allergy Clin Immunol 1984; 73:654–59.)*

between the magnitude of the early and late reactions, emphasizing the direct relationship between these events. The propensity to develop dual responses, as opposed to isolated immediate responses only, does not depend on the baseline level of airway reactivity or disease severity (Iikura et al., 1985). However, in children who develop dual responses, the rate of recovery from early reactions is slower, and this variable may be helpful in predicting at risk patients (Iikura et al., 1985).

C. Refractory Period

After exercise, 40-50% of asthmatic patients with EIA will be less responsive, or refractory, to an identical exercise task performed within 2 h (Schoeffel et al., 1980; Anderson, 1983). The refractory period is defined as the period during which repeated exercise under identical conditions induces less than 50% of the initial asthmatic response. When the initial exercise is strenuous and the resultant bronchoconstriction is extreme, more complete inhibition of asthma from subsequent exercise follows than with less strenuous exercise (Edmunds et al., 1978). However, the duration of the refractory period is unrelated to the severity of the initial episode of EIA (Lee & Anderson, 1985). Patients made refractory to exercise still develop bronchoconstriction to inhaled allergen (Weiler-Ravell & Godfrey, 1981). In addition to exercise, refractory periods following isocapnic hyperventilation have also been demonstrated by some investigators (Deal et al., 1979a and b; Chen et al., 1979; Bar-Yishay et al., 1983a; Ben-Dov et al., 1983b) but not all investigators (Tal et al., 1984).

The mechanisms by which a refractory state is induced following exercise are imprecisely known. Various theories have been advanced, including mediator depletion from mast cells and elevation in circulating levels of catecholamines. Recent work that demonstrated the ability of indomethacin to modulate these responses suggests that the refractory state may be dependent on a cyclooxygenase pathway product of arachidonic acid metabolism (O'Byrne & Jones, 1986).

A universal warm-up "prescription" that will consistently induce a refractory period has not been established. Schnall and Landau (1980) demonstrated that 30 s sprints could induce a refractory state to a 6 min exercise stimulus. However, factors such as the type of activity and the age of the patient must be taken into consideration before specific recommendations can be formulated. From a practical standpoint, various short periods of exercise related to the EIA-inducing event (i.e. short sprints before longer distance running events) can be tried until a consistent refractory state can be observed. Once a successful routine has been established, these warm-up exercises should be performed each time the patient begins exercising.

II. PATHOGENESIS

A. Physiologic Responses to Exercise

1. **Normal Individuals.** Exercise places numerous demands on the respiratory control system. Not only must the respiratory system maintain arterial blood gases, but this must be done in a manner that minimizes mechanical work, i.e. minimizes pressure development by the chest wall. For the most part, the normal individual can accomplish this. There are three important areas of control in maintaining homeostasis during exercise: 1) alveolar ventilation, 2) chest wall mechanics, and 3) gas exchange. The pulmonary physiology of exercise in the child has not been studied as extensively as in the adult. The following is a summary of known information compiled from research involving both adults and children.

The normal ventilatory response to exercise is an increase in ventilation accomplished mainly by an increase in tidal volume early in exercise; when tidal volumes reach approximately 60% of vital capacity, increases in frequency dominate. In the child, tidal volume plateaus at approximately the same percentage of the vital capacity; however, during maximal exercise, tidal volume may be smaller than in the adult. These factors help to minimize the fall in dynamic lung compliance (increased lung stiffness) that would result from the large lung volumes placing the lung at the nonlinear portion of its pressure volume curve (Figure 12-3). By not elevating ventilation solely by increases in frequency, work due to increased resistance to airflow will also be minimized. Both inspiratory and expiratory time are shortened proportionately so the ratio of inspiratory to total time is unchanged; this is important as a prolonged tension time index can jeopardize diaphragmatic blood flow and result in fatigue. The increase in ventilation is linear with oxygen consumption ($\dot{V}O_2$) and carbon dioxide production ($\dot{V}CO_2$) until about 60% of the maximal oxygen uptake. Thereafter, ventilation increases out of proportion to $\dot{V}O_2$ and $\dot{V}CO_2$ so that alveolar PCO_2 (P_ACO_2) is reduced and alveolar PO_2 (P_AO_2) rises sharply (Dempsey et al., 1984; Dempsey et al., 1985). Children slightly hyperventilate compared with the adult, so arterial PCO_2 (P_aCO_2) is lower.

The increases in ventilation must be achieved in a mechanically efficient manner, or else the ventilatory work becomes too costly and the ability to continue exercise becomes compromised. With the high, turbulent levels of flow rate seen during exercise, it is not

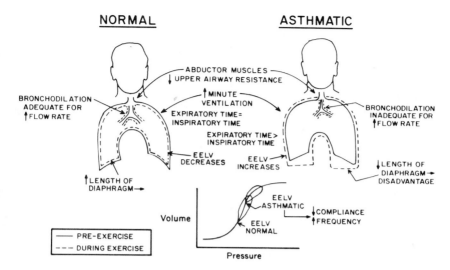

FIGURE 12-3. *Important physiologic changes that occur in both the normal and asthmatic individual during exercise.*

enough to maintain intra- or extra-thoracic airways at resting diameters. The abductor muscles of the extra-thoracic airway (the major site of resistance) are recruited (England & Bartlett, 1982), and bronchodilation of the intra-thoracic airway also occurs; the net effect of increased flow and an increased airway diameter is to maintain resistance at resting levels. The end-expiratory lung volume (EELV) decreases progressively as exercise intensity increases (Sharratt et al., 1987). (Figure 12-3). A decreased EELV lengthens the diaphragm, puts it on a more efficient portion of its length-tension curve, and makes it a more efficient pressure generator. The decrease in EELV is brought about by greatly augmenting expiratory flow rate in the presence of a reduced expiratory time. In turn, the increased expiratory flow is accomplished by the recruitment of expiratory muscles, most notably the abdominals (Grimby et al., 1976), combined with the removal of any "brakes" to expiratory flow, i.e. increases in airway diameter and cessation of antagonistic inspiratory muscle activity during the initial phase of expiration. Not only does the decrease in EELV help the diaphragm reach a more optimal length; the recoil of the chest wall when the abdominals are relaxed at the start of inspiration generates some inspiratory flow. Synchronous recruitment of the expiratory muscles and the inspiratory intercostals, scalenes, and sterno-mastoids assists the diaphragm in augmenting ventilation. This may spare the diaphragm and con- and conceivably prevent diaphragm fatigue. While the majority of

EXERCISE-INDUCED ASTHMA **473**

these observations have been made in adults, similar responses would be expected to occur in children during exercise.

Arterial blood gases are well-maintained during exercise until heavy exercise, when P_ACO_2 will decrease markedly. Arterial PO_2 stays constant despite decreased mixed venous O_2 content, increased pulmonary blood flow and a shortened time for alveolar-capillary diffusion. Two key responses are necessary: 1) increased P_AO_2, so that even though the difference between alveolar and arterial O_2 increases in moderate to heavy exercise, PaO_2 stays constant. Increased P_AO_2 results from an increased alveolar ventilation that is out of proportion to the increase in blood flow and oxygen consumption throughout exercise (Dempsey et al., 1985). 2) Pulmonary capillary blood volume increases 2-2.5 times during exercise so mean transit time is shortened as pulmonary blood flow increases, but is preserved at greater than its critical level.

2. Asthmatic Individuals. Most studies have focused mainly on post-exercise events, and therefore less is known about the respiratory response of people with asthma *during* exercise. The following will briefly compare what is known about the respiratory responses of asthmatics and compare them to those found in nonasthmatic individuals. The relationships are illustrated in Figure 12-3. As mentioned earlier, several studies have demonstrated that children and adults with EIA bronchodilate during exercise; however, there is some indication that this dilation may not be enough for them to mount a "normal" response to exercise. That is, if the child's baseline resistance is high, bronchodilation may only return resistance toward the normal resting level, which would not be sufficient. Cropp, for example, reported that in asthmatic children, expiratory flow does not increase as much as does inspiratory flow, indicating that they may be flow limited (Cropp, 1983). With this in mind, the finding of Kiers et al. (1980) that EELV increases during exercise in children with EIA is not surprising. While breathing at a higher lung volume can increase recoil pressure and help to maintain expiratory flow rates within the maximum flow volume curve, it is very costly to the individual. An increase in EELV shortens the diaphragm and other inspiratory muscles and decreases their ability to generate pressure, so they must be activated to a greater extent to maintain the appropriate ventilation. An increase in EELV combined with the higher tidal volumes that have been seen in asthma during exercise may put the lung on the upper nonlinear (i.e., stiffer) portion of the pressure volume curve and thus increase work (Figure 12-3). Martin et al. (1980) have demonstrated an increased tonic inspiratory muscle activity during bronchoconstriction. If this were to occur during exercise, this continuous activity of muscles already placed at a disadvantage would increase the "braking" of expiratory flow rate, thereby increasing flow resistive work. An increase in EELV also causes tachypnea, which would increase flow resistive work and cause inefficient increases in dead space ventilation.

A few investigators have measured arterial blood gases during exercise in asthmatics. P_AO_2 has been shown in increase, decrease, and remain unchanged (Anderson et al., 1972; Hedlin et al., 1986; Katz et al., 1971). Out of these three studies, only two patients actually became desaturated and most are able to lower P_ACO_2 (Anderson et al., 1972; Cropp, 1983). There is some evidence that, in some patients with more severe EIA, alveolar-arterial oxygen differences (A-aO_2) may be inappropriately widened during exercise. Bronchoconstriction (at rest) causes maldistribution of ventilation to perfusion so very high and very low ventilation/perfusion (V/Q) units exist in the lung. Certainly, if this so-called bimodal V/Q distribution described in the asthmatic were to persist *during* exercise, then the desaturated, mixed venous blood leaving a relatively underventilated portion of the lung would likely cause arterial desaturation.

Young et al. (1982) and Freyschuss et al. (1984) both report the appearance of bimodal V/Q distributions during post-exercise bronchoconstriction. These changes resulted from both increases in V/Q units > 10 and an increase in units from 0.1 to 1.0. With the return to normal of mixed venous blood after exercise, unless there is a significant increase in units of < 0.1, the shift in V/Q should not cause hypoxemia. An increase in these very low (<0.1) V/Q units has *not* been seen after exercise, and this is verified by the fact that hypoxemia rarely occurs during EIA (Cropp, 1983).

There is much to be learned about the response of the individual with EIA to exercise. Extrapolating from the material presented above, one would predict that much of the efficiency of this response and the ability to maintain blood gas homeostasis during exercise will depend critically on: 1) the pre-exercise level of bronchoconstriction (small and large airways); and 2) the ability of the asthmatic airways to show bronchodilation during exercise. A special case in this regard might be found in the elite endurance athlete with asthma or EIA. Even a significant number of non-asthmatic athletes reach apparent ventilatory "limitations" and experience significant arterial hypoxemia (-20–35 mmHg PaO_2, 84%–89% O_2 saturation) at their abnormally high maximal workloads (Dempsey et al., 1984). Thus, it is conceivable that even the "mildly" asthmatic athlete would experience even a higher incidence of gas exchange failure. The "room for error" in ventilatory response, red cell transit time in the lung, ventilation distribution, respiratory muscle pressure development, etc. become less and less as the reserve required for homeostatic gas exchange diminishes toward zero at exceptionally high metabolic demands.

B. Endogenous Catecholamines

The relationship between circulating catecholamines and EIA has recently been reviewed by Barnes (1986). Exercise causes a rise in circulating catecholamines in normal subjects. Some investigators (Barnes et al., 1981; Warren et al., 1982), but not all (Dosani et al., 1987; Belcher et al., 1988) have demonstrated that, in asthmatics, there is a blunted rise in norepinephrine and no rise in epinephrine (compared with a three-fold rise in normal subjects who perform the same test) (Barnes et al., 1981; Warren et al., 1982). The effects of beta-blockade recently analyzed by Warren et al. (1984) suggest that catecholamines may play a role in post-exercise bronchoconstriction, but not in the bronchodilation noted during exercise.

To investigate the importance of catecholamines in modulating airway tone in EIA, Pichurko et al. (1986) studied the relationships of endogenous and exogenous norepinephrine to exercise challenge. They demonstrated that a second exercise stimulus, begun at the peak of the exercise-induced obstructive response following the initial stimulus, can result in a second increase in circulating levels of norepinephrine with parallel increases in pulmonary function measurements. Further, in a separate series of experiments, exogenous administration of aerosolized norepinephrine to these same patients during their initial airway obstructive response to exercise resulted in resolution of their asthmatic symptoms. These results support the concept that circulating levels of catecholamines may play a role in modulating airway tone (Pichurko et al., 1986).

Plasma levels of cyclic AMP, which indirectly modulate the effects of catecholamines on beta adrenergic receptors in a variety of tissues, are also blunted in asthmatics following an exercise stimulus (Barnes et al., 1981). Interestingly, diminished responsiveness may be more characteristic of asthmatic patients who develop EIA than those who do not (Martinsson et al., 1985).

C. Heat and Water Loss

For many years, it was noted that certain types of exercise, such as running sports as opposed to swimming, were more likely to result in EIA. Various theories were proposed to explain these findings, but recent information regarding the importance of airway heat and water loss in triggering EIA has provided insight into possible physiologic explanations for these earlier observations (Bar-Or et al., 1977; Chen & Horton, 1977; McFadden, 1987a; Anderson, 1985).

During normal breathing, heat and water are transferred from the bronchial mucosa of the upper airways to the incoming air so the air is warmed to body temperature and fully saturated with water. This results in both convective and evaporative cooling of the airways. Data from a number of studies (McFadden et al., 1982; McFadden et al., 1985b) have demonstrated that the conditioning of inspired air is not confined to a single region of the tracheobronchial tree, but rather is a continuum that begins at the mouth or nose and involves as much of the airways as is necessary to complete the task. Although the ultimate depth of penetrance has not yet been determined, direct recordings demonstrate that substantive thermal exchanges between the air and mucosa routinely occur in airways less than 1.5 in internal diameter (well beyond the eighth to 10th generation of airways) (McFadden, 1987a).

On expiration, although some of the vaporized water condenses back to the airways and some heat is returned to the mucosa, the net effect of these exchanges results in a loss of both heat and water from the respiratory tract. About 80% of the heat loss is caused by vaporization of water when breathing in temperate climates; as the temperature of the inspired air is decreased, the contribution from convective cooling becomes greater. Since cold air is always dry, the magnitude of the respiratory heat loss will be greater when subjects breath air at subfreezing temperatures. As expired air is almost fully saturated with water, respiratory water loss during ventilation will depend on the concentration of water in the inspired air and on the temperature of the expired air.

In 1977, Chen and Horton reported that EIA could be prevented if subjects breathed fully humidified body temperature air during exercise, and suggested that the increased heat and/or water loss from the respiratory tract secondary to hyperpnea caused EIA to occur. Initial attention was primarily focused on respiratory heat loss as the major contributing factor. Deal and co-workers (1979a & b) made a number of observations that supported this concept. First, they noted that cold, dry air caused a greater fall in FEV_1 and specific airway conductance than did ambient or hot, dry air. Second, they noted that the calculated respiratory heat exchange correlated with the magnitude of the fall in FEV_1. And finally, in subsequent experiments (Deal et al., 1979c; McFadden et al., 1985a), they demonstrated that airway temperature actually fell during exercise. However, additional experiments, in which the inspiration of air as hot as 80° C caused no less bronchoconstriction than did dry air at 25° C, indicated that additional factors were also important.

In analyzing the mathematical formula describing respiratory heat loss in Figure 12-4, it is apparent that heat and water loss are closely related. As indicated, the water content of inspired air is a more important variable than its temperature because the latent heat of vaporization is so much greater than the heat capacity of dry air. Thus, water loss contributes substantially to the respiratory heat loss during exercise. Respiratory heat loss and water loss are therefore closely linked under most circumstances. When attempts have been made to analyze the potential contribution of each, neither heat loss or water loss, per se, could be established as the sole stimulus for bronchoconstriction following isocapnic hyperventilation (Eschenbacher & Sheppard, 1985).

In addition to augmenting respiratory heat loss, respiratory water loss may act as a stimulus for EIA through its direct effect in drying the airways (Lee & Anderson, 1985). During the hyperpnea of exercise, respiratory water loss may result in a transient state of hyperosmolarity of the fluids bathing the respiratory tract. Inhalation of either hypotonic or hypertonic aerosols of saline have been reported to produce bronchospasm (Shoeffel et al., 1981a) that is not the result of a direct effect of these nonisotonic solutions on airway smooth muscle tone (Finney et al., 1987). Changes in osmolarity could induce mast cell (Eggleston et al., 1984) or basophil degranulation (Findlay et al., 1981) to occur with resultant bronchospasm due to the local effects of released or generated mediators (Wasserman, 1983). Since substantial increases in osmolarity must occur (600 to 800 milliosmoles) for mast cells to release 20% of their histamine content in vitro, it has been argued that these independent observations are not physiologically reconcilable. However, in vivo challenge of nasal mucosa with hyperosmolar solutions results in mediator release (Silber et al., 1988). Moreover, cold, dry air challenge of the nose increases the osmolality of nasal secretions and is associated with the release of histamine (Togias et al., 1988a) and sulfidopeptide leukotrienes (Togias et al., 1986). These in vivo observations in the upper airway have been used to support a potential role for changes in osmolarity and mediator release in the lower airway.

In addition to their ability to promote bronchospasm, the effects of exercise, inhalation of hypertonic and hypotonic aerosols, and

---

$$\text{RHE} = \dot{V}_E \, [\text{HC} \, (T_i - T_e) + \text{HV} \, (\text{WC}_i - \text{WC}_e)]$$

FIGURE 12-4. RHE is the respiratory heat exchange, V_E is minute ventilation in $L \cdot min^{-1}$, HC is the heat capacity of air ($0.000304 \ kcal \cdot L^{-1}$), T_i is the inspired temperature, T_e is the expired temperature in degrees C, HV is the latent heat of vaporization of water ($0.580 \ kcal \cdot g^{-1}$), WC_i is the water content of the inspired air in mg $H_2O \cdot L^{-1}$ air, and WC_e is the water content of the expired air in mg $H_2O \cdot L^{-1}$ air.

isocapnic hyperventilation on airway responsiveness to methacholine and histamine have been analyzed. Smith, Anderson, and Black (1987) demonstrated in adults that the airway responsiveness to methacholine and hypertonic saline solutions were correlated, whereas the response to methacholine and hypotonic saline was not. Similar correlations for exercise and methacholine (Chatham et al., 1982) and isocapnic hyperventilation and methacholine (Weiss et al., 1983) have also been reported. Interestingly, although airway challenge with hypotonic aerosols induces bronchospasm and results in subsequent enhancement of airway reactivity to methacholine, airway challenge with hypertonic aerosols only produces bronchospasm (Smith et al., 1987). In related observations, interchangeable refractory periods can be demonstrated for both hypertonic aerosol challenge and exercise (Belcher et al., 1987). Taken together, these observations indicate that EIA and bronchospasm due to hyperosmolar challenge may share pathogenic mechanisms and further, that both are not associated with the induction of enhanced bronchial reactivity.

D. Airway Rewarming

In addition to the effects that heat loss, water loss, and/or osmolarity changes have during exercise, recent work has focused on the importance of thermal events that may be influential immediately following exercise (McFadden et al., 1986; Gilbert et al., 1987). In studies in which either the temperature and humidity of the inspired air during the recovery period from EIA, or the rate at which the decrease in post-challenge ventilation was varied, McFadden et al. (1986) demonstrated that the severity of EIA was dependent not only on airway cooling but also upon the rapidity and magnitude of post-challenge airway rewarming. In addition, measurements of temperature obtained at various points throughout the airway (posterior pharynx, glottis, mid-trachea, carina, right lower lobe bronchus, and anterior segmental bronchus), which permitted calculating values for water content, water flux, and osmolality, demonstrated no differences between normal and asthmatic patients prior to and immediately following cessation of exercise (Gilbert et al., 1987). These results indicated that heat, water, and osmolality differences could not account for the observed changes in pulmonary function. If the rate of rewarming of the airways contributed significantly to the observed EIA, it could have done so by two potential mechanisms. First, in vitro analysis of guinea pig airway smooth muscle demonstrates extreme sensitivity to thermal changes. When cooling of smooth muscle is followed by rapid rewarming, large, sustained contractions develop; similar changes are not seen following slow rewarming (Souhrada et al., 1983). Thus, if similar events occurred in humans, rapid rewarming of the airways would result in bronchospasm. Second, reactive hyperemia is seen following cooling and rewarming of the skin. If parallel events occurred in the bronchial vascular bed, engorgement and edema formation in the mucosa and submucosa would result. Thus, either or both of these mechanisms could compromise airflow and result in EIA.

E. Exercise Intensity

Finally, Noviski et al. (1987) have emphasized that exercise intensity may be the dominant factor in determining the degree of EIA rather than the climatic conditions that are present during the exercise stimulus. They performed exercise testing in eight children under two sets of conditions: first, more intense exercise/breathing room air, and second, less intense exercise/breathing cold, dry air. Despite equivalent respiratory heat losses during the two provocations, a greater decrease in FEV_1 was observed following the more intense exercise stimulus. While these results are provocative, an accompanying editorial by D. Sheppard (1987) emphasized that, despite equivalent heat and water losses as calculated from values obtained at the mouth, it is still possible to have significant local changes in these parameters that would influence bronchomotor tone. The level of minute ventilation can affect not only the distribution of heat and water transfer (nose and mouth vs. airways), but also regional blood flow that can replace local losses of both heat and water.

F. Mediators of Immediate Hypersensitivity and EIA

1. **Mast Cells, Basophils and Mediators.** Mast cells are present in connective tissue surrounding blood vessels, nerves, and sweat glands in virtually every organ of the body (Lemanske & Kaliner, 1985). In the lung, mast cells are present in the mucosal and submucosal regions, between epithelial cells, and free-floating in the alveolar fluid (Friedman & Kaliner, 1987). Morphologic heterogeneity of human pulmonary mast cells has been described, but it is uncertain if these different populations also exhibit functional heterogeneity (Barrett & Metcalfe, 1987). Mast cells bind IgE antibody through high affinity IgE receptors located on their membrane surface. Initiation of mediator release occurs when antigen bridges at least two antigen-specific IgE molecules. In addition to antigen interacting with membrane-bound IgE antibody, a number of other stimuli may induce mediator release through non-IgE-dependent mechanisms (Table 12-2). Thus, individuals do not have to be "allergic" for mediator release to occur.

Basophils are circulating polymorphonuclear leukocytes that also

TABLE 12-2. *Non-IgE-dependent methods of initiating mast cell mediator release*

1. Endogenous
   a. Complement fragments C5a > C3a > C4a
   b. Neuropeptides (substance P, somatostatin)
   c. ATP
   d. Adenosine (potentiates secretion)
   e. Neutrophil lysosomal proteins
   f. Eosinophil major basic protein
2. Exogenous
   a. Anesthetic agents (succinylcholine, d-tubocurare)
   b. Antibiotics (polymyxin B, vancomycin)
   c. Narcotics (morphine, codeine)
   d. Iodinated contrast material
   e. Hypertonic or hypotonic solutions

bind IgE antibody and undergo mediator release when appropriately stimulated. They can infiltrate tissues, but contrary to popular belief, they do not undergo differentiation into mast cells once they leave the bloodstream. Numbers of circulating basophils rise following exercise (Morgan et al., 1983), and spontaneous basophil histamine release has been reported to be increased in asthmatic patients (Howarth et al., 1984).

2. Measurement of Mediator Release During EIA. The ability to modulate EIA with drugs that work, at least in part, by preventing mast cell mediator release, as well as the demonstration that physical stimuli such as temperature changes can induce cutaneous mast cell mediator release (Wasserman et al., 1977), has led to investigations evaluating the role of mediators of immediate hypersensitivity in the pathogenesis of EIA. Although numerous mediators are released or generated following mast cell and/or basophil activation (Wasserman, 1983), only histamine and neutrophil chemotactic factor of anaphylaxis (NCF-A) have been measured in the peripheral bloodstream. Early work in this area was hampered due to the unavailability of assays sensitive enough to detect changes in blood histamine levels. Further, NCF-A is a putative mast cell mediator due to the fact that its activity can be measured in time courses similar to histamine release following the induction of allergic cutaneous (Wasserman et al., 1977) and pulmonary reactions (Atkins et al., 1977); the precise biochemical characterization and cell source of NCF-A have not yet been determined. Thus, in an analysis of the participation of mast cell mediators in EIA, measurements of NCF-A may not be relevant.

In patients with EIA, histamine levels have been reported either not to change following exercise (Deal et al., 1980; Howarth et al., 1984; Morgan et al., 1983) or to rise (Lee et al., 1982a; Barnes &

Brown, 1962). Levels of NCF-A have also been noted not to change following exercise (Morgan et al., 1983) or to rise (Lee et al., 1982a; Lee et al., 1982b). In contrast to EIA, isocapnic hyperventilation is not associated with detectable increases in either histamine or NCF-A (Lee et al., 1982b; Morgan et al., 1983; Howarth et al., 1984). The latter findings suggest that the pathogenesis of EIA and hyperventilation-induced asthma may differ.

The relevance of these findings to the clinical features of EIA is still not established. Some authors have argued that depletion of mediators may be at least one explanation for the refractory period that can be demonstrated in many patients following exercise. Further, since beta-agonists and cromolyn sodium inhibit pulmonary mast cell mediator release (Cockcroft & Murdock, 1987), these results may explain the utility of these drugs in the treatment of EIA. However, Belcher et al. (1988) recently demonstrated that rises in both histamine and NCF-A occurred during a second exercise challenge when the patient's airway response was refractory from a challenge performed one hour previously. Moreover, since rises in both histamine and NCF-A can occur following exercise in asthmatics who do not develop EIA (Lee et al., 1982a), and because late responses following exercise may be due to sampling artifact (Rubinstein et al., 1987) but occur in association with rises in NCF-A (Lee et al., 1983), changes in levels of these mediators in association with the physiologic events surrounding EIA may be epiphenomena (McFadden, 1987a).

G. Applications of Pathogenic Findings to Therapy

As reviewed, multiple mechanisms have been proposed for the pathogenesis of EIA. Based on these observations, treatment recommendations are summarized in Figure 12-5. As diagrammed, the type of exercise, the use of warm-up exercises, the climatic conditions during and following exercise, and medical therapy (see below) are all important considerations. Exercise performed in warm, moist air with an adequate warm-up period would be the least likely to provoke EIA. Thus, swimming preceded by multiple short laps in the pool as a warm-up would be advisable for individuals who have a history of difficulty with running events. If a child or young adult prefers running sports, longer distances preceded by short sprints as a warm-up would be preferable to events such as the half-mile or mile run. For small children playing outdoors in winter, the use of a scarf or a face mask during playtime would diminish respiratory heat and water loss (Gravelyn et al., 1987). Finally, as discussed below, the use of medications *prior to* exercise can also be very effective in attenuating or preventing EIA.

EIA TREATMENT

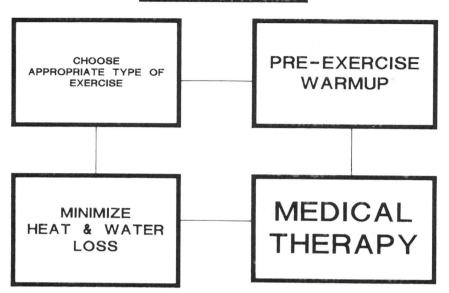

FIGURE 12-5. *Overall treatment approaches to individuals with exercise-induced asthma.*

III. TESTING PROCEDURES

A. Indications

In the majority of patients who give a good history for EIA, an appropriate trial of pharmaceuticals known to be efficacious (see below) is usually the most expeditious and least expensive method of management. However, in equivocal cases, quantitative assessment of EIA is best performed in the laboratory. It should be emphasized that exercise testing is a provocative challenge, and it should therefore not be performed on individuals with baseline airway obstruction (FEV_1 < 80% of predicted values) (Hsu et al., 1979) or known cardiac disease. Due to the ability of viral upper respiratory infections to enhance airway hyperreactivity, patients with "colds" should also be excluded.

The most frequent indications for this type of testing are: 1. to assess latent asthma; 2. to evaluate the severity of known EIA, especially in competitive athletes; and 3. to evaluate the effectiveness of acute or chronic medication in the prevention of symptoms of EIA (Souhrda & Kivity, 1983). In the assessment of airway reactivity, especially in athletes, methacholine bronchoprovocation may be a more sensitive method of analysis as compared with exercise (Shapiro, 1984). In challenging cases, or in circumstances in which it is important to have an accurate determination of cardiorespiratory fitness and EIA potential (in highly trained athletes), exercise challenge testing should be performed using exercise conditions that are an accurate reflection of those known to produce difficulty.

B. Medications

The advisability of withholding medication prior to challenge will depend on the purpose of the study. The times that each medication should be withheld will depend on the duration of action of each preparation. For example, sustained release theophylline preparations should be withheld for 24 h, beta agonists for 6–12 h and cromolyn sodium for 6–12 h. Prolonged steroid therapy may attenuate the immediate bronchospastic response to exercise (see below), a feature that should be considered in interpreting pulmonary function results. To avoid ambiguity, antihistamines should also be withheld for 24–48 h (see below). Since food intake may produce anaphylaxis following exercise in some patients (Novey et al., 1983; Kidd et al., 1983), testing should be done at least 2 to 3 h after a major meal [although in certain patients, longer intervals between testing and the ingestion of *specific* foods may be indicated (Novey et al., 1983)]

Once the diagnosis of EIA has been established, it is helpful to repeat the testing (similar workload) following premedication with various pharmaceuticals, warm-up exercises, or under relevant climatic conditions if possible. Obviously, the need to perform these repeat tests will be dependent on the patient's overall response to therapy once the diagnosis has been established. However, in challenging cases, information gained from these evaluations can be invaluable in determining the exact set of conditions that will best attenuate or block the asthmatic response to exercise.

C. Exercise Testing

The majority of pulmonary function laboratories conduct a 6 to 8 min high-intensity treadmill or cycle ergometer test. The cycle ergometer is cheaper and smaller; further, exercise is more easily quantitated on a cycle ergometer, and physiologic monitoring is easier (Eggleston, 1984). Once the patients, especially in the case of children, are familiar with the equipment and the testing procedure, they are connected to leads to monitor heart rate. The intensity of the exercise stress must be determined by some objective criteria such as heart rate or oxygen uptake. This response will depend on such factors as age, size, and fitness, but should increase heart rate to at least 80% of predicted maximum values or increase oxygen uptake to at least 30 to 35 ml $\cdot$ min $\cdot$ kg^{-1}. Maximum heart rate may be predicted from the following relationship: $HR_{max} = 209 - 0.74(x)$, where x is the age in yrs (Eggleston, 1984). A cycle ergometer can be adjusted to provide a precise resistance, and thus a quantifiable workload. An appropriate setting for reaching the target stress levels indicated above is 2.0 W $\cdot$ kg^{-1}. With a treadmill, work is related in a more complex way, but may be estimated from height and age values (Eggleston et al., 1979).

The patient is first asked to begin a slow run on the treadmill to establish balance and familiarity with the equipment. The workload is then increased until the patient becomes exhausted or the heart rate remains at 80% of predicted maximum for 6 min. In evaluations that are performed over a period of days, values for workload, the time of day the testing is done, and ambient temperature and humidity should all be kept constant. If these factors are controlled, the severity of EIA is reasonably reproducible in children with perennial asthma over at least a period of one year (Henriksen, 1986).

Following cessation of exercise, serial measurements of pulmonary functions are performed. The various individual measurements of pulmonary functions each have advantages and disadvantages (Cropp, 1983). For example, although measurements of specific airway conductance are more sensitive in detecting significant changes than are peak flow values, the former require relatively elaborate techniques, whereas the latter can be performed using an inexpensive peak flow meter. However, measurements of peak flow are more effort-dependent and therefore less reliable. Aronsson et al. (1977) and others have demonstrated that the forced oscillation technique is a sensitive measure of changes in resistance in asthmatics, which requires little subject cooperation. Flow volume loops with analysis of flow rates at 50% of vital capacity can also be used (Haas et al., 1985).

Measurements of pulmonary function can be made at various times but, in general, are performed every 5 min for the first 30 min and then at 60 min following exercise termination. If late reactions are being analyzed, more prolonged evaluation as well as a "placebo" challenge day are necessary to avoid false positive responses (Rubinstein et al., 1987). Criteria for scoring the functional severity of exercise-induced bronchospasm are listed in Table 12-3. As reviewed previously, measurements made *during* exercise can also be insightful in selected patients.

TABLE 12-3. *Criteria for scoring functional severity of exercise-induced bronchospasm (EIB)*

| Test | Post-exercise Measurements* |||
	Mild EIB	Moderate EIB	Severe EIB
Specific conductance (SG_{aw})	51–70	30–50	<30
Peak expiratory flows (PEFR)	61–75	40–60	<40
FEF_{25-75}	61–75	40–60	<40
FEV_1	66–80	50–65	<50
FVC	81–90	70–80	<70

* Percent of pre-exercise values
Modified with permission from: Cropp, G.J.A.: Exercise-induced asthma. In: *Allergy: Principles and Practice.* Vol. II, C.V. Mosby Co., St. Louis, 1983, Eds.: E. Middleton, C.E. Reed, E. Ellis, p. 1003–14.

D. Isocapnic Hyperventilation Testing

As discussed previously, when exercise testing cannot be performed due to medical reasons, an alternative method to assess bronchial reactivity is isocapnic hyperventilation. In this procedure, patients are asked to ventilate for 5 min at three different levels of effort, with 7 to 10 min intervals separating each ventilatory level. The patient inhales a mixture of room air (or compressed air) and CO_2 at a predetermined temperature and relative humidity; cold, dry air would provoke more airway obstruction than warm, moist air. Continuous analysis of expired CO_2 is made using an infrared CO_2 analyzer. Values of CO_2 are used to adjust the flow of CO_2, which is added into a gas-mixing chamber to maintain constant end-tidal pCO_2. Values of minute ventilation, tidal volume, and respiratory rate are usually visually displayed to the patients so they are able to maintain the desired level of ventilation. Pulmonary function tests are determined immediately before and at 3 to 5 min after each hyperventilation challenge. Pulmonary function changes usually revert to normal faster following hyperventilation than they do following exercise challenge.

IV. TREATMENT

In analyzing the effectiveness of various treatments in the prevention or attenuation of airway obstruction following exercise or isocapnic hyperventilation, it is important to recognize that results will depend on a number of factors, including drug dosage, time of administration, route of delivery, effect on baseline pulmonary function, and the criterion used for defining a statistically or clinically significant effect. For drugs, Anderson et al. (1979) have suggested that a significant protective effect of a drug occurs when the maximum FEV_1 drop after exercise is 50% of the decrease observed prior to drug administration. Alternatively, since normal subjects usually do not experience decreases in FEV_1 values greater than 10% following exercise, some authors have suggested that an acceptable method of evaluating drug efficacy would be to determine the number of subjects with FEV_1 decrements of less than 10% following treatment and exercise (Rohr et al., 1987). In many evaluations, however, statistical group comparisons are made without reference to the clinical relevance of the observed changes.

A. Cromolyn Sodium and Related Compounds

Cromolyn sodium is the disodium salt of 1,3 bis(2-carboxychromon-5-yloxy)-2-hydroxypropane and is available in the United States in three forms: solution for nebulization (20 mg·2.0 ml^{-1}), capsule of powder (20 mg) for inhalation using a device called a Spinhaler^R, and a metered dose inhaler (800 ug/spray). Oral cromolyn is not sufficiently absorbed and is therefore of no clinical use in asthma. Each inhaled preparation has been shown to be effective in the prevention of EIA in a significant percentage of patients (Bar-Yishay et al., 1983b; Patel et al., 1986). Estimates for the degree of protection have ranged from 40% for complete protection (percent fall in peak expiratory flow rates within normal range) to 73% for significant protection (percent fall with cromolyn less than half that with placebo) (Godfrey & Konig, 1976). For the nebulized solution, variations in response may be related to the fact that the standard solution is hypotonic (1% in distilled water) (Weiner et al., 1988). The heterogeneity observed in the immediate responsiveness to cromolyn may also be related to the refractory period in that patients who develop a refractory state following exercise are more likely to respond to cromolyn (Ben-Dov et al., 1983a). The duration of action of its protection is also quite variable among patients and differs depending on the dose and the method of delivery (Bar-Yishay et al., 1983b). Most studies have been able to demonstrate significant protection up to 2 h following inhalation, with maximum effects occurring within 15 to 30 min after inhalation. In comparison to single dosing, prolonged therapy (weeks) has been reported by some investigators (Eggleston et al., 1972), but not all (Rohr et al., 1987), to increase the drug's efficacy in modulating EIA. Cromolyn has also been shown to be protective in blocking bronchoconstriction due to isocapnic hyperventilation (Juniper et al., 1986).

The mechanism of action of cromolyn is presently unknown. It has been demonstrated to inhibit mediator release (Cox & Altounyan, 1970), inhibit phosphodiesterase activity (Roy & Warren, 1974), inhibit reflex mechanisms (Konig, 1984; Black et al., 1987), and modulate calcium flux across cell membranes (Foreman & Garland, 1976). Interestingly, in normal subjects, cromolyn has the ability to modify the airway response to respiratory heat loss (Fanta et al., 1981).

Agents with pharmaceutical profiles similar to cromolyn, but not yet available in the United States, have also demonstrated efficacy in antagonizing EIA. In adults, nedocromil sodium (the disodium salt of pyranoquinalone dicarboxylic acid), at a dose of 4 mg delivered by mete-dose inhaler was equivalent to cromolyn (at a dose of 20 mg delivered by a Spinhaler^R) 15 min prior to exercise; its duration of action, however, was less than that observed for cromolyn (Konig et al., 1987). Similar protective effects have been observed in children if nedocromil is administererd 30 min before exercise (Chudry et al., 1987). Orally active agents, such as M&B 22,948 (zaprinast; 2-o-propoxyphenyl-8-asapurin-6-one), have demonstrated protective effects in 42% of adults (Rudd et al., 1983) but not in children (Reiser et al., 1986).

B. Beta Adrenergic Agonists

Beta adrenergic agonists are the most potent bronchodilators and are considered to be the drugs of choice in the treatment of EIA. Beta agonists exert their biologic effects by stimulating beta receptors on the surface of cells. Two types of receptors have been described: a β_1 receptor, which is present in larger numbers in cardiac as opposed to bronchial smooth muscle, and β_2 receptors, which are present in larger numbers in the lung as opposed to the heart. For bronchial smooth muscle, stimulation of beta receptors results in increases in intracellular levels of cAMP, which are associated with smooth muscle relaxation. A variety of beta agonists has been developed; individual drugs may differ in their ability to act orally vs. the inhaled route, their duration of action, and their selectivity for stimulating the two subclasses of beta adrenergic receptors.

Although the precise mechanism by which beta agonists antagonize the development of EIA is not established, there are at least three ways in which they might work. First, the bronchodilation that they induce before exercise might compensate for asthma induced by exercise. Second, they might enhance bronchodilation during exercise, which might decrease or override the bronchoconstriction that follows exercise. Third, they might inhibit EIA either by inhibiting mediator release or by acting directly on smooth muscle to prevent bronchoconstriction (Sly, 1984). Interestingly, for some beta agonists, there appears to be a discordance between the duration of action of the bronchodilatory response and the duration of action of protection from EIA (Sly et al., 1967; Sly et al., 1968).

Isoproterenol is short-acting, not absorbed orally, and can stimulate both β_1 and β_2 receptors. When inhaled, it inhibits EIA within 5 min, and the duration of action may last 2 h (Sly et al., 1967).

Metaproterenol, a resorcinol derivative of isoproterenol, is active orally and by inhalation and stimulates both β_1 and β_2 receptors. Following inhalation, bronchodilation begins to occur in 5 min with maximal effects seen in approximately 15 min. Inhaled metaproterenol has been shown to inhibit EIA in most patients within 15 min and in some for up to 1 hour; despite continued bronchodilation at 2 h, it does not inhibit EIA 2 h after inhalation in most subjects (Schoeffel et al., 1981b; Konig et al., 1981). Following oral administration, it can decrease the severity of EIA for up to 1 h (Konig et al., 1981).

Albuterol, a saligenin derivative of isoproterenol, is felt to be more β_2 selective than isoproterenol and metaproterenol. It is active both orally and by aerosolization. When delivered by metered-dose inhaler, bronchodilation begins in 5 min with peak effects occurring 120 to 160 min later. Berkowitz et al. (1986) demonstrated that 15 min after two inhalations of either albuterol (0.18 mg) or metaproterenol (1.3 mg), protection from EIA was equivalent; however, when the same children were evaluated at 2 h, the duration of protection was found to be longer with albuterol. The duration of the protective effects of inhaled albuterol has been reported to range from 4–6 h (Silverman et al., 1973). Oral albuterol ($0.15 \text{ mg} \cdot \text{kg}^{-1}$) has been reported to have a similar duration of protection in comparison to inhaled albuterol (0.2 mg), although time to peak bronchodilation was more prolonged with the inhaled drug (120 vs. 40 min) (Francis et al., 1980). In comparison to inhalation of cromolyn capsules (20 mg), albuterol (180 μg) was better for prophylaxis 15 min prior to exercise (Rohr et al., 1987).

Tebutaline sulfate and fenoterol are both resorcinol derivatives. Terbutaline is currently available in the United States in both a metered-dose inhaler (0.2 mg/puff) and oral tablets (2.5 and 5.0 mg), while fenoterol is still awaiting release. Despite using a low inhaled dose (32.5 μg) of terbutaline delivererd through a coned space 15 min before challenge, Henriksen and Dahl (1983) noted significant protection from EIA in eight of 14 children. Higher inhaled doses (500 μg) have demonstrated protection up to one hour (Rosenthal et al., 1979), while oral terbutaline (2.5 or 5.0 mg) inhibits EIA 2–5 h after administration. Fenoterol has been shown to be effective in a number of forms. Inhaled powder (0.4 mg) significantly blocked EIA in 17 children 30 min before exercise and was significantly more effective than cromolyn sodium (20 mg) (Bundgaard et al., 1983). At doses of 0.4 and 0.8 mg by metered-dose inhaler, fenoterol demonstrated a significant protective effect 10 min following inhalation that lasted for 2 h but had abated 4 h later; no differences between the two doses were appreciated (Konig et al., 1984). One interesting feature of fenoterol has been the demonstration that it can produce bronchodilation if the metered-dose inhaler is sprayed against the buccal mucosa on the inside of the cheek; the relevance of this observation to clinical management has still not been defined (Symon et al., 1985).

C. Theophylline

Theophylline is a dimethylated xanthine that is similar in structure to the common dietary xanthines, caffeine and theobromine found in coffee and tea. The bronchodilating effects of theophylline have been appreciated since the 1920s (Weinberger, 1984), but its precise mechanism of action is still unknown. At concentrations tenfold higher than those usually attained clinically, theophylline inhibits the breakdown of cAMP through its action on phosphodiesterase (Bergstrand, 1980); increased levels of cAMP are associated with bronchial smooth muscle relaxation. Other proposed mechanisms of action include prostaglandin antagonism and inhibition of adenosine receptors. The latter property, however, is not shared with enprofylline, which has greater bronchodilator potency than does theophylline (Weinberger, 1984). The bronchodilator efficacy of theophylline is related to its serum concentration (Pollock et al., 1977). Various product formulations (short-acting oral tablets or liquids vs. sustained release tablets or capsules) have substantially different effects on fluctuations in peak and through levels; therefore, their potential in blocking EIA will depend on their time to peak, duration of action, and their bioavailability related to food intake (Pedersen, 1986).

The effects of theophylline on inhibiting EIA have recently been reviewed by Ellis (1984). The relationship between serum concentration and the physiologic effect is less clear in terms of inhibition of EIA than it is with bronchodilation (Seale et al., 1977; Pollock et al., 1977). Theophylline has been found to be effective in inhibiting EIA in about 80% of individuals tested in most studies (Ellis, 1984; Oppenheimer & Schuller, 1987; Laursen et al., 1985; Ioli et al., 1984), but not all studies (Seale et al., 1977; Cummings & Strunk, 1984). Interestingly, similar to the beta agonists, the ability of theophylline to serve as an adequate bronchodilator for chronic asthma management does not necessarily relate to its ability to block EIA in the same patient (Ellis, 1984). In most (Ellis, 1984), but not all (Oppenheimer & Schuller, 1987), comparison studies, theophylline is less effective in modulating EIA than are the beta agonists.

Theophylline also has extrapulmonary effects that are important to the athlete (Ellis, 1984). It has a positive inotropic effect on the heart (Matthay et al., 1982) and decreases both pulmonary artery pressure and pulmonary vascular resistance (Murphy et al., 1968). It also strengthens the contractions of skeletal muscles, including the diaphragm (Aubier et al., 1981). The precise contribution of these effects to overall athletic performance has not been systematically studied.

D. Cholinergic Antagonists

Atropine and other antimuscarinic antagonists are competitive antagonists of acetylcholine with the major site of action in the lung being postganglionic receptors on smooth muscle and exocrine glands. Since the vagus nerve is the major autonomic nervous system input in controlling bronchial smooth muscle tone, blockade of cholinergic innervation results in bronchodilation that is mechanistically different from the effects of the beta agonists or theophylline. The undesirable side effects of atropine, including mouth dryness, cardiovascular effects, visual problems, and psychologic changes, however, have historically prevented its usefulness as a routine bronchodilator in the treatment of asthma. Quaternary ammonium derivatives of atropine, such as ipratropium bromide, are not well absorbed and cross the blood brain barrier poorly; these properties reduce the side effects while maintaining their usefulness as bronchodilators.

The effects of ipratropium bromide on asthma and EIA have recently been reviewed by Furakawa (1984). In comparison with the beta agonists, the onset of action is later and the duration of action is somewhat longer. Further, not all asthmatic patients respond positively to this drug with regard to routine asthma management (Schlueter, 1986). Thus, studies evaluating the efficacy of ipratropium have to be interpreted with these factors in mind. Finally, from the information available, it appears that cholinergic mechanisms play, at best, a minor role in EIA (McFadden, 1987a). With this as a background, it is not surprising that some (Borut et al., 1977; Yeung et al., 1980), but not all investigators (Stemman & Koshe, 1975; Larsson, 1982; Poppius et al., 1986), have found ipratropium bromide to be effective in antagonizing EIA. Ipratropium bromide does not augment the effects of beta agonists when used in combination prior to exercise (Sanguinetti et al., 1986).

E. Calcium Channel Blockers

As recently reviewed by Middleton (1984), all of the pathogenic processes in asthmatic airways are calcium-dependent phenomena: excitation-contraction coupling in smooth muscle; stimulus-secretion coupling in mast cells and mucous glands; nerve impulse initiation and conduction; and the movement and activation of inflammatory cells. Calcium channel blockers, therefore, have been evaluated for their efficacy in asthma management. Both nifedipine (sublingual) and verapamil (oral or intravenous) have demonstrated protection for EIA (Barnes, 1985). In contrast, diltiazem, given orally in adults (Magnussen et al., 1984) or by inhalation in children (Foresi et al., 1987), has not. PY-108-068, a new calcium channel antagonist, not only attenuates EIA but also causes resting bronchodilation, the latter feature being unique among calcium channel blockers (Ben-Dov et al., 1986). Maximal bronchodilation occurs at about 2 h (Ben-Dov et al., 1986), a time at which protection against EIA can still be observed (Olive et al., 1986). It is possible that the continued development of newer generations of calcium channel blockers will result in agents with greater airway selectivity, thereby enhancing their usefulness in asthma therapy.

F.   Corticosteroids

In chronic asthma, airway obstruction is the result of bronchoconstriction, edema of the airways, increased mucus secretion, and inflammation. Since corticosteroids are potent anti-inflammatory agents and can inhibit mucous secretion, they are important adjuncts to asthma therapy when bronchodilators alone do not maximize lung function (Morris, 1983). Corticosteroids can be administered both orally and topically, the latter through a metered-dose inhaler currently available in the United States as beclomethasone diproprionate and triamcinolone acetonide.

In early studies, both oral and inhaled steroids were considered to be ineffective in EIA (Konig et al., 1974). However, subsequent studies both in adults using betamethasone valerate inhalation (Hartley et al., 1977), and in children using a more potent steroid, budesonide (Henriksen & Dahl, 1983; Henriksen & Wenzel, 1984; Henriksen, 1985), have demonstrated efficacy in EIA. In the studies performed in children, exercise testing was performed after the childrern had been receiving the medication for 1 to 4 wks; it is unknown what duration of therapy is required before positive effects can be noted. Since pulmonary mast cell mediator release cannot be inhibited by corticosteroids (Schleimer et al., 1983), it is unlikely that the protective effects noted were due to this mechanism. One possible explanation is that the chronic inhaled steroids reduced baseline airway reactivity (Dutoit et al., 1987), which is known to be related to the propensity to develop EIA.

G.   Other Treatment Modalities

Alpha adrenergic antagonists have been noted to have some beneficial effects on airway response to either exercise or cold air while having no effect on the response following chemical or antigen challenge (Walden et al., 1984). Antihistamines, including chlorpheniramine (O'Byrne et al., 1983), astemizole (Clee et al., 1984), and terfenadine (Patel, 1984) have been shown to affect the airway response to cold air and exercise. In addition to drug therapy, hypnosis (Ben-Zvi et al., 1982) as well as both real and sham acupuncture (Fung et al., 1986) can influence an individual's response to exercise. However, since even placebo therapy can affect the severity of EIA, it is essential to assess this response in any evaluation (Godfrey & Silverman, 1973).

H. Medications Acceptable in International Competition

Drugs permitted by the International Olympic Committee's Medical Commission for the treatment of asthma and allergic diseases in athletes are listed in Figure 12-6. (For additional listing of approved medications see Clarke, 1984). Medications approved for use in asthma include methylxanthines (caffeine is banned if urinary concentration exceeds 15 µg/ml), cromolyn, belladonna alkaloids, corticosteroids, and β_2 specific sympathomimetic amines (albuterol and terbutaline). Drugs banned include sympathomimetics with lack

ASTHMA & ALLERGY TREATMENT
INTERNATIONAL COMPETITION

APPROVED

METHYLXANTHINES*
SPECIFIC B-2
    AGONISTS
BELLADONNA ALKALOIDS
CORTICOSTEROIDS
CROMOLYN
ANTIHISTAMINES
NONOPIOIDS
(DEXTRAMETHORPHAN,
LEVOPROPOXYPHENE,
DIPHENHYDRAMINE

NOT APPROVED

NONSPECIFIC B-2
    AGONISTS
OPIOIDS (CODEINE, HY-
DROCODONE, DIHYDROCO-
DONE, PHOLCODINE, ETC.)
VASOCONSTRICTORS
(EPHEDRINE, PSEUDOEPHEDRINE,
PHENYLEPHRINE, PHENYLPRO-
PANOLAMINE, TETRAHYDRO-
ZOLINE)

FIGURE 12-6. *Medications approved and not approved for the treatment of allergic diseases and asthma in international competition. *Caffeine is banned if urinary excretion exceeds 15 µg/ml. (Summarized from Fitch, 1984).*

of β_2 specificity (epinephrine, ephedrine, isoproterenol, and meta-proterenol) and opioid analgesics and antitussives (codeine, hydro-codone, dihydrocodeine, pholcodine, etc.). Antihistamines and top-ical nasal cromolyn or corticosteroids but not sympathomimetic vasoconstrictors (ephedrine, pseudoephedrine, phenylephrine, phenylpropanolamine, tetrahydrozoline) are permitted for the con-comitant treatment of allergic rhinitis (Fitch, 1983). However, since policies may change periodically, it is important that athletes notify appropriate committees responsible for various competitive events to be sure that proper guidelines are followed well in advance of the competition.

I. PRACTICAL TREATMENT APPROACHES TO THE CHILD WITH EIA

Treatment for children with EIA will depend on their overall asthma treatment needs (Figure 12-7). Children with *daily* symp-toms that are influenced by a variety of triggering mechanisms can be placed on chronic bronchodilatory therapy in the form of the-ophylline or beta agonists. Depending on the age of the patient, oral or aerosolized beta agonists can be used. In the child less than 5–7 y, oral agents, nebulized agents, or metered-dose inhalers with

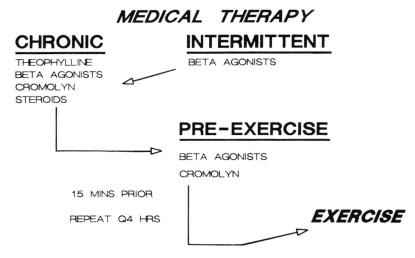

FIGURE 12-7. *Therapeutic strategies for the treatment of childhood asthma and exercise-induced asthma.*

spacing devices can be used. Since treatment side effects are less with inhaled vs. oral forms of beta agonists, this route of administration should be encouraged whenever possible. Cromolyn sodium is helpful in the chronic management of patients as well. In asthma not responding to bronchodilator therapy alone, inhaled or oral corticosteroids may be necessary. *Intermittent* breakthrough symptoms can be treated with beta agonists as they are rapid acting (5–15 mins) and can be repeated every 3 to 4 h. Children with chronic symptoms will undoubtedly have exacerbations of their asthma with exercise; alternatively, some children will only experience asthmatic symptoms following exercise. Both groups of children should be taught to premedicate 10 to 15 min *before* exercise with either a beta agonist or cromolyn sodium. Beta agonists are usually prescribed first as they can be used both prophylactically and as treatment should the child forget to premedicate. In cases not responding to beta agonists alone, the combination of beta agonists and cromolyn has been found to produce an additive effect (Latimer et al., 1983). In difficult-to-manage cases, theophylline could be added on a daily basis, and the addition of inhaled steroids should be considered.

V. EFFECTS OF PHYSICAL FITNESS ON EIA

A. Effects of Exercise on Cardiovascular Conditioning in Patients with EIA

At the 1984 Olympic Games in Los Angeles, 67 of 597 athletes on the U.S. team were identified as having asthma or exercise-induced bronchospasm (Voy, 1986); 41 medals were won by this group of athletes, indicating that EIA and outstanding athletic performance are not incompatible. The effects of physical training on exercise tolerance in asthmatics, both in terms of overall physiologic benefit as well as on the incidence and severity of bronchospasm provoked by exercise, has been evaluated by a number of investigators (Bundgaard et al., 1984; King et al., 1984; Henriksen & Nielsen, 1983; Svenonius et al., 1983; Szentagothai et al., 1987; Arborelius & Svenonius, 1984; Orenstein et al., 1985; Fitch et al., 1986; Nickerson et al., 1983; Haas et al., 1985; Haas et al., 1987).

Szentagothai et al. (1987) studied 121 asthmatic children who participated in a long-term physical exercise program that began with swimming and progressed to gymnasium exercises and outdoor running. During the first year, the number of days with asthmatic symptoms and medication use decreased. School absenteeism and hospitalization dropped markedly. Cardiovascular efficiency was better compared with a control group of nonasthmatic children. Orenstein et al. (1985) studied 20 children who participated in a four-month running program (30 min/day, 3 days/wk); each child premedicated with a β_2 agonist prior to each running session to prevent EIA. Despite significant increases in work tolerance and cardiopulmonary fitness, however, asthma severity judged by daily asthma diary scores and peak flow measurements did not change significantly. The investigators concluded that children with asthma can safely engage in a running program and increase work tolerance and fitness without worsening their asthma. It should be noted, however, that in studies attempting to evaluate the effects of exercise training on the frequency and intensity of asthmatic symptoms over a period of time, an appropriate age-matched control group that does not exercise but has the same number of visits to the physician or research personnel engaged in the study also be included. Inclusion of such a group would control for the effects that multiple physician-patient contacts may have on the observed outcomes.

B. Effect of Exercise Training on the Incidence and Severity of EIA

Studies evaluating the effects of physical training on EIA have yielded conflicting results. These disparate findings are most likely due to the method of analysis of EIA before and after the training period. For example, physical training increases fitness, which may mean less of a stimulus for EIA if the same workload is used during both evaluation periods; this factor could be controlled by exercising the patient at a workload to achieve the same level of minute ventilation for a given period of time.

Nickerson et al. (1983) studied 15 children with severe chronic asthma before and after a period in which patients ran progressively increasing distances 4 days a wk for 6 wks. Clinical status and need for treatment did not change. Fitness, as measured by the distance run in 12 min did significantly improve. However, EIA following a bicycle ergometer stress test to produce identical changes in heart rate, minute ventilation, and maximal oxygen consumption did not change following conditioning. Fitch et al. (1986) studied 26 children, 10 of whom were assigned to the treatment group. Children in the treatment group performed a series of diversified running group activities over a three-month period; children in the control group performed normal daily activities. Following treatment, the severity of EIA evaluated at 80% of maximal oxygen consumption before and after training was unchanged (as assessed by peak expiratory flow measurements).

In contrast to these results, studies by Henriksen and Nielsen (1983) and Svenonius et al. (1983) demonstrated that physical conditioning in children can significantly decrease their bronchospastic response to the same intensity of exercise. Finally, Haas et al. (1987) studied 22 adult asthmatic patients before and after a 36-session training sequence of aerobic exercise. Training did not change pulmonary function values, except for a small increase in maximal voluntary ventilation. After training, both external work at a given heart rate and peak oxygen consumption increased by 30% and 15%, respectively. When subjects were exercised at workloads that yielded similar minute ventilation rates, immediate post-exercise forced expiratory airflow was significantly higher after training, and reduction in forced expiratory airflow during the first 9 min post-exercise was significantly less after training as well.

Two important aspects of these analyses should not be overlooked: First, exercise has not been demonstrated to be harmful, and second, some studies have demonstrated that, after training, children can exercise at the same intensity as pre-training and have decreased bronchoconstriction. Since some studies have noted an improvement in general physical and psychologic well-being following physical training as well as this reduced incidence of EIA, asthmatic children and adolescents should be encouraged to participate to their fullest in both recreational and competitive athletics. If exercise does provoke attacks of asthma, safe and effective medications are available in a variety of delivery systems that can be individualized to fit each patient's age and desired level of performance.

SUMMARY

Asthma is the most common chronic respiratory disorder in children. Although multiple factors can trigger attacks of asthma, exercise is one of the more common precipitants. Exercise-induced asthma (EIA) can be recognized by the symptoms of cough, wheezing, or shortness of breath that occur in association with exercise. The propensity to develop EIA can be influenced by the climatic conditions (cold, dry conditions being the most likely to produce EIA), the type of exercise (short-distance running sports vs. swimming), and the baseline level of airway responsiveness (concurrent viral upper respiratory tract infection, allergen exposure, etc.). Although exercise can trigger attacks of asthma, exercise training programs for children with asthma should be encouraged as they will improve cardiorespiratory fitness and potentially decrease the asthmatic response to a given intensity of exercise. Since excellent treatment is available, children with asthma in general or solely EIA should not be restricted, but rather encouraged, to participate in a full range of exercise activities.

ACKNOWLEDGEMENTS

The authors wishes to express their gratitude to Drs. Jerome Dempsey, David Orenstein, and Bruce Johnson for their thorough review and thoughtful critique of this manuscript.

BIBLIOGRAPHY

1. American Thoracic Society. Chronic bronchitis, asthma and pulmonary emphysema. *American Review of Respiratory Disease.* 85:762–768, 1962.
2. Anderson, S., J.P. Seale, L. Ferris, R. Schoeffel, and D.A. Lindsay. An evaluation of pharmacotherapy for exercise-induced asthma. *Journal of Allergy and Clinical Immunology.* 64:612–618, 1979.
3. Anderson, S.D., J.D.S. McEvoy, and S. Bianco. Changes in lung volumes and airway resistance after exercise in asthmatic subjects. *American Review of Respiratory Disease.* 106:30–37, 1972.
4. Anderson, S.D., M. Silverman, P. Konig, and S. Godfrey. Exercise-induced asthma. *British Journal of Diseases of the Chest.* 69:1–10, 1975.
5. Anderson, S.D. Recent advances in the understanding of exercise-induced asthma. *European Journal of Respiratory Diseases.* 64(supplement 128):225–236, 1983.
6. Anderson, S.D. Issues in exercise-induced asthma. *Journal of Allergy and Clinical Immunology.* 76:763–772, 1985.
7. Arborelius, M., Jr., and E. Svenonius. Decrease of exercise-induced asthma after physical training. *European Journal of Respiratory Diseases.* 65(Supplement):25–31, 1984.
8. Arronson, H., L. Solymar, J.A. Dempsey, J. Bijure, T. Olsson, and B. Blake. A modified forced oscillation technique for measurements of respiratory resistance. *Journal Applied Physiology.* 42:650–655, 1977.
9. Atkins, P.C., M. Norman, H. Weiner, and B. Zweiman. Release of neutrophil chemotactic activity during immediate hypersensitivity reactions in humans. *Annals of Internal Medicine.* 86:415–418, 1977.
10. Aubier, M., A. DeTroyer, M. Sampson, P.T. Macklem, and C. Roussos. Aminophylline improves diaphragmatic contractility. *New England Journal of Medicine.* 305:249–252, 1981.
11. Badger, D., A.D. Ramos, C.D. Lew, A.C.G. Platzker, M.W. Stabile, and T.G. Keens. Childhood sequelae of infant lung disease: Exercise and pulmonary function abnormalities after bronchopulmonary dysplasia. *Journal of Pediatrics.* 110:693–699, 1987.
12. Bar-Or, O., I. Neuman, and R. Dotan. Effects of dry and humid climates on exercise-induced asthma in children and preadolescents. *Journal of Allergy and Clinical Immunology.*60:163–68, 1977.
13. Barnes, P.J., and M.J. Brown. Venous plasma histamine in exercise and hyperventilation induced asthma in man. *Clinical Science.* 61:159–162, 1962.
14. Barnes, P.J., M.J. Brown, M. Silverman, and C.T. Dollery. Circulating catecholamines in exercise- and hyperventilation-induced asthma. *Thorax.* 36:435–438, 1981.
15. Barnes, P.J. Clinical studies with calcium antagonists in asthma. *British Journal of Clinical Pharmacology.* 20:289S–298S, 1985.
16. Barnes, P.J. Endogenous catecholamines and asthma. *Journal of Allergy and Clinical Immunology.* 77:791–793, 1986.
17. Barrett, K.E. and D.D. Metcalfe. Heterogeneity of mast cells in the tissues of the respiratory tract and other organ systems. *American Review of Respiratory Disease.* 135:1190–1195, 1987.
18. Bar-Yishay, E., I. Ben-Dov, and S. Godfrey. Refractory period following hyperventilation-induced asthma. *American Review of Respiratory Disease.* 127:572–574, 1983a.
19. Bar-Yishay, E., I. Gur, M. Levy, D. Volozui, and S. Godfrey. Duration of action of sodium cromoglycate on exercise-induced asthma: Comparison of 2 formulations. *Archives of Disease in Childhood.* 58:624–627, 1983b.
20. Belcher, N.G., R. Murdoch, N. Dalton, T.J.H. Clark, P.J. Rees, and T.H. Lee. Circulating concentrations of histamine, neutrophil chemotactic activity, and catecholamines during the refractory period in exercise-induced asthma. *Journal of Allergy and Clinical Immunology.* 81:100–110, 1988.
21. Belcher, N.G., P.J. Rees, T.J.H. Clark, and T.H. Lee. A comparison of the refractory periods induced by hypertonic airway challenge and exercise in bronchial asthma. *American Review of Respiratory Disease.* 135:822–825, 1987.
22. Ben-Dov, I., E. Bar-Yishay, and S. Godfrey. Heterogeneity in the response of asthmatic patients to pre-exercise treatment with cromolyn sodium. *American Review of Respiratory Disease.* 127:113–116, 1983a.

23. Ben-Dov, I., I. Gur, E. Bar-Yishay, and S. Godfrey. Refractory period following induced asthma: Contributions of exercise and isocapnic hyperventilation. *Thorax.* 38:849–853, 1983b.
24. Ben-Dov, I., D.Y. Sue, J.E. Hansen, and K. Wasserman. Bronchodilation and attenuation of exercise-induced bronchospasm by PY 108-068, a new calcium antagonist. *American Review of Respiratory Disease.* 133:116–119, 1986.
25. Ben-Zvi, Z., W.A. Spohn, S.H. Young, and M. Kattan. Hypnosis for exercise-induced asthma. *American Review of Respiratory Disease.* 125:392–395, 1982.
26. Bergstrand, H. Phosphodiesterase inhibition and theophylline. *European Journal of Respiratory Diseases.* 109Supplement:37–44, 1980.
27. Berkowitz, R., E. Schwartz, D. Bukstein, M. Grunstein, and H. Chai. Albuterol protects against exercise-induced asthma longer than metaproterenol sulfate. *Pediatrics.* 77:173–178.1986.
28. Bierman, C.W., S.G. Spiro, and I. Petheram. Characterization of the late response in exercise-induce asthma. *Journal of Allergy and Clinical Immunology.* 74:701–706, 1984.
29. Black, J.L., C.M. Smith, and S.D. Anderson. Cromolyn sodium inhibits the increased responsiveness to methacholine that follows ultrasonically nebulized water challenge in patients with asthma. *Journal of Allergy and Clinical Immunology.* 80:39–44, 1987.
30. Boner, A., E. Niero, I. Antolini, and J.O. Warner. Biphasic (early and late) asthmatic responses to exercise in children with severe asthma, resident at high altitude. *European Journal of Pediatrics.* 144:164–166, 1985.
31. Borut, T.C., D.P. Tashkin, T.J. Fisher, R. Katz, G. Rachelefsky, S.C. Siegel, E. Lee, and C. Harper. Comparison of aerosolized atropine sulfate and Sch-1000 on exercise-induced bronchospasm in children. *Journal of Allergy and Clinical Immunology.* 60:127–133, 1977.
32. Boulet, L., C. Legris, H. Turcotte, and J. Hebert. Prevalence and characteristics of late asthmatic responses to exercise. *Journal of Allergy and Clinical Immunology.* 80:655–662, 1987.
33. Bundgaard, A., D. Buch, A. Schmidt, and N. Bach-Mortensen. Pretreatment of exercise-induced asthma in children using disodium cromoglycate and fenoterol inhalation power. *European Journal of Respiratory Diseases.* 64(supplement 130):36–41, 1983.
34. Bundgaard, A., T. Ingemann-Hansen, and J. Halkjaer-Kristensen. Physical training in bronchial asthma. *International Rehabilitation Medicine.* 6:179–182, 1984.
35. Chatham, M., E.R. Bleeker, P.L. Smith, R.R. Rosenthal, P. Mason, and P.S. Norman. A comparison of histamine, methacholine, and exercise airway reactivity in normal and asthmatic subjects. *American Review of Respiratory Disease.* 126:235–240, 1982.
36. Chen, W.Y., and D.J. Horton. Heat and water loss from the airways and exercise-induced asthma. *Respiration.* 34:305–310, 1977.
37. Chen, W.Y., P.C. Weiser, and H. Chai. Airway cooling stimulus for exercise-induced asthma. *Scandinavian Journal of Respiratory Diseases.* 60:144–50, 1979.
38. Chudry, N., F. Correa, and M. Silverman. Nedocromil sodium and exercise induced asthma. *Archives of Disease in Childhood.* 62:412–414, 1987.
39. Clarke, K.S. Sports medicine and drug control programs of the U.S. Olympic Committee. *Journal of Allergy and Clinical Immunology.* 73:740–44, 1984.
40. Clee, M.D., C.G. Ingram, P.C. Reid, and A.S. Robertson. The effect of astemizole on exercise-induced asthma. *British Journal of Diseases of the Chest.* 78:180–183, 1984.
41. Cockcroft, D.W., and K.Y. Murdock. Comparative effects of inhaled salbutamol, sodium cromoglycate, and beclomethasone dipropionate on allergen-induced early asthmatic responses, late asthmatic responses, and increased bronchial responsiveness to histamine. *Journal of Allergy and Clinical Immunology.* 79:734–740, 1987.
42. Counahan, R., and M.B. Mearns. Prevalence of atopy and exercise-induced bronchial lability in relatives of patients with cystic fibrosis. *Archives of Disease in Childhood.* 50:477–481, 1975.
43. Cox, J.S.G., and R.E.C. Altounyan. Nature and modes of action of disodium cromoglycate (Lomudal). *Respiration.* 27(supplement):292–309, 1970.
44. Cropp, G.J.A. Exercise-induced asthma. In E. Middleton, C.E. Reed, and E. Ellis (eds.). *Allergy: Principles and Practice, Vol. II.* St. Louis:C.V. Mosby Co., 1983.
45. Cummings, N.P., and Strunk, R.C. Combination drug therapy in children with exercise-induced bronchospasm. *Annals of Allergy.* 53:395–400, 1984.
46. Deal, E.C., Jr., E.R. McFadden, Jr., R.H. Ingram, Jr., and J.J. Jaeger. Esophageal temperature during exercise in asthmatic and non-asthmatic subjects. *Journal of Applied Physiology.* 46:484–90, 1979a.
47. Deal, E.C., E.R. McFadden, R.H. Ingram, and J.J. Jaeger. Hyperpnea and heat flux: initial reaction sequence in exercise-induced asthma. *Journal of Applied Physiology, Respiratory Environmental Exercise Physiology.* 46:476–83, 1979b.
48. Deal, E.C., Jr., E.R. McFadden, Jr., R.H. Ingram, Jr., R.H. Strauss, and J.J. Jaeger. Role of respiratory heat exchange in production of exercise-induced asthma. *Journal of Applied Physiology.* 46:467–475, 1979c.

49. Deal, E.C., Jr., S.I. Wasserman, N.A. Soter, R.H. Ingram, Jr., and E.R. McFadden, Jr. Evaluation of role played by mediators of immediate hypersensitivity in exercise-induced asthma. *Journal of Clinical Investigation*. 65:659–665, 1980.
50. Dempsey, J.A., P. Hanson, and K. Henderson. Exercise-induced alveolar hypoxemia in healthy human subjects at sea level. *Journal of Physiology*. (London), 355:161–75, 1984.
51. Dempsey, J.A., E.H. Vidruk, and G.S. Mitchell. Pulmonary control systems in exercise: update. *Federation Proceedings*. 44:2260–70, 1985.
52. Dosani, R., G.R. Van Loon, and N.K. Burki. The relationship between exercise-induced asthma and plasma catecholamines. *American Review of Respiratory Disease*. 136:973–978, 1987.
53. Dutoit, J.I., C.M. Salome, and A.J. Woolcock. Inhaled corticosteroids reduce the severity of bronchial hyperresponsiveness in asthma but oral theophylline does not. *American Review of Respiratory Disease*. 136:1174–1178, 1987.
54. Edmunds, A.T., M. Tooley, and S. Godfrey. The refractory period after exercise-induced asthma: Its duration and relation to the severity of exercise. *American Review of Respiratory Disease*. 117:247–254, 1978.
55. Eggleston, P.A. Methods of exercise challenge. *Journal of Allergy and Clinical Immunology*. 73:666–69, 1984.
56. Eggleston, P.A., W.C. Bierman, W.E. Pierson, S.J. Stamm, and Van P.P. Arsdel, Jr. A double blind trial of the effect of cromolyn sodium on exercise-induced bronchospasm. *Journal of Allergy and Clinical Immunology*. 50:57–62, 1972.
56. Eggleston, P.A., A. Kagey-Sobotka, R.P. Schleimer, and L.M. Lichtenstein. Interaction between hyperosmolar and IgE-mediated histamine release from basophils and mast cells. *American Review of Respiratory Disease*. 130:86–91, 1984.
57. Eggleston, P.A., R.R. Rosenthal, S.A. Anderson, R. Anderton, C.W. Bierman, E.R. Bleecker, H. Chai, G.J. Cropp, J.D. Johnson, P. Konig, J. Morse, L.J. Smith, R.J. Summers, J.J. Trautlein, Guidelines for the methodology of exercise challenge testing of asthmatics. Study group on exercise challenge, bronchoprovocation committee, American Academy of Allergy. *Journal of Allergy and Clinical Immunology*. 64:6642–5, 1979.
58. Ellis, E. Inhibition of exercise-induced asthma by theophylline. *Journal of Allergy and Clinical Immunology*. 73:690–692, 1984.
59. England, S.J., and D. Bartlett, Jr. Changes in respiratory movements of the human vocal cords during hyperpnea. *Journal of Applied Physiology*. 52:780–785, 1982.
60. Eschenbacher, W.L., and D. Sheppard. Respiratory heat loss is not the sole stimulus for bronchoconstriction induced by isocapnic hyperpnea with dry air. *American Review of Respiratory Disease*. 131:894–901, 1985.
61. Fanta, C.H., E.R. McFadden, Jr., and R.H. Ingram. Effects of cromolyn sodium on the response to respiratory heat loss in normal subjects. *American Review of Respiratory Disease*. 123:161–164, 1981.
62. Findlay, S.R., A.M. Dvorak, A. Kagey-Sobotka, and L.M. Lichtenstein. Hyperosmolar triggering of histamine release from human basophils. *Journal of Clinical Investigation*. 67:1604–1613, 1981.
63. Finney, M.J.B., S.D. Anderson, and J.L. Black. The effect of non-isotonic solutions on human isolated airway smooth muscle. *Respiration Physiology*. 69:277–286, 1987.
64. Fitch, K.D. Management of allergic Olympic athletes. *Journal of Allergy and Clinical Immunology*. 73:722–727, 1984.
65. Fitch, K.D., J.D. Blitvich, and A.R. Morton. The effect of running training on exercise-induced asthma. *Annals of Allergy*. 57:90–94, 1986.
66. Foreman, J.C., and L.G. Garland. Cromoglycate and other antiallergic drugs. A possible mechanism of action. *British Medical Journal*. 1:820–821, 1976.
67. Foresi, A., S. Mattoli, G. Corbo, A. Verga, A. Sommaruga, and G. Ciappi. Late bronchial response and increase in methacholine hyperresponsiveness after exercise and distilled water challenge in atopic subjects with asthma with dual asthmatic response to allergen inhalation. *Journal of Allergy and Clinical Immunology*. 78:1130–1139, 1986.
68. Foresi, A., G.M. Corbo, G. Ciappi, S. Valente, and G. Polidori. Effect of two doses of inhaled diltiazem on exercise-induced asthma. *Respiration*. 51:241–247, 1987.
69. Francis, P.W.J., I.R.B. Krastins, and H. Levison. Oral and inhaled salbutamol in the prevention of exercise-induced bronchospasm. *Pediatrics*. 66:103–108, 1980.
70. Freyschuss, U., G. Hedlin, and G. Hedenstierna. Ventilation-perfusion relationships during exercise-induced asthma in children. *American Review of Respiratory Disease*. 130:888–894, 1984.
71. Friedman, R., M. Ackerman, E. Wald, M. Casselbrant, G. Friday, and P. Fireman. Asthma and bacterial sinusitis in children. *Journal of Allergy and Clinical Immunology*. 74:185–189, 1984.
72. Friedman, M.M., and M.A. Kaliner. Human mast cells and asthma. *American Review of*

Respiratory Disease. 135:1157–1164, 1987.

73. Fung, K.P., O.K.W.C. Chow, and S.Y. So. Attenuation of exercise-induced asthma by acupuncture. *Lancet.* 20:1419–1421, 1986.
74. Furukawa, C.T. Other pharmacologic agents that may affect bronchial hyperreactivity. *Journal of Allergy and Clinical Immunology.* 73:693–698, 1984.
75. Gergen, P.J., D.I. Mullally, and R. Evans. National survey of prevalence of asthma among children in the United States, 1977–80. *Pediatrics.* 81:1–7, 1988.
76. Gilbert, I.A., J.M. Fouke, and E.R. McFadden, Jr. Heat and water flux in the intrathoracic airways and exercise-induced asthma. *Journal of Applied Physiology.* 63:1681–91, 1987.
77. Godfrey, S., and M. Silverman. Demonstration of placebo response in asthma by means of exercise testing. *Journal of Psychosomatic Research.* 17:293–298, 1973.
78. Godfrey, S., and P. Konig. Inhibition of exercise-induced asthma by different pharmacological pathways. *Thorax.* 31:137–140, 1976.
79. Godfrey, S. Symposium on special problems and management of allergic athletes. *Journal of Allergy and Clinical Immunology.* 73:630–633, 1984.
80. Gravelyn, T.R., M. Capper, and W.L. Eschenbacher. Effectiveness of a heat and moisture exchanger in preventing hyperpnoea induced bronchoconstriction in subjects with asthma. *Thorax.* 42:877–80, 1987.
81. Grimby, G.M., M. Goldman, and J. Mead. Respiratory muscle action inferred from rib cage and abdominal V-P partitioning. *Journal of Applied Physiology.* 41:739–751, 1976.
82. Gross, N.J. What is this thing called love?—or defining asthma. *American Review of Respiratory Disease.* 121:203–204, 1980.
83. Haas, F., S. Pasierski, N. Levine, M. Bishop, K. Axen, P. Horacio, and A. Haas. Effect of aerobic training on forced expiratory airflow in exercising asthmatic humans, *Journal of Applied Physiology.* 63:1230–35, 1987.
84. Haas, F., H. Pineda, K. Axen, D. Gaudino, and A. Haas. Effects of physical fitness on expiratory airflow in exercising asthmatic people. *Medicine and Science in Sports and Exercise.* 17:585–92, 1985.
85. Halfon, N., and P.W. Newacheck. Trends in the hospitalization for acute childhood asthma, 1970–84. *American Journal of Public Health.* 76:1308–1311, 1986.
86. Hartley, J.P.R., T.J. Charles, and A. Seaton. Beclomethasone valerate inhalation and exercise-induced asthma in adults. *British Journal of Diseases of the Chest.* 71:253–258, 1977.
87. Hedlin, G., V. Graff-Lonnevig, and U. Freyschuss. Working capacity and pulmonary gas exchange in children with exercise-induced asthma. *Acta Paediatrica Scandinavica.* 75:947–954, 1986.
88. Henriksen, J.M., and R. Dahl. Effects of inhaled budesonide alone and in combination with low-dose terbutaline in children with exercise-induced asthma. *American Review of Respiratory Disease.* 128:993–997, 1983.
89. Henriksen, J.M., and T.T. Nielsen. Effect of physical training on exercise-induced bronchoconstriction. *Acta Paediatrica Scandinavica.* 72:31–36, 1983.
90. Henriksen, J.M., and A. Wenzel. Effect of an intranasally administered corticosteroid (Budesonide) on nasal obstruction, mouth breathing, and asthma. *American Review of Respiratory Disease.* 130:1014–1018, 1984.
91. Henriksen, J.M. Effect of inhalation of corticosteroids on exercise induced asthma: Randomized double blind crossover study of budesonide in asthmatic children. *British Medical Journal.* 291:248–249, 1985.
92. Henriksen, J.M. Reproducibility of exercise-induced asthma in children. *Allergy.* 41:225–231, 1986.
93. Honicky, R.E., J.S. Osborne, and C.A. Akpom. Symptoms of respiratory illness in young children and the use of wood-burning stoves for indoor heating. *Pediatrics.* 75:587–593, 1985.
94. Horn, C.R., R.M. Jones, D. Lee, and S.R. Brennan. Late response in exercise-induced asthma. *Clinical Allergy.* 14:307–309, 1984.
95. Howarth, P.H., G.J.K. Pao, M.K. Church, and S.T. Holgate. Exercise and isocapnic hyperventilation-induced bronchoconstriction in asthma: Relevance of circulating basophils to measurements of plasma histamine. *Journral of Allergy and Clinical Immunology.* 73:391–399, 1984.
96. Hsu, K.H.K., D.E. Jenkens, B.P. Hsi, E. Bourhofer, V. Thompson, N. Tanakawa, and G.S. Hsieh. Ventilatory functions of normal children and young adults, Mexican-American, white and black. I. Spirometry. *Journal of Pediatrics.* 95:14–23, 1979.
97. Iikura, Y., H. Inui, T. Nagakura, and T.H. Lee. Factors predisposing to exercise-induced late asthmatic responses. *Journal of Allergy and Clinical Immunology.* 75:285–289, 1985.
98. Ioli, F., C.F. Donner, C. Fracchia, A. Patessio, and C. Aprile. Sustained-release anhydrous theophylline in preventing exercise-induced asthma. *Respiration.* 46:105–113, 1984.
99. Juniper, E.F., K.M. Latimer, M.M. Morris, R.S. Roberts, and F.E. Hargreave. Airway re-

sponses to hyperventilation of cold dry air: Duration of protection by cromolyn sodium. *Journal of Allergy and Clinical Immunology.* 78:387–391, 1986.
100. Katz, R.M., B.J. Whipp, E.M. Heimlich, and K. Wasserman. Exercise-induced brornchospasm, ventilation and blood gases in asthmatic children. *Journal of Allergy.* 47:148–154, 1971.
101. Kidd, J.M., S.H. Cohen, A.J. Sosman, and J.N. Fink. Food-dependent exercise-induced anaphylaxis. *Journal of Allergy and Clinical Immunology.* 71:407–411, 1983.
102. Kiers, A., T.W. Van der Mark, M.G. Woldring, and R. Peset. Determination of the functional residual capacity during exercise. *Ergonomics.* 23:955–959, 1980.
103. King, J.T., M.R. Bye, and J.T. Demopoulos. Exercise programs for asthmatic children. *Comprehensive Therapy* 10:67–71, 1984.
104. Kock, G., and B.O. Ericksson. Effect of physical training on anatomical R-L shunt at rest and pulmonary diffusing capacity during near-maximal exercise in boys 11–13 years old. *Scandinavian Journal of Clinical and Laboratory Investigation* 31:95–103, 1972.
105. Konig, P., P. Jaffe, and S. Godfrey. Effects of corticosteroids on exercise-induced asthma. *Journal of Allergy and Clinical Immunology* 54:14–19, 1974.
106. Konig, P., P.A. Eggleston, and C.W. Serby. Comparison of oral and inhaled metaproterenol for prevention of exercise-induced asthma. *Clinical Allergy* 11:597–604, 1981.
107. Konig, P. The use of cromolyn in the management of hyperreactive airways and exercise. *Journal of Allergy and Clinical Immunology* 73:686–689, 1984.
108. Konig, P., N.L. Hordvik, and C.W. Serby. Fenoterol in exercise-induced asthma. Effect of dose on efficacy and duration of action. *Chest* 85:462–464, 1984.
109. Konig, P., N.L. Hordvik, and C. Kreutz. The preventive effect and duration of action of nedocromil sodium and cromolyn sodium on exercise-induced asthma (EIA) in adults. *Journal of Allergy and Clinical Immunology* 79:64–68, 1987.
110. Larsson, K. Oxitropium bromide, ipratropium bromide and fenoterol in exercise-induced asthma. *Respiration* 43:57–63, 1982.
111. Latimer, K.M., P.M. O'Byrne, M.M. Morris, R. Roberts, and F.E. Hargreave. Bronchoconstriction stimulated by airway cooling. Better protection with combined inhalation of terbutaline sulphate and cromolyn sodium than with either alone. *American Review of Respiratory Disease* 128:440–6, 1983.
112. Laursen, L.C., N. Johannesson, and B. Weeke. Effects of enprofylline and theophylline on exercise-induced asthma. *Allergy* 40:506–509, 1985.
113. Lee, T.H., M.J. Brown, L. Nagy, R. Causon, M.J. Walport, and A.B. Kay. Exercise-induced release of histamine and neutrophil chemotactic factor in atopic asthmatics. *Journal of Allergy and Clinical Immunology* 70:73–81, 1982a.
114. Lee, T.H., L. Nagy, T. Nagakura, M.J. Walport, and A.B. Kay. Identification and partial characterization of an exercise-induced neutrophil chemotactic factor in bronchial asthma. *Journal of Clinical Investigation* 69:889–892, 1982b.
115. Lee, T.H., T. Nagakura, N. Papageorgiou, Y. Iikura, and A.B. Kay. Exercise-induced late asthmatic reactions with neutrophil chemotactic activity. *New England Journal of Medicine* 308:1502–1505, 1983.
116. Lee, T.H., and S.D. Anderson. Heterogeneity of mechanisms in exercise induced asthma. *Thorax* 40:481–487, 1985.
117. Lemanske, R.F., and M. Kaliner. Late-phase allergic reactions. In E. Middleton, Jr., C.E. Reed, E.F. Ellis, N.F. Adkinson, Jr., J.W. Yunginger (Eds.). *Allergy: Principles and Practice.* Vol. 1. St. Louis, MO: C.V. Mosby Co., 1988.
118. Lemanske, R.F., and M. Kaliner. The biology of mast cell secretion and its pharmacologic modulation. In J.H. Hanson, and A. Szentivanyi (eds.). *The Reticuloendothelial System. A comprehensive treatise. Vol. 8.* New York:Plenum Press, 1985.
119. Loughlin, G.M., and L.M. Taussig. Pulmonary function in children with a history of laryngotracheobronchitis. *Journal of Pediatrics* 94:365–369, 1979.
120. Magnussen, H., V. Hartmenn, and G. Reuss. Influence of diltiazem on bronchoconstriction induced by cold air breathing during exercise. *Thorax* 39:579–582, 1984.
121. Markham, D., M. Chang, R. Evans III, and D. Mullally. Epidemiologic study of deaths from asthma among children in U.S. 1965–83. *Journal of Allergy and Clinical Immunology* 77:161A, 1986.
122. Martin, J., E. Powell, S. Shore, J. Emrich, and L.A. Engel. The role of respiratory muscles in the hyperinflation of bronchial asthma. *American Review of Respiratory Disease,* 121, 441–447, 1980.
123. Martinsson, A., K. Larsson, and P. Hjemdahl. Reduced β_2-adrenoceptor responsiveness in exercise-induced asthma. *Chest* 88:594–600, 1985.
124. Matthay, R.A., H.J. Berger, R. Davies, J. Loke, A. Gottschalk, and B.L. Zaret. Improvement in cardiac performance by oral long-acting theophylline in chronic obstructive pulmonary disease. *American Heart Journal* 104:1022–1025, 1982.

125. McFadden, E.R., Jr., D.M. Denison, J.R. Waller, B. Assoufi, A. Peacock, and T. Sopwith. Direct recordings of the temperatures in the tracheobronchial tree in normal man. *Journal of Clinical Investigation* 69:700–705, 1982.
126. McFadden, E.R., Jr., and B.M. Pichurko. Intra-airway thermal profiles during exercise and hyperventilation in normal man. *Journal of Clinical Investigation* 76:1007–1010, 1985a.
127. McFadden, E.R., Jr., B.M. Pichurko, K.F. Bowman, E. Ingenito, S. Burnes, N. Dowling, and J. Solway. Thermal mapping of the airways in man. *Journal of Applied Physiology* 58:564–570, 1985b.
128. McFadden, E.R., Jr., A.M. Lenner, and K.P. Strohl. Postexertional airway rewarming and thermally induced asthma. New insights into pathophysiology and possible pathogenesis. *Journal of Clinical Investigation* 78:18–25, 1986.
129. McFadden, E.R. Exercise-induced asthma. Assessment of current etiologic concepts. *Chest* 91:151S–157S, 1987a.
130. McFadden, E.R. Exercise and asthma. *New England Journal of Medicine* 317:502–503, 1987b.
131. Middleton, E., Jr. Airway smooth muscle, asthma, and calcium ions. *Journal of Allergy and Clinical Immunology* 73:643–650, 1984.
132. Minor, T.E., E.C. Elliot, A.N. DeMeo, J.J. Ouellette, M. Cohen, and C.E. Reed. Viruses as precipitants of asthmatic attacks in children. *Journal of the American Medical Association* 227:292–298, 1974.
133. Mitchell, R.G., and B. Dawson. Educational and social characteristics of children with asthma. *Archives of Disease in Childhood* 48:467–471, 1973.
134. Morgan, D.J.R., I. Moodley, M.J. Phillips, and R.J. Davies. Plasma histamine in asthmatic and control subjects following exercise: Influence of circulating basophils and different assay techniques. *Thorax* 38:771–777, 1983.
135. Morris, H.G. Pharmacology of corticosteroids in asthma. In C.E. Reed, E. Ellis, and E. Middleton (eds.). *Asthma: Principles and Practice. Vol 2, 2nd edition.* St. Louis:C.V. Mosby Co., 1983
136. Morse, J.L.C., N.L. Jones, and G.D. Anderson. The effect of terbutaline in exercise-induced asthma. *American Review of Respiratory Disease* 113:89–93, 1976.
137. Morton, A.R., S.R. Lawrence, K.D. Fitch, and A.G. Hahn. Duration of exercise in the provocation of exercise-induced asthma. *Annals of Allergy* 51:530–534, 1983.
138. Murphy, G.W., B.F. Schreiner Jr., and P.N. Yu. Effect of aminophylline on the pulmonary circulation and left ventricular performance in patients with valvular heart disease. *Circulation* 37:361–369, 1968.
139. Nickerson, B.G., D.B. Bautista, M.A. Namey, W. Richards, and T.G. Keens. Distance running improves fitness in asthmatic children without pulmonary complications or changes in exercise-induced bronchospasm. *Pediatrics* 71:147–152, 1983.
140. Novey, H.S., R.D. Fairshter, K. Salness, R.A. Simon, and J.G. Curd. Postprandial exercise-induced anaphylaxis. *Journal of Allergy and Clinical Immunology* 71:498–504, 1983.
141. Noviski, N., E. Bar-Yishay, I. Gur, and S. Godfrey. Exercise intensity determines and climatic conditions modify the severity of exercise-induced asthma. *American Review of Respiratory Disease* 136:592–594, 1987.
142. O'Byrne, P.M., N.C. Thomson, M. Morris, R.S. Roberts, E.E. Daniel, and F.E. Hargreave. The protective effect of inhaled chlorpheniramine and atropine on bronchoconstriction stimulated by airway cooling. *American Review of Respiratory Disease* 128:611–617, 1983.
143. O'Byrne, P.M., and G.L. Jones. The effect of indomethacin on exercise-induced bronchoconstriction and refractoriness after exercise. *American Review of Respiratory Disease* 134:69–72, 1986.
144. Olive, S.R., J.E. Hansen, D.Y. Sue, I. Ben-Dov, and K. Wasserman. Comparison of PY 108-068, a new calcium antagonist, with nifedipine in exercise-induced asthma. *Chest* 90:208–211, 1986.
145. Oppenheimer, P.J., and D.E. Schuller. Pulmonary function and cardiovascular responses to exercise in asthmatic children taking oral metaproterenol versus theophylline. *Pediatric Asthma Allergy Immunology* 1:95–101, 1987.
146. Orenstein, D.M., M.E. Reed, F.T. Grogan, and L.V. Crawford. Exercise conditioning in children with asthma. *Journal of Pediatrics* 106:556–560, 1985.
147. Patel, K.R. Terfenadine in exercise induced asthma. *British Medical Journal* 288:1496–1497, 1984.
148. Patel, K.R., W.M. Tullett, M.G. Neale, R.T. Wall, and K.M. Tan. Plasma concentrations of sodium cromoglycate given by nebulization and metered dose inhalers in patients with exercise-induce asthma: Relationship to protective effect. *British Journal of Clinical Pharmacology* 21:231–233, 1986.
149. Peckham, C., and N. Butler. A national study of asthma in childhood. *Journal of Epidemiology and Community Health* 32:79–85, 1978.
150. Pedersen, S. Absorption of Theo-Dur Sprinkle with food: Importance of types of meals

and medication times. *Journal of Allergy and Clinical Immunology* 78:653–660, 1986.

151. Pichurko, B.M., B. Sullivan, R.J. Porcelli, and E.R. McFadden. Endogenous adrenergic modification of exercise-induced asthma. *Journal of Allergy and Clinical Immunology* 77:796–801, 1986.

152. Pierson, W.E., W. Bierman, I. Kawabori, and P.P. Van Arsdel. The incidence of exercise-induced bronchospasm in "normal" and "atopic" children. *Journal of Allergy and Clinical Immunology* 49:129A–130A, 1972.

153. Pollock, J., F. Keichel, D. Cooper, and M. Weinberger. Relationship of serum theophylline concentration to inhibition of exercise-induced bronchospasm and comparison with cromolyn. *Pediatrics* 60:840–844, 1977.

154. Poppius, H., A.R.A. Sovijarvi, and L. Tammilehto. Lack of protective effect of high-dose ipratropium on bronchoconstriction following exercise with cold air breathing in patients with mild asthma. *European Journal of Respiratory Diseases* 68:319–325, 1986.

155. Rachelefsky, G.S., R.M. Katz, and S.C. Siegel. Chronic sinus disease with associated reactive airway disease in children. *Pediatrics* 73:526–529, 1984.

156. Reiser, J., Y. Yeang, and J.O. Warner. The effect of Zaprinast (M&B 22,948, an orally absorbed mast cell stabilizer) on exercise-induced asthma in children. *British Journal of Diseases of the Chest* 80:157–163, 1986.

157. Rohr, A.S., S.C. Siegel, R.M. Katz, G.S. Rachelefsky, S.L. Spector, and R. Lanier. A comparison of inhaled albuterol and cromolyn in the prophylaxis of exercise-induced bronchospasm. *Annals of Allergy* 59:107–109, 1987.

158. Rosenthal, R.R., J. Campbell, and P.S. Norman. The protective effects of inhaled terbutaline and isoproterenol on exercise induced bronchospasm. *American Review of Respiratory Disease* 119 (supplement):79–83, 1979.

159. Roy, A.C., and B.T. Warren. Inhibition of cAMP phosphodiesterase by disodium cromoglycate. *Biochemical Pharmacology* 23:917–920, 1974.

160. Rubinstein, I., H. Levison, A.S. Slutsky, H. Hak, J. Wells, N. Zamel, and A.S. Rebuck. Immediate and delayed bronchoconstriction after exercise in patients with asthma. *New England Journal of Medicine* 317:482–485, 1987.

161. Rudd, R.M., A.R. Gellert, P.R. Studdy, and D.M. Geddes. Inhibition of exercise-induced asthma by an orally absorbed mast cell stabilizer (M&B 22, 948). *British Journal of Diseases of the Chest* 77:78–86, 1983.

162. Sanguinetti, C.M., S. DeLuca, S. Gasparini, and V. Massei. Evaluation of Duovent in the prevention of exercise-induced asthma. *Respiration* 50 (supplement 2):181–185, 1986.

163. Schenker, M.B., J.M. Samet, and F.E. Speizer. Risk factors for childhood respiratory disease. The effect of host factors and home environmental exposures. *American Review of Respiratory Disease* 128:1038–1043, 1983.

164. Schleimer, R.P., E.S. Schulman, D.W. MacGlashan Jr., S.P. Peters, E.C. Hayes, G.K. Adams, L.M. Lichtenstein, and N.F. Adkinson. Effects of dexamethasone on mediator release from human lung fragments and purifies human lung mast cells. *Journal of Clinical Investigation* 71:1830–1835, 1983.

165. Schlueter, D.P. Ipratropium bromide in asthma. A review of the literature. *American Journal of Medicine* 81 (supplement 5A):55–59, 1986.

166. Schnall, R.P., and L.I. Landau. Protective effects of repeated short sprints in exercise-induced asthma. *Thorax* 35:828–32, 1980.

167. Schoeffel, R.E., S.D. Anderson, I. Gillam, and D.A. Lindsay. Multiple exercise and histamine challenges in asthmatic patients. *Thorax* 35:164–170, 1980.

168. Schoeffel, R.E., S.D. Anderson, and R.E.C. Altounyan. Bronchial hyperreactivity in response to inhalation of ultrasonically nebulized solutions of distilled water and saline. *British Medical Journal* 283:1285–1287, 1981a.

169. Schoeffel, R.E., S.D. Anderson, and J.P. Seale. The protective effect and duration of action of metaproterenol aerosol on exercise-induced asthma. *Annals of Allergy* 46:273–275, 1981b.

170. Seale, J.P., S.D. Anderson, and D.A. Lindsay. A comparison of oral theophylline and oral salbutamol in exercise-induced asthma. *Australian and New Zealand Journal of Medicine* 7:270–275, 1977.

171. Shapiro, G.G., J.J. McPhillips, K. Smith, C.T. Furukawa, W.E. Pierson, and C.W. Bierman. Effectiveness of terbutaline and theophylline alone and in combination in exercise-induced bronchospasm. *Pediatrics* 67:508–513, 1981.

172. Shapiro, G.G. Methacholine challenge—relevance for the allergic athlete. *Journal of Allergy and Clinical Immunology* 73:670–675, 1984.

173. Sharrat, M.T., K.G. Henke, D.F. Pegelow, E. Aaron, and J. Dempsey. Exercise-induced changes in functional residual capacity (FRC) *Respiration Physiology*, 70, 313–326, 1987.

174. Sheppard, D. What does exercise have to do with "exercise-induced" asthma? *American Review of Respiratory Disease* 136:547–549, 1987.

175. Silber, G., D. Proud, J. Warner, R. Naclerio, A. Kagey-Sobotka, L. Lichtenstein, and P.

504 *PERSPECTIVES IN EXERCISE*

Eggleston. In vivo release of inflammatory mediators by hyperosmolar solutions. *American Review of Respiratory Disease* 137:606–12, 1988.

176. Silverman, M., F.D. Hobbs, I.R. Gordon, and F. Carswell. Cystic fibrosis, atopy and airways lability. *Archives of Disease in Childhood* 53:873–877, 1978.

177. Silverman, M., P. Konig, and S. Godfrey. Use of serial exercise tests to assess the efficacy and duration of action of drugs for asthma. *Thorax* 28:574–578, 1973.

178. Sly, R.M., E.M. Heimlich, R.J. Busser, and L. Strick. Exercise-induced bronchospasm: Evaluation of isoproterenol, phenylephrine and the combination. *Annals of Allergy* 25:324–330, 1967.

179. Sly, R.M., E.M. Heimlich, J. Ginsburg, R.J. Busser, and L. Strick. Exercise-induced bronchospasm. Evaluation of metaproterenol. *Annals of Allergy* 26:253–258, 1968.

180. Sly, R.M. Beta-adrenergic drugs in the management of asthma in athletes. *Journal of Allergy and Clinical Immunology* 73:680–685, 1984.

181. Smith, C.M., S.D. Anderson, and J.L. Black. Methacholine responsiveness increases after ultrasonically nebulized water but not after ultrasonically nebulized hypertonic saline in patients with asthma. *Journal of Allergy and Clinical Immunology* 79:85–92, 1987.

182. Souhrada, J.F., and S. Kivity. Exercise testing. In S. Spector (ed.). *Provocative Challenge Procedures. Bronchial, Oral, Nasal and Exercise. Vol 2.* Boca Raton, Fla: CRC Press, Inc., 1983

183. Souhrada, J.F., D. Presley, and M. Souhrada. Mechanisms of the temperature effect on airway smooth muscle. *Respiration Physiology* 53:225–237, 1983.

184. Stemman, E.A., and F. Koshe. Comparison of the effect of Sch 1000 MDI, sodium cromoglycate and beta-adrenergic drugs on exercise-induced asthma in children. *Postgraduate Medical Journal* 51:105–106, 1975.

185. Stirling, D.R., D.J. Cotton, B.L. Graham, W.C. Hodgson, D.W. Cockcroft, and J.A. Dosman. Characteristics of airway tone during exercise in patients with asthma. *Journal of Applied Physiology*, 54, 934–42, 1983.

186. Svenonius, E., R. Kautto, and M. Arborelius Jr. Improvement after training of children with exercise-induced asthma. *Acta Paediatrica Scandinavica* 72:23–30, 1983.

187. Symon, D.N.K., G. Miller, and G. Russell. Buccal administration of fenoterol aerosol in childhood asthma. *European Journal of Respiratory Diseases* 67:37–40, 1985.

188. Szentagothai, K., I. Gyene, M. Szocska, and P. Osvath. Physical exercise program for children with bronchial asthma. *Pediatric Pulmonology* 3:166–172, 1987.

189. Tal, A., H. Pasterkamp, C. Serrette, F. Leahy, and V. Chernick. Response to cold air hyperventilation in normal and in asthmatic children. *Journal of Pediatrics* 104:516–521, 1984.

190. Togias, A.G., R.M. Naclerio, S.P. Peters, I. Nimmagadda, D. Proud, A. Kagey-Sobotka, N.F. Adkinson Jr., P.S. Norman, and L.M. Lichtenstein. Local generation of sulfidopeptide leukotrienes upon nasal provocation with cold, dry air. *American Review of Respiratory Disease* 133:1133–37, 1986.

191. Togias, A.G., D. Proud, L.M. Lichtenstein, G.K. Adams III., P.S. Norman, A. Kagey-Sobotka, and R.M. Naclerio. The osmolality of nasal secretions increases when inflammatory mediators are released in response to inhalation of cold, dry air. *American Review of Respiratory Disease* 137:625–29, 1988a.

192. Voy, R.O. The U.S. Olympic Committee experience with exercise-induced bronchospasm, 1984. *Medicine and Science in Sports and Exercise.* 18:328–330, 1986.

193. Walden, S.M., D.R. Bleecker, K. Chahal, E.J. Britt, P. Mason, and S. Permutts. Effect of alpha-adrenergic blockade on exercise-induced asthma and conditioned cold air. *American Review of Respiratory Disease* 130:357–362, 1984.

194. Warner, J.O., and J.F. Price. House dust mite sensitivity in childhood asthma. *Archives of Disease in Childhood* 53:710–713, 1978.

195. Warren, J.B., R.J. Keynes, M.J. Brown, D.A. Jenner, and M.W. McNicol. Blunted sympathoadrenal response to exercise in asthmatic subjects. *British Journal of Diseases of the Chest* 76:147–151, 1982.

196. Warren, J.B., S.J. Jennings, and T.J. Clark. Effect of adrenergic and vagal blockade on the normal human airway response to exercise. *Clinical Science (London)*, 66, 79–85, 1984.

197. Wasserman, S. Mediators of immediate hypersensitivity. *Journal of Allergy and Clinical Immunology* 72:101–114, 1983.

198. Wasserman, S.I., N.A. Soter, D.M. Center, and K.F. Austen. Cold urticaria. Recognition and characterization of a neutrophil chemotactic factor which appears in serum during experimental cold challenge. *Journal of Clinical Investigation* 60:189–196, 1977.

199. Weiler-Ravell, D., and S. Godfrey. Do exercise and antigen-induced asthma utilize the same pathways? *Journal of Allergy and Clinical Immunology* 67:391–397, 1981.

200. Weinberger, M. The pharmacology and therapeutic use of theophylline. *Journal of Allergy and Clinical Immunology* 73:525–540, 1984.

201. Weiner, P., M. Saaid, A. Reshef. Isotonic nebulized disodium cromoglycate provides bet-

ter protection against methacholine- and exercise-induced bronchoconstriction. *American Review of Respiratory Disease* 137:1309–11, 1988.

202. Weiss, J.W., T.H. Rossing, E.R. McFadden, and R.H. Ingram. Relationship between bronchial responsiveness to hyperventilation with col and methacholine in asthma. *Journal of Allergy and Clinical Immunology* 72:140–144, 1983.
203. Whipp, B.J., and K. Wasserman. Alveolar-arterial gas tension differences during graded exercise. *Journal of Applied Physiology* 27:361–365, 1969.
204. Yeung, R., G.M. Nolan, and H. Levison. Comparison of the effects of inhaled SCH-1000 and fenoterol on exercise-induced bronchospasm in children. *Pediatrics* 66:109–114, 1980.
205. Young, I.H., P. Corte, and R.E. Schoeffel. Pattern and time course of ventilation-perfusion inequality in exercise-induced asthma. *American Review of Respiratory Disease* 125:304–311, 1982.
206. Zimmerman, B., D. Stringer, S. Feanny, J. Reisman, H. Hak, N. Rashed, F. deBenedictis, J. McLaughlin, and H. Levison. Prevalence of abnormalities found by sinus X-rays in childhood asthma: Lack of relation to severity of asthma. *Journal of Allergy and Clinical Immunology* 80:268–273, 1987.

DISCUSSION

GISOLFI: In the normal child and in the unconditioned subject, there seems to be an enormous reserve capacity in the lung in terms of lung volumes and flow rates. How do we account for the feeling of breathlessness by some people when they exercise?

SUTTON: Breathlessness (or dyspnea) is a normal sensation, and if you actually get a range of individuals to exercise and try to quantify their perception of breathlessness, you find that they rate it fairly high as you go to exhaustion. It happens in Olympic athletes at a $\dot{V}O_2$ of about 5–6 l·min, if you apply it to the cross-country skiers. It will happen in normal individuals at a $\dot{V}O_2$ of something like 2–3 l·min. Although breathlessness is commonly thought of as a symptom reflecting an underlying disorder, the sensation of breathlessness will occur in any of the following situations or combinations of them: a) high ventilation, b) high impedance to breathing, and c) when the respiratory muscles are weak. So it is a normal sensation, and in the last few years there has been an attempt to try and understand the various factors that contribute to dyspnea. The two important aspects of the definition of dyspnea are the one by Makens back in the late '20s that dyspnea is the consciousness of the need to breathe. The other is by Comroe, when he was actually introducing a symposium devoted to the study of dyspnea, and he says most physiologists, when they are talking about dyspnea and trying to study dyspnea, are studying something quite different, such as the control of breathing, gas exchange, ventilation, etc. And in fact, it is a psychophysical sensation. It doesn't necessarily have anything to do with those other acts of ventilation and gas exchange, etc. So that's point one. The other aspects that have been clarified in recent time are that the components determining dyspnea in any individual will be the respiratory effort, the pressure generated by the respiratory muscles, and then to a smaller extent, the tidal volume and frequency of breathing. All of those have interactive contributions to the feeling of dyspnea. But we shouldn't ever think that dyspnea is abnormal. Dyspnea will occur in anyone if they do enough work. But the level at which that occurs in absolute terms will be very different across a range of people.

Actually, while I have the microphone, I do have one or two comments. Firstly, I think this has been an exemplary presentation. The quality of the presentation and the quality of the slides has really been marvelous, and I was very impressed. Now I think it may well be important when we consider the focus of the book, for us actually to bring out the fact that exercise-induced asthma is not an entity as such. It's asthma that occurs, in this particular instance, provoked by exercise. And many of those people in whom asthma is provoked by exercise will have asthma that is provoked by other factors as well. The other thing is that in terms of the diagnosis, now I know that Bob brought this out to some extent, but so often we get people who only get asthma when they are playing hockey, for instance. You bring them into the laboratory and you don't see anything. They don't actually have much of a response during a normal exercise test on the cycle ergometer or treadmill, and of course it's that combination of the cold and exercise that is required. So I think the most important thing in the diagnosis is a careful history. When does asthma occur? If the asthmatic response is clearly related to the combination of exercise in the cold environment, then you may need to reproduce these conditions. The other thing that we have sometimes found helpful is that if you don't demonstrate a drop in the FEV$_1$ during an exercise test, and yet you're convinced symptomatically that this is the diagnosis, then it may well be worthwhile doing a bronchial challenge with methacholine or histamine. Sometimes these provocative tests can be helpful as well.

Now the other point, when considering the whole diagnostic issue, is that one needs to remember that all that wheezes is not necessarily asthma. Many people diagnose asthma as soon as they hear of an athlete who gets a bit breathless. Again, the history will help you. If the maximum breathlessness occurs after the event, that's certainly more likely to be EIA than a person getting breathless during an event, although it's not mutually exclusive. We recently studied an Olympic class athlete who was breathless during exercise. His doctor started him on a variety of asthmatic medications, but this person was subsequently found to have significant pulmonary emboli. So I think one must keep a very clear mind about this, and if one can't historically justify what's going on, and if one's investigations do not confirm that it is in fact asthma, one needs to consider other possibilities.

Therapeutically, the entire list of medications was presented, but one should keep in mind that many asthmatics require a combination of medications. The combination of cromolyn together with a beta-agonist has been particularly advantageous.

SHEPHARD: One possible reason for the pathogenesis of exercise-induced bronchospasm is a failure to appreciate that, in the winter, conditions encountered in continental North America (e.g. ambient $-25°$ C), the air is almost devoid of water vapor (partial pressure 1–2 mmHg, 0.15–0.25 kPa). Water loss is thus provoked by exercise, whether this is performed indoors or out. The use of a facemask to humidify inspired air depends greatly on environmental conditions. One design for a mask, with a copper mesh heat exchanger, freezes up within 15–20 min exercise at $-15°$ C, particularly if there is a stiff breeze.

BAR-OR: In one of your very first slides, you showed that by modifying the intensity of exercise, one can also help the patient. With mild asthma, we would rather not even medicate them, but first give them the benefit of the doubt that just by modifying the exercise they can complete a task without any bronchial constriction. Warming up as a precaution can be very useful. Another aspect is how to avert the effects of a cold climate, and one thing that seems to work is to wear a face mask on a cold day.

Just a comment about a clinical finding that we have had in three or four adolescents. The only presentation of exercise-induced asthma was exertional chest pain, that could not be explained by any cardiological or other origin, but there was bronchial constriction after exercise, and both the pain and bronchial constriction responded to drug treatment.

Now something about interpretation of results of studies. You have mentioned the optimal duration and optimal intensity of exercise which is based, I think, on Anderson's and Silverman's observation about 10 to 12 years ago. One problem with that study was that they did not really look at any combinations of exercise and intensity. They had one set of experiments increasing the intensity and another set of experiments keeping the intensity constant and increasing the duration. There is a study by Omri Inbar showing that the Wingate Test, a very brief, highly intense, super-maximal provocation, induced bronchial constriction. It was primarily maximal expiratory flow rate that responded, which probably reflects smaller airways. But even a 30-second provocation can cause a reduction in forced expiratory measurements.

Finally, something about the Gilbert and McFadden study. I just thought of two comments, having looked at your data, and I don't really know the study. One is the fact that even if both the asthmatics and controls respond with the same changes in osmolality, this observation does not really negate Sandra Anderson's concept that osmolality may be an important contributing factor. If anything, both the asthmatics and controls respond with the same changes in temperature, although the asthmatics are more sensitive. Something else that I found very intriguing in one of the slides regarding that study is the rewarming phenomenon. It made me think that perhaps rewarming could explain, to some extent, why swimming is less asthmagenic than running because in swimming we do not really raise the core temperature as much as we do in running.

LEMANSKE: In regard to your comments on airway rewarming, work in guinea pig models has demonstrated that if you rapidly rewarm guinea pig smooth muscle it will undergo intense contraction, but if you slowly rewarm it, it will not. Similar events may be occurring following exercise in humans. Further, if an ice cube is placed on one's arm and then removed, reactive hyperemia of the skin occurs. Dr. McFadden suggests that in asthmatics, this hyperemic response, at least in the airway, might be exaggerated, and vascular engorgement develops that compromises airflow.

ROGOL: I have two short questions about the pharmacology. First the pharmacologic precept of acting at two different points along the same pathway often gives synergism, rather than additive effects. Is there any synergism among these drugs, and might that be of use to us in answer to John Sutton's question of using rational combinations rather than two or three drugs that work at the same point? And my second question, which is related to that: Are corticosteroids effective in this particular form of asthma?

LEMANSKE: In answer to your first question, the combination therapy that's really been looked at most extensively has been the beta-adrenergics with cromolyn sodium: the effects of both drugs in the treatment of exercise-induced asthma. First, does a drug completely block the response to exercise or, second, does it attenuate the response to exercise? Cromolyn sodium has been shown to block in about 50% and to attenuate in about 75% of cases of exercise-induced asthma. The beta-agonists are probably the most effective therapy for exercise-induced asthma, and they work in about 80–90% of patients. One additional benefit from beta-agonists is that one can use this class of drugs not only as prophylaxis but for treatment as well. So for the child who does not remember to take his medication prior to exercise, if he or she does develop asthma, he or she can reverse the attack with the beta-agonist, whereas he or she will not be able to do so with cromolyn. One approach with patients is to use the beta-agonist first and then, if the child still is not well-controlled, we consider adding cromolyn as well—the beta-agonist plus the cromolyn about 15 minutes prior to exercise.

In regard to your question with corticosteroids, some of the initial work that was done with corticosteroids suggested that this class of drugs was not effective in exercise-induced asthma. However, recently investigators have taken children who are not optimally controlled with beta-agonists and cromolyn in terms of preventing exercise-induced asthma and have placed them on corticosteroids—inhaled corticosteroids. In both adults and children, after two to four weeks of therapy, response to exercise was decreased, perhaps due to a decrease in underlying airway hyperresponsiveness. We know that if the airway is less reactive to begin with, the response to exercise will be diminished as well. So if steroids are working in exercise-induced asthma to prevent the response, they may be doing so by diminishing the airway hyperresponsiveness over a period of time.

MALINA: Is there anything that we should know about the growth and maturation of these youngsters that might be related to their exercise performance? We have also heard about the elite athletes who are diabetics or asthmatics, but what do we know about the motor skill development and strength of the general population of asthmatics or diabetics?

LEMANSKE: As far as I can tell from looking at the literature, we don't know much about that at all.

MORGAN: Kathy alluded to the psychogenic component and I'd just like to make a few comments. There is clearly an influence of trait anxiety on the sensation of breathlessness. That's number one. You can predict panic behavior and hyperventilation in scuba divers and firefighters as well with that particular personality variable with 70–80% accuracy. You can hypnotically change the perception. When you do that, the physiological parameter that always changes is the ventilatory minute volume. And so, there is that cognitive or psychogenic input that is very important. There is an extensive hypnotic literature involving the successful treatment of asthmatics with hypnosis. Now it may be, given what John said, that when asthmatics are successfully treated hypnotically, that they may not be true asthmatics. But there is an extensive literature suggesting that there is a psychogenic drive.

VAILAS: Has there been any work done in receptor responses of endothelial surfaces and with the susceptibility to shearing forces since shearing force is related to degree of turbulent flow?

LEMANSKE: The only receptor work that I'm familiar with is that which has been done with the beta-receptor. Years ago, the beta blockade theory of asthma was proposed, suggesting that one of the reasons that people get asthma is that their beta receptor responsiveness is diminished. Further, other work has demonstrated that alpha-adrenergic and cholinergic responsiveness are hyperresponsive in asthmatic patients. If one could think of a scenario that would make the airway at greatest risk of developing asthma and enhancing mast cell mediator release, it would be exactly that profile—a diminished beta-adrenergic response and an enhanced alpha adrenergic and cholinergic responsiveness. I did mention to you that there have been some reports in patients with exercise-induced asthma in whom circulating levels of catecholamines and cyclic AMP have been evaluated. Reported abnormalities seem to be dependent on the level of exercise. I am not aware of any particular studies looking at endothelial or epithelial cells within the respiratory tract.

13

Athletics and Menstrual Dysfunction in Young Women

Anne B. Loucks, Ph.D.

INTRODUCTION

Does athletic training disrupt the menstrual cycle? Does it do so in all women, or only in some? How does athletic training induce the disruption? Does athletic training delay maturation? Are menstrual disorders harmful to the health of athletes? Are the harmful effects reversible? What new responsibilities are incumbent upon

513

coaches and team physicians concerning possible harmful effects of athletic training upon the health of adolescent athletes? What changes in coaching and clinical practice are needed to meet these responsibilities?

I. THE MENSTRUAL CYCLE

Many centuries of folklore testify that hard physical labor and undernutrition are incompatible with fertility. Recently, folklore has been hardening into dogma. Medical textbooks and reviews testify to the disruptive impact of exercise and undernutrition on sexual development and fertility, almost always without reference or qualifications. To provide a perspective on menstrual disorders in young athletes, I shall briefly review the regulation of the adult menstrual cycle and what is known about its normal development.

A. The Adult Menstrual Cycle

1. Hormonal Rhythms. The menstrual cycle is regulated by the hypothalamic-pituitary-ovarian (HPO) axis (Figure 13-1), which includes negative and positive feedback mechanisms, as well as inputs from the central nervous system and other systems at various levels. The menstrual rhythms of the reproductive hormones are well-established (Figure 13-2). These hormones are secreted in a pulsatile fashion, however; and these pulsations are measurable in the blood for those hormones that are quickly metabolized. This pulsatile pattern can only be assessed by repeatedly sampling blood over 24 or more hours. It has been recognized in recent years that an optimal amplitude and frequency of secretion of gonadotropin releasing hormone (GnRH) by neurons in the arcuate nucleus of the hypothalamus is absolutely essential to the operation of the HPO axis (Knobil, 1980). The influence and mechanism of behavior and psychological factors upon this pulse generator are the focus of considerable basic and clinical research.

2. The Ovarian Cycle. Under pulsatile gonadotropin stimulation during the follicular phase, granulosa cells in the ovarian follicle produce a rising concentration of estrogen, which imposes negative feedback to regulate gonadotropin release and simultaneously tightens its squeeze on the positive feedback trigger (Figure 13-2). Eventually the trigger is pulled, gonadotropins surge, the ovarian follicle ruptures, and the remaining corpus luteum secretes its supply of progesterone, inhibiting the development of additional follicles. As the corpus luteum atrophies, this inhibition is released and the ovarian cycle is repeated.

3. The Endometrial Cycle. Under rising estrogen stimulation

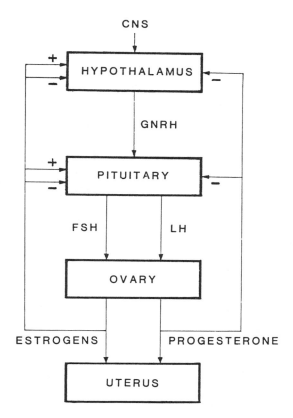

FIGURE 13.1. *The hypothalamic-pituitary-ovarian (HPO) axis regulates the female reproductive system. Within the HPO axis, the source and target organs of the principal sex hormones are shown. Note the feedback of ovarian sex steroids to regulate the activity of higher centers. The menstrual cycle depends upon the development of both negative and positive feedback mechanisms for estrogens. Neurological inputs from the central nervous system are indicated. Inputs from other physiological systems are not indicated.*

during the follicluar phase, the uterine endometrium proliferates (Figure 13-2). After ovulation, the endometrium is sustained by estrogen and progesterone until the corpus luteum regresses. Low progesterone secretion is thought to reduce endometrial susceptibility to implantation despite successful ovulation and conception, but luteal adequacy is not well-quantified. Because implantation does not occur until six to seven days after ovulation and because degeneration of the endometrium begins a few days prior to menses, luteal phases shorter than 10 days are also frequently infertile.

Figure 13-2 presents an idealized 28-day cycle. Actually, "there is no substantial justification for the widely held belief that women

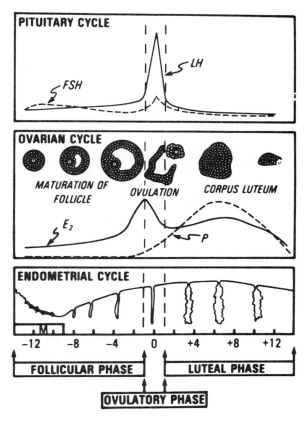

FIGURE 13-2. *The idealized changes in the gonadotropins, LH and FSH, ovarian steroids, E_2 and P, and follicles and uterine endometrium during the adult menstrual cycle. Information is centered about the day of the LH surge (day 0). Days of menstrual bleeding are indicated by M. Reprinted from Kustin & Rebar (1987) with permission.*

normally vary in menstrual interval about a value of 28 days common to all. Each woman has her own central trend and variation, both of which change with age" (Treloar et al., 1967) (Figures 13-3, 13-4). Nevertheless, in 50% of adult women, the standard deviation in the length of the menstrual cycle is no more than two to three days over a span of 20 years, with interruptions only by pregnancy.

B. Premenarchal Development

Detailed reviews of the development of the HPO axis are available (Styne & Grumbach, 1986; Reindollar & McDonough, 1987). The ovaries are the first component of the fetal HPO axis to begin to

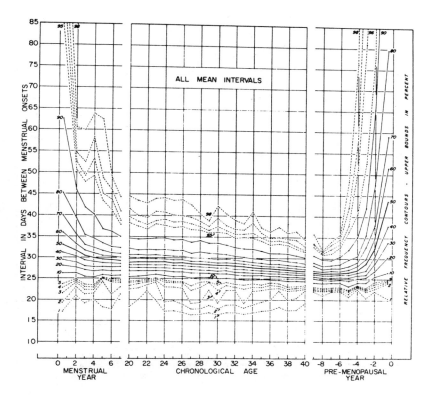

FIGURE 13-3. *Frequency distributions for the average length of the menstrual cycle, by age. Averages are calculated within individuals on a yearly basis. For adolescents, data are plotted by menstrual age (years since menarche). In most adolescents the length of the menstrual cycle decreases during adolescence. Data are based on 275,000 menstrual cycles reported by 2,700 women, mostly alumnae of the University of Minnesota. Reprinted from Treloar et al. (1967) with permission.*

develop under the influence of chorionic gonadotropin from the placenta. By the 10th week of gestation, the hypothalamic GnRH pulse generator is operative, and by the 12th week the pituitary has established pulsatile gonadotropin secretory patterns. The gonadotropins, luteinizing hormone (LH), and follicle stimulating hormone (FSH), quickly rise to levels equal to those in the adult (Figure 13-5). Primordial follicles in the ovary begin to develop into the lifetime supply of Graafian follicles present by four to six months after birth. A negative steroid feedback mechanism becomes progressively more sensitive after 150 days gestation as placental and fetal ovarian steroids, 100 times adult levels, gradually suppress gonadotropin production. The elevated sex steroids during late gestation are com-

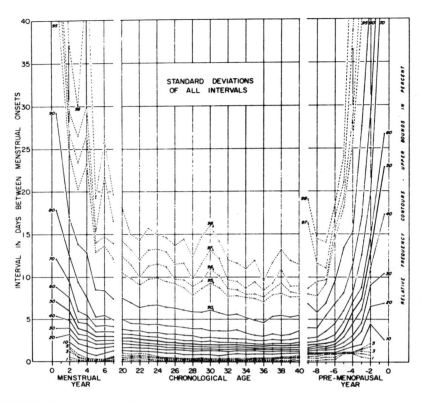

FIGURE 13-4. *Frequency distributions for the standard deviation in the length of the menstrual cycle, by age. Standard deviations are calculated within individuals on a yearly basis. Within individuals, the length of the menstrual cycle would have varied by approximately ±2 standard deviations during the year. For adolescents, data are plotted by menstrual age (years since menarche). In most adolescents, the length of the menstrual cycle does not reach adult stability for five years. In some women the menstrual cycle never stabilizes. Data are based on 275,000 menstrual cycles reported by 2,700 women, mostly alumnae of the University of Minnesota. Reprinted from Treloar et al. (1967) with permission.*

monly evident by breast budding in the newborn, and occasionally parents are alarmed by uterine bleeding due to the abrupt decline in placental steroids at birth.

This abrupt fall in steroids reduces the inhibition of gonadotropins. Within a few days, the hypothalamus is generating GnRH pulses again, and gonadotropins are secreted episodically, stimulating the infantile estrogen surge. In female infants, gonadotropins remain elevated at adult levels or higher for two years. Only then does the HPO axis enter the quiescent state from which it re-emerges at puberty.

Neither the mechanism by which the HPO axis is repressed in

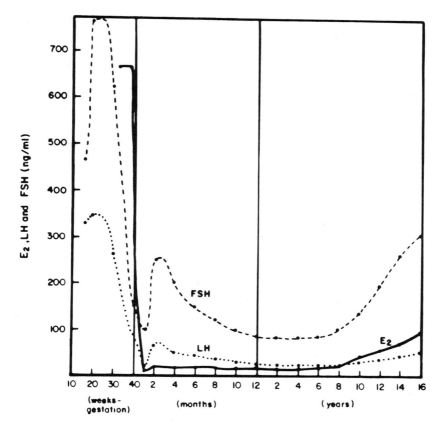

FIGURE 13-5. *Premenarchal development of the HPO axis. In the fetus and during infancy, the HPO axis is as active as in the adult, but without menstrual cycles. The HPO axis is repressed at about two years of age and then de-repressed at puberty, by which time the positive estrogen feedback mechanism triggering menstrual cycles has developed. The mechanisms of repression and de-repression are unknown. Reprinted from Lee (1985) with permission.*

late infancy nor the mechanism by which it is reactivated during puberty is understood. One theory derives from demonstrations of the extremely high sensitivity of the negative steroid feedback mechanism during childhood. This theory holds that the decline in HPO axis activity reflects the completion of this mechanism's development, which began in utero. By this feedback theory, some unidentified factor later reduces the sensitivity of the negative feedback mechanism and thereby reactivates the HPO axis.

The feedback theory fails to explain the observation that agonadal children display the same degree of HPO axis repression during childhood. These observations have led to the theory that a sex-steroid-independent intrinsic central nervous system mechanism for repressing HPO axis activity develops during infancy, and that the later deactivation of this central mechanism leads to puberty. The nature of this intrinsic mechanism is uncertain.

By whatever mechanism, reactivation of the HPO axis (gonadarche) begins with an extended asymptomatic prepubertal period. Intrinsic central nervous system (CNS) inhibition and the sensitivity to sex-steroid feedback are gradually reduced. The amplitude and frequency of GnRH pulsatility increase, initially only during sleep. Pituitary sensitivity to GnRH and secretion of gonadotropins increase; and ovarian sensitivity to gonadotropins and secretion of sex steroids also increase. As sex steroids rise, they stimulate breast budding (thelarche), the appearance of pubic and axillary hair (pubarche), and the release of growth hormone and somatomedin, which initiate the adolescent growth spurt at about age 11. These developments are well advanced before steroid levels have risen enough to trigger a new positive sex-steroid feedback mechanism in the HPO axis. This feedback mechanism initiates the first LH surge, ovulation, luteinization, progesterone withdrawal, and uterine bleeding (menarche).

Several observers have associated athletic training with an older age of menarche. The bases for skepticism about a causal effect of exercise training on premenarchal sexual development are discussed below.

C. The Adolescent Menstrual Cycle

The average age of menarche has declined dramatically over the past 150 years (Figure 13-6), with considerable social repercussions. At present, it is approximately 12.8 y in the United States. The vast majority of girls experience menarche from 10 to 16.5 y, but menarche occurs completely normally in some girls at even younger and older chronological ages. The test of normal sexual development is "bone age," as assessed by hand X-ray: menarche occurs normally at a bone age of 13 to 14 y. Abnormal development is extremely unlikely unless menarche occurs earlier than a bone age of 12.5 y or later than a bone age of 14.5 y. Nevertheless, social and psychological considerations frequently motivate medical interference in perfectly normal early or late development.

Among the many investigators who have studied physical growth and sexual development, almost all regard these processes as correlative rather than causally related (Zacharias et al., 1976). The weight of a girl at menarche is random with respect to her age. Height and ponderal index are slightly correlated, with women who mature early

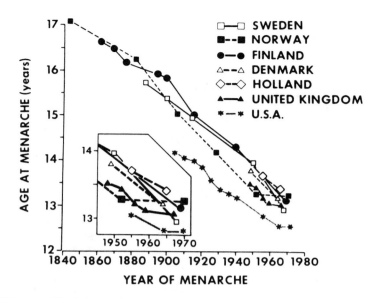

FIGURE 13-6. *The decline in the average age of menarche in northern Europe and the United States over the past 50 years. Reprinted from Styne & Grumback (1986) with permission.*

being more stout at menarche than women who mature later (Zacharias et al., 1976), but the inferential strength of such cross-sectional data are limited by the absence of anthropometric information on the late maturers when they were the age at which the early maturers reached menarche. Nor do correlations of body composition and sexual development establish the direction of causation, if any exists. Rising estrogen levels may be the cause rather than the consequence of increased body fatness, as well as being the finger that pulls the positive feedback trigger on menarche.

The average length of the menstrual cycle declines substantially during adolescence (Figure 13-3), as does variability in the length of the menstrual cycle (Figure 13-4). A menstrual experience of approximately 40 cycles is required before variability approaches that of maturity (Engle & Shelesnyak, 1934). Variation in age of menarche obscures the monotonicity of these postmenarchal trends if data are plotted by chronological rather than menstrual (gynecological) age, that is, years since menarche. During adolescence, the prevalence of cycles with full luteal expression also gradually increases for at least five years. The association of reduced progesterone secretion with movement out of the parental home indicates that the HPO axis is still not robust as late as eight years after menarche (Metcalf et al., 1983). Furthermore, the prevalence of cycles

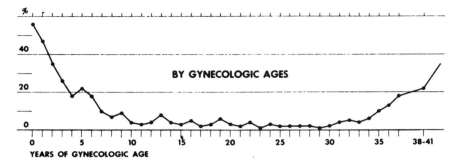

FIGURE 13-7. *The prevalence of menstrual cycles with no biphasic pattern in basal body temperature, by gynecological age (years since menarche). A biphasic basal body temperature pattern is associated with ovarian secretion of progesterone during the luteal phase. The high adolescent prevalence of monophasic patterns does not decline to the adult level for approximately 10 years. Data are based on 13,800 menstrual cycles reported by 524 women attending a medical clinic. Reprinted from Vollman (1977) with permission.*

with no luteal expression (Figure 13-7) and short luteal phases (Figure 13-8) are not minimized until 10 and 12 years after menarche.

Thus, the transition from the adolescent to the adult menstrual cycle is subtle but substantial, and for most women occurs gradually over several years. However, in some women, menstrual stability

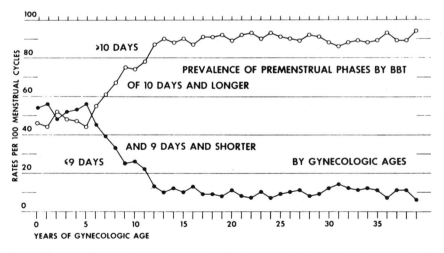

FIGURE 13-8. *The prevalence of menstrual cycles with short luteal phases, by gynecological age (years since menarche). Luteal phases shorter than 10 days often prevent implantation of a fertilized egg into the uterine endometrium. The high adolescent prevalence of short luteal phase does not decline to the adult level for approximately 12 years. Data are based on 13,800 menstrual cycles reported by 524 women attending a medical clinic. Reprinted from Vollman (1977) with permission.*

and luteal adequacy develop quickly, while in others they never do (Figures 13-3 and 13-4).

Several observers have associated athletic training with menstrual disorders in adolescents, but the causal influence of exercise and other factors upon postmenarchal sexual development has yet to be explored. The subtlety of this development and the wide range of individual variation in the adolescent menstrual cycle make research into this important issue especially difficult.

II. MENSTRUAL DISORDERS IN YOUNG ATHLETES

Studies of menstrual disorders in athletes have appeared with increasing frequency in the literature over the past 15 years. Preliminary surveys indicated a higher prevalence of menstrual disorders among athletes than among the general population. Associations with numerous lifestyle factors were made. Then case reports and small sample observations of endocrine parameters appeared. The accumulation of inconsistencies led to the appreciation of the need for careful subject selection, extensive subject description, sophisticated endocrine protocols, and well-planned experimental designs in subsequent studies. The motivation for such elaborate and expensive studies increased dramatically six years ago when reports of spinal demineralization in amenorrheic athletes began to appear.

More reliable data have been reported in recent years, but much information is lacking still; and because much of what is available was collected on women of advanced gynecological age, it is of questionable relevance to the much more unstable adolescent menstrual cycle. In preparing the following remarks, I have restricted myself to studies on subjects no older than their early twenties. Even so, some of these studies are more indicative of what data must be collected on younger women rather than what may reliably be inferred about them.

A. Primary Amenorrhea and Delayed Menarche

Primary amenorrhea is usually defined statistically as the occurrence of menarche more than 2.5 standard deviations above the average age of menarche in the population. In the United States, this presently corresponds to 16.0 y. Because the definition is statistical, many women who meet this criterion are developing at their own normal rate.

The occurrence of menarche in athletes has been extensively reviewed (Scott & Johnston, 1982; Malina, 1983). The later occurrence of menarche in athletes than in the general population was noted as early as 1931. Some have found that the age of menarche of athletes who begin training before menarche is later than that of those who begin training afterward. Such reports may be responsible for establishing the dogma that menarche is delayed by intense exercise during childhood.

Recently, however, Stager et al. (submitted) have shown that the observational process of comparing ages of menarche of girls who began training before and after menarche is statistically biased. Stager et al. used a computer to simulate a large population of adolescent athletes in whom age of menarche and age at initiation of training were completely uncorrelated. From this population, they randomly drew two samples of data corresponding to girls who began training before and after menarche. Comparing these samples, Stager et al. found two nonsensical results. First, although age of menarche and age at initiation of training were uncorrelated in the population, they were highly correlated in the samples. Second, even though the average age of menarche was identical at every age at initiation of training in the population, it was different in the two samples: age of menarche was later in the sample corresponding to girls who began training before menarche. These nonsensical results correspond to what has been observed retrospectively and demonstrate the need for experimental rather than observational data in the study of menarche.

Malina (1983) has attributed the apparent relationship between childhood athletics and age of menarche to selection and socialization. Athletes, he notes, are not selected at random. Due to their more linear physique, late maturers tend to perform better at motor tasks compared to their age-matched postmenarchal peers. Meanwhile, early maturing girls are diverted away from sports participation by new social roles and changing interests.

At present, the average age of menarche is later in athletes than non-athletes, but there is no experimental evidence that athletic training delays menarche in anyone.

B. Secondary Amenorrhea

Secondary amenorrhea is the cessation of menstrual cycles sometime after menarche. Numerous surveys attest to the disproportionately high prevalence of secondary amenorrhea among athletes. However, the estimated prevalence has varied widely (a) with the criteria used by specific investigators to judge whether menses have stopped, and (b) with the specific population of athletes studied (Loucks & Horvath, 1985).

Whatever the prevalence of secondary amenorrhea may be, the HPO axis of the athlete with secondary amenorrhea is now better characterized. It is clear that the GnRH pulse generator is not functioning properly (Veldhuis et al., 1985, Loucks et al., in press). This is reflected in the typically infrequent and disorderly appearance of LH pulses from the pituitary (Figure 13-9), despite the demonstrated capability of the pituitary to respond to GnRH stimulation (Figure 13-10). As a result, ovarian follicles are dormant and estradiol remains low, even compared with normal early follicular phase levels

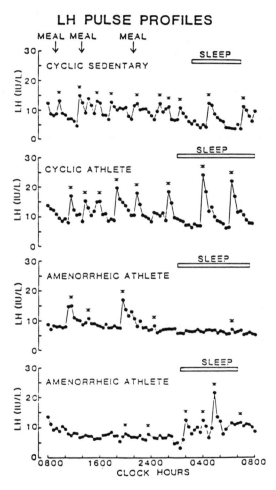

FIGURE 13-9. *Early follicular phase luteinizing hormone (LH) pulsatile patterns over 24 h in a typical regularly menstruating sedentary woman, a typical regularly menstruating athlete, and two typical athletes with secondary amenorrhea. Note the infrequent and irregular appearance of pulses in the amenorrheic athletes. The asterisks indicate pulses as identified by the Cluster pulse analysis program using a 2 × 1 cluster size and balanced T-criteria of 2.1.*

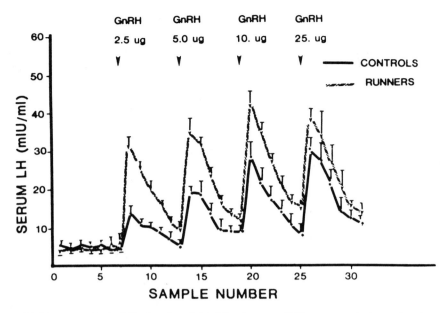

FIGURE 13-10. *Early follicular phase luteinizing hormone (LH) responses to increasing doses of gonadotropin releasing hormone (GnRH). Runners who had 0–3 menstrual cycles per year were capable of responding. The data imply that the GnRH pulse generator in the hypothalamus is not functioning properly in amenorrheic athletes. Reprinted from Veldhuis et al. (1985) with permission.*

(Cumming & Rebar, 1983; Loucks & Horvath, 1984). Estrone, however, a less potent estrogen largely derived from peripheral conversion of androgens in fat and muscle, is present at normal levels (Loucks & Horvath, 1984). That there is no malfunction below the level of the hypothalamus is demonstrated by the exogenous pulsatile administration of GnRH to amenorrheic athletes and other women, which has yielded ovulatory cycles, conceptions, and full-term deliveries (Liu et al., 1984; Sanborn et al., 1987).

Indeed, the GnRH pulse generator may also be responding properly to its own neuroendocrine stimulation. Abnormal CNS activity, or normal CNS responses to abnormal behavior, may culminate in the disruption of the GnRH pulse generator. Prolactin and androgens are no longer thought to mediate this effect because they are within normal range in amenorrheic athletes (Chang et al., 1984; Cumming & Rebar, 1983; Loucks & Horvath, 1984). At present, data concerning the effect of endogenous opiates on the GnRH pulse generator in amenorrheic athletes and other women are inconsistent (McArthur et al., 1980; Dixon et al., 1984; Khoury et al., 1987; Wildt et al., 1987). Recently, however, athletes and other women with secondary amenorrhea have shown evidence of increased hypothalamic-pituitary-adrenal (HPA) axis activity, which may inhibit the GnRH pulse generator directly or indirectly (Ding et al., 1988; Suh et al., 1988; Loucks et al., in press).

C. Luteal Phase Deficiency

Luteal phase deficiency is the occurrence of menstrual cycles with inadequate secretion of progesterone or premature atrophy of the corpus luteum as indicated by persistent infertility. Usually, luteal phase deficiency is completely asymptomatic. Thus, in the absence of an active effort to become pregnant, the functional inadequacy of the luteal phase is difficult to substantiate.

Diminished luteal function has been reported in adult athletes (Prior et al., 1982; Ellison & Lager, 1986), and declining luteal function has been observed prospectively in 28 young women of 10 y gynecological age who were suddenly subjected to a strenuous athletic program (Bullen et al., 1985). Although the women were moved away from home during the study, and although psychological stress about the intensity of the training program may have influenced results, this is the best evidence to date that strenuous exercise training, especially when combined with caloric restriction, disrupts the female reproductive system. Other efforts to induce menstrual disorders with less strenuous or less abruptly imposed training programs have been less effective at inducing menstrual disorders (Bullen et al., 1984; Boyden et al., 1983).

Since short luteal phases occur so commonly among adolescents (Figure 13-8), the relevance of luteal phase data from older athletes is questionable. This is evident in cross-sectional data presented by Bonen et al. (1981). In four swimmers of 2 to 4.5 y gynecological age, they found the average luteal phase length to be only 4.5 days compared to 13.4 days in adult women. In four moderately active gynecologically age-matched physical education students, the average luteal length was only 7.8 days, still longer than in the swimmers but less than in adults. In such a highly variable population, however, even gynecological age-matching may not have prevented large errors in the selection of small samples. Perhaps the mechanism responsible for secondary amenorrhea in athletes occurs to a lesser degree as diminished luteal function in a much larger group of asymptomatic women. On the other hand, diminished luteal function and amenorrhea may be the end points of distinct processes in separate groups of women. At this point, whether these conditions differ in degree or kind is unknown.

D. The Search for Causes

1. Preliminary Remarks. People commonly have very different ideas in mind when they speak of causation. When an event of interest has many necessary conditions, some people regard the finally occurring condition as the cause of the event, because the event follows immediately. Others regard the first condition, without which later occurring conditions would be ineffectual, as the cause. For still others, the cause is whatever condition they can and are willing to control.

Clearly, menstrual disorders in athletes require the presence of numerous conditions. Different groups interested in these disorders seek different information when they inquire about the causes. Neuroendocrinologists, for example, want to learn what neurotransmitter or hormone disturbs the hypothalamic GnRH pulse generator. Physicians want to learn whether pharmaceutical intervention is necessary to insure future fertility and to preserve peak bone mass and whether other clinical complications of this treatment may arise. Parents want to learn whether everything would be all right if only girls waited until after menarche to begin training. Athletes want to learn what change in fatness or weight or diet or training will return their menses. Meanwhile, coaches want to learn how altered training programs may affect performance.

To date there has been an implicit and tacit assumption among investigators that the menstrual disorders observed in athletes are all expressions of the same biological mechanism. By this assumption, there may be several behavioral and psychological conditions influencing young women, and the women themselves may vary in their susceptibility to these conditions, but basically the same thing is happening in all of them. This may not be true. Amenorrhea, delayed menarche, and diminished luteal function may be distinct processes occurring in separate groups of women. The delay of menarche by athletic training, for example, may simply not exist. Amenorrhea may occur in women who are incapable of the adjustment seen in women with diminished luteal function. Much more detailed information is needed to compare and contrast the separate neuroendocrine responses of these groups to various conditions.

Many of the hypothetical causes of menstrual disorders in athletes have arisen by extrapolation from other groups of women. Starving women, psychiatric patients, heroin addicts, nursing mothers, hirsute women, and physical laborers have all inspired theories about environmental conditions and physiological mechanisms affecting athletes. It is clear, now, that although some athletes share menstrual symptoms with other populations, their lifestyle and physiology are qualitatively different. Therefore, theories about the causes of menstrual disorders in athletes need to be based upon detailed, well-controlled experiments on athletes themselves.

Little information of this type is available. Of the data that are available, most have been collected in cross-sectional studies of adult athletes with secondary amenorrhea. Cross-sectional observations are incapable of proving causation, however, because they cannot demonstrate the proper temporal relationship between cause and effect. Randomized prospective cohort experiments are needed to distinguish causal relationships from random variations over time. Cross-sectional observations, however, do help to identify which risk factors and outcome variables merit prospective study. In the following discussion, I shall evaluate the extent to which neuroendocrine mechanisms have been shown to link menstrual disorders to various behavioral and psychological conditions in the athletic lifestyle.

2. **Body Composition.** Despite repeated criticism in the scientific literature, the explanation for menstrual disturbances in athletes most commonly cited in the popular literature (Frisch, 1988) and by many gynecologists is an overly lean body composition. In its original form, this hypothesis held that a critical weight was required for the onset of menses (Frisch & Revelle, 1971). Later, the hypothesis was revised to claim that a critical amount of body fat was required for the onset of menses (17% of body weight) and another amount (22% of body weight) to sustain regular menstrual cycles (Frisch & McArthur, 1974). Two endocrine mechanisms have been offered to explain how a lack of body fat would disrupt the reproductive system (Frisch, 1984). First, it was argued that because adipose tissue is a site for the conversion of the androgen androstenedione to the estrogen estrone, lean women would have insufficient estrogen for menstrual function. Second, it was argued that because adipose tissue is a site for estrogen metabolism, and because anorexic women have more catecholestrogens (so-called antiestrogens) than obese women (Fishman et al., 1975), an overly lean body composition might lead to inhibition of regular menstruation by catecholestrogens.

These hypotheses have been criticized on several levels. The interpretation of the statistical results in the original study of body weight at age of menarche has been questioned. The original data constitute a classic example of uncorrelated variables. The investigators concluded that the average weight in the group (48 kg) represented a critical weight for menarche. Yet the body weight at menarche within the data extends through a range of 30 kg.

The revision of the hypothesis to focus on body fat rather than body weight was based on estimates of body fatness from records of height and weight at menarche. These procedures for estimating body composition in peripubertal girls and athletes have been criticized as inaccurate and inappropriate (Billewicz et al., 1976). Trussel (1978) pointed out that an intermediary estimate of total body water was illusory, and that the estimates of fatness were based on nothing more than height and weight. Reeves (1979) reported that such estimates are in error by as much as 9 kg. Johnston (1982) determined that such errors are greatest for the leanest individuals, the precise group involved. Johnston concluded that "errors of this magnitude are simply not desirable in scientific research, and when that research is applied to clinical problems or to matters of public policy import, they are intolerable." Loucks et al. (1984) showed the errors to be so large that they were inappropriate for either individuals or groups of athletes, and that accurately measured body composition could not differentiate amenorrheic from cyclic athletes.

The body weight and composition hypotheses have also been criticized on temporal grounds. The temporal relationship between the occurrence of menses and changes in body composition are frequently inconsistent with causality (Warren, 1980).

The endocrine basis of the hypothesis has also been disputed. Longcope et al. (1978) demonstrated that muscle as well as adipose tissue converts androgens to estrogens and at roughly equal rates. Loucks and Horvath (1984) showed that estrone levels are well-maintained in amenorrheic runners, perhaps by their larger muscle mass. Among prepubertal gymnasts and swimmers, estrone levels were found to be related to androgen levels, as would be expected, and not to body fatness (Peltenburg et al., 1984). Finally, although by their structure catecholestrogens have the potential to affect gonadotropin secretions, they do so only when given in doses that produce blood levels as high or higher than those seen in late pregnancy (Merriam et al., 1983). The highest catecholestrogen concentrations measured in athletes (Russell et al., 1984) were 4,000 times lower than those seen in pregnancy (Adlercreutz and Fotsis, 1983).

3. **Exercise.** Exercise, which is obviously inherent in athletic training, has been proposed to induce menstrual disorders via several neuroendocrine mechanisms. Experience with nursing mothers and women with pituitary tumors led to the hypothesis that exercise disrupts the female reproductive system in athletes by means of high basal levels or transient elevations in the pituitary hormone prolactin; however, cross-sectional comparisons of regularly menstruating and amenorrheic runners dispelled this idea. Basal levels of prolactin were within the normal range, and increments in response to

exercise occurred only in regularly menstruating runners (Cumming & Rebar, 1984; Loucks & Horvath, 1984).

Experience with hyperandrogenic women with amenorrhea led to the idea that elevated basal androgen levels or transient elevations in response to exercise disrupt the female reproductive system in athletes. Research studies revealed that basal androgen levels and androgen responses to exercise are similar in menstruating and amenorrheic athletes (Cumming & Rebar, 1984; Loucks & Horvath, 1984).

The hypersecretion of corticotropin releasing factor (CRF), the hypothalamic factor that activates the HPA stress axis, has also been proposed to disrupt the HPO axis in women athletes. The GnRH pulse generator may be inhibited either directly by CRF or indirectly via cortisol or endogenous opiates. In animals, CRF inhibits hypothalamic release of GnRH (Gambacciani et al., 1986) and pituitary release of LH (Ono et al., 1984; Rivier & Vale, 1984), while cortisol reduces pituitary sensitivity to GnRH (Mann et al., 1982). Furthermore, drugs that block opiate receptors mitigate the influence of CRF (Almeida et al., 1988). Nevertheless, this does not prove that exercise, as commonly practiced in athletics, activates the HPA axis to induce menstrual disorders.

Recent cross-sectional studies have revealed mildly elevated cortisol levels in amenorrheic athletes as well as in women with other types of functional hypothalamic amenorrhea (Ding et al., 1988; Suh et al., 1988; Loucks et al., in press). Whether this mild hypercortisolism develops in response to exercise training (or depression or anorexia nervosa, etc.) or was pre-existing is not clear.

Once again, it is appropriate to mention the study of Bullen et al. (1985). This is the only prospective investigation to date in which the imposition of an exercise program was associated with diminished luteal function, anovulation, and the absence of menses. It substantially strengthens the case that abruptly imposed strenuous exercise may be inherently inhibitory to the HPO axis. Whether conventional athletic training has similar effects is unknown.

4. **Undernutrition.** In many sports, dieting is as integral a part of the training program as exercise. In addition, eating disorders are a frequent occurrence in young athletes (Zucker et al., 1985). Hence, experience with starvation led to the idea that athletes with menstrual disorders are simply undernourished.

It should be noted that nutrition is highly confounded with body weight and body composition. Very careful metabolic and biochemical experiments will be necessary to distinguish the effects of these potential risk factors.

Several cross-sectional observations have found various combinations of certain micronutrients to be below the U.S. RDA in athletes with menstrual disorders (Marcus et al., 1985; Duester et al., 1986). Findings are usually not different from those in menstruating athletes, however, and may imply more about the U.S. RDA or about the data bases used in the dietary analyses than they do about the effects of micronutrients on the HPO axis. No experiments have manipulated the micronutrient content of athletes' diets and monitored indices of menstrual function.

Several investigators have reported dietary protein consumption in athletes with menstrual disorders, usually finding it to be adequate or not different from menstruating and amenorrheic groups (Schwartz et al., 1981; Drinkwater et al., 1984; Marcus et al., 1985; Nelson et al., 1986). Yet, none have reported on the dietary amino acid balance, and this may be important in light of the prevalence of vegetarianism among women athletes (Brooks et al., 1984).

By far, the dominant nutritional theory of menstrual disorders in athletes is caloric deficiency or "energy drain" (Warren, 1980). Although few cross-sectional studies have found athletes with menstrual disorders to consume less energy than sedentary women, neither have they found them to consume the extra energy that would be expected for their level of physical activity (Nelson et al., 1986; Richards et al., 1985). Typically, though, the weight and even the body composition of these athletes have been reported to be stable. This has led to the idea that a compensatory reduction in basal metabolic rate reestablishes and maintains caloric balance (Marcus et al., 1985), inhibiting the HPO axis at some level in the process. I have never been persuaded by the teleological argument that the HPO axis is inhibited to avoid expending the tens of thousands of kilocalories of *future* and *hypothetical* energy cost needed for pregnancy and lactation. Besides, it is a cultural cliche for women to begin eating for two *after* becoming pregnant. Perhaps, though, the energetic advantage of inhibiting the HPO axis would be the *immediate* avoidance of follicular synthesis of proteins and steroids.

Again, the prospective intense exercise study by Bullen et al. (1985), in which caloric consumption was restricted in some subjects, provides the best available evidence that caloric deficiency contributes to the occurrence of menstrual disorders in athletes.

5. Psychological Stress. Menstrual disorders have been noted in cases of severe psychological stress and psychiatric disorders. Accordingly, investigators have inquired whether menstrual disorders in athletes may be of psychological origin. The results of psychometric tests and psychiatric interviews on athletes themselves are inconsistent and unconvincing (Schwartz et al., 1981; Galle et al., 1983; Loucks & Horvath, 1984; Gadpaille et al., 1987).

6. Other Conditions. An increased prevalence of menstrual disorders has been noted in young, nulligravid athletes (cited in Loucks & Horvath, 1985). Given the instability of the adolescent menstrual cycle described above, these observations are not surprising. Age, however, is not a factor of pragmatic interest: Few young athletes are willing to postpone their athletic careers for 10 years. Gravidity is also of little practical interest: no one is going to propose that girls get pregnant to protect themselves from menstrual disorders. These conditions must be accepted as the context in which menstrual disorders are to be expected, while their prevention is achieved via more readily controlled conditions.

III. CONCLUSIONS AND RECOMMENDATIONS

Conclusions about menstrual disorders in young athletes must be tentative in light of our lack of important basic knowledge about the development and regulation of the menstrual cycle. The high variability of the adolescent menstrual cycle obscures our ability to distinguish the effects of behavioral conditions upon it. The inability of informal observations to identify causes of menstrual disorders is exaggerated by the late occurrence of perceptible symptoms. To date, no specific behavior has been conclusively shown to induce menstrual disorders of any kind. Exercise and caloric restriction are the most strongly implicated for secondary amenorrhea and luteal phase deficiency, but there is little evidence that athletic training as practiced in childhood delays menarche. Furthermore, no physiological mechanism linking athletic training to menstrual disorders has been demonstrated. In particular, the widespread idea that menstrual disorders in athletes result from a too lean body composition has not been substantiated. Nor is it known whether all women are equally susceptible to behavioral factors which might disturb menstrual function.

A. Potential Clinical Consequences

To date, there have been no long-term studies of birth rates among former athletes. Births to famous athletes are widely publicized. These may not correctly imply that fertility among athletes and former athletes is normal, however, since infertility is not publicized. Therefore, we cannot predict the likelihood that a particular adolescent athlete with menstrual disturbances will spontaneously regain normal fertility in later life. Nevertheless, adolescent athletes with menstrual disturbances should not be distressed because effective pharmacological means for inducing fertility are available.

So far as we know today, the most serious clinical consequence of secondary amenorrhea in athletes is progressive skeletal demin-eralization (Cann et al., 1984; Drinkwater et al., 1984; Marcus et al., 1985; Lindberg et al., 1984; Cann et al., 1985; Drinkwater et al., 1986; Nelson et al., 1986; Lindberg et al., 1987). Athletes are not different from any other type of hypoestrogenic woman in this regard. Low spinal bone density places these women at grave risk of premature osteoporotic fractures in later life with their attendant pain, dis-ability, and deformity.

There is some concern about the effect of primary amenorrhea and delayed menarche on skeletal integrity. Important risk factors in the occurrence of postmenopausal osteoporosis include the age of menopause and peak adult bone mass. Reassuringly, a recent study of 30,000 women found no correlation between the ages of menarche and menopause (Kikuchi, 1987). To my knowledge, no data relating age of menarche and peak bone mass are available.

Since pregnancy is rarely desired by adolescents, reduced fer-tility due to luteal phase deficiency would not seem to be a problem. Unpredictable fertility may very well be a problem, though. Other possible consequences of luteal phase deficiency may include pre-menopausal cancer of the breast (Sherman & Korenman, 1974; Cowan et al., 1981; Mauwais-Jarvis et al., 1982) and cancer of the endo-metrium. To date, however, no pathological consequences of di-minished luteal function in young athletes have been reported.

B. The Position of the American Academy of Pediatrics

The Sports Medicine Committee of the American Academy of Pediatrics, with the approval of the Council on Child and Adoles-cent Health, has issued a statement on "Amenorrhea in Adolescent Athletes" (American Academy of Pediatrics Committee on Sports Medicine, in press). This statement recognizes the obscure etiology of primary and secondary amenorrhea in adolescent athletes and stresses the need for their aggressive treatment.

Athletes younger than 16 y who have not achieved menarche should receive thorough physical examinations to rule out extra-neous pathologies in which amenorrhea is an incidental symptom. Pregnancy should also be ruled out. Athletes 16 y or older who have not yet achieved menarche, athletes whose age of menarche is more than one year beyond the age of menarche of other female family members, and athletes whose menses have ceased for six months or more should also receive a thorough endocrine evaluation.

Amenorrheic athletes younger than 16 y are encouraged to de-crease the intensity of their exercise and to improve their nutritional intake. While routine administration of estrogen supplements is not recommended for athletes younger than 16, their use in the form of low-dose oral contraceptives is regarded as reasonable for older athletes to reduce the risk of osteoporosis. Calcium should be supplemented to maintain an intake of 1200 to 1500 mg·day^{-1}. Furthermore, an extensive educational and counseling program is recommended for athletes, parents, and coaches regarding the nutrients necessary for normal growth and development, along with routine monitoring of menstrual function, growth, diet, changes in weight, and skinfold thickness.

The American Academy of Pediatrics should be applauded for providing these recommendations. I only question whether (a) our current understanding of the influence of exercise and caloric restriction on the menstrual cycle warrants interference in an athletic training program, (b) the instability of the adolescent menstrual cycle permits any confidence in the effectiveness of behavior modifications in specific cases, and (c) serious athletes are likely to comply with AAP recommendations. In my experience, amenorrheic athletes are loath to change their training habits and rarely even accept estrogen and progesterone supplementation until they have stared at their spinal mineral density reports.

I would like to add my encouragement, however, to the AAP call for an aggressive educational program for athletes, parents, and coaches. Beyond that, I believe a major reform is needed in education of all adolescent girls about exercise and nutrition. Physical education programs should be reformed to encourage all girls (not only those who excel) to participate in athletics, to nourish themselves optimally, and to strive for high bone density, strength, and cardiovascular fitness. It is incumbent upon those of us who urge these reforms to ensure that athletic training programs to improve performance in specific events during youth do not compromise general health in later life.

BIBLIOGRAPHY

1. Adlercreutz, H., and T. Fotsis. Chemical assays of catecholestrogens and their monomethyl ethers. In G.R. Merriam and M.B. Lipsett (eds.). *Proceedings of the International Workshop on Catechol Estrogens.* New York: Raven Press, 1983.
2. Almeida, O.F.X., K.E. Nikolarakis, and A. Herz, Evidence for the involvement of endogenous opioids in the inhibition of luteinizing hormone by corticotropin-releasing factor. *Endocrinology* 122:1034–1041, 1988.
3. American Academy of Pediatrics Committee on Sports Medicine. "Amenorrhea in Adolescent Athletes." *Pediatrics.* (In press).
4. Billewicz, W.Z., H.M. Fellowes, and C.A. Hytten. Comments on the critical metabolic mass and age of menarche. *Annals of Human Biology* 3:51–59, 1976.
5. Bonen, A., A.N. Belcastro, W.Y. Ling, and A.A. Simpson. Profiles of selected hormones during menstrual cycles of teenage athletes. *Journal of Applied Physiology* 50:545–551, 1981.
6. Boyden, T.W., R.W. Pamenter, P. Stanforth, T. Rotkis, and J.H. Wilmore. Sex steroids and endurance running women. *Fertility and Sterility* 39:629–632, 1983.
7. Brooks, S.M., C.F. Sanborn, B.H. Albrecht, and W.W. Wagner, Jr., Diet in athletic amenorrhea. *Lancet* 1:559–560, 1984.

8. Bullen, B.A., G.S. Skrinar, I.Z. Beitins, D.B. Carr, S.M. Reppert, C.O. Dotson, D.M. Fencl, E.V. Gervino, and J.W. McArthur. Endurance training effects on plasma hormonal responsiveness and sex hormone excretion. *Journal of Applied Physiology* 56:1453–1463, 1984.
9. Bullen, B.A., G.S. Skrinar, I.A. Beitins, G. von Mering, B.A. Turnbull, and J.W. McArthur. Induction of menstrual disorders by strenuous exercise in untrained women. *New England Journal of Medicine* 312:1349–1353, 1985.
10. Cann, C.E., M.C. Martin, H.K. Genant, and R.B. Jaffe. Decreased spinal mineral content in amenorrheic women. *Journal of the American Medical Association* 251:626–629, 1984.
11. Cann, C.E., M.C. Martin, and R.B. Jaffe. Duration of amenorrhea affects rate of bone loss in women runners: implications for therapy. *Medicine and Science in Sports and Exercise* 17:214, 1985.
12. Chang, F.E., S.R. Richards, H.K. Moon, and W.B. Malarkey. Twenty four-hour prolactin profiles and prolactin responses to dopamine in long-distance running women. *Journal of Clinical Endocrinology and Metabolism* 59:631–635, 1984.
13. Cowan, L.D., L. Gordis, J.A. Tonascia, and G.S. Jones. Breast cancer incidence in women with a history of progesterone deficiency. *American Journal of Epidemiology* 114:209–217, 1981.
14. Cumming, D.C., and R.W. Rebar. Exercise and reproductive function in women. *American Journal of Industrial Medicine* 4:113–125, 1983.
15. Ding, J.H., C.B. Sheckter, B.L. Drinkwater, M.R. Soules, and W.J. Bremner. High serum cortisol levels in exercise-associated amenorrhea. *Annals of Internal Medicine* 108:530–534, 1988.
16. Dixon, G., P. Eurman, B.E. Stern, B. Schwartz, and R.W. Rebar. Hypothalamic function in amenorrheic runners. *Fertility and Sterility* 42:377–383, 1984.
17. Drinkwater, B.L., K. Nilson, C.H. Chesnut, III, W.J. Bremner, S. Shainholtz, and M.B. Southworth. Bone mineral content of amenorrheic and eumenorrheic athletes. *New England Journal of Medicine* 311:277–281, 1984.
18. Drinkwater, B.L., K. Nilson, S. Ott, and C.H. Chesnut, III. Bone mineral density after resumption of menses in amenorrheic athletes. *Journal of the American Medical Association* 256:380–382, 1986.
19. Duester, P.A., S.B. Kyle, P.B. Moser, R.A. Vigersky, A. Singh, and E.B. Schoomaker. Nutritional intake and status of highly trained amenorrheic and eumenorrheic women runners. *Fertility and Sterility* 46:636–643, 1986.
20. Ellison, P.T., and C. Lager. Moderate recreational running is associated with lowered salivary progesterone profiles in women. *American Journal of Obstetrics and Gynecology* 154:1000–1003, 1986.
21. Engle, E.T., and M.C. Shelesnyak. First menstrual and subsequent menstrual cycles of pubertal girls. *Human Biology* 6:431–453, 1934.
22. Fishman, J., R.M. Boyar, and L. Hellman. Influence of body weight on estradiol metabolism in young women. *Journal of Clinical Endocrinology and Metabolism* 41:989–991, 1975.
23. Frisch, R.E. Body fat, puberty, and fertility. *Biological Reviews* 59:161–188, 1984.
24. Frisch, R.E. Fatness and fertility. *Scientific American* 258:88–95, 1988.
25. Frisch, R.E., and J.W. McArthur. Menstrual cycles: Fatness as a determinant of minimum weight for height necessary for their maintenance or onset. *Science* 185:949–951, 1974.
26. Frisch, R.E., and R. Revelle. Height and weight in young athletes. *Archives of Disease in Childhood* 46:695–701, 1971.
27. Gadpaille, W.J., C.F. Sanborn, and W.W. Wagner. Athletic amenorrhea, major affective disorders, and eating disorders. *American Journal of Psychiatry* 144:939–942, 1987.
28. Galle, P.C., E.W. Freeman, M.G. Galle, G.R. Huggins, and S.T. Sondheimer. Physiologic and psychologic profiles in a survey of women runners. *Fertility and Sterility* 39:633–639, 1983.
29. Gambacciani, M., S.S.C. Yen, and D.D. Rasmussen. GnRH release from the mediobasal hypothalamus: in vitro inhibition by corticotropin-releasing factor. *Neuroendocrinology* 43:533–536, 1986.
30. Johnston, F.E. . Relationships between body composition and anthropometry. *Human Biology* 54:221–245, 1982.
31. Khoury, S.A., N.E. Reame, R.P. Kelch, and J.C. Marshall. Diurnal patterns of pulsatile luteinizing hormone secretion in hypothalamic amenorrhea: Reproducibility and responses to opiate blockade and an alpha$_2$-adrenergic agonist. *Journal of Clinical Endocrinology and Metabolism* 64:755–762, 1987.
32. Kikuchi, T. Interrelation between menopausal age and frequency of ovulatory cycles in life. *Hokkaido Journal of Medical Science* 62:469–475, 1987.
33. Knobil, E. The neuroendocrine control of the menstrual cycle. *Recent Progress in Hormone Research* 36:53–88, 1980.
34. Kustin, J., and R.W. Rebar. Menstrual disorders in the adolescent age group. *Primary Care* 14:139–166, 1987.

35. Lee, P.A. Neuroendocrine maturation. In J.P. Lavery and J.S. Sanfilippo (eds.). *Pediatric and Adolescent Obstetrics and Gynecology*. New York: Springer-Verlag, 1985.
36. Lindberg, J.S., W.B. Fears, M.M. Hunt, M.R. Powell, D. Boll, and C.E. Wade. Exercise-induced amenorrhea and bone density. *Annals of Internal Medicine* 101:647–649, 1984.
37. Lindberg, J.S., M.R. Powell, M.M. Hunt, D.E. Ducey, and C.E. Wade. Increased vertebral bone mineral in response to reduced exercise in amenorrheic runners. *Western Journal of Medicine* 146:39–42, 1987.
38. Liu, J.H., and S.S.C. Yen. The use of gonadotropin-releasing hormone for the induction of ovulation. *Clinical Obstetrics and Gynecology* 27:975–982, 1984.
39. Longcope, C., J.H. Pratt, S.H. Schneider, and S.E. Fineberg. Aromatization of androgens by muscle and adipose tissue *in vivo*. *Journal of Clinical Endocrinology and Metabolism* 46:146–152, 1978.
40. Loucks, A.B., and S.M. Horvath. Exercise-induced stress responses of amenorrheic and eumenorrheic runners. *Journal of Clinical Endocrinology and Metabolism* 59:1109–1120, 1984.
41. Loucks, A.B., and S.M. Horvath. Athletic amenorrhea: a review. *Medicine and Science in Sports and Exercise* 17:56–72, 1985.
42. Loucks, A.B., S.M. Horvath, and P.S. Freedson. Menstrual status and validation of body fat prediction in athletes. *Human Biology* 56:383–392, 1984.
43. Loucks, A.B., J.F. Mortola, L. Girton, and S.S.C. Yen, (in press). Alterations in the hypothalamic-pituitary-ovarian (HPO) and the hypothalamic-pituitary-adrenal (HPA) axes in athletic women. *Journal of Clinical Endocrinology and Metabolism*.
44. Malina, R.M. Menarche in athletes: a synthesis and hypothesis. *Annals of Human Biology* 10:1–24 1983..
45. Mann, D.R., G.G. Jackson, and M.S. Blank. Influence of adrenocorticotropin and adrenalectomy on gonadotropin secretion in immature rats. *Neuroendocrinology* 34:20–26, 1982.
46. Marcus, R., C. Cann, P. Madvig, J. Minkoff, M. Goddard, M. Bayer, M. Martin, L. Gaudiani, W. Haskell, and H. Genant. Menstrual function and bone mass in elite women distance runners: endocrine and metabolic features. *Annals of Internal Medicine* 102:158–163, 1985.
47. Mauvais-Jarvis, P., R. Sitruk-Ware, and F. Kuttenn. Luteal phase defect and breast cancer genesis. *Breast Cancer Research and Treatment* 2:139–150, 1982.
48. McArthur, J.W., B.A. Bullen, I.Z. Beitins, M. Pagano, T.M. Badger, and A. Klibansksi. Hypothalamic amenorrhea in runners of normal body composition. *Endocrine Research Communications* 7:13–25, 1980.
49. Merriam, G.R., D.L. Loriaux, and M.B. Lipsett. Effects of catechol estrogens on gonadotropins and prolactin in man. In G.R. Merriam and M.B. Lipsett (eds.). *Proceedings of the International Workshop on Catechol Estrogens*. New York: Raven Press, 1983.
50. Metcalf, M.G., D.S. Skidmore, G.F. Lowry, and J.A. MacKenzie. Incidence of ovulation in the years after the menarche. *Journal of Endocrinology* 97:213–219, 1983.
51. Nelson, M.E., E.C. Fisher, P.D. Catsos, C.N. Meredith, R.N. Turksoy, and W.J. Evans. Diet and bone status in amenorrheic runners. *American Journal of Clinical Nutrition* 43:910–916, 1986.
52. Ono, N., M.D. Lumpkin, W.K. Samson, J.K. McDonald, and S.M. McCann. Intrahypothalamic action of corticotropin-releasing factor (CRF) to inhibit growth hormone and LH release in the rat. *Life Sciences* 35:1117–1123, 1984.
53. Peltenburg, A.L., W.B.M Erich, J.J.H. Thijssen, W. Veeman, M. Jansen, M.J.E. Bernink, M.L. Zonderland, J.L. van den Brande, and I.A. Huisveld. Sex hormone profiles of premenarcheal athletes. *European Journal of Applied Physiology* 52:385–392, 1984.
54. Prior, J.C., K. Cameron, B. Ho Yuen, and J. Thomas. Menstrual cycle changes with marathon training: anovulation and short luteal phase. *Canadian Journal of Applied Sport Sciences* 7:173–177, 1982.
55. Reeves, J. Estimating fatness. *Science* 204:881, 1979.
56. Reindollar, R.H., and P.G. McDonough. Neuroendocrine processes relevant to the childhood years. *Clinical Obstetrics and Gynecology* 30:633–642, 1987.
57. Richards, S.R., F.E. Chang, B. Bossetti, W.B. Malarkey, and M.H. Kim. Serum carotene levels in female long-distance runners. *Fertility and Sterility* 43:79–81, 1985.
58. Rivier, C., and W. Vale. Influence of corticotropin-releasing factor on reproductive functions in the rat. *Endocrinology* 114:914–921, 1984.
59. Russell, J.B., D.E. Mitchell, P.I. Musey, and D.C. Collins. The role of B-endorphins and catechol estrogen on the hypothalamic-pituitary axis in female athletes. *Fertility and Sterility* 42:690–695, 1984.
60. Sanborn, C.F., B.H. Albrecht, and W.W. Wagner, Jr. Medically induced reversal of infertility in athletic amenorrhea. *Medicine and Science in Sports and Exercise* 19:Supplement S5, 1987. .
61. Schwartz, B., D.C. Cumming, E. Riordan, M. Selye, S.S.C. Yen, and R.W. Rebar. Exercise-

associated amenorrhea: A distinct entity? *American Journal of Obstetrics and Gynecology* 141:662–670, 1981.

62. Scott, E.C., and F.E. Johnston. Critical fat, menarche, and the maintenance of menstrual cycles. *Journal of Adolescent Health Care* 2:249–260, 1982.

63. Sherman, B.M., and S.G. Korenman. Inadequate corpus luteum function: a pathophysiological interpretation of human breast cancer epidemiology. *Cancer* 33:1306–1312, 1974.

64. Stager, J.M., J.K. Wigglesworth, and L.K. Hatler, (submitted). Interpreting the relationship between age of menarche and prepubertal training. *Medicine and Science in Sports and Exercise.*

65. Styne, D.M., and M.M. Grumbach. Puberty in the male and female: Its physiology and disorders. In S.S.C. Yen and R.B. Jaffe (eds.). *Reproductive Endocrinology.* Philadelphia: W.B. Saunders Company, 1986.

66. Suh, B.Y., J.H. Liu, S.L. Berga, M.E. Quigley, G.A. Laughlin, and S.S.C. Yen. Hypercortisolism in patients with functional hypothalamic-amenorrhea. *Journal of Clinical Endocrinology and Metabolism* 66:733–739, 1988.

67. Treloar, A.E., R.E.Boynton, B.G.Behn, and B.W. Brown. Variation of human menstrual cycle through reproductive life. *International Journal of Fertility* 12:77–126, 1967.

68. Trussell, J. Menarche and fatness: Reexamination of the critical body composition hypothesis. *Science* 200:1506–1509, 1978.

69. Veldhuis, J.D., W.S. Evans, L.M. Demers, M.O. Thorner, D. Wakat, and A.D. Rogol. Altered neuroendocrine regulation of gonadotropin secretion in women distance runners. *Journal of Clinical Endocrinology and Metabolism* 61:557–563, 1985.

70. Vollman, R.F. The menstrual cycle. In E.A. Friedman (ed.). *Major Problems in Obstetrics and Gynecology.* Vol. 7. Philadelphia: W.B. Saunders Co., 1977

71. Warren, M.P. The effects of exercise on pubertal progression and reproducive function in girls. *Journal of Clinical Endocrinology and Metabolism* 51:1150–1157, 1980.

72. Wildt, L., and G. Leyendecker. Induction of ovulation by the chronic administration of naltrexone in hypothalamic amenorrhea. *Journal of Clinical Endocrinology* 64:1334–1335, 1987.

73. Zacharias, L., W.M. Rand, and R.J. Wurtman. A prospective study of sexual development in American Girls: The statistics of menarche. *Obstetrical and Gynecological Survey* 31(Supplement):325–337, 1976.

74. Zucker, P., J. Avener, S. Bayder, A. Brotman, K. Moore, and J. Zimmerman. Eating disorders in young athletes. *The Physician and Sports Medicine* 13(11):89–106, 1985.

14

Exercise and Diabetes in Youth

EDWARD S. HORTON, M.D.

INTRODUCTION

Prior to the discovery of insulin, diet and exercise were the principal therapies used in the treatment of diabetes mellitus. Even today, standard medical doctrine holds that optimum blood glucose control in patients of all ages with insulin-dependent (type I) diabetes depends on a carefully managed interaction among food intake, physical exercise, and insulin administration. Although the

539

beneficial effects of exercise in treating diabetes were recognized centuries ago (Sushruta, 1938), it was not until 1919 that it was first demonstrated that exercise lowers the blood glucose concentration and transiently improves glucose tolerance in diabetic patients (Allen et al., 1919). Shortly after the discovery of insulin, Lawrence (1926) demonstrated that exercise potentiates the hypoglycemic effect of injected insulin; it was soon recognized that the combination of insulin and exercise may lead to acute symptomatic hypoglycemia and decreased insulin requirements in many insulin-treated diabetic patients. More recently, it has also been recognized that exercise may result in a further rise in blood glucose and the rapid development of ketosis in insulin deficient diabetics in poor metabolic control (Berger et al., 1977). Furthermore, even in well-controlled diabetic individuals, exercise of high intensity may produce sustained hyperglycemia (Mitchell et al., 1988).

Because of these problems with regulation of blood glucose and ketone metabolism during or after exercise, many insulin-treated youths with diabetes have found it difficult to participate in sports or other recreational activities in which physical exercise may be intermittent and of varied intensity and duration. In fact, it is not uncommon that young, physically active, and otherwise healthy people with type I diabetes are not allowed to participate in organized athletics and are discouraged from participation in recreational sports because of these risks. As more is learned about the multiple neural and endocrine factors that regulate blood glucose and other metabolic fuels during and after exercise, this information can be used to develop strategies to make it both possible and safe for the youth with type I diabetes to participate in sports or other forms of vigorous physical activity.

Regular physical exercise is now recognized to have several benefits to health, not only for those with diabetes, but for everyone. In addition to lowering blood glucose (Berger et al., 1977, Kemmer et al., 1979) and increasing insulin sensitivity (Bjorntorp et al., 1970, Sato et al., 1984, Soman et al., 1979), regular exercise improves several of the recognized risk factors for cardiovascular disease. Serum cholesterol and triglyceride concentrations may decline with physical training, due to decreases in low density and very low density lipoproteins (Huttenen et al., 1979, Lipson et al., 1980), and high density lipoprotein cholesterol increases (Ruderman et al., 1979, Wood et al., 1976, Wood & Haskell, 1979). Also, mild to moderate hypertension is reduced (Horton 1981), resting pulse rate and cardiac work are decreased, and physical working capacity, usually measured as maximal aerobic capacity ($\dot{V}O_2$max), is increased with physical training. Since young people with diabetes are at increased risk for developing long-term complications, including premature cardiovascular disease, retinopathy, nephropathy, and neuropathy, all of the above effects of regular physical exercise may have long-term benefits to health and provide the rationale for encouraging exercise as part of daily life. Psychological benefits of exercise such as an increased sense of well-being, improved self-esteem, and an enhanced quality of life are also important for youths with diabetes who have to cope with the anxieties and limitations of living with a chronic disease.

On the other hand, it is now recognized that exercise also presents several risks for diabetics and that these risks must be weighed against the potential benefits when advising youths with diabetes about participation in vigorous physical activity. As noted above, hypoglycemia may occur during or after exercise in insulin-treated individuals, and, when exercise is superimposed on the insulin deficient state, rapid increases in blood glucose and the development of ketosis may occur. Even in well-controlled individuals, brief periods of high intensity exercise may cause hyperglycemia.

In adults, exercise may precipitate angina pectoris, myocardial infarction, cardiac arrhythmias, or sudden death if there is underlying coronary artery disease. In addition, several of the long-term complications of diabetes may be worsened by exercise. Individuals who have proliferative retinopathy are at increased risk for developing retinal or vitreous hemorrhages during vigorous exercise, and retinal detachment may occur. Vigorous exercise also increases proteinuria (Mogensen & Vittinghus, 1975, Viberti et al., 1978), although this is probably a transient hemodynamic response, and it has not been shown that there is any deleterious effect of exercise on the progression of renal disease.

In patients with peripheral neuropathy, soft tissue and joint injuries are more likely to occur and may go unrecognized. In those with autonomic neuropathy, physical working capacity may be significantly decreased (Storstein & Jervell, 1979). This is associated with an increased resting pulse rate and a decreased cardiovascular response to exercise (Hilsted et al., 1979, Kahn et al., 1986, Margonato et al., 1986), lower VO_2max (Rubler, 1981), and an impaired response to dehydration.

However, recent epidemiological data from long-term follow-up of children with Type I diabetes suggest that regular physical activity early in life is not associated with an adverse effect on health and, in fact, may be beneficial (LaPorte et al., 1986). This has led many diabetologists to recommend that physical exercise be encouraged in people with diabetes if there are no specific contraindications, but that exercise should not be considered to be a part of the therapeutic prescription for every diabetic. Instead, the goal should be to develop educational programs for those with diabetes who want to participate in sports or other forms of physical exercise. These educational programs should be designed to enable diabetics to maintain good metabolic control before, during, and after exercise and to avoid or minimize the various complications of exercise.

During the past 10 years, much new information has been acquired about the hormonal and metabolic adaptations that occur during physical exercise, and several excellent reviews have been written on exercise and diabetes (Bjorkman, 1986; Horton, 1988; Kemmer & Berger, 1983; Vitug et al., 1988; Vranic & Berger, 1979; Zinman & Vranic, 1985). In this chapter, current concepts regarding the regulation of glucose and other metabolic fuels during and after exercise will be reviewed, and comparisons will be made between the normal condition and the abnormalities observed in Type I diabetes mellitus. This information may be used to develop strategies for the management of exercise in youths with diabetes who wish to participate in sports or other vigorous recreational activities.

I. METABOLIC FUEL HOMEOSTASIS DURING AND AFTER EXERCISE

During exercise, numerous cardiovascular, hormonal, and neural responses occur in a highly integrated fashion to ensure the delivery of oxygen and metabolic fuels to working muscle groups and the removal of metabolic end products. Increased oxygen delivery and carbon dioxide removal from tissues are accomplished by increased respiration, increased cardiac output, redistribution of blood flow, and increased capillary perfusion of working muscles. Metabolic fuels are made available by a more complex system that involves breakdown of glycogen and triglyceride stores within muscle itself and by increased delivery of substrates via the blood. Glucose and fatty acids, the major metabolic fuels for muscle, are released into the circulation from the liver and adipose tissue, respectively, and amino acids are made available by increased release from muscle.

In the resting, postabsorptive state, the blood glucose concentration is maintained at a constant level by a closely matched balance between glucose utilization and hepatic glucose production (Figure 14-1). Approximately 50% of glucose turnover is accounted for by uptake in the brain, where glucose is the major (usually the only) metabolic substrate utilized. Thirty to 35% is taken up by other tissues, including blood cells, kidneys, and the splanchnic bed, and only 15 to 20% is used by muscles. Hepatic glucose production is

GLUCOSE PRODUCTION   GLUCOSE UTILIZATION

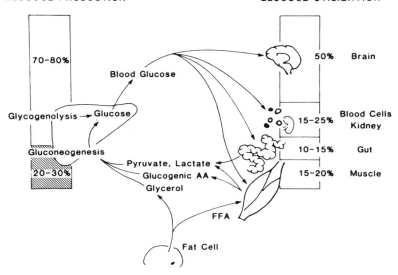

FIGURE 14-1. *Schematic representation of glucose turnover in the basal (overnight-fasted) resting state in normal man. The liver is the sole site of glucose production, via glycogenolysis (75) and gluconeogenesis (25). The brain is the major site of glucose utilization, consuming approximately half the output. Smaller amounts of glucose are taken up by blood cells, the renal medulla, the gut, and skeletal muscle. The last is a source of glucose precursors in the form of amino acids, primarily alanine and two glycolytic intermediaries, lactate and pyruvate. The adipocyte contributes small amounts of glycerol for gluconeogenesis. Reproduced from Bjorkman and Wahren (1988) with permission.*

maintained by a combination of breakdown of hepatic glycogen stores through glycogenolysis and the formation of new glucose by gluconeogenesis. In normal subjects in the postprandial state, hepatic glucose production is due predominantly to glycogenolysis, with only approximately 25% coming from gluconeogenesis (Felig & Wahren, 1975), whereas in diabetes, gluconeogenesis proceeds at a much higher rate and may account for as much as 40% of hepatic glucose production (Bjorkman, 1986). The major gluconeogenic precursors (lactate, pyruvate, alanine, and glycerol) are derived from glycolysis and oxidation of amino acids in muscle and other peripheral tissues and from lipolysis in adipose tissue. Free fatty acids are also released by lipolysis and provide a major substrate for energy production.

At rest, approximately 10% of the energy generated in skeletal muscle comes from glucose oxidation, 85–90% is from the oxidation of fatty acids, and only 1–2% is from amino acids (Ahlborg et al., 1974). With the onset of exercise, carbohydrate utilization in muscle increases abruptly and is associated with the rapid breakdown of muscle glycogen stores. The marked increase in glycolysis results in the formation of lactate, which accumulates in muscle and is released into the circulation. Within the first few minutes of exercise, blood flow to the muscles is increased, glucose uptake from the circulation occurs, and lactate release declines as aerobic metabolism is established. The increase in glucose uptake by exercising muscles is closely matched by increased hepatic glucose production, and blood glucose concentrations stay relatively constant for up to several hours during sustained, moderate intensity exercise.

The onset of exercise is also associated with the activation of lipolysis in adipose tissue and the release of free fatty acids (FFA) and glycerol into the circulation. Concentrations of FFA rise, and FFA are taken up and utilized by exercising muscle in proportion to their concentration in plasma (Ahlborg et al., 1974). Lactate, pyruvate, alanine, and other gluconeogenic amino acids released from both exercising and non-exercising muscle and glycerol released from adipose tissue are extracted by the liver and utilized for gluconeogenesis.

A. Factors Affecting Metabolic Fuel Utilization During Exercise

Several factors influence the relative amounts of carbohydrate and FFA utilized during exercise. These include the intensity and duration of exercise, the level of physical training, the antecedent diet, and the effects of meals taken shortly before or during exercise.

1. **Intensity.** As the *intensity* of exercise is increased, carbohydrate becomes a progressively more important substrate for energy production. During exercise of moderate intensity, e.g., at 50% of $\dot{V}O_2$max, muscle derives approximately 50% of its energy from carbohydrate oxidation. At intensities of 70–75% $\dot{V}O_2$max, carbohydrate becomes the predominant metabolic fuel, and when exercise is at or near 100% of $\dot{V}O_2$max, nearly all of the energy is derived from carbohydrate oxidation. Amino acids ordinarily contribute less than 7% of the energy required for muscular contraction at all intensities of exercise, and the contribution to energy production from oxidation of lipids ranges from 80% at low intensities of exercise to near 0% at maximal, high power exercise. During very high intensity exercise, carbohydrate oxidation rates are markedly increased, muscle glycogen stores are depleted rapidly, and glucose uptake from the circulation is high. If hepatic glycogen stores are adequate, hepatic glucose production is able to match or exceed peripheral utilization, and blood glucose concentrations remain constant or may actually increase.

2. Duration. With increasing *duration* of low to moderate intensity exercise, muscle and hepatic glycogen stores fall, and plasma FFA concentrations increase in conjunction with increased lipolysis in adipose tissue. Fatty acid oxidation by exercising muscle increases gradually, and carbohydrate oxidation decreases so that after 2–3 h of continuous exercise, FFA becomes the major substrate for energy production.

With increasing duration of exercise, hepatic glucose production decreases and becomes progressively more dependent on gluconeogenesis but is usually sufficient to maintain normal blood glucose concentrations. Hypoglycemia rarely develops, but it may occur during prolonged, exhaustive exercise such as long distance running or cycling. This is usually associated with glycogen depletion in muscle and liver and the consequent inability of hepatic glucose production to keep up with the high rates of peripheral glucose utilization.

3. Physical Training. *Physical training* has a major effect on the pattern of metabolic fuel utilization during exercise. Compared with untrained individuals, trained subjects perform the same amount of work at a lower percentage of $\dot{V}O_2$max and thus utilize less carbohydrate and more FFA. Even when exercising at the same relative intensity, i.e. the same percent $\dot{V}O_2$max, trained subjects utilize less carbohydrate and more FFA than untrained subjects. This results in a slower rate of decline of muscle and liver glycogen stores and is associated with greater endurance.

4. Diet. The *antecedent diet* is also an important factor in determining substrate utilization during exercise and endurance. In 1939, Christensen and Hansen demonstrated that the feeding of a carbohydrate-rich diet is associated with increased rates of carbohydrate oxidation during exercise and that endurance during cycle exercise is greater after feeding a high carbohydrate diet compared to a high fat diet (Christensen & Hansen, 1939). Subsequent studies revealed that the dietary effects on endurance during high intensity cycle exercise (75% $\dot{V}O_2$max) are correlated with the pre-exercise muscle glycogen content (Bergstrom et al., 1967). It was also observed that the highest muscle glycogen concentration can be obtained if subjects first deplete their glycogen stores by exercise, remain on a low carbohydrate diet for several days, then eat a diet rich in carbohydrates for another three days (Bergstrom & Hultman, 1966, Bergstrom et al., 1972, Hultman & Bergstrom, 1967). The "supercompensation" of muscle glycogen stores that occurs under these conditions has led to the common practice of "carbohydrate loading" among endurance athletes. More recent studies have demonstrated that the low carbohydrate diet phase is not necessary to achieve supercompensation of muscle glycogen stores following glycogen-depleting exercise (Sherman et al., 1981), and this phase is now generally omitted from carbohydrate loading regimens.

The effects of feeding sugar-sweetened drinks or raising FFA concentrations 30–60 min before starting exercise on metabolic fuel utilization and exercise performance have been examined by several groups during the past few years. Costill et al. (1977) demonstrated that when FFA concentrations were increased prior to exercise by injection of heparin and feeding a high fat meal, carbohydrate oxidation was reduced and muscle glycogen spared. However, when 75 g glucose was ingested 45 min prior to exercise, plasma insulin concentrations were increased, FFA concentrations decreased, and carbohydrate utilization was increased. This was associated with an increased utilization of muscle glycogen and a fall in blood glucose to hypoglycemic levels. However, more recent studies (Fielding et al., 1987; Koivisto et al., 1985) have found no increase in glycogen use during 30 min of exercise when subjects were given pre-exercise feedings of glucose.

Levine et al. (1983) subsequently demonstrated that fructose ingestion prior to exercise had a much smaller effect on plasma insulin and glucose concentrations, did not result in hypoglycemia, and had a sparing effect on muscle glycogen utilization. In contrast, Fielding et al. (1987) and Koivisto et al. (1985) did not find a sparing effect of fructose on muscle glycogen utilization during exercise.

Recent studies by Devlin et al. (1986) have shown that a snack meal (candy bar) containing a mixture of carbohydrates, fats, and proteins did not cause any alteration in metabolic fuel utilization during exercise and was associated with better maintenance of blood glucose concentrations during and after exercise compared with a non-caloric, placebo drink. These studies suggest that pre-exercise feeding of a mixed snack may be preferable to feeding pure glucose and comparable with feeding fructose for maintenance of normal glucose homeostasis during exercise and that postexercise recovery may be more rapid when food is ingested prior to exercise.

The effects of glucose, glucose polymer, or complex carbohydrate ingestion during exercise have also been examined (Coyle et al., 1983, Ivy et al., 1979, Ivy et al., 1983). There is little evidence to suggest any advantage of complex carbohydrates over simple sugars as an energy source during exercise. Hyperglycemia and hyperinsulinemia do not occur if the carbohydrate is given during, rather than before, moderate intensity exercise. Carbohydrate oxidation rates are increased, FFA oxidation rates are decreased, and blood glucose concentrations are better maintained after 2 h of exercise with carbohydrate feeding. In most studies, carbohydrate feeding during prolonged exercise has been associated with increased endurance, presumably by providing a source of glucose for energy.

Following exercise, glucose uptake by muscle continues to be increased and is utilized to rebuild muscle glycogen stores. Without feeding, muscle glycogen stores are replenished rather slowly, depending on continued hepatic glucose production and maintenance of normal plasma glucose concentrations. With feeding, muscle glycogen stores are replenished more rapidly, reaching normal levels within 12–14 h after exercise (Maehlum et al., 1977, Maehlum et al., 1978, Maehlum & Hermansen, 1978). Ingested glucose is taken up preferentially in previously exercised muscle groups, probably due to increased insulin sensitivity and activation of glycogen synthase by the prior exercise. Hepatic glycogen stores recover at a slower rate. When studied 12–14 h following high intensity cycle exercise, glucose oxidation and turnover rates are lower than in the non-exercised state, and FFA oxidation rates are increased (Devlin & Horton, 1985). In response to insulin infusion, total glucose disposal is increased only slightly, but there is a marked change in the metabolic pathways of glucose metabolism. Following glycogen-depleting exercise, glucose oxidation rates are decreased, and nonoxidative glucose disposal, presumably representing primarily glycogen synthesis, is markedly increased. Thus, part of the increased insulin sensitivity and glucose utilization following exercise is related to the resynthesis of depleted muscle glycogen stores (Bogardus et al., 1983, Devlin & Horton, 1985).

B. The Role of the Neuro-Endocrine System in the Metabolic Response to Exercise

The hormonal response to exercise is a complex, highly integrated system that involves activation of the sympathetic nervous system and the hypothalamic pituitary axis, as well as the suppression or release of a large number of hormones that regulate the mobilization and/or metabolism of glucose, FFA, and amino acids, or alter fluid and electrolyte balance. The magnitude and pattern of the hormonal adaptation to physical activity depends on multiple factors that include the intensity and duration of the exercise performed, the level of physical training and the physiological state under which exercise is being performed, including factors such as body and environmental temperature, hydration, the supply of oxygen, and the availability of glucose and other metabolic substrates to working muscles. These responses have been reviewed extensively by Galbo (1983) and Sutton and Farrell (1988), and key points relevent to the youth with diabetes are summarized below.

1. Sympathetic Nervous System. Physical activity is associated with activation of the sympathetic nervous system and a rise in plasma norepinephrine and epinephrine concentrations. The increase in plasma norepinephrine represents a spillover from sympathetic nerve terminals and gives only a rough approximation of sympathetic nerve stimulation. Plasma norepinephrine increases with increasing work intensity and responses correlate well with the relative workload being performed, both in physically trained and untrained individuals. A greater response is observed when a fixed amount of work is being done by a small muscle mass than when the same work is performed by larger muscle groups, supporting the concept that the sympathetic nervous system activation is proportional to the intensity of work being performed by specific muscle groups.

In addition to intensity of physical activity, plasma norepinephrine also increases with increased duration of exercise (Galbo et al., 1975). Several other factors also increase the norepinephrine response to exercise; these include hypoxemia, hypovolemia, exposure to hot or cold environments, and performance of work in an upright position. Norepinephrine responses are lower in physically trained individuals than in the untrained at the same absolute workload.

Plasma epinephrine, derived from adrenal medullary secretion, does not increase significantly during low intensity exercise but does increase during exercise of high intensity or prolonged duration. A major factor in regulating the epinephrine response is a decrease in blood glucose concentration (Galbo et al., 1975; Gray et al., 1980; Rizza et al., 1979). In general, epinephrine responses are less than the increases in norepinephrine and are seen primarily with exercise of high intensity or in response to a falling blood glucose concentration. In response to insulin-induced hypoglycemia, children have greater increases in plasma epinephrine levels than adults, a fact that may be important in glucose regulation during exercise in youths with diabetes (Amiel et al., 1988).

The major physiological effects of sympathetic nervous system activation during exercise are to increase heart rate and cause vasoconstriction in the vascular beds supplying the splanchnic circulation, kidneys, and non-exercising muscles. This results in a redistribution of blood flow away from these areas and increases flow to exercising muscle groups. In addition, increased sympathetic nervous system activity during exercise stimulates perspiration and thus plays an important role in body cooling and perhaps potassium homeostasis. It also stimulates the renin-angiotensin system and plays an important role in decreasing renal sodium and water excretion.

Norepinephrine and epinephrine also play major roles in the regulation of metabolic fuel mobilization and utilization, both by direct and indirect mechanisms (Clutter et al., 1988). Insulin secretion is suppressed by alpha-adrenergic stimulation, lipolysis is stimulated by beta-adrenergic stimulation, and catecholamines stimulate glycogenolysis in both liver and muscle tissue, making glucose available to provide energy for muscular contraction.

    2. **Insulin.** Insulin plays an important role in the regulation of metabolic fuel delivery and utilization during exercise. As mentioned above, insulin secretion is suppressed during physical activity in response to alpha-adrenergic inhibitory effects on the pancreatic beta cells (Hartley et al., 1972, Hermanssen et al., 1970, Wahren et al., 1971). In addition, increased blood flow to working muscles results in increased insulin delivery to these tissues. The falling insulin concentrations in plasma have major effects on glucose, lipid, and amino acid metabolism, making these fuels more readily available for energy production. Insulin is the major inhibitor of hepatic glucose production, and the fall in plasma insulin during exercise, coupled with no change or a rise in plasma glucagon, results in increased hepatic glucose output. This is closely correlated with peripheral glucose utilization and maintenance of blood glucose concentration in a normal range. In addition, the falling insulin concentrations decrease the inhibitory effects on lipolysis in adipose tissue and release of amino acids from muscle. Since little or no insulin is needed for glucose uptake in exercising muscle (Berger et al., 1975, Richter et al., 1985), the fall in plasma insulin concentrations does not impair glucose utilization by this vital tissue.

    3. **Glucagon.** During exercise, glucagon is secreted from pancreatic alpha-cells, primarily in response to falling glucose concentrations. Glucagon responses are minimal during mild to moderate intensity exercise. However, with high intensity or prolonged exercise, glucagon concentrations increase and play a role in maintaining glucose homeostasis (Bjorkman et al., 1981). Glucagon responses are greater in untrained than trained individuals. The major role of glucagon is to increase uptake of amino acids in liver and to stimulate gluconeogenesis. Glucagon also has glycogenolytic activity in the liver and, with epinephrine, is the major glucose counter-regulatory hormone during exercise (Kemmer and Vranic, 1981; Vranic et al., 1976; Vranic et al., 1982; Wasserman et al., 1984).

    4. **Other Hormones.** During physical activity, growth hormone and cortisol concentrations increase with increasing work-rates. This response is less in trained than untrained subjects, even when measured at the same relative work intensity. Cortisol and growth hormone may be important in maintaining glucose levels

during prolonged exercise. Cortisol and growth hormone antagonize insulin action in peripheral tissues and may serve to limit glucose utilization in non-exercising, insulin-sensitive tissues, making more glucose available to working muscle.

Several other hormones increase during physical activity, although much less is known about their physiological roles or their relevance to metabolic homeostasis during exercise in diabetes mellitus.

In trying to integrate the hormonal adaptations to physical activity, two major areas emerge. First, there is marked activation of the sympathetic nervous system with release of norepinephrine and secondary inhibition or stimulation of several other hormones that play an important role in the cardiovascular and metabolic responses to exercise. In addition, there is activation of the hypothalamic-pituitary axis with release of several anterior pituitary hormones including growth hormone, adrenocorticotrophic hormone, prolactin, and possibly thyroid-stimulating hormone.

In response to these hormonal changes, several physiological responses occur to increase delivery of oxygen and metabolic fuels to working muscles for energy production and to maintain other body homeostatic mechanisms, including regulation of body temperature, circulating blood volume, and electrolyte balance. It is clear that these responses to physical activity are complex, highly integrated, and interdependent. They vary considerably, depending on the intensity and duration of exercise and the physiological state of the organism. There appears to be considerable redundancy in the adaptive responses so that deficiency of one hormonal system may be compensated by overactivity of another. This is particularly evident in regulation of glucose homeostasis, where deficiencies of catecholamines or glucagon may be compensated without major disruption of glucose homeostasis in certain defined circumstances. On the other hand, major deficiencies of one or more of the counter-regulatory hormones may result in the development of hyper- or hypoglycemia during exercise and impaired work performance.

II. EFFECTS OF INSULIN DEPENDENT DIABETES MELLITUS ON METABOLIC FUEL HOMEOSTASIS DURING EXERCISE

Whereas changes in blood glucose are very small in normal subjects during exercise, several factors may complicate glucose regulation during and following exercise in patients with insulin-treated diabetes. Shortly after the introduction of insulin, Lawrence (1926) demonstrated that exercise potentiates the hypoglycemic effect of injected insulin (Figure 14-2), and it was soon discovered that regular physical activity leads to decreased insulin requirements and an increased risk of hypoglycemic reactions in insulin-treated diabetics. Several studies in both man and animals have confirmed that physical training increases sensitivity to insulin (Bjorntorp et al., 1970, 1972, 1973), although the mechanism by which this occurs is still not well understood. Athletes have normal or increased tolerance to oral glucose in conjunction with low basal and glucose stimulated insulin responses (Lohman et al., 1978), and physical inactivity rapidly results in decreased glucose tolerance (Lipman et al., 1972). Both normal control subjects and patients with type II diabetes have been shown to have a 30–35% increase in insulin stimulated glucose disposal after physical training when studied by the hyperinsulinemic-euglycemic clamp technique (DeFronzo et al., 1983; Soman et al.,

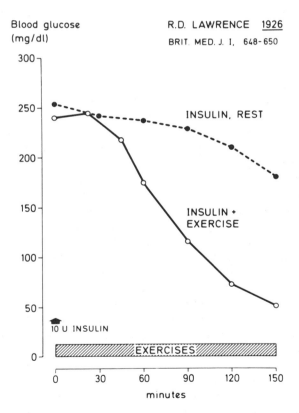

FIGURE 14-2. *Effect of subcutaneously injected insulin on blood glucose concentrations in a type I diabetic patient. Adapted from Lawrence (1926) by Vranic & Berger (1979). Reproduced with permission.*

1979; Trovati et al., 1984). This increase in insulin sensitivity correlates well with the training-induced increase in $\dot{V}O_2$max (Rosenthal et al., 1983; Sato et al., 1984; Yki-Jarvinen & Koivisto, 1983) and is thought to be due primarily to increased glucose uptake by muscle, since no changes have been observed in hepatic glucose production rates.

Acute exercise in untrained subjects is also associated with increased insulin sensitivity and glucose metabolism, which persists for several hours following the exercise (Bogardus et al., 1983; Fahlen et al., 1972; Pruett & Oseid, 1970). This is related to both the need for replenishment of decreased muscle and liver glycogen stores and to increased glucose metabolism in muscle. However, the mechanisms by which exercise and physical training result in increased sensitivity to insulin are not yet clear. The binding of ^{125}I-insulin to monocytes is increased after acute exercise in untrained individuals and after a period of physical training (Koivisto et al., 1979; Koivisto & Yki-Jarvinen, 1985), the former effect being due to increased receptor affinity and the latter due to increased receptor number. However, increased insulin binding to muscle or adipose cells has not been demonstrated in trained animals, and increased glucose transport and changes in intracellular glucose metabolism appear to be the major causes of the increased insulin effect (Wardzala et al., 1982).

The blood-glucose-lowering effects of exercise led Joslin (1959) and others to advocate physical exercise as a major method for improving blood glucose control in insulin-treated diabetics, and for many years regular physical exercise has been considered, with diet and insulin, a key part of the triad of good diabetic management. Recent studies, however, have failed to show a beneficial effect of exercise on long-term metabolic control in type I diabetes (Wallberg-Henriksson et al., 1982, 1986). One possible explanation for this is suggested by the studies of Zinman et al., (1984), in which the effects of cycle exercise training for 12 weeks on acute blood glucose responses, long-term glucose control, and dietary intake were measured in a group of subjects with type I diabetes and in normal controls. They found that each 45-min exercise session had an acute glucose-lowering effect in the diabetic patients, but that fasting plasma glucose and glycohemoglobin concentrations remained unchanged. This appeared to be due to the fact that caloric intake was significantly increased on the training days, both in anticipation of and in response to the exercise. Whereas the above studies utilized blood glucose and glycohemoglobin levels to determine the effects of exercise on diabetic control, another recent study (Stratton et al., 1987) using blood glucose and glycosylated serum albumin as indices of metabolic control, concluded that, if no compensatory increase in food intake is allowed, an exercise program of eight weeks duration does result in improved blood glucose control.

The questionable effects of physical training on long-term glucose control, coupled with the acute risks and complications of exercise, have cast substantial doubt on the concept that exercise should be advocated for all diabetics. Most diabetologists now believe that the best advice is to encourage exercise for those who do not have any significant contraindications and who wish to participate, but not to recommend it for everyone. The youth or young adult who wants to exercise and is free of complications should be educated about the effects of exercise on blood glucose regulation, and strategies should be developed to avoid hypoglycemia during or after exercise and to prevent exercise-induced hyperglycemia. These individuals should also be taught to postpone exercise and take corrective steps when exercise is contraindicated by poor metabolic control. With proper instruction, careful monitoring, appropriate adjustments in insulin and food intake, and individual experience, many youths with insulin-treated diabetes can learn to exercise safely. Most patients with type I diabetes show normal cardiovascular and peripheral adaptations to physical training, with the possible exception of deficient proliferation of capillaries in skeletal muscle (Mandroukas et al., 1986), and many have achieved the status of world class athletes.

A. Glucose Regulation During Exercise

One of the major problems for the youth with insulin-dependent diabetes is that plasma insulin concentrations do not respond to exercise in a normal manner, thus upsetting the balance between peripheral glucose utilization and hepatic glucose production. In normal individuals, plasma insulin concentrations decrease to low levels during exercise. This, in conjunction with constant or increasing plasma concentrations of glucagon, promotes increased hepatic glucose production to match the increased rate of peripheral glucose utilization. The low insulin concentration during exercise also increases the lipolytic response to catecholamines, making FFA available for oxidation by exercising muscle and making glycerol available to the liver for gluconeogenesis. In insulin-treated diabetics, plasma insulin concentrations do not decrease during exercise and may even increase substantially if exercise is undertaken within an hour or so of an insulin injection (Berger et al., 1978, 1979, 1982; Kemmer et al., 1979). As illustrated in Figure 14-3, this is due to increased absorption of insulin from the subcutaneous tissue. This effect of exercise on insulin absorption is most marked if regular

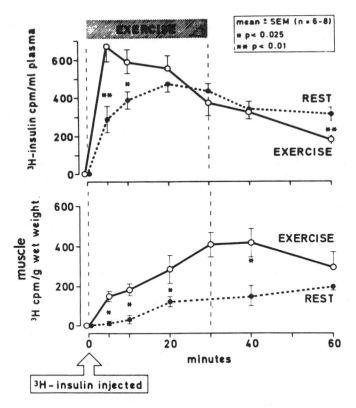

FIGURE 14-3. *(A) Effect of treadmill running (EXERCISE) on plasma levels of intact ^{3}H-insulin after subcutaneous (s.c.) injections of 10^6 cpm ^{3}H-insulin/kg body weight in normal, fed rats. ^{3}H-insulin was separated from its labeled degradation products by gel chromatography. (B) Effects of treadmill running (EXERCISE) on total ^{3}H concentrations of skeletal muscle after s.c. injections of 10^6 and ^{3}H-insulin/kg body weight in normal, fed rats. From Berger et al. (1978) with permission.*

insulin is used and if the injection site is in an exercising part of the body (Koivisto & Felig, 1978). At rest, human insulin is absorbed more rapidly than is porcine insulin, but during exercise this difference disappears, both types of insulin being absorbed more rapidly than in the resting condition. The increased absorption rate during exercise is not associated with increased cutaneous blood flow, but may be due to mechanical stimulation of the injection site (Fernqvist et al., 1986).

Enhanced insulin absorption during exercise is most likely to occur when the insulin injection is given immediately before or within a few minutes of the onset of exercise. The longer the interval between injection and onset of exercise, the less significant this effect will be and the less important it is to choose the site of injection to avoid an exercising area. There is considerable variation in insulin absorption rates from different injection sites, such as the thigh, abdomen, or arm, and this variation may have more of an effect on the rate of insulin absorption than the exercise itself (Berger et al., 1982; Susstrunk et al., 1982). To avoid this problem, a good plan is to postpone vigorous exercise for at least 60–90 min after an insulin injection. However, even with this precaution, plasma insulin concentrations do not fall normally during exercise in insulin-treated patients, and glucose homeostasis may be impaired.

The sustained concentrations of circulating insulin in exercising diabetics enhance peripheral glucose uptake and stimulate glucose oxidation by exercising muscle. However, the major effect of these higher-than-normal concentrations of insulin is an inhibition of hepatic glucose production (Kawamori & Vranic, 1977; Zinman et al., 1977). Both glycogenolysis and gluconeogenesis are inhibited by the high insulin levels, and, even though counter-regulatory hormone responses may be normal or even enhanced, the hepatic glucose production rate cannot match the rate of peripheral glucose utilization; thus, blood glucose concentration falls. During mild to moderate exercise of short duration, this may be considered to be a beneficial effect of exercise, but during more prolonged exercise, hypoglycemia may result. This is particularly true in some diabetics who have glucagon deficiency because the combination of high insulin and low glucagon concentrations may result in decreased gluconeogenesis and impaired hepatic glucose production.

Gerich et al. (1973) were the first to demonstrate that some patients with type I diabetes have deficient glucagon responses to hypoglycemia, although the mechanism by which this occurs remains unclear. Since responses to other stimuli in these individuals are often normal or increased (Unger et al., 1970; Wise et al., 1973), the defect in glucagon secretion may be related to a specific abnormality in the glucose sensor mechanism of the pancreatic alpha-cell, rather than to a more generalized loss of glucagon secretory capacity.

When the glucagon response to hypoglycemia is impaired, some delay in restoration of normoglycemia may occur, but this is usually not a severe problem because catecholamines, particularly epinephrine, also serve as potent glucose counter-regulatory hormones (Cryer and Gerich, 1985). However, when both glucagon and epinephrine responses are impaired, severe, prolonged hypoglycemia may occur (Rizza, Haymond, et al., 1979).

Several factors may affect the epinephrine response to hypoglycemia in youths with diabetes. It is now well-recognized that one of the "trade offs" for tight metabolic control is an increased incidence of severe hypoglycemic reactions (Caspari & Ewing, 1985; DCCT Research Group, 1986; Goldstein et al., 1981; Lauritzen et al., 1983; Tchobroutsky et al., 1981), many of which are associated with exercise. One possible mechanism for the increased incidence of exercise-induced hypoglycemia in patients who undergo intensive insulin therapy is a subnormal response of epinephrine, growth hormone, and cortisol when blood glucose is lowered to 50 mg/dL (Simonson et al., 1985). This observation, coupled with the finding of DeFronzo et al. (1977) that epinephrine secretion is stimulated in diabetics, but not in non-diabetics, when blood glucose is decreased rapidly from 200 to 100 mg/dL, is consistent with the hypothesis that the preceding plasma glucose concentration has a major effect on the magnitude of the counter-regulatory hormone response to a falling blood glucose level (Amiel et al., 1988). Furthermore, Amiel et al. (1986, 1987) have clearly demonstrated that strict control of blood glucose by insulin pump therapy results in a significant decrease in the concentration of blood glucose that stimulates epinephrine and growth hormone release as well as an increase in the sensitivity of the liver to insulin for inhibition of glucose production. Thus, intensively treated patients achieve much lower blood glucose concentrations before counter-regulatory mechanisms become activated and hepatic glucose production increases.

Another factor that may contribute to exercise-induced hypoglycemia is autonomic neuropathy. Defective autonomic nervous system function has been associated with decreased catecholamine responses and inadequate glucose counter-regulation to insulin-induced hypoglycemia in a group of patients who experienced frequent hypoglycemic reactions during intensive insulin therapy (White et al., 1983). In addition, patients with autonomic neuropathy often do not develop the classic warning signs of hypoglycemia before developing severe neuroglucopenia, which further compounds the problem of exercise-induced hypoglycemia (Hoeldtke et al., 1982).

Strategies to avoid hypoglycemia during prolonged, vigorous exercise include decreasing insulin dosage before exercise and taking supplemental carbohydrate feedings before and during exercise. For example, in exhaustive, competitive events such as marathon running, insulin-dependent diabetics may omit their usual insulin dose altogether and start with an elevated blood glucose concentration, which gradually falls to a normal range during the first 60–90 min of the run. As long as insulin deficiency is not severe enough to result in ketosis before exercise, metabolic fuel regulation during exercise is fairly normal, although lactate and pyruvate concentrations are greater and several of the glucose counter-regulatory hormones, including glucagon, catecholamines, growth hormone, and cortisol, increase more in diabetics than in non-diabetics (Meinders et al., 1988). This counter-regulatory response is probably a key factor in preventing hypoglycemia from occurring.

Because the vast majority of young people with type I diabetes do not participate in marathon running or similar exhausting events, it is important to develop strategies for managing more moderate forms of exercise. The metabolic responses to moderate intensity exercise performed 30 min after breakfast have been studied in insulin-dependent diabetics and compared to normals (Caron et al., 1982, Nelson et al., 1982). In normal subjects, the expected postprandial rise in blood glucose and insulin concentrations is rapidly reversed by exercise, returning to fasting levels within 45 min. When exercise is stopped, there is a moderate rebound increase in glucose and insulin concentrations, which do not exceed those occurring after breakfast alone. Thus, 45 min of cycle exercise started 30 min after a meal has a significant but transient effect to lower blood glucose concentrations.

In subjects with Type I diabetes treated with a closed loop "artificial endocrine pancreas," blood glucose responses following breakfast and in response to exercise are similar to those in normal subjects, and there is an appropriate 30% decrease in insulin requirement during exercise. When insulin is infused at a constant rate, i.e., not decreased during exercise, symptomatic hypoglycemia occurs, further demonstrating the interaction between insulin and exercise in lowering blood glucose concentrations in insulin treated subjects (Nelson et al., 1982).

In patients treated with subcutaneous insulin, responses to exercise started 30 min after breakfast have been found to be variable, with the majority having improved (lowered) blood glucose concentrations that persist through lunch. Some subjects, however, show improved glucose levels during lunch only, and a few show no significant improvement at all (Caron et al., 1982). Thus, the effect of exercise following meals on blood glucose concentrations and the appropriate adjustments in insulin dosage may vary considerably; individual responses should be determined to achieve improved glucose control and avoid symptomatic hypoglycemia.

B. Postexercise Hypoglycemia

Another major problem for the youth with insulin-treated diabetes is the occurrence of postexercise hypoglycemia. Many diabetics experience increased insulin sensitivity and have hypoglycemic reactions several hours after exercise, in some cases even the next day. In one recent study (MacDonald, 1987) 16% of 300 young patients with Type I diabetes who were followed prospectively for

2 y experienced postexercise, late onset hypoglycemia, usually occurring at night, 6–15 h after the completion of unusually strenuous exercise or play. Although the mechanism of postexercise-hypoglycemia is not well-understood, it is most likely due to increased glucose uptake and glycogen synthesis in the previously exercised muscle groups; these phenomena are associated with increased insulin sensitivity and activation of glycogen synthase in skeletal muscle (Bogardus et al., 1983, Devlin & Horton, 1985).

Hepatic glycogen stores also recover following exercise, but at a slower rate than occurs in muscle, so that increased requirements for dietary carbohydrate may persist for up to 24 h after prolonged, glycogen depleting exercise. Various strategies have been used to prevent postexercise hypoglycemia, including decreasing pre-exercise doses of intermediate or short-acting insulin and taking supplemental feedings after exercise (Campaigne et al., 1987), but no universal guidelines are totally effective, and treatment regimens must be individualized.

C. Exercise-Induced Hyperglycemia

In contrast to moderate intensity, sustained exercise, during which blood glucose concentrations remain constant or decrease slightly, short-term, high intensity exercise at 80% of $\dot{V}O_2$max or greater is normally associated with a transient increase in blood glucose levels (Mitchell et al., 1988). The rise in blood glucose during exercise reaches a peak 5–15 min after exercise is stopped and then gradually returns to the pre-exercise level within 40–60 min. This glycemic response to intense exercise is caused by a marked stimulation of hepatic glucose production that exceeds the rate of glucose uptake in muscle and is associated with activation of the sympathetic nervous system, a sharp rise in glucose counter-regulatory hormones (particularly epinephrine), and a suppression of insulin secretion. The energy for muscular contraction is provided predominantly by glucose derived from breakdown of muscle glycogen stores, and glucose uptake from the circulation increases only gradually. Hepatic glucose production, on the other hand, is stimulated rapidly by the decrease in portal vein insulin concentration, an increase in the glucagon to insulin ratio, and the rapid rise in plasma epinephrine. When exercise is stopped, there is a rapid, two- to threefold increase in plasma insulin, which has an inhibitory effect on hepatic glucose production and may enhance postexercise glucose uptake in muscle. As a result, the transiently elevated blood glucose concentration returns rapidly to normal (Calles et al., 1983; Hermanssen et al., 1970).

In the youth with insulin-dependent diabetes, this highly integrated response to brief, high intensity exercise is abnormal, and sustained hyperglycemia may occur. Mitchell et al. (1988) recently studied the effects of exercise to exhaustion at 80% VO_2max on glucose substrate and hormone responses in type I diabetics treated with continuous subcutaneous insulin infusion (CSII) and in controls. In contrast to the controls, blood glucose rose to much higher levels during postexercise recovery in the diabetic subjects and remained elevated for the entire 2 h postexercise observation period (Figure 14-4). The pattern of postexercise hyperglycemia was influenced by the initial, pre-exercise glucose concentration, being considerably greater when the pre-exercise level was elevated.

The most likely mechanism for the sustained hyperglycemic response to the high intensity, exhausting exercise in this study was the absence of any increase in plasma insulin during postexercise recovery in the diabetic subjects (Berk et al., 1985). In fact, free insulin concentrations in plasma actually declined in those subjects who had pre-exercise hyperglycemia (Figure 14-4, group 2). There were no differences in plasma glucagon, norepinephrine, or epinephrine responses; changes in FFA, while higher in the less well-controlled diabetic subjects, probably do not account for the sustained postexercise hyperglycemia.

Because many sports and recreational activities require relatively short periods of high intensity exercise, the sustained hyperglycemic response to this type of exercise may present a problem

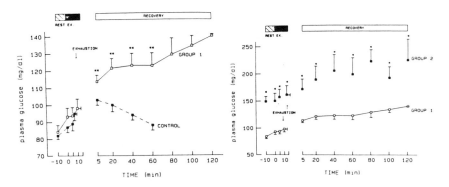

FIGURE 14-4. *Plasma glucose concentrations during intense exercise in control and diabetic subjects. Values are shown for 10-min rest period before exercise, exercise period at 80 VO_2max, and 2 h of recovery. Vertical arrows are mean time of exhaustion. Data are means ± SE for control vs. group 1 diabetic subjects (left panel), and group 1 vs. group 2 diabetic subjects (right panel). *Values significantly different from group 1 and control group (P <0.05). **Group 1 values different from control values (P <0.01). Reproduced from Mitchell et al. (1988) with permission.*

for youths with diabetes. At present, there are no clear-cut guidelines for prevention or management of this response, although it is possible that the administration of small doses of insulin following exercise might shorten the period of hyperglycemia. Careful self-monitoring of blood glucose levels before, during, and after exercise of different intensities and duration may provide the individual patient with useful information that will allow the development of strategies to minimize the risks of either hyperglycemia or hypoglycemia.

D. Exercise-Induced Ketosis

Another problem encountered by insulin treated diabetics occurs when exercise is undertaken in the presence of severe insulin deficiency. In this situation, plasma insulin concentrations are low or absent, and hyperglycemia and ketosis are present. With the onset of exercise, peripheral glucose utilization is impaired, lipolysis is enhanced, and hepatic glucose production and ketogenesis are stimulated. This results in a rapid rise in the already elevated blood glucose concentration and the rapid development of ketosis (Berger et al., 1977) (Figure 14-5). In this situation, the already poor metabolic control rapidly becomes worse, and, instead of lowering blood glucose, the exercise causes a rapid deterioration of the metabolic

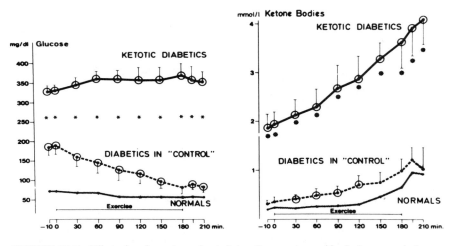

FIGURE 14-5. *Effect of prolonged, moderate intensity exercise on blood glucose and plasma ketone body concentrations in normal controls, diabetic patients in moderate control, and ketotic diabetic patients. Encircled values are significantly different from the control groups at P < 0.005. Stars indicate statistically significant differences between corresponding values of the two groups of diabetic patients at P < 0.05. From Vranic and Berger (1979) with permission.*

state. The mechanism for the rapid development of ketosis is not altogether clear, but recent studies suggest that there is a defect in peripheral clearance of ketones rather than a marked increase in ketogenesis during exercise in insulin-deprived individuals (Fery et al., 1987). To avoid this, youths with insulin-dependent diabetes should check their blood glucose concentration and urine ketones before undertaking vigorous physical activity. If blood glucose is greater than 250 mg/dL and ketones are present in urine or blood, the exercise should be postponed and supplemental insulin taken to reestablish good metabolic control. Likewise, if blood glucose is less than 100 mg/dL and the individual has taken insulin within the past 60–90 min, supplemental feedings should be taken before and during exercise to avoid hypoglycemia.

III. STRATEGIES FOR MANAGEMENT OF EXERCISE IN INSULIN-TREATED DIABETIC PATIENTS

A list of factors to consider before beginning exercise is provided in Table 14-1. Obviously, it is impossible to predict all situations because physical exercise is often spontaneous, intermittent, and varies greatly in intensity and duration from one time to the next. However, a number of strategies that may be useful to avoid either hypoglycemia or hyperglycemia are outlined in Table 14-2. If exercise can be anticipated, ideally it should occur 1–3 h following a meal when the starting blood glucose is above 100 mg/dL. If exercise is prolonged and vigorous, frequent carbohydrate feedings should be taken during exercise, as well as extra food following exercise to avoid postexercise hypoglycemia. If exercise is intermittent, of high intensity, and short duration, hyperglycemia may be a problem, and small supplemental doses of insulin may be needed during postexercise recovery.

There are no precise guidelines regarding how much carbohydrate should be eaten during prolonged exercise to avoid hypoglycemia. However, one can make some estimate of energy requirements based on the intensity and duration of the physical exercise to be performed. For example, if one is planning to go jogging, cycling, backpacking, or swimming, it might be estimated that the activity will require 600 kcal/h or 10 kcal/min. This might represent 50% of the patient's maximum aerobic capacity, an exercise intensity at which about 50% of the energy would be derived from carbohydrate oxidation. Thus, the energy requirement from carbohydrate would be approximately 5 kcal/min, which is equivalent to 1.25 gm glucose/min. A 30-min period of exercise at this intensity would utilize 37.5 gm of carbohydrate, part coming from glycogen break-

TABLE 14-1. *Factors for youths with diabetes to consider before starting exercise*

1. The Exercise Plan
    a. Is the planned exercise habitual or unusual?
    b. What is the anticipated intensity of exercise?
    c. Is the exercise appropriate to the level of physical training?
    d. How long will the exercise last?
    e. Will the exercise be continuous or intermittent?
    f. How many calories will be expended during exercise?

2. The Plan for Meals and Supplemental Feedings
    a. When was the last meal eaten in relation to the start of exercise?
    b. Should a high-carbohydrate snack be eaten before starting exercise?
    c. Should supplemental carbohydrate feedings be taken during exercise?
       If so, how much, and how often?
    d. Will extra food be required after exercise to avoid postexercise hypoglycemia?

3. The Insulin Regimen
    a. What is the usual insulin mixture and dosage? Should it be modified before or after exercise?
    b. What is the interval between the last insulin injection and the start of the exercise?
    c. Should the injection site be changed to avoid muscles that will be exercised?

4. The Pre-Exercise Blood Glucose Concentration
    a. Is the blood glucose concentration in a safe range to exercise (100 to 250 mg/dL)?
    b. If blood glucose is less than 100 mg/dL, a pre-exercise carbohydrate snack should be taken to decrease the risk of exercise-induced hypoglycemia.
    c. If blood glucose is greater than 250 mg/dL, urine ketones should be checked. If they are negative, it is generally safe to exercise. If they are positive, supplemental insulin should be taken, and exercise should be delayed until ketones are negative and blood glucose is less than 250 mg/dL.

down in muscle and part coming from circulating glucose. Since glucose uptake by muscle can range from 0.2 to 0.8 g/min in a 70 kg person during cycling for up to 40 min (Wahren et al., 1971) and up to 1.1 g/min after 3 h of cycling at 70% $\dot{V}O_2$max (Coggan and Coyle, 1987), the precise amount of exogenous carbohydrate needed to maintain a normal blood glucose concentration is difficult to determine. Youths, because of their smaller muscle mass, will generally require less exogenous carbohydrate during exercise than adults. Based on an estimated glucose uptake of 0.5 to 0.8 g/min in the example given, the patient might be instructed to eat a carbohydrate snack containing 15–25 g carbohydrate every 30 min to maintain a normal blood glucose concentration during exercise.

Obviously, this kind of calculation is only approximate, and actual carbohydrate requirements will depend on multiple factors, such as the intensity and duration of exercise, the level of physical conditioning, the antecedent diet, the circulating insulin levels, and the

TABLE 14-2. *Suggested strategies to avoid hypoglycemia or hyperglycemia during and after physical exercise*

1. Adjustments to the Insulin Regimen
   a. Take insulin at least 1 h before exercise. If less than 1 h before exercise, inject insulin in muscle that will not be extensively used during exercise.
   b. Decrease the dose of both short-acting and intermediate-acting insulin before exercise
   c. Alter daily insulin schedule.

2. Meals and Supplemental Feedings
   a. Eat a meal 1–3 h before exercise and check to see that blood glucose is in a safe range (100 to 250 mg/dL) before starting exercise.
   b. Take supplemental carbohydrate feedings during exercise, at least every 30 min if exercise is vigorous and of long duration. Monitor blood glucose during exercise if necessary to determine size and frequency of feedings needed to maintain safe glucose levels.
   c. Increase food intake for up to 24 h after exercise, depending on intensity and duration of exercise, to avoid late-onset post-exercise hypoglycemia.

3. Self-monitoring of blood glucose in urine ketones.
   a. Monitor blood glucose before, during, and after exercise to determine the need for and effect of changes in insulin dosage and feeding schedule.
   b. Delay exercise if blood glucose is <100 mg/dL or >250 mg/dL and if ketones are present in blood. Use supplemental feedings or insulin to correct glucose and metabolic control before starting exercise.
   c. Learn individual glucose responses to different types, intensities, and conditions of exercise. Determine effects of exercise at different times of the day (e.g., morning, afternoon, or evening) and effects of training versus competition on blood glucose responses.

relative need for exogenous carbohydrate to maintain blood glucose concentration in a normal range. For example, lower intensity exercise would decrease the requirements initially, but if exercise is continued for several hours, muscle and liver glycogen levels will become depleted and more exogenous carbohydrate will be required to prevent hypoglycemia. It is often helpful to monitor blood glucose at frequent intervals during exercise of different types and duration to determine individual responses and learn from experience.

If the exercise is planned in advance, the insulin dosage and schedule may be altered to decrease the likelihood of hypoglycemia during or following exercise. Individuals who take a single dose of intermediate acting insulin may decrease the dose by 30–35% on the morning prior to exercise or may change to a split dose regimen, taking two-thirds of the usual dose in the morning and one-third before the evening meal, if supplemental insulin is needed following the exercise. Those who are taking a combination of intermediate- and short-acting insulin may decrease the short-acting insulin by 50% or omit it altogether prior to exercise. They may also decrease the intermediate-acting insulin before exercise and take supplemental doses of short-acting insulin later if needed.

For those on multiple dose therapy with short-acting insulin, the dose before exercise may be decreased by 30–50% and postexercise doses adjusted based on glucose monitoring and experience with postexercise hypoglycemia. If insulin infusion devices are used, the basal infusion rate may be decreased during exercise and premeal boluses decreased or omitted. If this is not done, hypoglycemia may occur during exercise (Schiffrin et al., 1984), although this has not been a universal finding in studies of the effects of moderate intensity exercise on glucose homeostasis in patients treated with continuous subcutaneous insulin infusion (Martin et al., 1982). In practice, the basal insulin infusion rates both during and after exercise and pre-meal insulin boluses can be adjusted on the basis of glucose monitoring and personal experience. In advising a patient regarding these strategies, it is important to stress the individual nature of the problem and the need for careful glucose monitoring and experience. If exercise patterns are relatively consistent with respect to time of day and the intensity and duration of exercise, a routine program can often be developed to avoid either hypoglycemia or hyperglycemia during and following exercise. If exercise is unusual, then frequent glucose monitoring will be helpful to make adjustments in insulin dosage and in the frequency and size of supplemental feedings.

Although youths with diabetes are frequently free of any long-term complications of the disease, a final comment should be made about the necessity for a thorough medical evaluation before undertaking unusual or particularly vigorous exercise programs. Diabetics should be screened carefully for the presence of cardiovascular disease, proliferative retinopathy, nephropathy, and both peripheral and autonomic neuropathy, all of which present increased risks for exercise. Some types of exercise should be avoided if specific risks are present. For example, those with proliferative retinopathy should not do heavy lifting or straining and should avoid low head positions or excessive jarring of the head, all of which may precipitate a vitreous hemorrhage. Those with peripheral neuropathy should be particularly careful to avoid cuts, blisters, and pounding exercises of the legs and feet (e.g., jogging or running sports), and those with autonomic neuropathy should be careful to maintain appropriate fluid and electrolyte balance during prolonged exercise in the heat.

SUMMARY

As more is understood about the physiology of exercise, both in normal subjects and in diabetics, the role of exercise in the treatment of diabetes is becoming better defined. While youths and young adults with diabetes may derive many benefits of regular physical exercise, there are also several hazards that make exercise difficult to manage. In insulin-treated diabetics, there are risks of hypoglycemia during or after exercise or of worsening metabolic control if exercise is of high intensity or if insulin deficiency is present.

A number of strategies can be employed to avoid hypoglycemia in youths with insulin-treated diabetes, and those who want to participate in vigorous exercise should be examined carefully for long-term complications of their disease that may be made worse by exercise.

ACKNOWLEDGEMENTS

The author is grateful for the expert assistance of Linda Del Hagen in the preparation of the manuscript. The work was supported in part by United States Public Health Service grants R01-AM-26317 and RR-109 (General Clinical Research Center).

BIBLIOGRAPHY

1. Ahlborg, G., P. Felig, L. Hagenfeldt, R. Hendler, and J. Wahren. Substrate turnover during prolonged exercise *Journal of Clinical Investigation* 53:1080–1090, 1974.
2. Allen, F.M., E. Stillman, and R. Fitz. Total dietary regulation in the treatment of diabetes. In: *Exercise*, Chapter V. New York: Rockefeller Institute of Medical Research, monograph #11, 1919.
3. Amiel, S.A., R.S. Sherwin, and W.V. Tamborlane. Intensive insulin therapy lowers glucose thresholds for counterregulation: a risk factor for hypoglycemia in diabetes. *Diabetes* 35(1):4A, 1986.
4. Amiel, S.A., W.V. Tamborlane, D.C. Simonson, and R.S. Sherwin. Defective glucose counterregulation after strict control of insulin-dependent diabetes mellitus. *New England Journal of Medicine* 316:1376–1383, 1987.
5. Amiel, S.A., W.V. Tamborlane, L. Sacca, and R.S. Sherwin. Hypoglycemia and glucose counterregulation in normal and insulin-dependent diabetic subjects. *Diabetes/Metabolism Reviews* 4:71–89, 1988.
6. Berger, M., S.A. Hagg, and N.B. Ruderman. Glucose metabolism in perfused skeletal muscle. Interaction of insulin and exercise on glucose uptake. *Biochemical Journal* 146:231–238, 1975.
7. Berger, M., P. Berchtold, H.-J. Cuppers, H. Drost, H.K. Kley, W.A. Muller, W. Wiegelmann, H. Zimmermann-Telschow, F.A. Gries, H.L. Kruskemper, and H. Zimmerman. Metabolic and hormonal effects of muscular exercise in juvenile type diabetics. *Diabetologia* 13:355–365, 1977.
8. Berger, M., P.A. Halban, W.A. Muller, R.E. Offord, A.E. Renold, and M. Vranic. Mobilization of subcutaneously injected tritiated insulin in rats: effects of muscular exercise. *Diabetologia* 15:133–40, 1978.
9. Berger, M., P.A. Halban, J.P. Assal, R.E. Offord, M. Vranic, and A.E. Renold. Pharmacokinetics of subcutaneously injected tritiated insulin: effects of exercise, in M. Vranic, J. Wahren, and S. Horvath, (eds): Proceedings of a Conference on Diabetes and Exercise. *Diabetes* 28 (Suppl 1):53–57, 1979.
10. Berger, M., H.-J. Cuppers, H. Hegner, V. Jorgens, and P. Berchtld. Absorption kinetics and biological effects of subcutaneously injected insulin preparations. *Diabetes Care* 5:77–91, 1982.
11. Bergstrom, J., and E. Hultman. Muscle glycogen synthesis after exercise: An enhancing factor localized to the muscle cells in man. *Nature* 210:309–310, 1966.
12. Bergstrom, J., L. Hermansen, E. Hultman, and B. Saltin. Diet, muscle glycogen and physical performance. *Acta Physiologica Scandinavica* 71:140–150, 1967.
13. Bergstrom, J., E. Hultman, and A.E. Roch-Norlund. Muscle glycogen synthetase in normal subjects: Basal values, effect of glycogen depletion by exercise and of a carbohydrate rich diet following exercise. *Scandinavian Journal of Clinical and Laboratory Investigation* 29:231–236, 1972.

14. Berk, M.A., W.E. Clutter, D.A. Skor, S.D. Shah, R.P. Gingerich, C.A. Parvin, and P.E. Cryer. Enhanced glycemic responsiveness to epinephrine in insulin dependent diabetes mellitus is the result of the inability to secrete insulin. *Journal of Clinical Investigation* 75:1842–1851, 1985.
15. Bjorkman, O., P. Felig, L. Hagenfeldt, and J. Wahren. Influence of hypoglucagonemia on splanchnic glucose output during leg exercise in man. *Clinical Physiology* 1:43–57, 1981.
16. Bjorkman, O. Fuel metabolism during exercise in normal and diabetic man. *Diabetes/Metabolism Reviews* 1:319–357, 1986.
17. Bjorkman, O., and J. Wahren. Glucose homeostasis during and after exercise. In E.S. Horton, and R.L. Terjung, (eds): *Exercise, Nutrition and Energy Metabolism*. New York: Macmillan. 100–115, 1988.
18. Bjorntorp, P., K. de Jounge, L. Sjostrom, and L. Sullivan. The effect of physical training on insulin production in obesity. *Metabolism* 19:631–637, 1970.
19. Bjorntorp, P., M. Fahler, G. Grimby, A. Gustafson, J. Holm, P. Renström, and T. Schersten. Carbohydrate and lipid metabolism in middle aged physically well-trained men. *Metabolism* 21:1037–1042, 1972.
20. Bjorntorp, P., K. de Joung, L. Sjostrom, and L. Sullivan. Physical training in human obesity. II. Effects of plasma insulin in glucose intolerant subjects without marked hyperinsulinemia. *Scandinavian Journal of Clinical and Laboratory Investigation* 32:42–45, 1973.
21. Bogardus, C., P. Thuillez, E. Ravussin, B. Vasquez, M. Narimiga, and S. Azhar. Effect of muscle glycogen depletion on in vivo insulin action in man. *Journal of Clinical Investigation* 72:1605–10, 1983.
22. Calles, J., J.J. Cunningham, L. Nelson, N. Brown, E. Nadel, R.S. Sherwin, and P. Felig. Glucose turnover during recovery from intensive exercise. *Diabetes* 32:734–738, 1983.
23. Campaigne, B.N., H. Wallberg-Henriksson, and R. Gunnarsson. Glucose and insulin responses in relation to insulin dose and caloric intake 12 h after acute physical exercise in men with IDDM. *Diabetes Care* 10:716–721, 1987.
24. Caron, D., P. Poussier, E.B. Marliss, and B. Zinman. The effect of postprandial exercise on meal-related glucose intolerance in insulin-dependent diabetic individuals. *Diabetes Care* 5:364–369, 1982.
25. Caspari, A.F., and L.D. Ewing. Severe hypoglycemia in diabetic patients: frequency, causes, prevention. *Diabetes Care* 8:141–145, 1985.
26. Christensen, E.H., and O. Hansen. Zur methodik der respiratorischen quotient-bestimmungen in ruhe und bei arbeit. II. Untersuchungen ueber die verbrennungsvorgaenge bei langdaurnder, schwerer muskelarbeit: Arbeits faehigkeit und ernahrung. *Skandinavisches Archiv für Physiologie* 81:138–171, 1939.
27. Clutter, W.E., R.A. Rizza, J.E. Gerich, and P.E. Cryer. Regulation of glucose metabolism by sympathochromaffin catecholamines. *Diabetes/Metabolism Reviews* 4(1):1–15, 1988.
28. Coggan, A.R., and E.F. Coyle. Reversal of fatigue during prolonged exercise by carbohydrate infusion or ingestion. *Journal of Applied Physiology* 63:2388–2395, 1987.
29. Costill, D.L., E. Coyle, G. Dalsky, W. Evans, W. Fink, and D. Hoopes. Effects of elevated plasma FFA and insulin on muscle glycogen usage during exercise. *Journal of Applied Physiology* 43:695–699, 1977.
30. Coyle, E.F., J.M. Hagberg, B.F. Hurley, W.H. Mardin, A.A. Ehsani, and J.O. Holloszy. Carbohydrate feeding during prolonged strenuous exercise can delay fatigue. *Journal of Applied Physiology* 55:230–235, 1983.
31. Cryer, P.E., and J.E. Gerich. Glucose counterregulation, hypoglycemia, and intensive therapy of diabetes mellitus. *New England Journal of Medicine* 313:232–241, 1985.
32. The DCCT Research Group. Results of the feasibility phase of the Diabetes Control and Complications Trial (DCCT): glycemic control, follow-up the complications of therapy. *Diabetes* 35(1):3A, 1986.
33. DeFronzo, R.A., R. Andres, T.A. Bledsoe, G. Boden, G.A. Faloona, and J. Tobin. A test of the hypothesis that the rate of glucose fall triggers a counterregulatory hormone response to hypoglycemia. *Diabetes* 26:445–452, 1977.
34. DeFronzo, R.A., E. Ferrannini, and V. Koivisto. New concepts in the pathogenesis and treatment of non-insulin dependent diabetes mellitus. *American Journal of Medicine* 74:52–81, 1983.
35. Devlin, J.T., and E.S. Horton. Effects of prior high-intensity exercise on glucose metabolism in normal and insulin-resistant men. *Diabetes* 34:973–978, 1985.
36. Devlin, J.T., J. Calles-Escandon, and E.S. Horton. Effects of pre-exercise snack feeding on endurance cycle exercise. *Journal of Applied Physiology* 60:980–985, 1986.
37. Fahlen, M., J. Stenberg, and P. Bjorntorp. Insulin secretion in obesity after exercise. *Diabetologia* 8:141–144, 1972.
38. Felig, P., and J. Wahren. Fuel homeostasis in exercise. *New England Journal of Medicine* 293:1078–1084, 1975.

39. Fernqvist, E., B. Linde, J. Ostman, and R. Gunnarsson. Effects of physical exercise on insulin absorption in insulin-dependent diabetics. A comparison between human and porcine insulin. *Clinical Physiology* 6:489–498, 1986.
40. Fery, F., V. de Maertelaer, and E.O. Balasse. Mechanism of the hyperketonaemic effect of prolonged exercise in insulin-deprived type 1 (insulin-dependent) diabetic patients. *Diabetologia* 30:298–304, 1987.
41. Fielding, R.A., D.L. Costill, W.J. Fink, D.S. King, J.E. Kovaleski, and J.P. Kirwan. Effects of pre-exercise carbohydrate feedings on muscle glycogen use during exercise in well-trained runners. *European Journal of Applied Physiology* 55(2):225–229, 1987.
42. Galbo, H., J.J. Holst, and J. Christensen. Glucagon and plasma catecholamine response to graded and prolonged exercise in man. *Journal of Applied Physiology* 38:70–75, 1975.
43. Galbo, H. *Hormonal and Metabolic Adaptation to Exercise.* New York:Thieme-Stratton Inc, 1983.
44. Gerich, J.E., M. Langloise, C. Noacco, J.H. Karam, and P.H. Forsham. Lack of a glucagon response to hypoglycemia in diabetes: evidence for an intrinsic pancreatic alpha-cell defect. *Science* 182:171–173, 1973.
45. Goldstein, D.E., J.D. England, and R. Hess. A prospective study of symptomatic hypoglycemia in young diabetic patients. *Diabetes Care* 4:601–605, 1981.
46. Gray, D., L. Lickley, and M. Vranic. Physiologic effects of epinephrine on glucose turnover and plasma free fatty acid concentrations mediated independently of glucagon. *Diabetes* 29:600–608, 1980.
47. Hartley, L.H., J.W. Mason, R.P. Hogan, L.G. Jones, T.A. Kotchen, E.H. Mougey, L.L. Pennington, and T. Ricketts. Multiple hormonal responses to graded exercise in relation to physical training. *Journal of Applied Physiology* 33:602–606, 1972.
48. Hermansen, L., E.D.R. Pruett, J.B. Osnes, and F.A. Giere. Blood glucose and plasma insulin in response to maximal exercise and glucose infusion. *Journal of Applied Physiology* 29:13–16, 1970.
49. Hilsted, J., H. Galbo, and N.J. Christensen. Impaired cardiovascular responses to graded exercise in diabetic autonomic neuropathy. *Diabetes* 28:313–319, 1979.
50. Hoeldtke, R.D., G. Boden, C.R. Shuman, and O.E. Owen. Reduced epinephrine secretion and hypoglycemia unawareness in diabetic autonomic neuropathy. *Annals of Internal Medicine* 96:459–462, 1982.
51. Horton, E.S. The role of exercise in the treatment of hypertension in obesity. *International Journal of Obesity*, 5 (Suppl. 1):165–171, 1981.
52. Horton, E.S. Role and management of exercise in diabetes mellitus. *Diabetes Care* 11:201–11, 1988.
53. Hultman, E., and J. Bergstrom. Muscle glycogen synthesis in relation to diet studied in normal subjects. *Acta Medica Scandinavica* 182:109–117, 1967.
54. Huttunen, J.K., E. Lansimies, E. Voutilainen, C. Ehnholm, F. Hietanen, I. Panttila, O. Siitonen, and R. Rauramua. Effect of moderate physical exercise on serum lipoprotein. *Circulation* 60:1220–1229, 1979.
55. Ivy, J.L., D.L. Costill, W.J. Fink, and R.W. Lower. Influence of caffeine and carbohydrate feedings on endurance performance. *Medicine and Science in Sports and Exercise* 11:6–11, 1979.
56. Ivy, J.F., W. Miller, V. Power, L.G. Goodyear, W.M. Sherman, S. Farrell, and H. Williams. Endurance improved by ingestion of a glucose polymer supplement. *Medicine and Science in Sports and Exercise* 15(6):466–471, 1983.
57. Joslin, E.P. The treatment of diabetes mellitus. In: *Treatment of Diabetes Mellitus.* E.P. Joslin, H.F. Root, P. White, and A. Marble, (eds.) Philadelphia:Lea and Febiger, 243–300, 1959.
58. Kahn, J.K., B. Zola, J.E. Juni, and A.I. Vinik. Decreased exercise heart rate and blood pressure response in diabetic subjects with cardiac autonomic neuropathy. *Diabetes Care* 9:389–394, 1986.
59. Kawamori, R., and M. Vranic. Mechanism of exercise-induced hypoglycemia in depancreatized dogs maintained on long-acting insulin. *Journal of Clinical Investigation* 59:331–337, 1977.
60. Kemmer, F.W., P. Berchtold, M. Berger, A. Starke, H.-J. Cuppers, F.A. Gries, and H. Zimmermann. Exercise-induced fall of blood glucose in insulin-treated diabetics unrelated to alteration of insulin mobilization. *Diabetes* 28:1131–1137, 1979.
61. Kemmer, F.W., and M. Vranic. The role of glucagon and its relationship to other glucoregulatory hormones in exercise. In: *Glucagon, Physiology, Pathophysiology and Morphology of the Pancreatic A-Cells.* R.H. Unger, and L. Orci, (eds.) New York:Elsevier. 297–331, 1981.
62. Kemmer, F.W., and M. Berger. Exercise and diabetes mellitus: Physical activity as a part of daily life and its role in the treatment of diabetic patients. *International Journal of Sports Medicine* 4:77–88, 1983.

EXERCISE AND DIABETES **567**

63. Koivisto, V., and P. Felig. Effects of leg exercise on insulin absorption in diabetic patients. *New England Journal of Medicine* 298:77–83, 1978.
64. Koivisto, V.A., V. Soman, P. Conrad, R. Hendler, E. Nadel, and P. Felig. Insulin binding to monocytes in trained athletes. *Journal of Clinical Investigation* 64:1011–1015, 1979.
65. Koivisto, V.A., and H. Yki-Jarvinen. Influence of prolonged exercise on insulin binding and glucose transport in adipocytes. *Diabetes* 34 (Suppl 1):26A, 1985.
66. Koivisto, V.A., M. Harkonen, S-L. Karonen, P.H. Groop, R. Elovainio, E. Ferrannini, L. Sacca, and R.A. DeFronzo. Glycogen depletion during prolonged exercise: Influence of glucose, fructose and placebo. *Journal of Applied Physiology* 58:731–737, 1985.
67. LaPorte, R.E., J.S. Dorman, N. Tajima, K.J. Cruickshanks, T.J. Orchard, D.E. Cavender, D.J. Becker, and A.L. Drash. Pittsburgh insulin-dependent diabetes mellitus morbidity and mortality study: Physical activity and diabetic complications. *Pediatrics* 78:1027–1033, 1986.
68. Lauritzen, T., K. Frost-Larsen, H.-W. Larsen, and T. Deckert, Steno Study Group. Effect of 1 year near-normal blood glucose levels on retinopathy in insulin-dependent diabetics. *Lancet* 1:200–204, 1983.
69. Lawrence, R.D. The effects of exercise on insulin action in diabetes. *British Medical Journal* 1:648–52, 1926.
70. Levine, L., W.J. Evans, B.S. Cadarette, E.C. Fisher, and B.A. Bullen. Fructose and glucose ingestion and muscle glycogen use during submaximal exercise. *Journal of Applied Physiology: Respiratory, Environmental, and Exercise Physiology* 55(6):1767–1771, 1983.
71. Lipman, R.L., P. Raskin, T. Love, J. Triebwasser, F.R. LeCocq, and J.J. Schnure. Glucose intolerance during decreased physical activity in man. *Diabetes* 21:101–107, 1972.
72. Lipson, L.C., R.W. Bonow, E.J. Schaefer, H. Brewer, and F.T. Lindgren. Effect of exercise conditioning on plasma high density lipoprotein and other lipoproteins. *Atherosclerosis* 37:529–538, 1980.
73. Lohmann, D., F. Liebold, W. Heilmann, H. Senger, and A. Pohl. Diminished insulin response in highly trained athletes. *Metabolism* 27:521–542, 1978.
74. MacDonald, M.J. Postexercise late-onset hypoglycemia in insulin-dependent diabetic patients. *Diabetes Care* 10:584–588, 1978.
75. Maehlum, S., A.T. Horstmark, and L. Hermansen. Synthesis of muscle glycogen during recovery after prolonged severe exercise in diabetic and non-diabetic subjects. *Scandinavian Journal of Clinical and Laboratory Investigation* 37:309–316, 1977.
76. Maehlum, S., P. Felig, and J. Wahren. Splanchnic glucose and muscle glycogen metabolism after glucose feeding during post-exercise recovery. *American Journal of Physiology* 235:E255–E260, 1978.
77. Maehlum, S., and L. Hermansen. Muscle glycogen concentrations during recovery after prolonged severe exercise in fasting subjects. *Scandinavian Journal of Clinical and Laboratory Investigation* 38:557–560, 1978.
78. Mandroukas, K., M. Krotkiewski, G. Holm, G. Stromblad, G. Grimby, H. Lithell, Z. Wroblewski, and P. Bjorntrop. Muscle adaptations and glucose control after physical training in insulin-dependent diabetes mellitus. *Clinical Physiology* 6:39–52, 1986.
79. Margonato, A., P. Gerundini, G. Vicedomini, M.C. Gilardi, G. Pozza, and F. Fazio. Abnormal cardiovascular response to exercise in young asymptomatic diabetic patients with retinopathy. *American Heart Journal* 112:554, 1986.
80. Martin, M.J., D.C. Robbins, R. Bergenstal, B. LaGrange, and A.H. Rubenstein. Absence of exercise-induced hypoglycaemia in type I (insulin-dependent) diabetic patients during maintenance of normoglycaemia by short-term, open-loop insulin infusion. *Diabetologia* 23:337–342, 1982.
81. Meinders, A.E., F.L.A. Willekens, and L.P. Heere. Metabolic and hormonal changes in IDDM during long-distance run. *Diabetes Care* 11:1–7, 1988.
82. Mitchell, T.H., G. Abraham, A. Schiffrin, L.A. Leiter, and E.B. Marliss. Hyperglycemia after intense exercise in IDDM subjects during continuous subcutaneous insulin infusion. *Diabetes Care* 11:311–317, 1988.
83. Mogensen, C.E., and E. Vittinghus. Urinary albumin excretion during exercise in juvenile diabetes. *Scandinavian Journal of Clinical and Laboratory Investigation* 35:295–300, 1975.
84. Nelson, J.D., P. Poussier, E.B. Marliss, A.M. Albisser, and B. Zinman. Metabolic response of normal man and insulin-infused diabetics to postprandial exercise. *American Journal of Physiology* 242:E309–E316, 1982.
85. Pruett, E.D.S., and S. Oseid. Effect of exercise on glucose and insulin response to glucose infusion. *Scandinavian Journal of Clinical and Laboratory Investigation* 26:277–285, 1970.
86. Richter, E.A., T. Ploug and H. Galbo. Increased muscle glucose uptake following exercise: No need for insulin during exercise. *Diabetes* 34:1041–1048, 1985.
87. Rizza, R., M. Haymond, P. Cryer, and J. Gerich. Differential effects of epinephrine on glucose production and disposal in man. *American Journal of Physiology* 237:E356–E362, 1979.

88. Rizza, R.A., P.E. Cryer, and J.E. Gerich. Role of glucagon, catecholamines and growth hormone in human glucose counterregulation. Effects of somatostatin and combined alpha- and beta-blockade on plasma glucose recovery and glucose flux rates after insulin-induced hypoglycemia. *Journal of Clinical Investigation* 64:62–71, 1979.

89. Rosenthal, M., W.L. Haskell, R. Solomon, A. Widstrom, and G.M. Reaven. Demonstration of a relationship between level of physical training and insulin stimulated glucose utilization in normal humans. *Diabetes* 32:408–411, 1983.

90. Rubler, S. Asymptomatic diabetic females—exercise testing. *New York State Journal of Medicine* 81:1185–1191, 1981.

91. Ruderman, N.B., O.P. Ganda, and K. Johansen. Effects of physical training on glucose tolerance and plasma lipids in maturity onset diabetes mellitus. *Diabetes* 28(Suppl. 1):89–92, 1979.

92. Sato, Y., A. Iguchi, and N. Sakamoto. Biochemical determination of training effects using insulin clamp technique. *Hormone and Metabolic Research* 16:483–486, 1984.

93. Schiffrin, A., S. Parikh, E.B. Marliss, and M.M. Desrosier. Metabolic response to fasting exercise in adolescent insulin-dependent diabetic subjects treated with continuous subcutaneous insulin infusion and intensive conventional therapy. *Diabetes Care* 7:255–260, 1984.

94. Sherman, W.M., D.L. Costill, W.J. Fink, and J.M. Miller. Effect of exercise-diet manipulation on muscle glycogen and its subsequent utilization during performance. *International Journal of Sports Medicine* 2(2):114–118, 1981.

95. Simonson, D.C., W.V. Tamborlane, R.A. DeFronzo, and R.S. Sherwin. Intensive insulin therapy reduces the counterregulatory hormone responses to hypoglycemia in patients with Type I diabetes. *Annals of Internal Medicine* 103:184–190, 1985.

96. Soman, V.J., V.A. Koivisto, D. Deibert, P. Felig, and R.A. DeFronzo. Increased insulin sensitivity and insulin binding to monocytes after physical training. *New England Journal of Medicine* 301:1200–1204, 1979.

97. Storstein, L., and J. Jervell. Response to bicycle exercise testing of long standing juvenile diabetics. *Acta Medica Scandinavica* 205:227–230, 1979.

98. Stratton, R., D.P. Wilson, R.K. Endres, and D.E Goldstein. Improved glycemic control after supervised eight-week exercise program in insulin-dependent diabetic adolescents. *Diabetes Care* 10:589–593, 1987.

99. Sushruta, S.C.S. *Vaidya Jadavaji Trikamji Acharia.* Bombay, Nirnyar Sagar Press. The original book was published in 500 B.C, 1938.

100. Susstrunk, H., B. Morell, W.H. Ziegler, and E.R. Froesch. Insulin absorption from the abdomen and the thigh in healthy subjects during rest and exercise: blood glucose, plasma insulin, growth hormone, adrenaline and noradrenaline levels. *Diabetologia* 22:171–174, 1982.

101. Sutton, J.R., and P.A. Farrell. Endocrine responses to prolonged exercise. In: D.R. Lamb and R. Murray (eds.). *Perspectives in Exercise Science and Sports Medicine, Vol. 1, Prolonged Exercise.* Indianapolis: Benchmark Press. 153–212, 1988.

102. Tchobroutsky, G., C. Goldgewicht, L. Papoz, T.P. Weissbrod, A. Basdevant, and E. Eschwege. Hypoglycemic reactions in 319 insulin-treated diabetics. *Diabetologia* 2:335, 1981.

103. Trovati, M., Q. Carta, F. Cavalot, S. Vitali, C. Banaudi, P.G. Lucchina, F. Fiocchi, G. Emanuelli, and G. Lenti. Influence of physical training on blood glucose control, glucose tolerance, insulin secretion, and insulin action in non-insulin-dependent diabetic patients. *Diabetes Care* 7:416–420, 1984.

104. Unger, R.H., E. Aquilar Parada, W.A. Muller, and A.M. Eisentraut. Studies of pancreatic alpha cell function in normal and diabetic subjects. *Journal of Clinical Investigation* 49:837–848, 1970.

105. Viberti, G.C., R.J. Jarrett, M. McCartney, and H. Keen. Increased glomerular permeability to albumin induced by exercise in diabetic subjects. *Diabetologia* 14:293–300, 1978.

106. Vitug, A., S.H. Schneider, and N.B. Ruderman. Exercise and type I diabetes mellitus. *Exercise and Sports Sciences Reviews* 16:285–304, 1988.

107. Vranic, M., S. Kawamori, S. Pek, N. Kovacevic, and G.A. Wrenshall. The essentiality of insulin and the role of glucagon in regulating glucose utilization and production during strenuous exercise in dogs. *Journal of Clinical Investigation* 57:245–255, 1976.

108. Vranic, M., and M. Berger. Exercise and diabetes mellitus. *Diabetes* 28:147–163, 1979.

109. Vranic, M., F.W. Kemmer, P. Berchtold, and M. Berger. Hormonal interaction in control of metabolism during exercise in physiology and diabetes. In: *Diabetes Mellitus: Theory and Practice.* 2nd ed. M. Ellenberg, and H. Rifkin, eds. New York:Medical Examination Publishing Corporation. 567–590, 1982.

110. Wahren, J., P. Felig, G. Ahlborg, and L. Jorfeldt. Glucose metabolism during leg exercise in man. *Journal of Clinical Investigation* 50:2715–2725, 1971.

111. Wallberg-Henriksson, H., R. Gunnarson, J. Henriksson, R. DeFronzo, P. Felig, J. Ostman,

and J. Wahren. Increased peripheral insulin sensitivity and muscle oxidative enzymes but unchanged blood glucose control in type-I-diabetics after physical training. *Diabetes* 31:1044–1050, 1982.

112. Wallberg-Henriksson, H., R. Gunnarsson, S. Rossner, and J. Wahren. Long-term physical training in female type I (insulin-dependent) diabetic patients: Absence of significant effect on glycaemic control and lipoprotein levels. *Diabetologia* 29:53–57, 1986.

113. Wardzala, L.J., E.D. Horton, M. Crettaz, B. Jeanrenaud, and E.S. Horton. Physical training of lean and genetically obese Zucker rats: effect on fat cell metabolism. *American Journal of Physiology* 243:E418–426, 1982.

114. Wasserman, D.H., H.L.A. Lickley, and M. Vranic. Interactions between glucagon and other counterregulatory hormones during normoglycemic and hypoglycemic exercise in dogs. *Journal of Clinical Investigation* 74:1404–1413, 1984.

115. White, N.H., D. Skor, P.E. Cryer, D.M. Bier, L. Levandoski, and J.V. Santiago. Identification of type I diabetic patients at increased risk for hypoglycemia during intensive therapy. *New England Journal of Medicine* 308:485–491, 1983.

116. Wise, J.K., R. Hendler, and P. Felig. Evaluation of alpha-cell function by infusion of alanine in normal, diabetic and obese subjects. *New England Journal of Medicine* 288:487–490, 1973.

117. Wood, P.D., W. Haskell, H. Klein, S. Lewis, M.P. Stern, and J.W. Farquhar. Distribution of plasma lipoproteins in middle aged male runners. *Metabolism* 25:1249–1257, 1976.

118. Wood, P.D., and W.L. Haskell. Effect of exercise on plasma high density lipoproteins. *Lipids* 14:417–427, 1979.

119. Yki-Jarvinen, H., and V.A. Koivisto. Effects of body composition on insulin sensitivity. *Diabetes* 32:965–969, 1983.

120. Zinman, B., F.T. Murray, M. Vranic, A.M. Albisser, B.S. Leibel, P.A. McClean, and E.B. Marliss. Glucoregulation during moderate exercise in insulin treated diabetics. *Journal of Clinical Endocrinology and Metabolism* 45:641–652, 1977.

121. Zinman, B., S. Zuniga-Guajardo, and D. Kelly. Comparison of the acute and long-term effects of exercise on glucose control in type I diabetes. *Diabetes Care* 7:515–519, 1984.

122. Zinman, B., and M. Vranic. Diabetes and exercise. *Medical Clinics of North America* 69:145–157, 1985.

DISCUSSION

BAR-OR: I have a comment regarding the dosing of the nutritional supplement for diabetics before exercise. You don't mention anything about consideration of the size of the individual, i.e., the body weight of the individual. This has been also an omission made by most diabetologists in their recommendations. They assume a standard caloric equivalence of exercise, but this obviously would be different for a 30 kg child than for a 70 kg individual. The food requirements should be completely different for these two individuals. We have attempted to define something which we call "exercise exchanges" in analogy to food exchanges or carbohydrate exchanges. One exercise exchange is equivalent to 15 g of carbohydrate, and, assuming that approximately 60% of energy expenditure would be from carbohydrates, one exercise exchange is equivalent to 100 kcal of exercise. Correction for body size of the individual should be made when one calculates the calorie requirements.

We see young diabetic patients who are sent to us basically for control of their obesity. Can you give us some sort of natural approach to help such children who may have a balanced glucohomeostasis before they come to us, but when we start fiddling with their food intake and exercise dosage, we may be throwing them off balance?

Also, there have been several publications that claim that an exercise provocation can induce proteinuria in diabetics who do not yet have nephropathy. It was even suggested that this exercise-induced proteinuria can be a predictor of future diabetic nephropathy. I would like to hear your opinion about that.

Finally, is the hypoglycemic response to exercise something typical for a given patient? In other words, in some patients we see a precipitous drop in blood glucose with exercise, but in others the drop is quite a bit slower. Can I assume that if I test the same patients who have taken the same dosage of insulin and eaten the same food with the same time interval, I should expect that this patient will respond several times in the same way? This is, I think, important as far as management is concerned.

HORTON: I must say that I put in a specific recommendation for feeding prior to exercise somewhat under duress, because I think it's very difficult to give specific advice to diabetics about this kind of formula. I really like your idea of coming up with an exercise exchange. The problem I have with constructing a table of exercise exchanges, however, is that people look at numbers and tables and believe that it's gospel. I don't beieve these are gospel numbers. If they are guidelines, they may be helpful. What I have neglected to do in my calculations is to take into consideration the fact that we should not be trying to provide the total carbohydrate need for exercise by exogenous glucose feeding. We should allow for a certain amount of energy to be coming from continued muscle glycogen breakdown. Obviously, the requirements for exogenous glucose are going to be different early in exercise, when there are adequate muscle glycogen stores, than late in prolonged exercise, when muscle glycogen becomes depleted and one is progressively more dependent on exogenous glucose. Thus, not only do we have to take into consideration the age and size of the individual and the intensity of the exercise, but also the duration of exercise and the preceding muscle glycogen stores. There are so many factors that go into this equation, that I get really nervous about putting them down in a table.

Regarding the reproducibility of individual glucose responses to exercise, I really wish I knew the answer to that question. There are no good scientific data on that point that I have been able to find. I don't know anybody who has put a patient through a series of different types of exercise conditions and then repeated it to see whether or not the same glucose response occurs on a different day. I suspect there is going to be a fair amount of variation, because it depends a little bit on where the patient starts. Not everybody starts their exercise under the same baseline conditions. If the patient begins with a low glucose level, he may have a different set of problems than if he starts with high glucose. So it's not just the exercise itself that will determine the response; pre-exercise condition is also critical. I suspect that it's going to be somewhat difficult to determine how reproducible the glucose response to exercise really is.

The practical problems are that people don't do the same exercise from day to day. The timing of the exercise is different, and one has to try to develop strategies for different conditions. As an example, one of my patients is a high school basketball player. His problem is that all of his practices are in the late afternoon after school, but all of his games are in the evening. And he has to develop a totally different eating strategy for a game day versus a practice day. I keep coming back to the principle that the best way to work with our young diabetics is to educate them about the physiology of diabetes and let them come up with the answers. I have learned a tremendous amount from people like Bill Carlson, who is the first Type 1 diabetic to ever do the Hawaiian Ironman; a fellow named Charlie Clark, who is also a triathlete and marathon runner; and people working in other sports who gave us the tricks of the trade. For example, I have told all of my diabetics that the one thing I absolutely do not want them to do is to become scuba divers. But several people at a recent meeting of diabetic athletes said they scuba dive all the time. They know how to take glucose when they are 30 feet under the water. So I think we have a lot of practical tricks to learn.

Your final question had to do with proteinuria. That's a confusing area to me. Not being in pediatrics, I haven't followed it terribly closely, but my understanding from talking to people who work in the area is that it has not proven to be a reliable predictive test for preclinical nephropathy.

SUTTON: Because we are directing our attention to the youth, we almost need to solely concern ourselves with the Type 1 diabetic. Are there any subtle differences apart from the learning experience of the very young, that we need to remember when we are looking at the very young diabetic child? And secondly, since you brought up the point about scuba diving, why was it that you were rather fearful of scuba diving by Type 1 diabetics, apart from the obvious hypoglycemia?

HORTON: The concern that most people have about scuba diving is that since a diabetic is prone to developing hypoglycemia reactions with exercise, it's not a particularly healthy situation to be far under water and have a hypoglycemia reaction. People who are into the sport use the buddy system; they are aware of the signs and symptoms to look for, and they have found that it's possible to take oral glucose underwater. With glucose packets one can just pop the mask off, suck up the glucose, and put the mask back on. It may be that with appropriate training and tricks of the trade, it's not so dangerous.

There are very few Type 2 diabetics in the childhood age range. There is a syndrome called maturity onset diabetes of the young, which is an autosomal dominate genetic trait, but that's quite rare. The main problem that should be considered for diabetics below 10 years of age is that they are often not the ones who are in control of their own environments. Their mother is feeding them; they may or may not administer their own insulin; they probably don't understand glucose counterregulatory hormone responses very well, and, probably more importantly, their exercise is much more erratic and spontaneous. The spontaneity is wonderful, but it can raise havoc. In talking with the parents of kids in that age range, another major problem is educating the teachers in school and the other people around who are scared to death of diabetes and who don't want the kids to do anything.

MORGAN: Robin Ewart, in the 1980 proceedings of the Undersea Medical Society Workshop, suggested that some diabetics may not recognize slowly developing symptoms of oncoming hypoglycemia while scuba diving. Therefore, diabetics must be extremely cautious in undertaking such activities.

HORTON: I agree. I don't mean to suggest that there is no need for concern when a diabetic undertakes a scuba diving venture.

BALDWIN: My question addresses the training response of the Type 1 diabetic. Is there an improvement in the course of the disease in a chronically trained youngster compared to the untrained. Does any such effect carry over into adulthood?

HORTON: There are only a few studies on the trainability of people with Type 1 diabetes. The data indicate that a Type 1 diabetic can essentially get the same training response as a nondiabetic individual, with one possible exception; in recent reports, there has been a failure to observe an increased capillary density in muscle as a response to training. The cardiovascular system, unless there is autonomic neuropathy, seems to respond in the normal way. The peripheral muscular adaptations are normal, with that possible exception of the capillarity of muscle.

There are very few studies on the carryover effect of training in diabetics. Ron Laporte has recently published a paper suggesting that certainly exercise in the pediatric age group is not deleterious, i.e., exercise does not increase either mortality or morbidity complications later on and is probably beneficial.

BLAIR: We have preliminary data from older subjects in our population who have a history of diabetes that, of course, have a much higher all-cause mortality rate compared to the apparently healthy population. But within the diabetic subgroup, when we stratify the men by degree of fitness, the high-fit individuals have a much lower death rate than the low-fit individuals.

HORTON: Steve, that's really good news to hear, and I think those will be very important data. Most of the studies that have looked at beneficial effects of regular exercise in the Type 1 diabetic population have really focused on improvement in glucose control. The results are quite mixed. There are studies that fail to show improvement in glucose regulation over the long haul. An early study in this regard by the group in Toronto showed that there was no improvement in long-term blood glucose regulation with a training program. They felt that there was a compensatory increase in food intake that counterbalanced the increased energy requirements. A study from the group in Stockholm also failed to show improvement in glucose control on the long-term basis. Furthermore, they have a study failing to show improvement in lipid profiles.

COYLE: One hypothesis is that in normal subjects the increase in capillary density within the exercise-trained musculature aids in glucose uptake. If diabetics don't increase capillary density in their muscles with training, do you think that might suggest that the exercise-trained diabetic may not be as capable of increasing muscle glucose uptake as a normal individual?

HOLLOSZY: I just want to emphasize that we cannot extrapolate health benefits of exercise in Type 2 diabetics to Type 1 diabetics. Exercise has a very powerful, beneficial effect on a number of risk factors in Type 2 diabetes, including high glucose levels, high insulin levels, high lipid levels, etc., most of which are not relevant to juvenile, Type I diabetes.

In relation to the question Ed asked about the role of capillarization in maximum glucose uptake, we've done euglycemic clamp studies on very highly trained athletes, who have a large increase in muscle capillary density, and in sedentary individuals. There is a large difference in insulin sensitivity, with the trained people having a greater insulin sensitivity, but no difference in responsiveness to insulin, which reflects the maximal capacity to take up glucose in the resting state. So at least under those conditions, the capillaries are not limiting in terms of maximal glucose intake.

Epilogue

Everest

J. R. SUTTON, PH.D.

INTRODUCTION

Everest is more than a mere mountain, more than the highest mountain in the world (Fig. 1). In fact, the term "Everest" is ingrained in our language in such a way that we use it very much as a descriptive term to imply the ultimate achievement, the highest goal attainable. This is fitting because George Everest (Fig. 2), superintendent of the Great Trigonometrical Survey of India from 1823 to 1843 and Surveyor General of India from 1830 to 1843, was a perfectionist. He arrived in India as an artillery cadet in 1806 and held various government positions, but his grand conception was the "gridiron system of triangulation" for the entire Indian subcontinent. His contributions to the survey of India were such that he was responsible for measuring the great meridial arc passing from the southern tip of India through the center of the subcontinent to the Himalayas. In surveying terms, his contribution was the basis on which all official heights of the Himalayan Mountains were measured, the so-called "Everest spheroid." It is said that no man before or since has made a more important contribution to the geography of Asia. Upon his retirement, it was remarked that his contribution was "one of the most stupendous works in the whole history of science. No scientific man ever had a grander monument to his name than the great meridial arc of India." Although this is not widely appreciated outside geographic circles, it is clear that his contribution was immense. (Mason, 1955).

Although it is known as Choma Lungma in Tibet and Sagarmatha in Nepal, the word "Everest" was not applied to the mountain that bears that name until 1865. It was proposed by Andrew Waugh, the Surveyor General of India at that time. The popular

FIGURE 1. *Painting of Everest from the north, from the 1922 expedition.*

legend as to how this mountain was found to be the highest in the world is as follows.

In Calcutta, the Bengali chief computer Radhanath Sikhdar rushed into Waugh's office exclaiming breathlessly, "Sir, I have discovered the highest mountain in the world!" That was in 1852, several years after the actual field survey work had been performed. Although rather romantic, this account has been disputed (Mason, 1955).

The Himalayan range and that part of central Asia was a hotly disputed territory between the empires of Britain and Russia; a "great game" was being played out between these two powers for influence in this region bordering Afghanistan–what is now northern Pakistan, India, Chinese Turkestan, Nepal, Sikkim, Bhutan, and Tibet. Nepal and Tibet were "off limits" to European travelers, yet there was great desire to know the location of these fabled places of Lhasa, Gilgit, and Yarkand. It fell to Captain T. G. Montgomerie, of the Great Trigonometrical Survey, to train Indian explorers to carry out these surveys in disguise. So a new era of the pundit explorers evolved, the first of whom were Nain Singh and his cousin Mani Singh from northern India. They were given two years' training in Dehra Dun, where they were taught simple astronomy, the use of the compass and sextant, and the measurement of altitude by the boiling water method. They were also taught to count and record their paces exactly, using a modified Tibetan rosary that had 100

FIGURE 2. *Sir George Everest.*

beads rather than the traditional 108. At every hundredth pace, a bead was slipped. Each complete circuit of the rosary, therefore, was 10,000 paces, or precisely five miles in the case of Nain Singh. Prayer wheels were also modified for Montgomerie's surveying purposes to conceal compasses, and scrolls were painted detailing the route, rate, and so forth. After being turned back initially, Nain Singh crossed the Himalayan range into Tibet and joined a caravan going to Lhasa. He reached Lhasa on the 10th of January, 1866, and lived there for three months. From his trip, he brought back enough details for a map of the southern trade route of Tibet and the course of the Tsangpo River for nearly 600 miles (Mason, 1955).

The first of the pundits to circuit Everest was Hari Ram, who, in 1871, set out from Darjeeling. Part of his mission was to determine local names for mountains, which he did for many, but he was unable to find one for Everest itself. He crossed the main Himalayan range into Tibet and returned through the Himalayas to Katmandu.

There are many other legendary explorers, including a group of Punjabis from Peshawar; however, it is the story of Kinthup, who was sent to Tibet by Captain H. J. Harman to establish the route of the Tsangpo River and where it flowed into the Brahmaputra, which is most remarkable. Harman's idea was that Kinthup would reach the banks of the Tsangpo, cut up logs, release 50 each day for 10 consecutive days, and Captain Harman would have observers downstream on the Brahmaputra to await the arrival of the logs. Kinthup managed to send a message to Captain Harman and, at the agreed time, began releasing 50 logs each day. Unfortunately, his message never got through. The 500 specially marked logs had floated unobserved down the Tsangpo into the Brahmaputra and into the Bay of Bengal. On return to Darjeeling, Kinthup's travel accounts were not believed, and he sank into obscurity, his incredible privation unappreciated. In fact, it was 30 years before Col. Eric Bailey, traveling in the same area as Kinthup, recognized exactly how accurate the early observations were. Bailey found Kinthup working as a tailor in Darjeeling and, after much lobbying, had the British Raj recognize his contribution (Mason, 1955).

ATTEMPTS TO CLIMB EVEREST

Nepal was closed to British travelers from 1885 onward, as was Tibet. It was not until the Younghusband Expedition reached Lhasa and signed a treaty in September 1904 that an uneasy truce was made that set the scene for the prewar British expeditions to Everest.

The first documented discussions of an expedition to Everest were between Carl Bruce and Francis Younghusband in 1893. In 1907, Alfred Mumm, Bruce and Tom Longstaff planned an expedition that never eventuated. In 1913, Captain John Noel visited the area, but it wasn't until 1921 that a reconnaissance party was sent out to prepare the way for the first formal assault on the mountain in 1922. On the reconnaissance mission, Alexander M. Kellas, the expedition's physician, died of "heart failure." On the 1922 expedition, seven Sherpas were swept into a crevasse and killed; this tragedy ended the first assault venture. The 1924 expedition, on which George Leigh Mallory and Andrew Irving disappeared, was probably the most notable of all the prewar attempts. Mallory had been on the 1921 reconnaissance and the 1922 expeditions. He and Irving were last seen about 250 m from the summit, going strongly, on June 8, 1924. To this very day, debate has raged as to whether or not they reached the summit (Fig. 3). Mallory's response, "Because it is there," to the question of why one would want to climb Everest is Mallory's memorial.

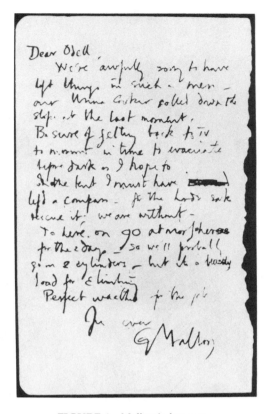

FIGURE 3. *Mallory's last note.*

Several more expeditions were mounted before the outbreak of World War II; the last was led by Bill Tillman in 1938. The possibility of climbing Everest via the southern route was first appreciated by Oscar Houston's party in 1950. Houston's son, Charles, with Tillman, recognized that a route could be forced through the icefall to the Western Cwm. This was followed by Eric Shipton's reconnaissance in 1951, which determined the final route to be chosen. In 1952, the Swiss made two attempts on Everest. In the meantime, Shipton organized an expedition to Cho Oyo in Nepal to select mountaineers, test the oxygen equipment, and perform some basic physiological studies. This was a blessing in disguise, for the work of physiologist Griffith Pugh determined several crucial facts (Fig. 4). The first was that oxygen equipment could be used successfully. The second was that malnutrition and dehydration were perhaps equally as important as the lack of oxygen to the success or failure

FIGURE 4. *Physiologist Griffith Pugh testing oxygen equipment.*

of an assault attempt at extreme altitude. By making these measurements in the field, Pugh was able to suggest a variety of solutions. In particular, he determined that the main reason for dehydration of mountaineers was the inefficient stoves and insufficient fuel necessary to melt the considerable volumes of snow required to provide drinking fluids at high altitudes. This was an important prelude to what became the successful climb (Pugh, 1952; 1953). On May 27th, 1953, Charles Evans and Tom Bourdillon reached the south summit at 8,750 m (28,700 ft); difficulty with Evans' oxygen apparatus had delayed their start, with the result that they had insufficient time and oxygen to complete their climb. It remained for Edmund Hillary and Tenzing Norgay to cap the expedition's work. They reached the south summit at 9 a.m. on May 29th and examined the last difficult ridge, which was heavily corniced. Their next hurdle was the great rocky step, about 12 m in height, which has

FIGURE 5. *Edmund Hillary and Sherpa Sutton.*

been christened "The Hillary Step." From there on, progress was extremely slow—about one foot per minute—but at 11:30, they were on the roof of the world. This settled for all time the question of whether the highest summit could be achieved (Hunt, 1953) (Fig. 5).

Over the next 25 years, the physiologists' debate changed to whether the summit of Everest could be gained without the use of supplementary oxygen. On the notable Silver Hut Expedition to answer some of these questions, Griffith Pugh obtained data which, when extrapolated, suggested a very low maximal oxygen uptake on the summit of Everest by climbers breathing only ambient air. It was suggested that the maximal oxygen uptake would be of the order of 3–4 ml/kg body weight/min. Clearly, this would be sufficient to sustain life but little else, certainly not enough to permit climbing (Pugh, 1962).

A number of expeditions into the Himalayas, the Alps, the Andes, and to Mount Logan in Canada's Yukon studied exercise performance at extreme altitude; various predictions were made. However, it wasn't until the 1978 expedition to Everest that the most important experiment in this regard was conducted (Fig. 6). On May 8, 1978, Peter Habeler and Reinhold Messner became the first to reach the summit of Everest without the use of supplementary oxygen (Hobeler, 1979; Messner, 1979). An even more remarkable climb

FIGURE 6. *Members of the 1978 Austrian Expedition. Peter Habeler and Reinhold Messner (bottom left) were the first to climb Everest without the use of supplementary oxygen.*

occurred two years later when Reinhold Messner, climbing alone and again without the use of supplementary oxygen, reached the summit from the north. Although Everest has since been climbed many times without the use of supplementary oxygen, there is no doubt that it is just on the very limit of human capabilities (Fig. 7).

What other physiological prerequisites of elite climbers enable them to reach the summit of Everest without using supplementary oxygen? One of those considered to be most important is possession of a high maximal oxygen uptake that, while reduced with progressive gains in altitude, would still remain above that of the average person. However, direct measurements of Messner and Habeler have not shown extraordinarily high maximal oxygen uptakes, but rather the ability to perform well in spite of modest maximal oxygen uptakes. Clearly, other factors such as climbing and technical skills, strength, a high power/weight ratio, perhaps a low ventilatory response to hypoxia, increased cerebral tolerance of hypoxia, and extreme motivation all figure as important characteristics. It would be foolish to assume that just because those variables currently measured do not appear to be unusual, these clearly highly successful climbers are not remarkable individuals (Sutton et al., 1988).

FIGURE 7. *The last note of Peter Boardman and Joe Tasker, who disappeared in 1982 in a similar position to that at which Mallory and Irvine were last seen in 1924.*

Further attempts to gain insight into extreme high altitude physiology were the advances made by the American Medical Research Expedition to Everest (AMREE) expedition of 1981 in which, for the very first time, barometric pressure was recorded on the summit of Mount Everest. In itself, this was a noteworthy achievement, and Chris Pizzo was able to collect expired gas samples for the measurement of alveolar gas composition (West et al., 1983).

OPERATION EVEREST II

A final chapter in the Everest story is the Operation Everest II saga in which a group of eight subjects were gradually decompressed in a chamber, finally reaching the equivalent of the summit of Mount Everest with indwelling arterial lines and Swan-Ganz catheters which permitted direct measurement of arterial and mixed venous blood gases and cardiac output. Initially conceived by Charles Houston and John Sutton, Operation Everest II was modeled after a similar "expedition," Operation Everest, conducted in 1946 by Charles Houston and Richard Riley. In the intervening years, technology had become much more sophisticated, yet it was quite clear that, despite these advances, it would still be some time, if ever, that a climber could reach the summit of Mount Everest and be able to have arterial or mixed venous blood sampled. With this in mind, Houston and Sutton gained a third investigator, Dr. John Maher of the U.S. Army Research Institute of Environmental Medicine (USARIEM) in Natick, Massachusetts, to plan a unique study (Sutton, Maher et al., 1983). Dr. Maher's untimely death in 1983 left us without a hypobaric expert until Dr. Allen Cymerman, Dr. Maher's replacement at USARIEM, soon stepped into the breach.

In the autumn of 1985, this most recent chapter unfolded. Finally, six subjects reached the equivalent of the summit of Mount Everest (Houston et al., 1987). The "mountain" had taken its toll of two, one retiring from the fray at 5,486 m and the other at 7,620 m, but for the first time, we had direct measurements of arterial blood gases on the "summit" as well as direct measurements of maximal oxygen uptake. The following were the results: The partial pressures of oxygen and carbon dioxide in arterial blood were 30 Torr and 11 Torr, respectively, and maximal oxygen uptake was 15 milliliters per kilogram of body weight per minute (Table 1) (Sutton, Pugh et al., 1983).

Operation Everest II also gave us the opportunity to look in more depth at the mechanisms whereby a successful climb of Everest was possible physiologically. While a number of adaptations occurred at the cellular level, in the gross picture of oxygen transport, it was clear that the major mechanisms enabling a maximal oxygen uptake of 15 ml/kg/min to be achieved were the marked increase in ventilation (fourfold increase in alveolar ventilation); the increase of hemoglobin by one-third, thus increasing the oxygen-carrying capacity of the blood, and finally, the maximal extraction of oxygen, giving a mixed venous PO_2 of approximately 10 Torr.

Thus, we have looked at the entire Everest saga, from the history of the man who lent his name to the highest peak on Earth to the story of successive attempts to reach the summit, and finally, a physiological understanding of these achievements. After all of this, no matter how we view the mountaineering world, Everest will always be more than just another mountain.

TABLE 1. *Measured physiological variables on the "summit" of Everest.*

P_B	250 Torr
P_IO_2	43 Torr
PaO_2	30 Torr
$PaCO_2$	11 Torr
pH	7.56
VO_2max	15 ml/kg/min.

REFERENCES

1. Habeler, P. *Everest the Impossible Victory*. London: Arlington Books, 1979.
2. Houston, C.S., J.R. Sutton, A. Cymerman, and J.T. Reeves. Operation Everest II: Man at extreme altitude. Journal of Applied Physiology 63:877–882, 1987.
3. Hunt, J. *The Ascent of Everest*. London: Hodder and Stoughton, 1953.
4. Mason, K. *Abode of Snow*. London: Rupert Hart-Davis, 1955.
5. Messner, R. *Everest, Expedition to the Ultimate*. London: Kaye and Ward, 1975.
6. Norton, E.F. *The Fight for Everest, 1924*. London: Edward Arnold, 1925.
7. Pugh, L.G.C.E. Physiological and medical aspects of the Himalayan Scientific and Mountaineering Expedition, 1960–61. British Medical Journal 2:621–634, 1962.
8. Pugh, L.G.C.E. Mount Cho Oyu, 1952, Mt. Everest, 1953. In: *Hypoxia: Man at Altitude*. J.R. Sutton, N.L. Jones and C.S. Houston (eds.), New York: Thieme-Stratton, 1982, pp. 105–112.
9. Sutton, J.R., J.T. Maher, and C.S. Houston. Operation Everest II. In: *Hypoxia, Exercise and Altitude*, edited by J.R. Sutton, C.S. Houston, and N.L. Jones, New York: Alan R. Liss, 1983, pp. 221–236.
10. Sutton, J.R., J.T. Reeves, P.D. Wagner, B.M. Groves, A. Cymerman, M.K. Malconian, P.R. Rock, P.M. Young, S.D. Walter, and C.S. Houston. Operation Everest II: Oxygen transport during exercise at extreme simulated altitude. Journal of Applied Physiology 64:1309–1321, 1988.
11. Sutton, J.R., L.G.C.E. Pugh, and N.L. Jones. Exercise at altitude. In: *Annual Review of Physiology*, vol. 45. Palo Alto: Annual Reviews Inc., 1983, pp. 427–437.
12. West J.B., S.J.H. Boyer, D.J. Graber, P.H. Hackett, K.H., Maret, J.S. Milledge, R.M. Peters, M. Samaja, F.H. Sarnquist, R.B. Schoene, and R.M. Winslow. Maximal exercise at extreme altitude on Mount Everest. Journal of Applied Physiology. 55:688–698, 1983.

Index

Abusive exercise, 64
Activity patterns, effect of obesity, 275-276
Acute exercise, state anxiety, 62
Adiposity, relationship of caloric intake, 276-278
Adoptees, in blood pressure studies, 435-437
Adult fitness, and hypertension, 443
Adult menstrual cycle, 514-538
Aerobic capacity, 10th grade males, 444
Aerobic power, measure of, 295; standards for, 410-415
Age, and physical fitness, 19-25; correlational analysis of strength, 119-122
Age related differences in strength, 104-111
Aggressive behavior, controlled by sports, 53-54; fostered by sports, 53-54
Altruism, 52
Amenorrhea, primary, 523-526
Amenorrheic athletes, 526
Androstenedione, endocrinological influence on strength, 148
Angle of pennation of muscle, 147
Anorectics, and exercise, 64
Antecedent diet, 545-547
Anxiety, in young athletes, 55
Arteriovenous oxygen (A-VO₂), effect of exercise on, 306-308
Asthma, exercise-induced, 465-512; in children, 466-467
Athletic performance, effect of strength training, 168-170
Attitudes, among athletes, 49-50

Basal metabolic rate, 372
Basophils, 480-481
Behavior, affected by sports activity, 47-98
Behavioral interventions, of physical activity, 76-77
Bent-knee curl-ups, 10
Beta adrenergic agonists, 488-490
Biogenic amines, 440
Biological maturation, 235-242
Biomechanical influences, on strength, 144-147
Blood cholesterol levels, 192
Blood lactate, 313-314
Blood pressure, 421-463; adoptive studies, 435-437; affect on fitness, 443-446; effect of exercise on, 306-308; family aggregation, 434, 437-438; left ventricular mass, 446-447; levels in children, 450; obesity, 438; physical activity, 443-447; race, 438-439; tracking, 432-433
Body composition, 11-12, 20-21; as cause of menstrual disorders, 529-530; cross-cultural

comparison, 33; somatic growth, 226-233; standards for, 415-416
Body density, measurement of, 228-233
Body fat, inheritance, 280-282; tracking, 274-275
Body image, and self-esteem, 64-65
Body mass, cross-cultural comparison, 32
Body size, correlational analysis of strength, 122-125; relation to fitness, 19-20; somatic growth, 224-225
Body surface area, 337-338
Body weight, to determine nutritional requirements, 371-373; training effects on, 249-252

Calcium, required for skeletal development, 373-374, 386-387; sources of, 374
Calcium channel blockers, 491-492
Cardiac function, effects of RST, 191-193
Cardiac hypertrophy, 192
Cardiac output response to exercise, 295-298
Cardiac transplants, response to exercise, 325-326
Cardiorespiratory endurance, 8-10, 21-23
Cardiovascular measurements, effect of training, 315-317
Cardiovascular responses to exercise, 293-334
Characteristics of physical fitness, 18-38
Cholinergic antagonists, 491
Chromium, required during adolescence, 376
Comparisons, limitations of, 31
Components of fitness, 4-7
Composite growth curve, age-associated, 125
Composite strength, 107-110; measurements, 107-109
Concepts of physical fitness, 3-8
Congenital heart disease, cardiovascular response, 321-325
Cooperative attitude, 52-53
Coronary heart disease, 407-408
Coronary risk factors, young boys, 444
Correlational analysis of strength, 118-151
Corticosteroids, 492
Creatinine excretion rates, estimating muscle mass, 125-127
Cromolyn sodium, 487
Cross-cultural comparisons, 31-38

Delinquent behavior, deterred by sports, 54
Densitometry, 228
Depression, 62
Determinants, of physical activity, 69-76; of stress, 58-60

Developmental stages of physical activity, 82-88
Developmental status, 18
Deyhdroepiandrosterone-sulphate, 258-259
Diabetes, exercise management, 561-565
Diabetes mellitus, exercise, 550-561
Diet, effects on metabolic fuel utilization, 545-547
Dynamic exercise tests, 294
Dynamometers, isokinetic, 10; isometric, 10

Elbow extensor strength, 115
Elbow flexion, 110-111, 114-115
Emotional stress, caused by sports activity, 54-58
Endocrinological influences, in determining strength, 147-150
Endogenous catecholamines, with exercise-induced asthma, 476
Endometrial cycle, adult menstrual cycle, 514-515
Energy, required during adolescence, 371, 377-379
Environmental temperatures, 350-355
Epinephrine excretion, stress indicator, 54
Evoked contraction strength, 183-186
Exercise, abusive, 64; and self-image, 65-66; cause of menstrual disorders, 530-531; medically supervised, 62; physiologic responses to, asthmatic individuals, 472-476; physiologic responses to, normal individuals, 472-476; regulation of glucose, 553-557
Exercise duration, metabolic fuel utilization, 545
Exercise electrocardiography, 308-312
Exercise-induced asthma, 465-512; airway rewarming, 479-480; characteristics of, 467-472; effects of physical fitness on, 495-497; endogenous catecholamines, 476; exercise intensity, 480; heat loss, 476-479; isocapnic hyperventilation testing, 486; measuring mediator release, 481-482; medications, 484-495; testing procedures, 483-486; therapy, 482; treatment, 486-495; water loss, 476-479
Exercise intensity, metabolic fuel utilization, 544-555

Familial aggregation, blood pressure, 437-438
Fast-twitch muscles, 131-135
Fat distribution, 233-235
Fat mass, measurement of, 229-233
Fat-free mass, measurement of, 229-233
Fat-free weight, 275
Fitness, effect of blood pressure, 443-446; and blood pressure, 443-446; components of, 4-7; motor, 3-6
FITNESSGRAM, 410-414, 416-418
Flexed arm hang test, 23-24
Flexibility, 11, 25; cross-cultural comparison, 37

Gender, and physical fitness, 19-25
Gender related, differences in strength, 104; mental disorders, 63

Genetic components of blood pressure, 434-437
Genetic endowment, 18
Genetic influences, on strength, 150-151
Genetic mechanism, blood pressure, 434
Geometric characteristics, temperature regulation, 337-348
Glucagon, 549
Glucose regulation during exercise, 553-557
Gonadarche, 520
Goniometer, 11
Grip strength, 102-107
Growth hormone, 256-261
Growth, biosocial perspective, 245-246; during adolescence, 370-371; effects of training, 245-261; Peak Height Velocity (PHV), 242-245; rate of maturation, 242

Handgrip force, cross-cultural comparison, 37
Handicapped children, self-esteem, 67
Health-related fitness tests, 29-30
Health-related physical fitness, defined, 3-4
Heat acclimatization, 355-356
Height, cross-cultural comparison, 32
Heredity, effect on physical activity, 79-81
Hormonal rhythms, adult menstrual cycle, 514
Hormones, effect on maturation, 256-261; luteinizing, 256-257
Hydrometry, 228
Hyperinsulinemia, 442
Hypertension, and salt sensitivity, 439-440; clinical implications, 447-455; exercise response, 321; inheritable, 434
Hypertension markers, 440
Hypoglycemia, exercise-induced, 558-560
Hypothalamic-pituitary-ovarian (HPO) axis, 514

Injuries, prevention, 209-211; types of strength training, 207-209
Insulin sensitivity, 552
Insulin, affecting metabolic fuel utilization, 549
Interpersonal problems, reason for withdrawal, 59
Iron, as nutritional requirement, 375, 389
Isokinetic dynamometers, 10
Isokinetic knee extensor strength, 111
Isokinetic strength, 113-117
Isometric dynamometers, 10
Isometric exercise, effect on blood pressure, 308
Isometric strength, 102-107
Isometric tests, 294
Isotonic one-repetition maximum test, 10

Ketosis, exercise-induced, 560-561
Kinetic therapy, 62-63
Knee extensor strength, 111
Knee flexion, 111-113, 115-117

Left ventricular mass (LVM), 446
Leighton flexometer, 11
Lipoprotein lipase, 279-280

Psychological theories, on physical activity, 79-81
Psychology, in children, in sport programs, 48
Pubarche, 520
Puberty, growth rate, 370
Pubescent children, resistance strength training, 168

Race, and blood pressure, 438-439
Resistance strength training, 166-194

Salt sensitivity, and hypertension, 439-440
Secondary amenorrhea, 524-526
Secular trends of physical fitness, 26-27
Self-image, and physical fitness, 65-66
Self-esteem, and physical fitness, 66-69
Sex related differences in strength, 104-111
Sexual maturation, 239-241, 254-256
Sickle cell anemia, effects on cardiovascular response, 317-320
Sit-and-reach, 11, 25
Sit-ups, 10, 24
Skeletal maturation, 235-236, 254
Skin blood flow, 347-348
Skinfold thickness measurements, 11-12, 20-21, 26-27
Slow-twitch muscles, 131-135
Social learning theory, 50
Sodium-lithium countertransport, 441-442
Sodium-potassium co-transport pathway, 440
Somatic growth, 224-235
Somatic maturation, 236-239
Speed sit-up, cross-cultural comparison, 37
Sport aggression, 53
Sports psychology, 47-98
Sportsmanship, 50
Stand-and-reach, 11
Standardization of test protocols, 18
State anxiety, associated with acute exercise, 62
Strength, composite, 107-110; correlational analysis, 118-151; evoked contraction, 183-186; grip, 102-107; isokinetic, 113-117; isometric, 102-107; muscular, 100-164; voluntary, 167-183
Strength training, 165-222; injuries, 207-211; integration of endurance training, 207; order of exercises, 205; periodization, 206-

207; principles, 194-201; program design, 201-207; progression, 198-199; selection of equipment, 201-204; set systems, 204-205; specificity, 199-200; split routine, 205-206; volume, 200-201; warm-up, 206
Stress, emotional, 54-58; metabolically induced, 54
Stroke volume, 298-306
Structural developmental approach, 50
Sweat patterns, 338-347
Sympathetic nervous system, 548-549

Temperature regulation, during exercise, 348-354, 356-358; geometric characteristics, 337-348; physical principles, 336-337; physiologic characteristics, 337-348; physiologic principles, 336-337
Temperature responses to exercise, 335-368
Test batteries, physical fitness, 12-13
Test performances, interpretation, 13-18
Test protocols, standardization, 18
Testing, physical fitness applications, 13
Testosterone, endocrinological influence, on strength, 147-148
Tests, motor fitness, 27-29
Thelarche, 520
Theophylline, 490-491
Total body water, measurement of, 228-233
Trace elements, required during adolescence, 375-377, 389-391
Tracking blood pressure in children, 432
Trainability of children, 170-177
Training, defined, 247; effects on body weight, 249-252; effects on maturation, 253-256; effects on physique, 252-253; effects on statural growth, 247-249
Training overload, 194-198
Treadmill exercise, 299
Twins, blood pressure levels, 434-435

Undernutrition, 531

Value orientation, toward competition, 49
Ventilatory threshold, 312-315
$\dot{V}O_2$, 413-415
Voluntary strength, 167-183

Zinc, required during adolescence, 376, 389-391